SYMBIOSIS

the pearson custom library
for the biological sciences

Miami Dade College North Campus
General Biology
BSC2010/2011L

Pearson Learning Solutions

New York Boston San Francisco
London Toronto Sydney Tokyo Singapore Madrid
Mexico City Munich Paris Cape Town Hong Kong Montreal

Senior Vice President, Editorial and Marketing: Patrick F. Boles
Senior Sponsoring Editor: Natalie Danner
Development Editor: Annette Fantasia
Editorial Assistant: Jill Johnson
Executive Marketing Manager: Nathan L. Wilbur
Operations Manager: Eric M. Kenney
Database Production Manager: Jennifer Berry
Art Director: Renée Sartell
Cover Designer: Kristen Kiley

Cover Art: Courtesy of Michael R. Martin, Darryl Johnson, Photodisk, DK Images, and Prentice-Hall, Inc.

This special edition published in cooperation with Pearson Learning Solutions.

Printed in the United States of America.

V0UD

Please visit our web site at *www.pearsoncustom.com/.*

Attention bookstores: For permission to return unused stock, contact us at *pe-uscustomreturns@pearson.com.*

Pearson Learning Solutions, 501 Boylston Street, Suite 900, Boston, MA 02116
A Pearson Education Company
www.pearsoned.com

PEARSON

ISBN 10: 0-536-13899-0
ISBN 13: 978-0-536-13899-6

Laboratory Safety: General Guidelines

1. Notify your instructor immediately if you are pregnant, color blind, allergic to any insects or chemicals, taking immunosuppressive drugs, or have any other medical condition (such as diabetes, immunologic defect) that may require special precautionary measures in the laboratory.
2. Upon entering the laboratory, place all books, coats, purses, backpacks, etc. in designated areas, not on the bench tops.
3. Locate and, when appropriate, learn to use exits, fire extinguisher, fire blanket, chemical shower, eyewash, first aid kit, broken glass container, and cleanup materials for spills.
4. In case of fire, evacuate the room and assemble outside the building.
5. Do not eat, drink, smoke, or apply cosmetics in the laboratory.
6. Confine long hair, loose clothing, and dangling jewelry.
7. Wear shoes at all times in the laboratory.
8. Cover any cuts or scrapes with a sterile, waterproof bandage before attending lab.
9. Wear eye protection when working with chemicals.
10. Never pipet by mouth. Use mechanical pipeting devices.
11. Wash skin immediately and thoroughly if contaminated by chemicals or microorganisms.
12. Do not perform unauthorized experiments.
13. Do not use equipment without instruction.
14. Report *all* spills and accidents to your instructor immediately.
15. Never leave heat sources unattended.
16. When using hot plates, note that there is no visible sign that they are hot (such as a red glow). Always assume that hot plates are hot.
17. Use an appropriate apparatus when handling hot glassware.
18. Keep chemicals away from direct heat or sunlight.
19. Keep containers of alcohol, acetone, and other flammable liquids away from flames.
20. Do not allow any liquid to come into contact with electrical cords. Handle electrical connectors with dry hands. Do not attempt to disconnect electrical equipment that crackles, snaps, or smokes.
21. Upon completion of laboratory exercises, place all materials in the disposal areas designated by your instructor.
22. Do not pick up broken glassware with your hands. Use a broom and dustpan and discard the glass in designated glass waste containers; never discard with paper waste.
23. Wear disposable gloves when working with blood, other body fluids, or mucous membranes. Change gloves after possible contamination and wash hands immediately after gloves are removed.
24. The disposal symbol indicates that items that may

    have come in contact with body fluids should be placed in your lab's designated container. It also refers to liquid wastes that should not be poured down the drain into the sewage system.
25. Leave the laboratory clean and organized for the next student.
26. Wash your hands with liquid or powdered soap prior to leaving the laboratory.
27. The biohazard symbol indicates procedures that

    may pose health concerns.

The caution symbol points out instruments,

substances, and procedures that require special attention to safety. These symbols appear throughout this manual.

Measurement Conversions

Metric to American Standard	American Standard to Metric
Length	
1 mm = 0.039 inches	1 inch = 2.54 cm
1 cm = 0.394 inches	1 foot = 0.305 m
1 m = 3.28 feet	1 yard = 0.914 m
1 m = 1.09 yards	1 mile = 1.61 km
Volume	
1 mL = 0.0338 fluid ounces	1 fluid ounce = 29.6 mL
1 L = 4.23 cups	1 cup = 237 mL
1 L = 2.11 pints	1 pint = 0.474 L
1 L = 1.06 quarts	1 quart = 0.947 L
1 L = 0.264 gallons	1 gallon = 3.79 L
Mass	
1 mg = 0.0000353 ounces	1 ounce = 28.3 g
1 g = 0.0353 ounces	1 pound = 0.454 kg
1 kg = 2.21 pounds	

Temperature

To convert temperature:

$$°C = \frac{5}{9}(F - 32) \qquad °F = \frac{9}{5}C + 32$$

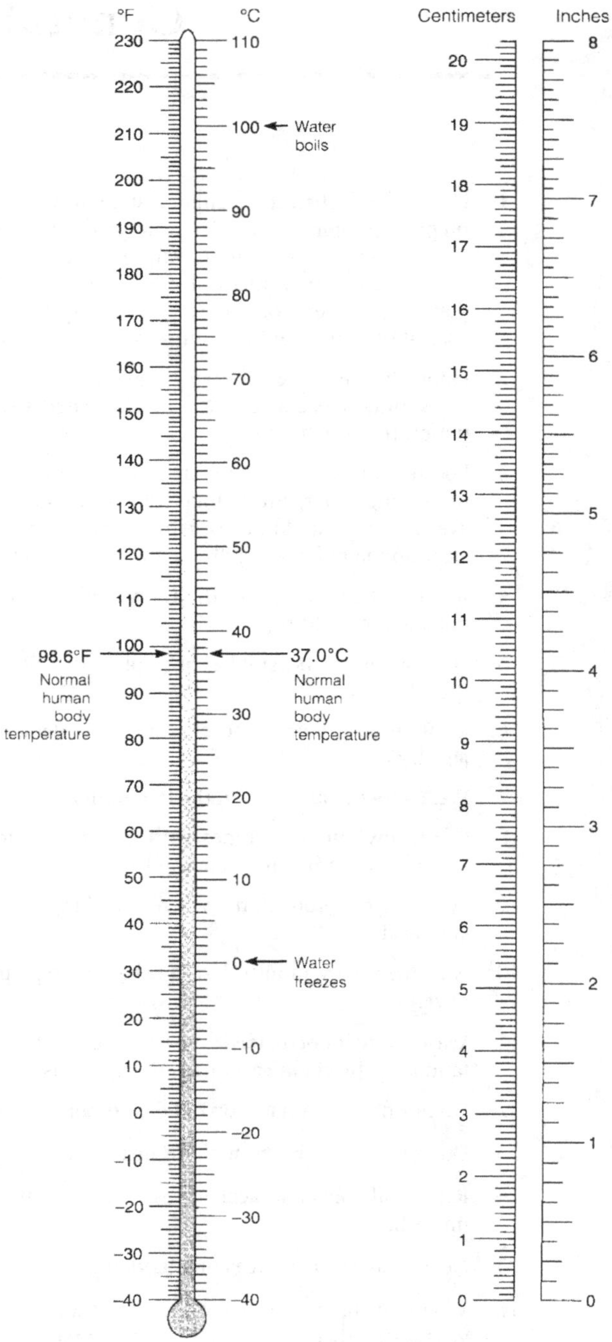

Contents

Preface

For the scientist the formulation of questions is almost the whole thing.
The answers, when found, only lead on to other questions.

D. W. Winnicott

Our knowledge of the biological world is based on the scientific enterprise of asking questions and testing hypotheses. An important aspect of learning biology is participating in the process of science and developing creative and critical reasoning skills. Our goal in writing this laboratory manual is to present a laboratory curriculum that encourages participation in the scientific process. We want students to experience the excitement of discovery and the satisfaction of solving problems and connecting concepts. For us, investigating biology is more than just doing experiments; it is an approach to teaching and learning.

The laboratory exercises are designed to encourage students to ask questions, to pose hypotheses, and to make predictions before they initiate laboratory work. Students are required to synthesize results from observations and experiments, then draw conclusions from evidence. Finally, whenever possible, students apply their results to new problems and are encouraged to pursue open-ended investigations of their own design. Scientific writing is emphasized throughout the laboratory manual.

We are convinced that involving students in the process of science through their investigating of biological phenomena is the best way to teach. The organization of this laboratory manual complements this approach to teaching and learning.

Lab Topics are designated as *Directed, Thematic,* or *Open-Ended Investigations* in the table of contents.

Scientific Communication—Writing and Speaking

Scientists must communicate their results in writing and in presentations to research groups and at meetings. Undergraduates need instruction in writing and an opportunity to practice these skills; however, instructors do not have the time to critique hundreds of student research reports for each exercise. Throughout this lab manual, teams of students work together on improving their skills. They are asked to organize and present their results to their peers during the discussion and summary sessions in the laboratory. Students are also required to write as part of each laboratory. They summarize and discuss their results and then apply information to new problems in the questions at the end of the laboratory.

We have also incorporated scientific writing into our lab manual in a stepwise fashion. Students must answer questions and summarize results within the context of the laboratory exercises. For directed investigations, students are required to submit one section of a scientific paper. For example, they might submit the Results section for one experiment, and the Discussion section for another experiment. Once students have experience writing each section, they write at least one complete scientific paper for an open-ended investigation.

See Appendix A and the Teaching Plans for additional information on scientific writing.

Integration of Other Sciences and Mathematics

Students often view biology as a separate and isolated body of knowledge. We have attempted to integrate biology, chemistry, some physics, and geology whenever possible. We provide opportunities for students to quantify observations, analyze and summarize results in tables and figures, and, ultimately, to use these data to construct arguments in support of their hypotheses.

Special Features

Questions for Review: Students review basic content and terminology at the end of each lab topic.

Applying Your Knowledge: As instructors, we want our students to be challenged to think and to develop critical thinking skills. Throughout this manual, students are asked to work logically through problems, critique results, and modify hypotheses. To emphasize these skills further, we have developed a section in each laboratory topic called Applying Your Knowledge, in which students are asked to apply their knowledge to other aspects of biology, to medicine, or to daily life.

Safety considerations: Safety concerns are noted in the text by the use of icons for general safety and for biohazards. Laboratory safety is also addressed in the teaching plans at the end of each lab topic in the Instructor's Edition.

Notes to students: To assure student success, cautionary reminders and notes of special interest are also highlighted in the text.

Appendixes: Information needed in several laboratory topics is included in the appendixes: scientific writing, using chi-square analysis, and dissection terminology.

Color insert: Color photographs are particularly helpful in the study of cells and organisms. Photos and illustrations in the color insert are cross-referenced to the text.

Scientific Investigation

Before going to lab, read the Introduction and Exercises 1 and 2. Be prepared to answer all questions and contribute your ideas in a class discussion.

Laboratory Objectives

After completing this lab topic, you should be able to:

1. Identify and characterize questions that can be answered through scientific investigation.
2. Define *hypothesis* and explain what characterizes a good scientific hypothesis.
3. Identify and describe the components of a scientific experiment.
4. Summarize and present results in tables and graphs.
5. Discuss results and critique experiments.
6. Design a scientific experiment.
7. Interpret and communicate results.

Introduction

Biology is the study of the phenomena of life, and biological scientists—researchers, teachers, and students—observe living systems and organisms, ask questions, and propose explanations for those observations. Scientific investigation is a way of testing those explanations. Science assumes that biological systems are understandable and can be explained by fundamental rules or laws. Scientific investigations share some common elements and procedures, which are referred to as the *scientific method.* Not all scientists follow these procedures in a strict fashion, but each of the elements is usually present. Science is a creative human endeavor that involves asking questions, making observations, developing explanatory hypotheses, and testing those hypotheses. Scientists closely scrutinize investigations in their field, and each scientist must present his or her work at scientific meetings or in professional publications, providing evidence from observations and experiments that supports the scientist's explanations of biological phenomena.

In this lab topic, you will not only review the process that scientists use to ask and answer questions about the living world, but you will develop the skills to conduct and critique scientific investigations. Like scientists, you will work in research teams in this laboratory and others, collaborating as you ask questions and solve problems. Throughout this laboratory manual, you will be investigating biology using the methodology of scientists, asking questions, proposing explanations, designing experiments, predicting results, collecting and analyzing data, and interpreting your results in light of your hypotheses.

EXERCISE 1
Questions and Hypotheses

This exercise explores the nature of scientific questions and hypotheses. Before going to lab, read the explanatory paragraphs and then be prepared to present your ideas in the class discussion.

Lab Study A. Asking Questions

Scientists are characteristically curious and creative individuals whose curiosity is directed toward understanding the natural world. They use their study of previous research or personal observations of natural phenomena as a basis for asking questions about the underlying causes or reasons for these phenomena. For a question to be pursued by scientists, the phenomenon must be well defined and testable. The elements must be measurable and controllable.

There are limits to the ability of science to answer questions. Science is only one of many ways of knowing about the world in which we live. Consider, for example, this question: Do excessively high temperatures cause people to behave immorally? Can a scientist investigate this question? Temperature is certainly a well-defined, measurable, and controllable factor, but morality of behavior is not scientifically measurable. We probably could not even reach a consensus on the definition. Thus, there is no experiment that can be performed to test the question. Which of the following questions do you think can be answered scientifically?

1. Is there a link between childhood vaccinations and autism?
2. Can cross-pollination occur between genetically engineered turf grass and non-engineered grass?
3. Should human embryonic stem cells be used to treat Parkinson's disease?
4. Do cactus spines reduce herbivory?
5. Did the use of the herbal supplement ephedra cause the death of the 18-year old soccer player?

How did you decide which questions can be answered scientifically?

Lab Study B. Developing Hypotheses

As questions are asked, scientists attempt to answer them by proposing possible explanations. Those proposed explanations are called **hypotheses.** A hypothesis tentatively explains something observed. It proposes an answer to a question. Consider question 5, preceding. One hypothesis based on this question might be "Spines on cacti reduce herbivory." The hypothesis has suggested a possible explanation for the observed spines.

A scientifically useful hypothesis must be testable and falsifiable (able to be proved false). To satisfy the requirement that a hypothesis be falsifiable, it must be possible that the test results do not support the explanation. In our example, if spines are removed from test cacti and the plants are not eaten by animals, then the hypothesis has been falsified. *Even though the hypothesis can be falsified, it can never be proved true.* The evidence from an investigation can only provide support for the hypothesis. In our example, if cacti without spines were eaten, the hypothesis has not been proved, but has been supported by the evidence. Other explanations still must be excluded, and new evidence from additional experiments and observations might falsify this hypothesis at a later date. In science seldom does a single test provide results that clearly support or falsify a hypothesis. In most cases, the evidence serves to modify the hypothesis or the conditions of the experiment.

Science is a way of knowing about the natural world (Moore, 1993) that involves testing hypotheses or explanations. The scientific method can be applied to the unusual and the commonplace. You use the scientific method when you investigate why your once-white socks are now blue. Your hypothesis might be that your blue jeans and socks were washed together, an assertion that can be tested through observations and experimentation.

Students often think that controlled experiments are the only way to test a hypothesis. The test of a hypothesis may include experimentation, additional observations, or the synthesis of information from a variety of sources. Many scientific advances have relied on other procedures and information to test hypotheses. For example, James Watson and Francis Crick developed a model that was their hypothesis for the structure of DNA. Their model could only be supported if the accumulated data from a number of other scientists were consistent with the model. Actually, their first model (hypothesis) was falsified by the work of Rosalind Franklin. Their final model was tested and supported not only by the ongoing work of Franklin and Maurice Wilkins but also by research previously published by Erwin Chargaff and others. Watson and Crick won the Nobel Prize for their scientific work. They did not perform a controlled experiment in the laboratory but tested their powerful hypothesis through the use of existing evidence from other research. Methods other than experimentation are acceptable in testing hypotheses. Think about other areas of science that require comparative observations and the accumulation of data from a variety of sources, all of which must be consistent with and support hypotheses or else be inconsistent and falsify hypotheses.

The information in your biology textbook is often thought of as a collection of facts, well understood and correct. It is true that much of the knowledge of biology has been derived through scientific investigations, has been thoroughly tested, and is supported by strong evidence. However, scientific knowledge is always subject to novel experiments and new technology, any aspect of which may result in modification of our ideas and a better understanding of biological phenomena. The structure of the cell membrane is an example of the self-correcting nature of science. Each model of the membrane has been modified as new results have negated one explanation and provided support for an alternative explanation.

Application

Before scientific questions can be answered, they must first be converted to hypotheses, which can be tested. For each of the following questions, write an explanatory hypothesis. Recall that the hypothesis is a statement that explains the phenomenon you are interested in investigating.

1. Does UVB radiation cause limb deformities in amphibians?

2. Does increasing calories in school lunches on test days improve mental ability?

Scientists often propose and reject a variety of hypotheses before they design a single test. Discuss with your class which of the following statements would be useful as scientific hypotheses and could be investigated using scientific procedures. Give the reason for each answer by stating whether it could possibly be falsified and what factors are measurable and controllable.

1. Mole rats navigate through tunnels by orienting to the earth's magnetic field.
2. Crime rates increase during the full moon.
3. Positive emotions prolong life.
4. Exposure to the pesticide endosulfan affects hormone levels in boys.
5. The extinct Moa is closely related to other large flightless birds, such as ostriches and rheas.

EXERCISE 2
Designing Experiments to Test Hypotheses

The most creative aspect of science is designing a test of your hypothesis that will provide unambiguous evidence to falsify or support a particular explanation. Scientists often design, critique, and modify a variety of experiments and other tests before they commit the time and resources to perform a single experiment. In this exercise, you will follow the procedure for experimentally testing hypotheses, but it is important to remember that other methods, including observation and the synthesis of other sources of data, are acceptable in scientific investigations. An experiment involves defining variables, outlining a procedure, and determining controls to be used as the experiment is performed. Once the experiment is defined, the investigator predicts the outcome of the experiment based on the hypothesis.

Read the following description of a scientific investigation of the effects of sulfur dioxide on soybean reproduction. Then in Lab Study A you will determine the types of variables involved, and in Lab Study B, the experimental procedure for this experiment and for others.

Investigation of the Effect of Sulfur Dioxide on Soybean Reproduction

Agricultural scientists were concerned about the effect of air pollution, sulfur dioxide in particular, on soybean production in fields adjacent to coal-powered power plants. Based on initial investigations, they proposed that sulfur dioxide in high concentrations would reduce reproduction in soybeans. They designed an experiment to test this hypothesis (Figure 1). In this experiment, 48 soybean plants, just beginning to produce flowers, were divided into two groups, treatment and no treatment. The 24 treated plants were divided into four groups of 6. One group of 6 treated plants was placed in a fumigation chamber and exposed to 0.6 ppm (parts per million) of sulfur dioxide for 4 hours to simulate sulfur dioxide emissions from a power plant. The experiment was repeated on the remaining three treated groups. The no-treatment plants were divided similarly into four groups of 6. Each group in turn was placed in a second fumigation chamber and exposed to filtered air for 4 hours. Following the experiment, all plants were returned to the greenhouse. When the beans matured, the number of bean pods, the number of seeds per pod, and the weight of the pods were determined for each plant.

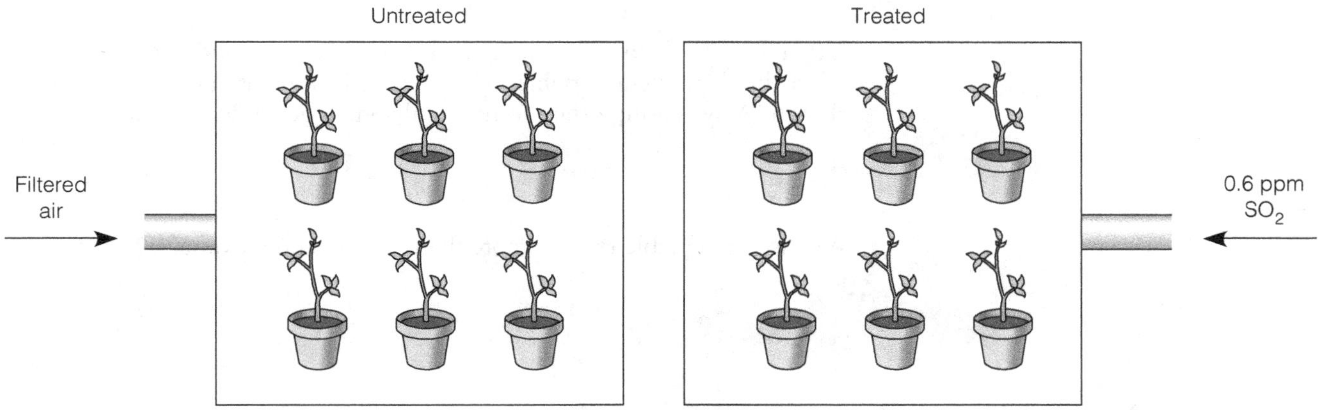

Figure 1.
Experimental design for soybean experiment. The experiment was repeated four times. Soybeans were fumigated for 4 hours.

Lab Study A. Determining the Variables

Read the description of each category of variable; then identify the variable described in the preceding investigation. The variables in an experiment must be clearly defined and measurable. The investigator will identify and define *dependent, independent,* and *controlled variables* for a particular experiment.

The Dependent Variable

Within the experiment, one variable will be measured or counted or observed in response to the experimental conditions. This variable is the **dependent variable.** For the soybeans, several dependent variables are measured, all of which provide information about reproduction. What are they?

The Independent Variable

The scientist will choose one variable, or experimental condition, to manipulate. This variable is considered the most important variable by which to test the investigator's hypothesis and is called the **independent variable.** What was the independent variable in the investigation of the effect of sulfur dioxide on soybean reproduction?

Can you suggest other variables that the investigator might have changed that would have had an effect on the dependent variables?

Although other factors, such as light, temperature, time, and fertilizer, might affect the dependent variables, only one independent variable is usually chosen. Why is it important to have only one independent variable?

Why is it acceptable to have more than one dependent variable?

The Controlled Variable

Consider the variables that you identified as alternative independent variables. Although they are not part of the hypothesis being tested in this investigation, they would have significant effects on the outcome of this experiment. These variables must, therefore, be kept constant during the course of the experiment. They are known as the **controlled variables.** The underlying assumption in experimental design is that the selected independent variable is the one affecting the dependent variable. This is only true if all other variables are controlled. What are the controlled variables in this experiment? What variables other than those you may have already listed can you now suggest?

Lab Study B. Choosing or Designing the Procedure

The **procedure** is the stepwise method, or sequence of steps, to be performed for the experiment. It should be recorded in a laboratory notebook before initiating the experiment, and any exceptions or modifications should be noted during the experiment. The procedures may be designed from research published in scientific journals, through collaboration with colleagues in the lab or other institutions, or by means of one's own novel and creative ideas. The process of outlining the procedure includes determining control treatment(s), levels of treatments, and numbers of replications.

Level of Treatment

The value set for the independent variable is called the **level of treatment.** For this experiment, the value was determined based on previous research and preliminary measurements of sulfur dioxide emissions. The scientists may select a range of concentrations from no sulfur dioxide to an extremely high concentration. The levels should be based on knowledge of the system and the biological significance of the treatment level. In some experiments however, independent variables represent categories that do not have a level of treatment (for example, gender). What was the level of treatment in the soybean experiment?

Replication

Scientific investigations are not valid if the conclusions drawn from them are based on one experiment with one or two individuals. Generally, the same procedure will be repeated several times (**replication**), providing consistent results. Notice that scientists do not expect exactly the same results inasmuch as individuals and their responses will vary. Results from replicated experiments are usually averaged and may be further analyzed using statistical tests. Describe replication in the soybean experiment.

Control

The experimental design includes a **control** in which the independent variable is held at an established level or is omitted. The control or control treatment serves as a benchmark that allows the scientist to decide whether the predicted effect is really due to the independent variable. In the case of the soybean experiment, what was the control treatment?

What is the difference between the control and the controlled variables discussed previously?

Lab Study C. Making Predictions

The investigator never begins an experiment without a prediction of its outcome. The **prediction** is always based on the particular experiment designed to test a specific hypothesis. Predictions are written in the form of if/then statements: "If the hypothesis is true, then the results of the experiment will be . . ."; for example, "if cactus spines reduce herbivory, then removal of the spines will result in greater surface area removed by herbivores." Making a prediction provides a critical analysis of the experimental design. If the predictions are not clear, the procedure can be modified before beginning the experiment. For the soybean experiment, the hypothesis was: "Exposure to sulfur dioxide reduces reproduction." What should the prediction be? State your prediction.

To evaluate the results of the experiment, the investigator always returns to the prediction. If the results match the prediction, then the hypothesis is supported. If the results do not match the prediction, then the hypothesis is falsified. Either way, the scientist has increased knowledge of the process being studied. Many times the falsification of a hypothesis can provide more information than confirmation, since the ideas and data must be critically evaluated in light of new information. In the soybean experiment, the scientist may learn that the prediction is true (sulfur dioxide does reduce reproduction at the concentration tested). As a next step, the scientist may now wish to identify the particular level at which the effect is first demonstrated.

Review your hypotheses for the numbered questions. Consider how you might design an experiment to test the first hypothesis. For example, you might measure "limb deformities" by recording the number of frog legs and their shape. The prediction might be:

> **If** UVB radiation increases limb deformities in amphibians (*a restatement of the hypothesis*), **then** frogs exposed to UVB radiation will have more (or fewer) legs and deformed legs (*predicting the results from the experiment*).

Now consider an experiment you might design to test the second hypothesis. How will you measure "mental ability"?

State a prediction for this hypothesis and experiment. Use the if/then format:

The actual test of the prediction is one of the great moments in research: No matter the results, the scientist is not just following a procedure but truly testing a creative explanation derived from an interesting question.

Discussion

1. From this exercise, list the components of scientific investigations from asking a question to carrying out an experiment.

2. From this exercise, list the variables that must be identified in designing an experiment.

3. What are the components of an experimental procedure?

EXERCISE 3
Designing an Experiment

Materials

steps or platform, 8 in. high
clock with a second hand
metronome

Introduction

In this exercise, your entire class, working together, will practice investigating a question using what you have learned so far about the scientific process.

Question

Cardiovascular fitness can be determined by measuring a person's pulse rate and respiration rate before and after a given time of aerobic exercise. A person who is more fit may have a relatively slower pulse rate and a lower respiratory rate after exercise, and his or her pulse rate should return to normal more quickly than that of a person who is less fit. Your assignment is to investigate the effect of a well-defined, measurable, controllable independent variable on cardiovascular fitness.

In your research teams, take about 10 minutes to discuss several *specific* questions that you can ask about an independent variable related to the *broad* topic of cardiovascular fitness. List your questions in the space provided. For example, your question might be "Does cigarette smoking have an effect on cardiovascular fitness?" Choose your best question and propose a testable hypothesis. Contribute your question and hypothesis to a class list recorded by the instructor.

The entire class decides on the hypothesis, the experimental design, and the predicted results. The same experiment is performed by all teams.

Hypothesis

Record the hypothesis chosen by the class.

The Experiment

If you were performing an independent investigation, at this time you would go to the library and read relevant scientific articles or texts to determine an accepted procedure used by scientists to test cardiovascular fitness. You might discover that there is a test, called the *step test,* that is used for this purpose (Kusinitz and Fine, 1987). Here are the basic elements of this test:

1. The subject steps up and down on a low platform, approximately 8 in. from the ground, for 3 minutes at a rate of 30 steps per minute. (Using a metronome to count steps ensures that all subjects maintain a constant step rate.) The subject should step up and then step down again, keeping the rate constant (Figure 2).
2. The subject's pulse rate is measured before the test and immediately after the test. The subject should be sitting quietly when the pulse is counted. Use three fingers to find the pulse in the radial artery (the artery in the wrist, above the thumb). Count the number of beats per minute. (Count the beats for 30 seconds and multiply by 2.)
3. Additionally, the pulse rate is measured at 1-minute intervals after the test until the pulse rate returns to normal (recovery time). Count the pulse for 30 seconds, rest 30 seconds, count 30 seconds, and rest 30 seconds. Repeat this procedure until the pulse returns to normal. Record the number of minutes to return to the normal pulse rate. (Do not record the pulse rate.)

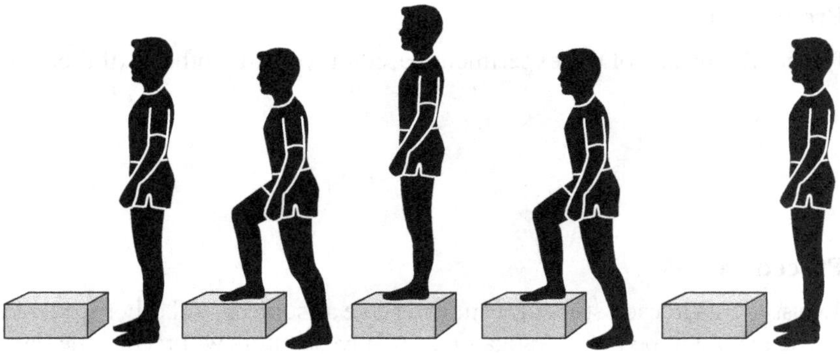

Figure 2.
The step test. Step up on the platform, and then step down again, keeping the rate constant.

As a class, design the experiment. Record the components of your experiment by completing the information below.

Dependent variable(s):

Independent variable:

Controlled variables:

Control:

Level of treatment:

Replication:

Summarize the experiment designed by your class:

Prediction

Predict the results of the experiment based on your hypothesis (if/then).

Procedure

Two students in each student team will serve as subjects. All other students in the team will be the investigators. The investigators will record the data for the two subjects.

Students with respiratory or circulatory disorders should not be the subjects in this experiment.

List in numerical order each exact step of your procedure. Begin with recruitment of the subjects in each treatment category. Refer to the description of the experimental test. Remember to designate persons to time the experiment and record the measurements.

Performing the Experiment

Following the procedures established by your investigative team, perform the experiment and record your results.

Results

Record the results for your team in Table 1. Record total class results in Table 2. Identify the treatment conditions at the top of the table.

Table 1
Results of Step Test for Your Team (Pulse rates are beats per minute.)

	Treatment 1: ______	**Treatment 2:** ______
Before step test Pulse rate		
After step test Pulse rate		
Recovery time (min)		

Table 2
Results of Step Test for All Teams (Pulse rates are beats per minute.)

Treatment 1: ______________________________

Subject	1	2	3	4	5	6	**Average**
Before step test Pulse rate							
After step test Pulse rate							
Recovery time (min)							

Treatment 2: ______________________________

Subject	1	2	3	4	5	6	**Average**
Before step test Pulse rate							
After step test Pulse rate							
Recovery time (min)							

EXERCISE 4
Presenting and Analyzing Results

Once the data are collected, they must be organized and summarized so that the scientists can determine if the hypothesis has been supported or falsified. In this exercise, you will design **tables** and graphs; the latter are also called **figures.** Tables and figures have two primary functions. They are used (1) to help you analyze and interpret your results and (2) to enhance the clarity with which you present the work to a reader or viewer.

Lab Study A. Tables

You have collected data from your experiment in the form of a list of numbers that may appear at first glance to have little meaning. Look at your data. How could you organize the data set to make it easier to interpret? You could *average* the data set for each treatment, but even averages can be rather uninformative. Could you use a summary table to convey the data (in this case, averages)?

Table 3 is an example of a table using data averages of the number of seeds per pod and number of pods per plant as the dependent variables and exposure to sulfur dioxide as the independent variable. Note that the number of replicates and the units of measurement are provided in the table and table legend.

Table 3
Effects of 4-Hour Exposure to 0.6 ppm Sulfur Dioxide on Average Seed and Pod Production in Soybeans

Treatment	Number	Seeds per Pod	Pods per Plant
Control	24	3.26	16
SO_2	24	1.96	13

Tables are used to present results that have a few to many data points. They are also useful for displaying several dependent variables. For example, average number of bean pods, average number of seeds per pod, and average weight of pods per plant for treated and untreated plants could all be presented in one table.

The following guidelines will help you construct a table:

- All values of the same kind should read down the column, not across a row. Include only data that are important in presenting the results and for further discussion.
- Information and results that are not essential (for example: test-tube number, simple calculations, or data with no differences) should be omitted.
- The headings of each column should include units of measurement, if appropriate.

- Tables are numbered consecutively throughout a lab report or scientific paper. For example: Table 4 would be the fourth table in your report.
- The **title,** which is located at the top of the table, should be clear and concise, with enough information to allow the table to be understandable apart from the text. Capitalize the first and important words in the title. Do not capitalize articles (a, an, the), short prepositions, and conjunctions. The title does not need a period at the end.
- Refer to each table in the written text. Summarize the data and refer to the table; for example, "The plants treated with sulfur dioxide produced an average of 1.96 seeds per pod (Table 3)." Do not write, "See the results in Table 3."
- If you are using a database program, such as Excel, you should still sketch your table on paper before constructing it on the computer.

Application

1. Using the data from your experiment, design a summary table to present the results for *one* of your dependent variables, pulse rate. Your table need not be the same size or design as the sample. In your table, provide units of the dependent variable (pulse rate). Tell the reader how many replications (if any) were used to calculate the averages.
2. Compose a title for your table. Refer to the guidelines in the previous section.

Lab Study B. Graphs

The results of an experiment usually are presented graphically, showing the relationships among the independent and dependent variable(s). A graph or figure provides a visual summary of the results. Often, characteristics of the data are not apparent in a table but may become clear in a graph. By looking at a graph, then, you can visualize the effect that the independent variable has on the dependent variable and detect trends in your data. Making a graph may be one of the first steps in analyzing your results.

The presentation of your data in a graph will assist you in interpreting and communicating your results. In the final steps of a scientific investigation, you must be able to construct a logical argument based on your results that either supports or falsifies your starting hypothesis. Your graph should be accurately and clearly constructed, easily interpreted, and well annotated. The following guidelines will help you to construct such a graph.

- Use graph paper and a ruler to plot the values accurately. If using a database program, you should first sketch your axes and data points before constructing the figure on the computer.
- The independent variable is graphed on the *x* axis (horizontal axis, or abscissa), and the dependent variable, on the *y* axis (vertical axis, or ordinate).
- The numerical range for each axis should be appropriate for the data being plotted. Generally, begin both axes of the graph at zero (the extreme left corner). Then choose your intervals and range to maximize the use of the graph space. Choose intervals that are logically spaced and therefore will allow easy interpretation of the graph, for example, intervals of 5s or 10s. To avoid generating graphs with wasted space, you may signify unused graph space by two perpendicular tic marks between the zero and your lowest number on one or both axes.
- Label the axes to indicate the variable and the units of measurement. Include a legend if colors or shading is used to indicate different aspects of the experiment.
- Choose the type of graph that best presents your data. Line graphs and bar graphs are most frequently used. The choice of graph type depends on the nature of the variable being graphed.
- Compose a title for your figure, and write it below your graph. Graphs, diagrams, drawings, and photographs are all called *figures* and should be numbered consecutively throughout a lab report or scientific paper. Each figure is given a caption or title that describes its contents, giving enough information to allow the figure to be self-contained. Capitalize only the first word in a figure title and place a period at the end.

The Line Graph

Line graphs show changes in the quantity of the chosen variable and emphasize the rise and fall of the values over their range. Use a line graph to present continuous data. For example, changes in the dependent variable pulse rate, measured over time, would be depicted best in a line graph.

- Plot data as separate points.
- Whether to connect the dots or draw a best fit curve depends on the type of data and how they were collected. To show trends, draw smooth curves or straight lines to fit the values plotted for any one data set. Connect the points dot to dot when emphasizing meaningful changes in values on the *x* axis.
- If more than one set of data is presented on a graph, use different colors or symbols and provide a key or legend to indicate which set is which.
- A boxed graph, instead of one with only two sides, makes it easier to see the values on the right side of the graph.

Note the features of a line graph in Figure 3, which shows that young males are the most likely victims of car crashes based on data from 2000.

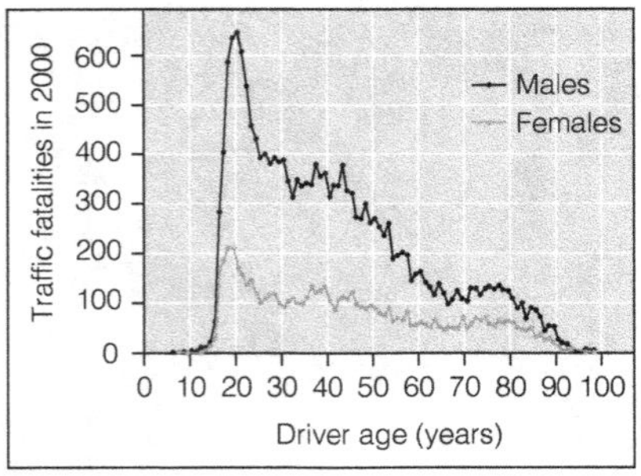

Figure 3.
Differences in traffic fatalities in 2000 for male and female drivers by age. (After Evans, 2002)

The Bar Graph

Bar graphs are constructed following the same principles as for line graphs, except that vertical bars, in a series, are drawn down to the horizontal axis. Bar graphs are often used for data that represent separate or discontinuous groups or non-numerical categories, thus emphasizing the discrete differences between the groups. For example, a bar graph might be used to depict differences in number of seeds per pod for treated and untreated soybeans. Bar graphs are also used when the values on the *x* axis are numerical but grouped together. These graphs are called histograms.

Note the features of a bar graph in Figure 4, which depicts the worldwide prevalence of anemia in children and pregnant women in 1998.

You will be asked to design graphs throughout this laboratory manual. Remember, the primary function of the figure is to present your results in the clearest manner to enhance the interpretation of your data.

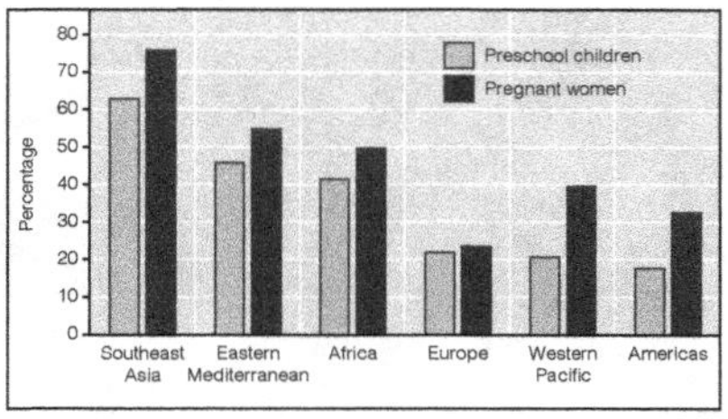

Figure 4.
Prevalence of anemia in preschool children and pregnant women worldwide, by region, 1998. (After Chrispeels and Sadava, 2003.)

Application

1. Using data from your experiment and the grid provided below, design a bar graph that shows the relationship between the dependent and independent variables in this experiment. Discuss with your teammates how to design this figure so that it includes the data for pulse rate before and after exercise for the treatments selected for your experiment. Draw and label the figure, and compose a title for it.

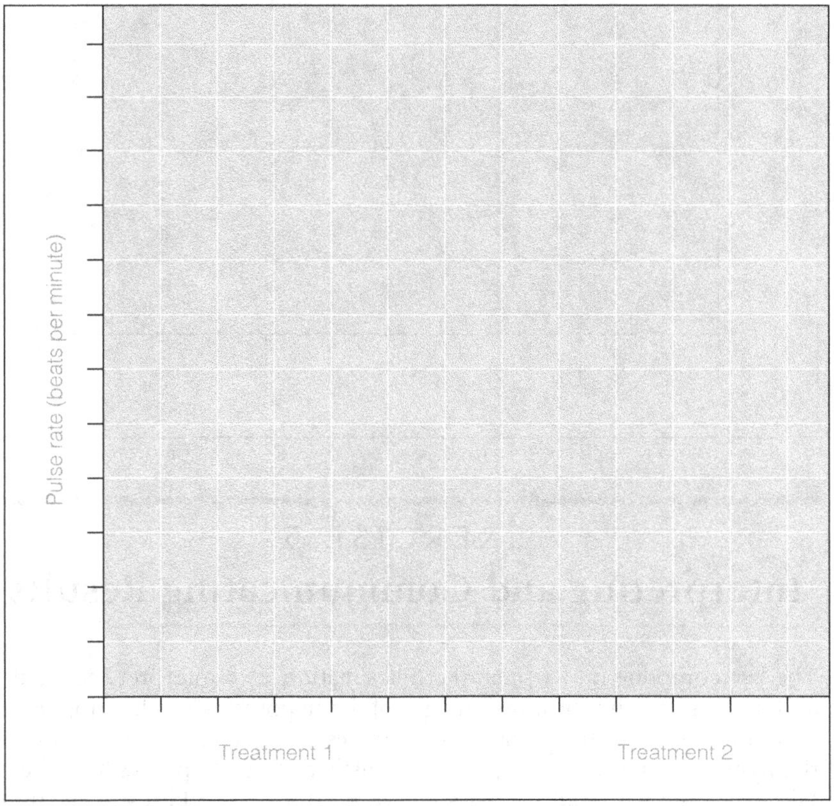

Figure 1.
Average pulse rate in athletes and nonathletes before and after exercise.

a. What was your independent variable (treatment)?

b. Write the dependent variable on the appropriate axis. Write the independent variable on the appropriate axis.

2. Design an additional figure that will assist with interpreting the results of your experiment. You might use the data for recovery time or the difference in pulse rate before and after the step test for each treatment.
3. Draw, label, and compose a title for that figure using the grid provided on the next page.

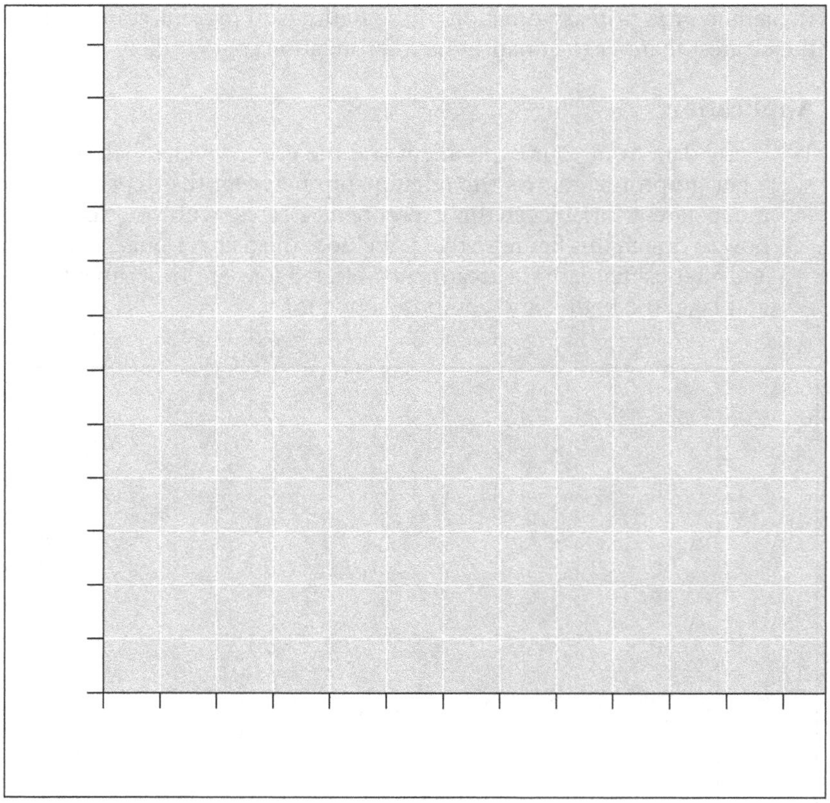

EXERCISE 5

Interpreting and Communicating Results

The last component of a scientific investigation is to interpret the results and discuss their implications in light of the hypothesis and its supporting literature. The investigator studies the tables and graphs and determines if the hypothesis has been supported or falsified. If the hypothesis has been falsified, the investigator must suggest alternate hypotheses for testing. If the hypothesis has been supported, the investigator suggests additional experiments to strengthen the hypothesis, using the same or alternate methods.

Scientists will thoroughly investigate a scientific question, testing hypotheses, collecting data, and analyzing results, until they are satisfied that they can explain the phenomenon of interest. The final phase of a scientific investigation is the communication of the results to other scientists. Preliminary results may be presented within a laboratory research group and at scientific meetings where the findings can be discussed. Ultimately, the completed project is presented in the form of a scientific paper that is reviewed by scientists within the field and published in a scientific journal. The ideas, procedures, results, analyses, and conclusions of all scientific investigations are critically scrutinized by other scientists. Because of this, science is sometimes described as *self-correcting,* meaning that errors that may occur are usually discovered within the scientific community.

Scientific communication, whether spoken or written, is essential to science. During this laboratory course, you often will be asked to present and interpret your results at the end of the laboratory period. Additionally, you will write components of a scientific paper for many lab topics.

Application

1. Using your tables and figures, analyze your results and discuss your conclusions with your group.
2. Write a summary statement for your experiment. Use your results to support or falsify your hypothesis. Be prepared to present your conclusions to the class.

3. Critique your experiment. What weaknesses do you see in the experiment? Suggest improvements.

Weaknesses in Experiment	Improvement
1.	
2.	
3.	
4.	
5.	

4. Suggest additional and modified hypotheses that might be tested. Briefly describe your next experiment.

5. Briefly describe the four major parts of a scientific paper. What is the abstract? What information is found in a References Cited section?

Questions for Review

1. Review the major components of an experiment by matching the following terms to the correct definition: *control, controlled variables, level of treatment, dependent variable, replication, procedure, prediction, hypothesis, independent variable.*
   a. Variables that are kept constant during the experiment (variables not being manipulated)

   b. Tentative explanation for an observation

   c. What the investigator varies in the experiment (for example, time, pH, temperature, concentration)

   d. Process used to measure the dependent variable

   e. Appropriate values to use for the independent variable

   f. Treatment that eliminates the independent variable or sets it at a standard value

   g. What the investigator measures, counts, or records; what is being affected in the experiment

h. Number of times the experiment is repeated

i. Statement of the expected results of an experiment based on the hypothesis

2. Identify the dependent and independent variables in the following experiments. (*Circle* the dependent variable and *underline* the independent variable.)

   a. The rate of carbon dioxide produced for yeast cells growing with and without the spice cinnamon.

   b. The beak length and depth for medium ground finches recorded over 5 years.

   c. Number and size of cubs born to polar bears living in habitats reduced by melting sea ice.

3. Suggest a control treatment for each of the following experiments.

   a. Frogs are captured from ponds where the parasitic worm *Robeiroia* is abundant. The number of limb deformities is recorded.

      Control treatment:

   b. Alzheimer patients aged 40–55 are tested for the presence of three copies of chromosome 21.

      Control treatment:

   c. Black worms are exposed to a solution of kava kava, an herbal supplement. Worm heart rates are recorded at 2-minute intervals.

      Control treatment:

4. In a recent study of 10,000 women (JAMA, Feb. 18, 2004), scientists reported that women who had breast cancer had a history of heavier antibiotic use than women who did not have breast cancer. What possible explanations for this correlation can you suggest?

5. What is the essential feature of science that makes it different from other ways of understanding the natural world?

Applying Your Knowledge

Interpreting Graphed and Tabular Data

1. The winning times for men and women competing in the Boston Marathon from 1972 to 1990 are presented in Figure 5. Women were allowed to compete for the first time in 1972. Write a statement summarizing these results.

   a. For men:

   b. For women:

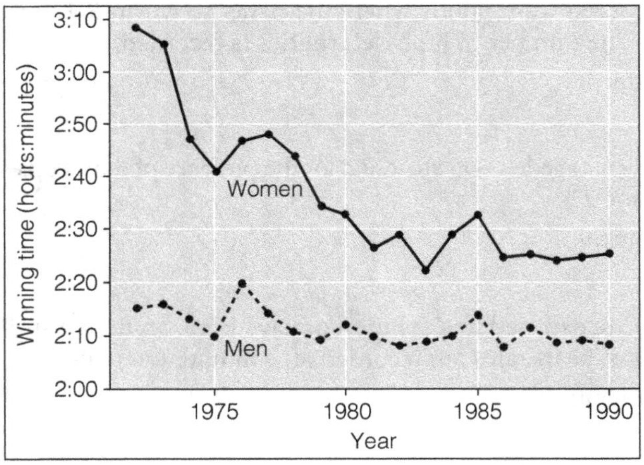

Figure 5.
Winning times for the Boston Marathon for men and women from 1972 to 1990. (After Gould, 1996.)

   c. Compare the slope of the two lines from 1972 to 1980. What possible explanation can you suggest for the rapid improvement in women's times compared to men's during this time period? During the 1980s, why did women's times level off?

d. What is the independent variable?

What is the dependent variable?

2. Rosemary and Peter Grant have studied the Galápagos finches on the Island of Daphne Major for 30 years. They have identified, marked, and measured every finch on the island. They recorded the parents and offspring for generations of finch species. The medium ground finches, *Geospiza fortis*, are medium-sized, seed-eating birds. The Grants determined the relationship between seed size and hardness with beak depth (Figure 6). Which finches are able to crack the hardest seeds? State the trend.

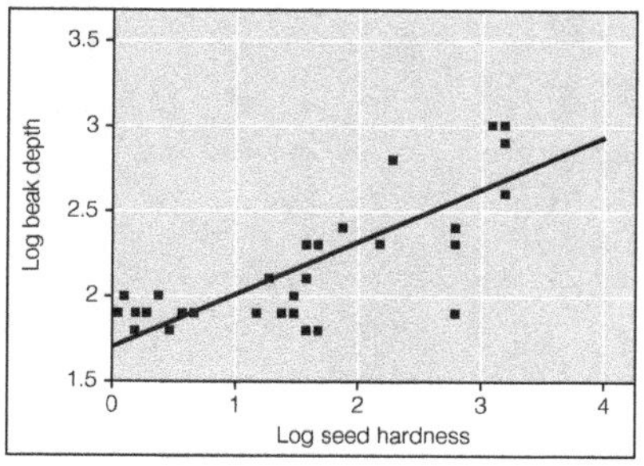

Figure 6.
The relationship of beak depth in ground finches and the maximum hardness of seeds they can crack. (After Grant and Grant, 2003)

In 1977 the Galápagos Islands experienced a severe drought that resulted in the death of many plants, severe competition for seeds among the finches, and death of many birds. Beak size for the medium ground finch offspring born in 1976 before the drought and those born in 1978, the year following the drought, are shown in Figure 7 (Grant and Grant, 2003).

Compare the average beak depth for the offspring from 1976 and 1978.

Approximately how many birds in the population each year had beaks larger than 9.3 mm?

During the drought of 1977 which group of medium ground finches were more successful in finding food and reproducing, those with large beaks or those with small beaks? Explain.

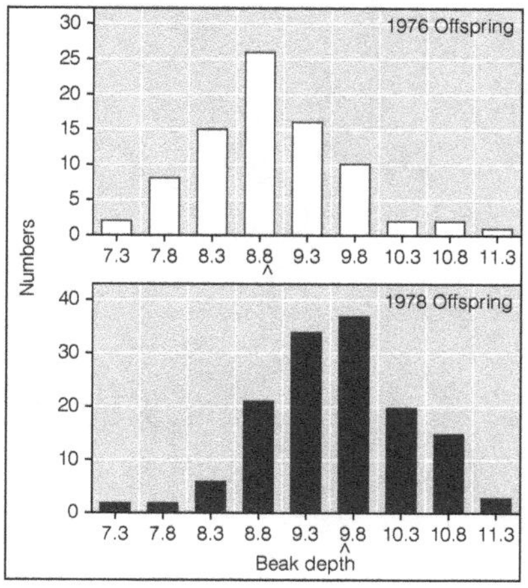

Figure 7.
Evolutionary change in beak depth in the population of the medium ground finch on the Galápagos Island of Daphne Major. The carets indicate the means for the population. (After Grant and Grant, 2003.)

Based on Figure 6 and 7 what kind of seeds were available in 1977, soft or hard?

Using guidelines for graphs, how could you improve the axes labels on this figure?

3. Review the guidelines for graphs and critique Figure 8 below. This figure illustrates the changes in risk factors that are important in chronic diseases such as coronary heart disease, lung cancer, diabetes, and stroke.

Figure 8.
RISK-FACTOR PREVALENCE IN U.S.

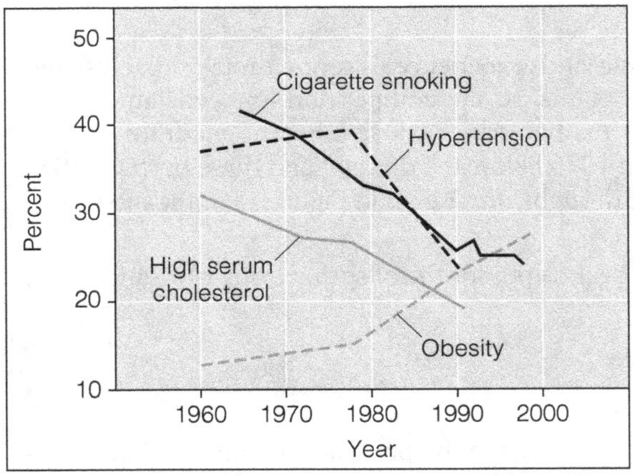

Source: Centers for Disease Control and Prevention. (After Doyle, 2001.)

4. Non-native invasive species are considered a serious threat to biodiversity and in particular to species already threatened by extinction. The percentage of threatened vertebrate species affected by invasive species differs on the continental mainlands versus the islands of the world (Table 4).

   a. Make a general statement about the effect of invasive species on threatened animals on the mainland compared to those on islands.

b. Which taxonomic category has a higher percentage of mainland species affected than island species?

Table 4
Percentage of Threatened Terrestrial Vertebrate Species on Continental Mainlands and Islands Affected by Invasive Species (The number of threatened species is in parentheses.)

	Mainland Areas		**Insular Areas**	
Taxonomic Group	**%**	**(n)**	**%**	**(n)**
Mammals	19.4	(283)	11.5	(61)
Birds	5.2	(250)	38.2	(144)
Reptiles	15.5	(84)	32.9	(76)
Amphibians	3.3	(30)	30.8	(13)
Total for all groups considered	12.7	(647)	31.0	(294)

(After McNeely, 2000.)

c. Is there a greater number of threatened species among birds or mammals?

Practicing Experimental Design

1. Scientists have become increasingly alarmed by the occurrence of limb deformities in amphibians during the last decade. Malformations have been detected in 60 species in 46 states with rates as high as 80% of the population. Deformities include missing and extra limbs, limbs extending from the stomach region, nubs, and malformed webbing. Scientists have hypothesized that one or more factors might be responsible, including exposure to UV radiation, infection by parasitic worms, agricultural runoff, and chemical pollutants.

   Several researchers hypothesized that the trematode (parasitic flatworm) *Ribeiroia* was responsible for the increased deformities in frogs. *Ribeiroia* has a complicated life cycle in which the adults live in the digestive systems of birds such as herons, and the trematode eggs are released in bird feces into ponds. The eggs hatch and larvae infect aquatic snails, forming large numbers of another larval stage called the cercariae. These larvae infect the tadpoles forming cysts in the developing legs. The frogs in turn are eaten by the birds, thus completing the cycle (Figure 9). Results from laboratory experiments confirmed that infection by the trematodes did cause limb deformities in frogs.

   Kiesecker (2002) investigated the role of *Ribeiroia* and the effect of agricultural runoff in field experiments. Six ponds were selected; three received runoff from agricultural fields. At each pond, experimental enclosures were built: 3 were covered with mesh that allowed the trematode larvae to enter

Figure 9.
Life cycle of the trematode, *Ribeiroia*. (After Kiesecker et al, 2004.)

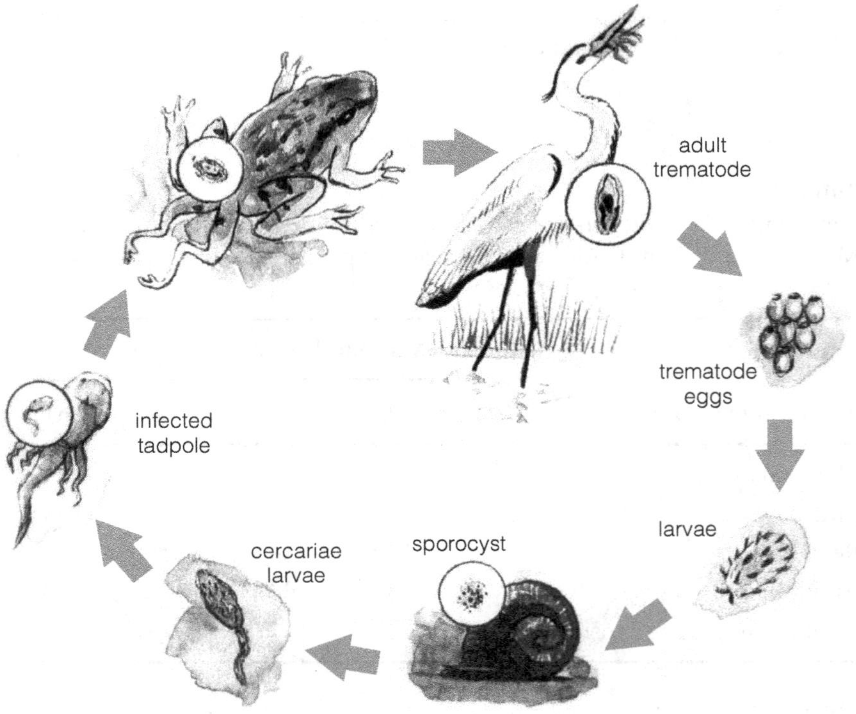

and 3 were covered with mesh too small for the parasitic larvae to penetrate. Ten wood frog tadpoles were added to each enclosure. When the tadpoles metamorphosed, they were collected and scored for limb deformities. The results were averaged and the proportion of the frogs with limb deformities was calculated. The results are shown in Figure 10.

In this complex experiment, more than one independent variable was investigated. What were the independent variables?

What were the dependent variables?

Figure 10.
Limb deformities in wood frogs following exposure to trematodes and agricultural runoff in six ponds. (After Kiesecker et al, 2004.)

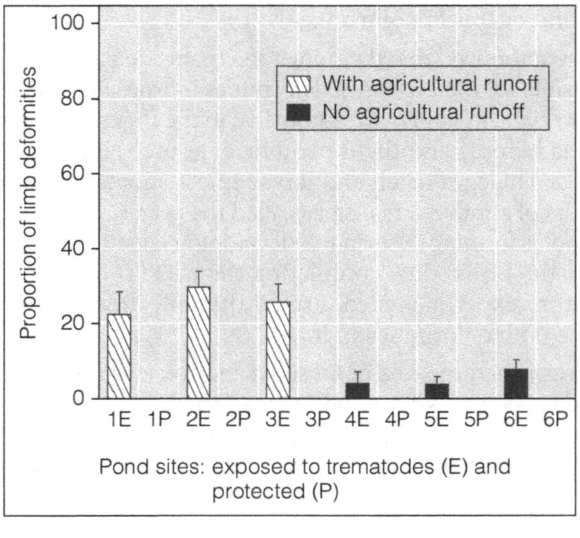

Identify the control treatments for the experiment.

How many replicates were used?

What controlled variables might need to be considered in designing this experiment?

Refer to Figure 10 and write a statement describing the proportion of limb deformities in frogs reared in protected vs. exposed enclosures at the 6 pond sites.

Under what conditions was the highest proportion of limb deformities produced?

Pesticides in agricultural runoff may have reacted with the trematode larvae to increase limb deformities. On separate paper, design a *laboratory* experiment to test the effect of a common pesticide on limb deformity. Include two levels of treatment for the pesticide.

Write a hypothesis and prediction for your experiment:

Hypothesis:

Prediction:

References

Campbell, N., and J. Reece. *Biology,* 7th ed. San Francisco, CA: Benjamin Cummings, 2005.

Chrispeels, M. J. and D. E. Sadava. *Plants, Genes and Crop Biotechnology,* 2nd ed. Sudbury, MA: Jones and Bartlett, 2003.

Doyle, R. "Lifestyle Blues," *Scientific American,* vol. 284 (2001) p. 30.

Evans, L. "Traffic Crashes." *American Scientist,* 2002, vol. 90, pp. 244–253.

Gould, S. *Full House*. New York: Random House, 1996.

Grant, B. R. and P. R. Grant. "What Darwin's Finches Can Teach Us about the Evolutionary Origins of Biodiversity," *BioScience*, 2003, vol. 53, pp. 965–975.

Kiesecker, J. M. "Synergism Between Trematode Infection and Pesticide Exposure: A Link to Amphibian Limb Deformities in Nature?" *PNAS*, 2002, vol. 99, pp. 9900–9904.

Kiesecker, J. M., L. K. Belden, K. Shea, and M. J. Rubbo. "Amphibian Decline and Emerging Disease," *American Scientist*, 2004, vol. 92, pp. 138–147.

Knisely, K. *A Student Handbook for Writing in Biology*, Sunderland, MA: Sinauer Associates, 2002. (Instructions for making graphs using Excel, Appendix 2.)

Kusinitz, I., and M. Fine. *Your Guide to Getting Fit*, 3rd ed. Palo Alto, CA: Mayfield, 1995.

McNeely, J. A. "The Future of Alien Invasive Species: Changing Social Views." In *Invasive Species in a Changing World*, eds. H. A. Mooney and R. J. Hobbs. Washington, D.C.: Island Press, 2000.

Moore, J. *Science as a Way of Knowing*. Cambridge, MA: Harvard University Press, 1993.

Pechenik, J. *A Short Guide to Writing about Biology*, 4th ed. San Francisco, CA: Addison Wesley Longman, 2001.

Velicer, C. M., S. R. Heckbert, J. W. Lampe, J. D. Potter, C. A. Robertson, and S. H. Taplin. "Antibiotic Use in Relation to the Risk of Breast Cancer," *JAMA*, 2004, vol. 291, pp. 827–835.

The format and many ideas in this lab topic were based on an exercise written by Jean Dickey, published in J. Dickey, *Laboratory Investigations for Biology*, Menlo Park, CA: Addison Wesley Longman, 1995.

Microscopes and Cells

Laboratory Objectives

After completing this lab topic, you should be able to:

1. Identify the parts of compound and stereoscopic microscopes and be proficient in their correct use in biological studies.
2. Describe procedures used in preparing materials for electron microscopy and compare these with procedures used in light microscopy.
3. Identify cell structures and organelles from electron micrographs and state the functions of each.
4. Describe features of specific cells and determine characteristics shared by all cells studied.
5. Discuss the evolutionary significance of increasing complexity from unicellular to multicellular organization and provide examples from the lab.

Introduction

According to cell theory, the *cell* is the fundamental biological unit, the smallest and simplest biological structure possessing all the characteristics of the living condition. All living organisms are composed of one or more cells, and every activity taking place in a living organism is ultimately related to metabolic activities in cells. Thus, understanding the processes of life necessitates an understanding of the structure and function of the cell.

The earliest known cells found in fossilized sediments 3.5 billion years old (called **prokaryotic** cells) lack nuclei and membrane-bound organelles. Cells with a membrane-bound nucleus and organelles (**eukaryotic** cells) do not appear in the fossil record for another 2 billion years. But the eventual evolution of the eukaryotic cell and its internal compartmentalization led to enormous biological diversity in single cells. The evolution of loose aggregates of cells ultimately to colonies of connected cells provided for specialization, so that groups of cells had specific and different functions. This early division of labor included cells whose primary function was locomotion or reproduction. The evolution of multicellularity appears to have originated more than once in eukaryotes and provided an opportunity for extensive adaptive radiation as organisms specialized and diversified, eventually giving rise to fungi, plants, and animals. This general trend in increasing complexity and specialization seen in the history of life will be illustrated.

Given the fundamental role played by cells in the organization of life, one can readily understand why the study of cells is essential to the study of life. Cells, however, are below the limit of resolution of the human eye. We cannot study them without using a microscope. The microscope has probably contributed more than any other instrument to the development of biology as a science. Two types of microscopes are named according to the source of illumination used: light microscopes and electron microscopes. We will be using light microscopes exclusively in our study of cells, and we will view electron micrographs of cell structures not visible with the light microscope.

Microscopes of one kind or another are used by all biologists in numerous subdisciplines: genetics, molecular biology, neurobiology, cell biology, evolution, and ecology. The knowledge and skills you develop today will be used and enhanced throughout this course and throughout your career in biology. It is important, therefore, that you take the time to master these exercises thoroughly.

EXERCISE 1
Parts of the Microscope

Materials

compound microscope

Introduction

The microscope is designed to make objects visible that are too difficult or too small to see with the unaided eye. There are many different kinds of light microscopes, including phase-contrast, darkfield, polarizing, and UV. These differ primarily in the source and manner in which light is passed through the specimen to be viewed.

The microscopes in biology lab are usually compound binocular or monocular light microscopes, some of which may have phase-contrast attachments. **Compound** means that the scopes have a minimum of two magnifying lenses (the ocular and the objective lenses). **Binocular microscopes** have two eyepieces, **monoculars** have only one eyepiece, and **light** refers to the type of illumination used, that is, visible light from a lamp.

Your success in and enjoyment of a large portion of the laboratory work in introductory biology will depend on how proficient you become in the use of the microscope. When used and maintained correctly, these precision instruments are capable of producing images of the highest quality.

Although there are many variations in the features of microscopes, they are all constructed on a similar plan (Figure 1). In this exercise you will be introduced to the common variations found in different models of compound microscopes and asked to identify those features found on your microscope.

Please treat these microscopes with the greatest care!

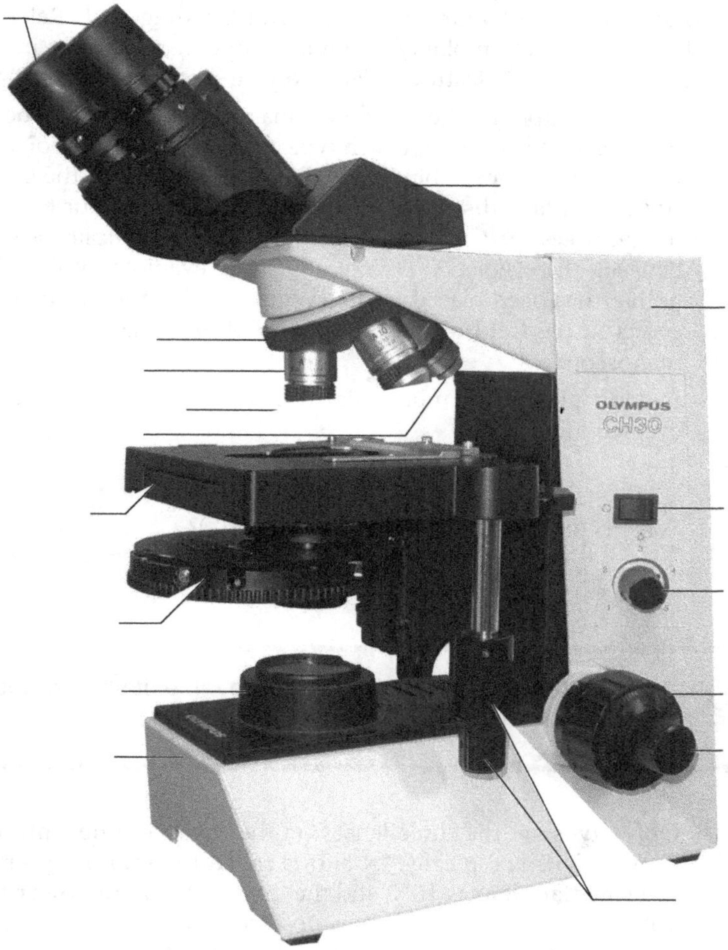

a.

b.

Figure 1.

a. **The compound binocular light microscope.** Locate the parts of your microscope described in Exercise 1 and label this photograph. Indicate in the margin of your lab manual any features unique to your microscope.

b. **Enlarged photo of compound light microscope as viewed from under the stage.** This microscope is equipped with phase-contrast optics. Locate the condenser, condenser adjustment knob, phase-contrast revolving turret, and iris diaphragm on your microscope (if present) and label them on the diagram.

Procedure

1. Obtain a compound light microscope, following directions from your instructor. To carry the microscope correctly, hold the arm with one hand, and support the base with your other hand. Remove the cover, but do not plug in the microscope.

2. Locate the parts of your microscope, and label Figure 1. Refer to the following description of a typical microscope. In the spaces provided, indicate the specific features related to your microscope.

   a. The **head** supports the two sets of magnifying lenses. The **ocular** is the lens in the eyepiece, which typically has a magnification of 10X. If your microscope is binocular, the distance between the eyepieces (**interpupillary distance**) can be adjusted to suit your eyes. Move the eyepieces apart, and look for the scale used to indicate the distance between the eyepieces. Do not adjust the eyepieces at this time. A pointer has been placed in the eyepiece and is used to point to an object in the **field of view**, the circle of light that one sees in the microscope.

      Is your microscope monocular (one eyepiece) or binocular (two eyepieces)?

      What is the magnification of your ocular(s)?

Although the eyepiece may be removable, it should not be removed from the microscope.

   b. **Objectives** are the three lenses on the **revolving nosepiece.** The shortest lens is typically 4X and is called the **scanning lens.** The **intermediate lens** is 10X, and the longest, the **high-power lens,** is 40X (the fourth position on the nosepiece is empty). It is important to clean both the objective and ocular lenses before each use. Dirty lenses will cause a blurring or fogging of the image. Always use lens paper for cleaning! Any other material (including Kimwipes®) may scratch the lenses.

      What is the magnification of each of your objectives? List them in order of increasing magnification.

   c. The **arm** supports the stage and condenser lens. The **condenser lens** is used to focus the light from the **lamp** through the specimen to be viewed. The height of the condenser can be adjusted by an **adjustment knob.** The **iris diaphragm** controls the width of the circle of light and, therefore, the amount of light passing through the specimen.

      If your microscope has phase-contrast optics, the condenser may be housed in a **revolving turret.** When the turret is set on 0, the normal optical arrangement is in place. This condition is called **bright-field microscopy.** Other positions of the turret set phase-contrast optics in place. To use phase-contrast, the turret setting must correspond to the magnifying power of the objective being used.

      Is your microscope equipped with phase-contrast optics?

The **stage** supports the specimen to be viewed. A mechanical stage can be moved right and left and back and forth by two **stage adjustment knobs.** With a stationary stage, the slide is secured under **stage clips** and moved slightly by hand while viewing the slide. The distance between the stage and the objective can be adjusted with the **coarse** and **fine focus adjustment knobs.**

Does your microscope have a mechanical or stationary stage?

d. The **base** acts as a stand for the microscope and houses the lamp. In some microscopes, the intensity of the light that passes through the specimen can be adjusted with the **light intensity lever.** Generally, more light is needed when using high magnification than when using low magnification. Describe the light system for your microscope.

EXERCISE 2
Basic Microscope Techniques

Materials

clear ruler
coverslips
prepared slides: letter and crossed thread
lens paper
blank slides
Kimwipes®
dropper bottle with distilled water

Introduction

In this exercise, you will learn to use the microscope to examine a recognizable object, a slide of the letter *e*. Recall that microscopes vary, so you may have to omit steps that refer to features not available on your microscope. Practice adjusting your microscope to become proficient in locating a specimen, focusing clearly, and adjusting the light for the best contrast.

Procedure

1. Clean microscope lenses.

   Each time you use the microscope, you should begin by cleaning the lenses. Using lens paper moistened with a drop of distilled water, wipe the ocular, objective, and condenser lenses. Wipe them again with a piece of dry lens paper.

Use only lens paper on microscope lenses. Do not use Kimwipes®, tissues, or other papers.

2. Adjust the focus on your microscope:
   a. Plug your microscope into the outlet.
   b. Turn on the light. Adjust the light intensity to mid-range if your microscope has that feature.

c. Rotate the 4X objective into position using the revolving nosepiece ring, not the objective itself.

d. Take the letter slide and wipe it with a Kimwipe® tissue. Each time you study a prepared slide, you should first wipe it clean. Place the letter slide on the stage, and center it over the stage opening.

Slides should be placed on and removed from the stage only when the 4X objective is in place. Removing a slide when the higher objectives are in position may scratch the lenses.

e. Look through the ocular and bring the letter into rough focus by slowly focusing upward using the coarse adjustment.

f. For binocular microscopes, looking through the oculars, move the oculars until you see only one image of the letter *e*. In this position, the oculars should be aligned with your pupils. In the margin of your lab manual, make a note of the **interpupillary distance** on the scale between the oculars. Each new lab day, before you begin to use the microscope, set this distance.

g. Raise the condenser to its highest position, and fully close the iris diaphragm.

h. Looking through the ocular, slowly lower the condenser just until the graininess disappears. Slowly open the iris diaphragm just until the entire field of view is illuminated. This is the correct position for both the condenser and the iris diaphragm.

i. Rotate the 10X objective into position.

j. Look through the ocular and slowly focus upward with the coarse adjustment knob until the image is in rough focus. Sharpen the focus using the fine adjustment knob.

Do not turn the fine adjustment knob more than two revolutions in either direction. If the image does not come into focus, return to 10X and refocus using the coarse adjustment.

k. For binocular microscopes, cover your left eye and use the fine adjustment knob to focus the fixed (right) ocular until the letter *e* is in maximum focus. Now cover the right eye and, using the diopter ring on the left ocular, bring the image into focus. The letter *e* should now be in focus for both of your eyes. Each new lab day, as you begin to study your first slide, repeat this procedure.

l. You can increase or decrease the contrast by adjusting the iris diaphragm opening. Note that the maximum amount of light provides little contrast. Adjust the aperture until the image is sharp.

m. Move the slide slowly to the right. In what direction does the image in the ocular move?

n. Is the image in the ocular inverted relative to the specimen on the stage?

o. Center the specimen in the field of view; then rotate the 40X objective into position while watching from the side. *If it appears that the objective will hit the slide, stop and ask for assistance.*

✱ Most of the microscopes have **parfocal** lenses, which means that little refocusing is required when moving from one lens to another. If your scope is *not* parfocal, ask your instructor for assistance.

p. After the 40X objective is in place, focus using the fine adjustment knob.

✱ Never focus with the coarse adjustment knob when you are using the high-power objective.

q. The distance between the specimen and the objective lens is called the **working distance.** Is this distance greater with the 40X or the 10X objective?

3. Compute the total magnification of the specimen being viewed. To do so, multiply the magnification of the ocular lens by that of the objective lens.

   a. What is the total magnification of the letter as the microscope is now set?

   b. What would be the total magnification if the ocular were 20X and the objective were 100X (oil immersion)? This is the magnification achieved by the best light microscopes.

4. Measure the diameter of the field of view. Once you determine the size of the field of view for any combination of ocular and objective lenses, you can determine the size of any structure within that field.

   a. Rotate the 4X objective into position and remove the letter slide.

   b. Place a clear ruler on the stage, and focus on its edge.

   c. The distance between two lines on the ruler is 1 mm. What is the diameter (mm) of the field of view?

d. Convert this measurement to micrometers, a more commonly used unit of measurement in microscopy (1 mm = 1,000 μm).

e. Measure the diameters of the field of view for the 10X and 40X objectives, and enter all three in the spaces below to be used for future reference.

4X ≈ ________ 10X ≈ ________ 40X ≈ ________

f. What is the relationship between the size of the field of view and magnification?

5. Determine spatial relationships. The **depth of field** is the thickness of the specimen that may be seen in focus at one time. Because the depth of focus is very short in the compound microscope, focus up and down to clearly view all planes of a specimen.

   a. Rotate the 4X objective into position and remove the ruler. Take a slide of crossed threads, wipe it with a Kimwipe, and place the slide on the stage. Center the slide so that the region where the two threads cross is in the center of the stage opening.

   b. Focus on the region where the threads cross. Are both threads in focus at the same time?

   c. Rotate the 10X objective into position and focus on the cross. Are both threads in focus at the same time?

   Does the 4X or the 10X objective have a shorter depth of field?

   d. Focus upward (move the stage up) with the coarse adjustment until both threads are just out of focus. Slowly focus down using the fine adjustment. Which thread comes into focus first? Is this thread lying under or over the other thread?

   e. Rotate the 40X objective into position and slowly focus up and down, using the fine adjustment only. Does the 10X or the 40X objective have a shorter depth of field?

6. At the end of your microscope session, use these procedures to store your microscope:

   a. Rotate the 4X objective into position.

   b. Remove the slide from the stage.

   c. Return the phase-contrast condenser to the 0 setting if you have used phase-contrast.

d. Set the light intensity to its lowest setting and turn off the power.
e. Unplug the cord and wrap it around the base of the microscope.
f. Replace the dust cover.
g. Return the microscope to the cabinet using two hands; one hand should hold the arm, and the other should support the base.

These steps should be followed every time you store your microscope.

EXERCISE 3

The Stereoscopic Microscope

Materials

stereoscopic microscope
dissecting needles
living *Elodea*
microscope slides
droppers of water
coverslips

Introduction

The stereoscopic (dissecting) microscope has relatively low magnification, 7X to 30X, and is used for viewing and manipulating relatively large objects. The binocular feature creates the stereoscopic effect. The stereoscopic microscope is similar to the compound microscope except in the following ways: (1) The depth of field is much greater than with the compound microscope, so objects are seen in three dimensions, and (2) the light source can be directed down onto as well as up through an object, which permits the viewing of objects too thick to transmit light. Light directed down on the object is called **reflected** or **incident light.** Light passing through the object is called **transmitted light.**

Procedure

1. Remove your stereoscopic microscope from the cabinet and locate the parts labeled in Figure 2. Locate the switches for both incident and transmitted light. In the margin of your lab manual, note any features of your microscope that are not shown in the figure. What is the range of magnification for your microscope?
2. Observe an object of your choice at increasing magnification. Select an object that fits easily on the stage (e.g., ring, coin, finger tip, pen, ruler).
   a. Place the object on the stage and adjust the interpupillary distance (distance between the oculars) by gently pushing or pulling the oculars until you can see the object as a single image.
   b. Change the magnification and note the three-dimensional characteristics of your object.
   c. Adjust the lights, both reflected and transmitted. Which light gives you the best view of your object?
3. Prepare a **wet mount** of *Elodea.* Living material is often prepared for observation using a wet mount. (The material is either in water or covered with water prior to adding a coverslip.) You will use this technique to view living material under the dissecting and compound microscopes (Figure 3).
   a. Place a drop of water in the center of a clean microscope slide.
   b. Remove a single leaf of *Elodea,* and place it in the drop of water.

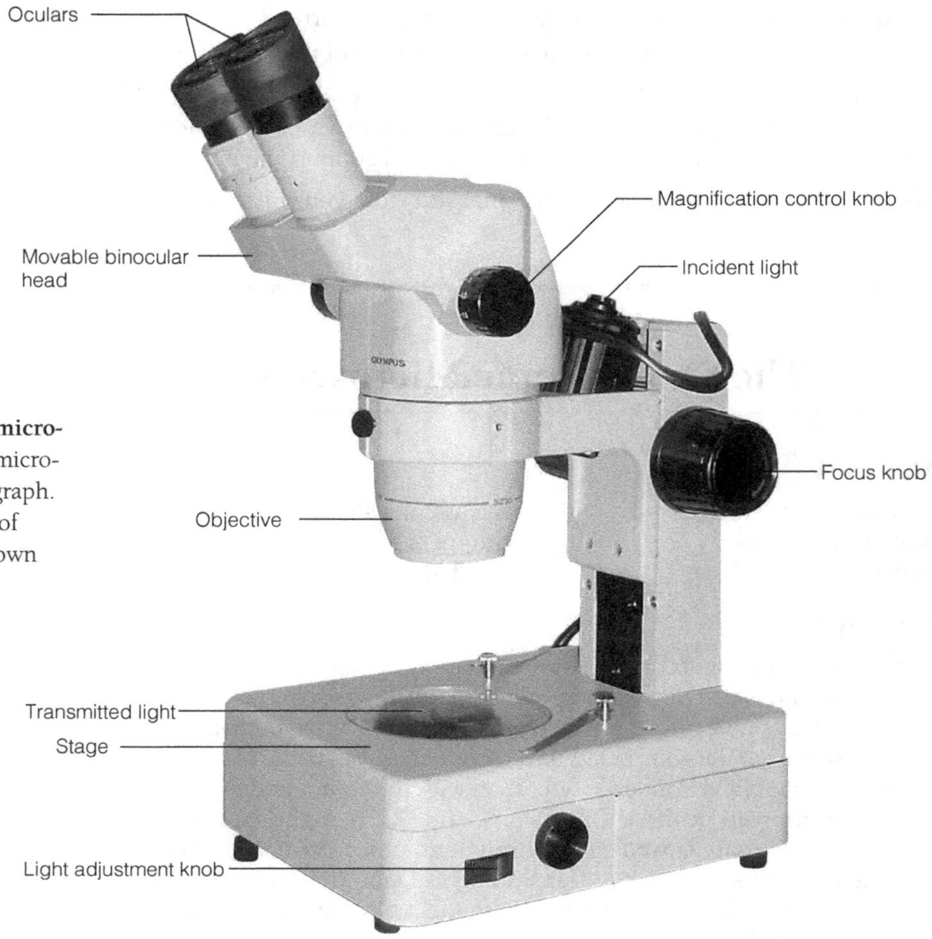

Figure 2.
The stereoscopic (dissecting) microscope. Locate the parts of your microscope by referring to this photograph. Note in the margin any features of your microscope that are not shown in the photograph.

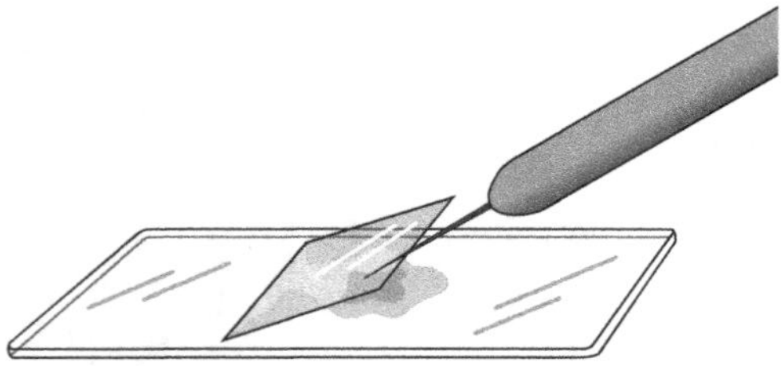

Figure 3.
Preparation of a wet mount. Place a drop of water and your specimen on the slide. Using a dissecting needle, slowly lower a coverslip onto the slide, being careful not to trap air bubbles in the droplet.

c. Using a dissecting needle, place a coverslip at a 45° angle above the slide with one edge of the coverslip in contact with the edge of the water droplet, as shown.

d. Lower the coverslip slowly onto the slide, being careful not to trap air bubbles in the droplet. The function of the coverslip is threefold: (1) to flatten the preparation, (2) to keep the preparation from drying out, and (3) to protect the objective lenses. Over long periods of time, the preparation may dry out, at which point water can be added to one edge of the coverslip.

Specimens can be viewed without a coverslip using the stereoscopic microscope, but a coverslip must always be used with the compound microscope.

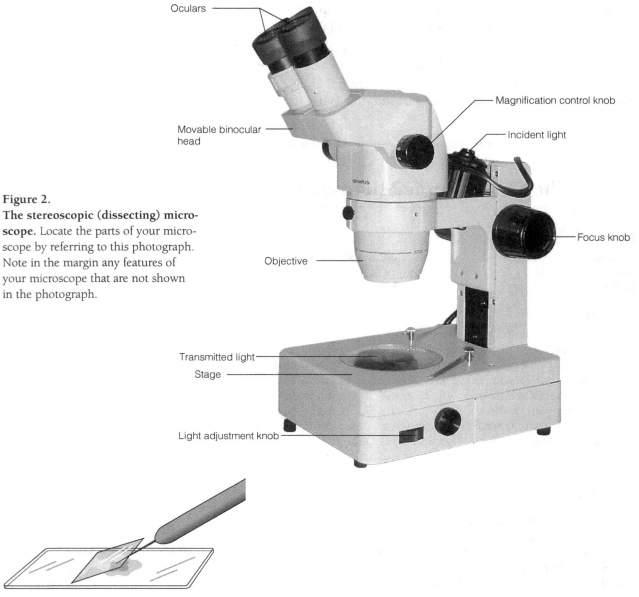

4. Observe the structure of the *Elodea* leaf at increasing magnification.
   a. Place the leaf slide on the stage and adjust the focus. Change the magnification and note the characteristics of the leaf at increased magnification.
   b. Sketch the leaf in the margin of your lab manual and list, in the space below, the structures that are visible at low and high magnification.

      Low:

      High:

      Is it possible to see cells in the leaf using the stereoscopic microscope?

      Organelles?

   c. Save your slide for later study. In Exercise 5, Lab Study C, you will be asked to compare these observations of *Elodea* with those made while using the compound microscope.

EXERCISE 4

The Electron Microscope

Materials

demonstration resources for the electron microscope
electron micrographs

Introduction

The electron microscope magnifies objects approximately 1,000X larger than a light microscope can (up to 1,000,000X). This difference depends on the **resolving power** of the electron microscope, which allows the viewer to see two objects of comparable size that are close together and still be able to recognize that they are two objects rather than one. Resolving power, in turn, depends on the wavelength of light passed through the specimen: the shorter the wavelength, the greater the resolution. Because electron microscopes use electrons as a source of illumination and electrons have a much shorter wavelength than does visible light, the resolving power of electron microscopes is much greater than that of light microscopes. Both the electron and light microscopes can be equipped with lenses that allow for tremendous magnification, but only the electron microscope has sufficient resolving power to make these lenses useful.

Procedure

1. Compare the features of the light and electron microscopes (Figure 4).
   a. Name three structures found in both microscopes.

   b. What is the energy source for the electron microscope?

   For the compound microscope?

   c. Describe how the lenses differ for the two microscopes.

2. Using the resources provided by your instructor, review the procedures and materials for preparing a specimen for electron microscopy.

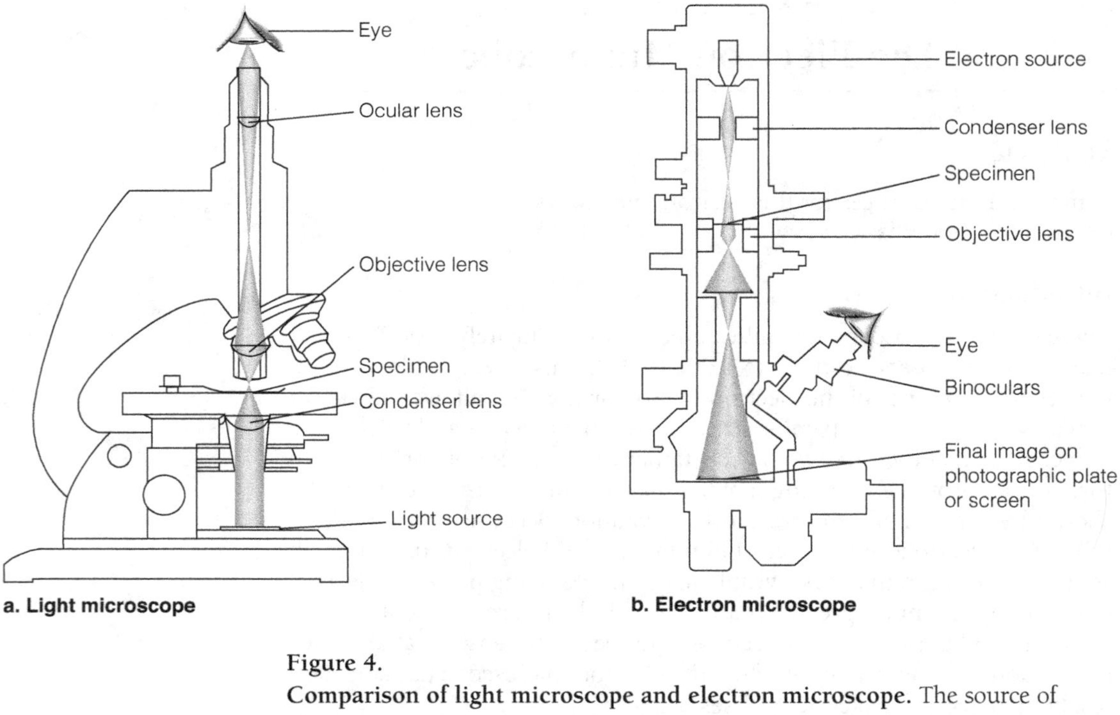

Figure 4.
Comparison of light microscope and electron microscope. The source of illumination is light for the light microscope and electrons for the electron microscope. The image is magnified by glass objectives in light microscopy and by electromagnets in electron microscopy.

3. Define the following terms on separate paper or in the margin of your lab manual:

fixation	*staining with heavy metals*
embedding	*electromagnetic lenses*
ultramicrotome	*fluorescent screen*
boat on diamond or glass knife	*vacuum*
copper grids	*electron micrographs*

4. Observe the electron micrographs on demonstration in the laboratory. Use these and your textbook to complete Table 1.

EXERCISE 5

The Organization of Cells

In this exercise, you will examine the features common to all eukaryotic cells that are indicative of their common ancestry. However, you will observe that all cells are not the same. Some organisms are **unicellular** (single-celled), with all living functions (respiration, digestion, reproduction, and excretion) handled by that one cell. Others form random, temporary **aggregates,** or clusters, of cells. Clusters composed of a consistent and predictable number of cells are called **colonies.** Simple colonies have no physiological connections but maintain a predictable multicellular structure. Complex colonies have physiological connections and specialization of groups of cells. **Multicellular** organisms have large numbers of cells with specialized structure and function, and no one cell can exist successfully by itself.

In this exercise, you will examine selected unicellular, aggregate, colonial, and multicellular organisms.

Lab Study A. Unicellular Organisms

Materials

microscope slides
culture of *Amoeba*
living termites
forceps
coverslips
dissecting needles
insect Ringers

Introduction

Unicellular eukaryotic organisms may be **autotrophic** (photosynthetic) or **heterotrophic** (deriving food from other organisms or their by-products). These diverse organisms, called protists, will be studied in detail later.

Table 1
Characteristics of Cellular Organelles; EM = Electron Microscope, LM = Light Microscope

Organelle	Size (μm); Visualization	Function	Where Present: Plants and Autotrophic Protists	Where Present: Animals and Heterotrophic Protists
Plasma membrane	$7–9 \times 10^{-3}$ (thickness); EM			
Cell wall	Variable; a single fibril is as thick as the plasma membrane; LM, EM			
Nucleus	4–10 (diameter); LM, EM			
Chloroplast	8 (length); LM, EM			
Mitochondria	0.5–10 (diameter); EM			
Vacuole	Variable; LM, EM			
Golgi apparatus	Variable; EM			
Peroxisomes	0.2–1.5 (diameter); EM			
Lysosomes	0.2–0.5 (diameter); EM			
Endoplasmic reticulum	0.005–0.01 (tube diameter); EM			
Ribosomes	$1.7–2.3 \times 10^{-3}$ (diameter); EM			
Flagella, cilia	0.2 (diameter); 2–150 (length); LM, EM			

Procedure

1. Examine a living *Amoeba* (Figure 5) under the compound microscope. Amoebas are aquatic organisms commonly found in ponds. To transfer a specimen to your slide, follow these procedures:
   a. Place the culture dish containing the amoeba under the dissecting microscope, and focus on the bottom of the dish. The amoeba will appear as a whitish, irregularly shaped organism attached to the bottom.
   b. Using a clean pipette (it is important not to interchange pipettes between culture dishes), transfer a drop with several amoebas to your microscope slide. To do this, squeeze the pipette bulb *before* you place the tip under the surface of the water. Disturbing the culture as little as possible, pipette a drop of water with debris from the *bottom* of the culture dish. You may use your stereoscopic microscope to scan the slide to locate amoebas before continuing.
   c. Cover your preparation with a clean coverslip.
   d. Under low power on the compound scope, scan the slide to locate an amoeba. Center the specimen in your field of view; then switch to higher powers.
   e. Identify the following structures in the amoeba:

      Cell membrane is the boundary that separates the organism from its surroundings.

      Ectoplasm is the thin, transparent layer of cytoplasm directly beneath the cell membrane.

      Endoplasm is the granular cytoplasm containing the cell organelles.

      The **nucleus** is the grayish, football-shaped body that is somewhat granular in appearance. This organelle, which directs the cellular activities, will often be seen moving within the endoplasm.

      Contractile vacuoles are clear, spherical vesicles of varying sizes that gradually enlarge as they fill with excess water. Once you've located a vacuole, watch it fill and then empty its contents into the surrounding environment. These vacuoles serve an excretory function for the amoeba.

      Food vacuoles are small, dark, irregularly shaped vesicles within the endoplasm. They contain undigested food particles.

      Pseudopodia ("false feet") are fingerlike projections of the cytoplasm. They are used for locomotion as well as for trapping and engulfing food in a process called **phagocytosis.**

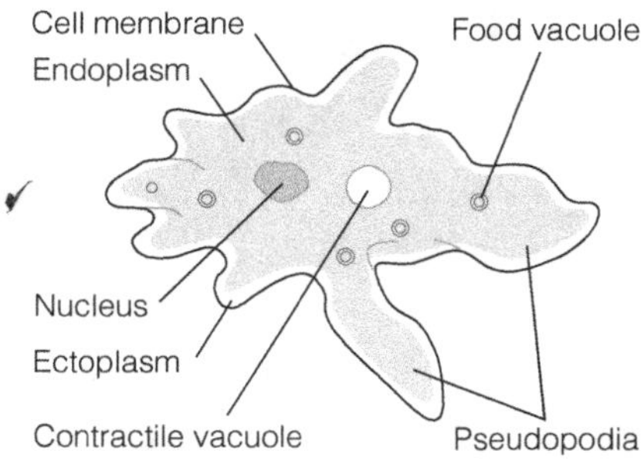

Figure 5.
Amoeba. An *Amoeba* moves using pseudopodia. Observe the living organisms using the compound microscope.

2. Examine *Trichonympha* under a compound microscope. You will first have to separate the *Trichonympha* (Figure 6) from the termite with which it lives in a symbiotic relationship. *Trichonympha* and other organisms occupy the gut of the termites, where they digest wood particles eaten by the insect. Termites lack the enzymes necessary to digest wood and are dependent on *Trichonympha* to make the nutrients in the wood available to them. *Trichonympha* has become so well adapted to the environment of the termite's gut that it cannot survive outside of it.

   To obtain a specimen:
   a. Place a couple of drops of **insect Ringers** (a saline solution that is isotonic to the internal environment of insects) on a clean microscope slide.
   b. Using forceps or your fingers, transfer a termite into the drop of Ringers.

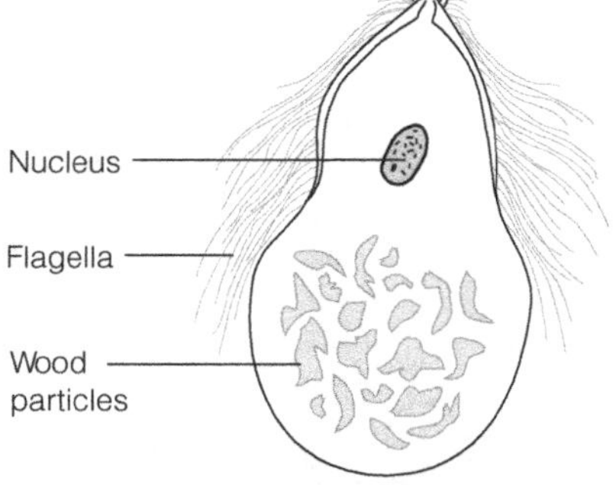

Figure 6.
Trichonympha. A community of microorganisms, including *Trichonympha,* inhabits the intestine of the termite. Following the procedure in Exercise 5, Lab Study A, disperse the microorganisms and locate the cellular structures in *Trichonympha.*

c. Place the slide under the dissecting microscope.
d. Place the tips of dissecting needles at either end of the termite and pull in opposite directions.
e. Locate the long tube that is the termite's intestine. Remove all the larger parts of the insect from the slide.
f. Using a dissecting needle, mash the intestine to release the *Trichonympha* and other protozoa and bacteria.
g. Cover your preparation with a clean coverslip.
h. Transfer your slide to the compound microscope and scan the slide under low power. Center several *Trichonympha* in the field of view and switch to higher powers.

Several types of protozoans and bacteria will be present in the termite gut.

i. Locate the following structures under highest power:

Flagella are the long, hairlike structures on the outside of the organism. The function of the flagella is not fully understood. Within the gut of the termite, the organisms live in such high density that movement by flagellar action seems unlikely and perhaps impossible.

The **nucleus** is a somewhat spherical organelle near the middle of the organism.

Wood particles may be located in the posterior region of the organism.

Lab Study B. Aggregate and Colonial Organisms

Materials

microscope slides
dissecting needles
forceps
coverslips
broken glass chips
cultures of *Protococcus*, *Scenedesmus*, and *Volvox*

Introduction

Unlike unicellular organisms, which live independently of each other, colonial organisms are cells that live in groups and are to some degree dependent on one another. The following organisms show an increasing degree of interaction among cells.

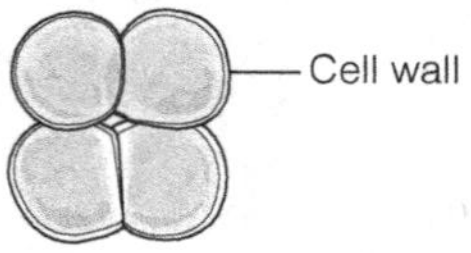

Figure 7.
Protococcus. *Protococcus* is a terrestrial green alga that forms loose aggregates on the bark of trees.

Procedure

1. Examine *Protococcus* under the compound microscope. *Protococcus* (Figure 7) is a terrestrial green alga that grows on the north sides of trees and is often referred to as "moss."

a. To obtain a specimen, use a dissecting needle to brush off a small amount of the green growth on the piece of tree bark provided into a drop of water on a clean microscope slide. Avoid scraping bark onto the slide. Cover the preparation with a clean coverslip.

b. Observe at highest power that these cells are **aggregates:** The size of the cell groupings is random, and there are no permanent connections between cells. Each cell is surrounded by a cell membrane and an outer **cell wall.**

c. Observe several small cell groupings and avoid large clumps of cells. Cellular detail may be obscure.

2. Examine living *Scenedesmus* under the compound microscope. *Scenedesmus* (Figure 8) is an aquatic green alga that is common in aquaria and polluted water.

   a. To obtain a specimen, place a drop from the culture dish (using a clean pipette) onto a clean microscope slide, and cover it with a clean coverslip.

   b. Observe that the cells of this organism form a **simple colony:** The cells always occur in groups of from four to eight cells, and they are permanently united.

   c. Identify the following structures:

   The **nucleus** is the spherical organelle in the approximate middle of each cell.

   Vacuoles are the transparent spheres that tend to occur at either end of the cells.

   Spines are the transparent projections that occur on the two end cells.

   Cell walls surround each cell.

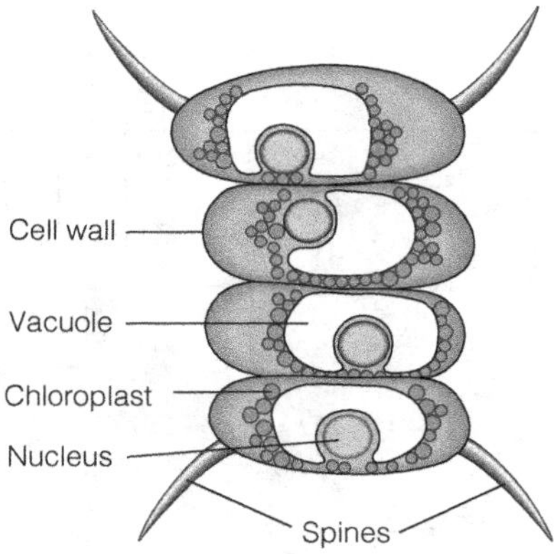

Figure 8.
Scenedesmus. *Scenedesmus* is an aquatic alga that usually occurs in simple colonies of four cells connected by an outer cell wall.

3. Examine living *Volvox* under the compound microscope. *Volvox* (Figure 9) is an aquatic green alga that also is common in aquaria, ponds, and lakes.

   a. To obtain a specimen, prepare a wet mount as you did for *Scenedesmus* with the following addition: Before placing a drop of the culture on your slide, place several glass chips on the slide. This will keep the coverslip from crushing these spherical organisms.

   b. Observe that the cells of this organism form a large **complex colony.** Approximately 500 to 50,000 cells (depending on the species) are permanently united, there are cytoplasmic connections between cells, and some cells are specialized for reproduction.

   c. Identify the following structures:

   Individual cells all possess the following structures: **cell wall, nucleus, vacuole, chloroplasts, flagella** (two per cell).

   Cytoplasmic strands form connections between adjacent cells.

   Daughter colonies are smaller spheres within the larger colony. These are produced asexually, and when they are large enough, they will be discharged from the parent colony into the surrounding environment.

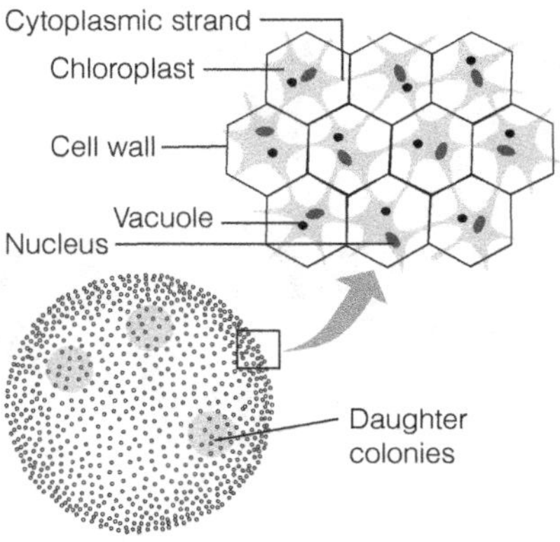

Figure 9.
Volvox. In this complex colony, the individual cells are interconnected by cytoplasmic strands to form a sphere. Small clusters of cells, called daughter colonies, are specialized for reproduction.

Lab Study C. Multicellular Organisms

Materials

microscope slides
dropper bottles of water
toothpicks
coverslips
Elodea
methylene blue
finger bowl with disinfectant

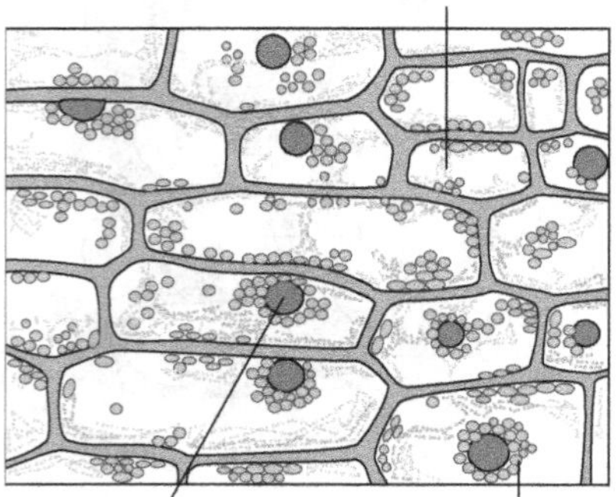

Figure 10.
Elodea. *Elodea* is an aquatic plant commonly grown in freshwater aquaria. The cell structures may be difficult to see because of the three-dimensional cell shape and the presence of a large central vacuole.

Introduction

Multicellular organisms are composed of groups of specialized cells, called **tissues,** that together perform particular functions for the organism. Tissues, in turn, may be grouped to form **organs,** and organs may be grouped into **organ systems.** In this lab study, you will examine some of the cells that compose the basic tissue types of plants and animals.

Procedure

Plant Cells

1. The major characteristics of a typical plant cell are readily seen in the leaf cells of *Elodea,* a common aquatic plant (Figure 10). Prepare a wet mount and examine one of the youngest (smallest) leaves from a sprig of *Elodea* under the compound microscope.
2. Identify the following structures:

   The **cell wall** is the rigid outer framework surrounding the cell. This structure gives the cell a definite shape and support. It is not found in animal cells.

   Protoplasm is the organized contents of the cell, exclusive of the cell wall.

   Cytoplasm is the protoplasm of the cell, exclusive of the nucleus.

   The **central vacuole** is a membrane-bound sac within the cytoplasm that is filled with water and dissolved substances. This structure serves to store metabolic wastes and gives the cell support by means of turgor pressure. Animal cells also have vacuoles, but they are not as large and conspicuous as those found in plants.

   Chloroplasts are the green, spherical organelles often seen moving within the cytoplasm. These organelles carry the pigment chlorophyll that is involved in photosynthesis. As the microscope light heats up the cells, cytoplasm and chloroplasts may begin to move around the central vacuole in a process called *cytoplasmic streaming,* or *cyclosis.*

   The **nucleus** is the usually spherical, transparent organelle within the cytoplasm. This structure controls cell metabolism and division.
3. What three structures observed in *Elodea* are unique to plants?

4. Compare your observations of *Elodea* using the compound scope with those made in Exercise 3 using the stereoscopic scope. List the structures seen with each:

   Stereoscopic:

   Compound:

Animal Cells

1. Animals are multicellular heterotrophic organisms that ingest organic matter. They are composed of cells that can be categorized into four major tissue groups: epithelial, connective, muscle, and nervous tissue. In this lab study, you will examine epithelial cells. Similar to the epidermal cells of plants, **epithelial cells** occur on the outside of animals and serve to protect the animals from water loss, mechanical injury, and foreign invaders. In addition, epithelial cells line interior cavities and ducts in animals. Examine the epithelial cells (Figure 11) that form the lining of your inner cheek. To obtain a specimen, follow this procedure:
   a. With a clean toothpick, gently scrape the inside of your cheek several times.
   b. Roll the scraping into a drop of water on a clean microscope slide, add a small drop of methylene blue, and cover with a coverslip. Discard the used toothpick in disinfectant.
   c. Using the compound microscope, view the cells under higher powers.
2. Observe that these cells are extremely flat and so may be folded over on themselves. Attempt to locate several cells that are not badly folded, and study their detail.
3. Identify the following structures:

   The **cell membrane** is the boundary that separates the cell from its surroundings.

   The **nucleus** is the large, circular organelle near the middle of the cell.

   Cytoplasm is the granular contents of the cell, exclusive of the nucleus.

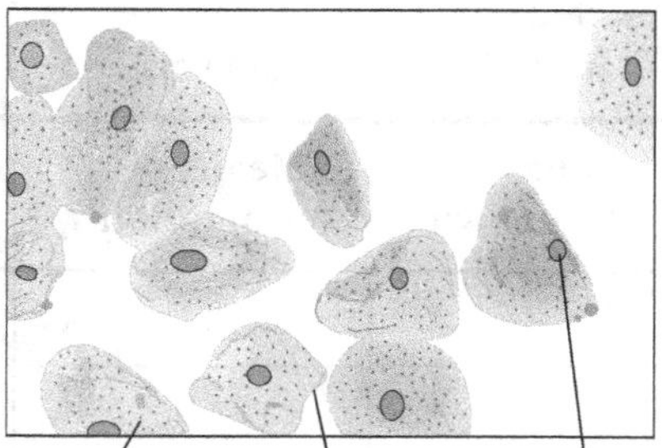

Figure 11.
Human epithelial cells. The epithelial cells that line your cheek are thin, flat cells that you can remove easily from your cheek by scraping it with a toothpick.

Lab Study D. Unknowns

Materials

microscope slides
coverslips
pond water or culture of unknowns

Introduction

Use this lab study to see if you have met the objectives of this lab topic. As you carry out this lab study, (1) think carefully about using correct microscopic techniques; (2) distinguish organisms with different cellular organization or configuration; (3) note how the different organisms are similar yet different; and (4) note cell differences.

Procedure

1. Examine several drops of the culture of pond water that you collected, or examine the unknown culture provided by the instructor.
2. Record in Table 2 the characteristics of at least four different organisms.

Table 2
Characteristics of Organisms Found in Pond Water

Tube Unknown	Means of Locomotion	Cell Wall (+/–)	Chloroplasts (+/–)	Organization
1				
2				
3				
4				
5				

Questions for Review

1. List several organelles that are visible with the electron microscope but that were not visible with your microscope.

2. Describe at least two types of materials or observations that would necessitate the use of the stereoscopic microscope.

3. What characteristics do all eukaryotic cells have in common?

4. a. What cellular features differentiate plants from animals?

   b. How are the structures that are unique to plants important to their success?

Applying Your Knowledge

1. In your own words, describe the evolutionary trend for increasing organismal complexity, using examples from this lab to illustrate your answer.

2. We often imply that multicellular organisms are more advanced (and therefore more successful) than unicellular or colonial organisms. Explain why this is not true, using examples from this lab or elsewhere.

3. Following is a list of tissues that have specialized functions and demonstrate corresponding specialization of subcellular structure. Match the tissue with the letter of the cell structures and organelles listed to the right that would be abundant in these cells. (Refer to Table 1.)

Tissues

- Enzyme (protein)-secreting cells of the pancreas
- Insect flight muscles
- Cells lining the respiratory passages
- White blood cells that engulf and destroy invading bacteria
- Leaf cells of cacti

Cell Structures and Organelles

a. plasma membrane
b. mitochondria
c. Golgi apparatus
d. chloroplast
e. endoplasmic reticulum
f. cilia and flagella
g. vacuole
h. ribosome
i. lysosome
j. peroxisomes

4. One organism found in a termite's gut is *Mixotricha paradoxa.* This strange creature looks like a single-celled swimming ciliate under low magnification. However, the electron microscope reveals that it contains spherical bacteria rather than mitochondria and has on its surface, rather than cilia, hundreds of thousands of spirilla and bacilla bacteria. You are the scientist who first observed this organism. How would you describe this organism—single-celled? aggregate? colony? multicellular? Can the structure of this organism give you any insight into the evolution of eukaryotic cells?

References

Alberts, B., D. Bray, J. Lewis, M. Raff, K. Roberts, and J. Watson. *Molecular Biology of the Cell,* 3rd ed. New York: Garland, 1994.

Becker, W. M., L. J. Kleinsmith, and J. Hardin. *The World of the Cell,* 5th ed. Redwood City, CA: Benjamin Cummings, 2003.

Cooper, G. M. and R. E. Hausman. *The Cell: A Molecular Approach,* 3rd ed. Sunderland, MA: ASM Press/Sinauer Associates, 2003.

Margulis, L., and D. Sagan. "The Beast with Five Genomes," *Natural History,* 2001, vol. 110, pp. 38–41.

Websites

http://www.cellsalive.com
http://www.ou.edu/research/electron/www-vl/

Diffusion and Osmosis

Laboratory Objectives

After completing this lab topic, you should be able to:

1. Describe the mechanism of diffusion at the molecular level.
2. List several factors that influence the rate of diffusion.
3. Describe a selectively permeable membrane, and explain its role in osmosis.
4. Define *hypotonic, hypertonic,* and *isotonic* in terms of relative concentrations of osmotically active substances.
5. Discuss the influence of the cell wall on osmotic behavior in cells.
6. Explain how incubating plant tissues in a series of dilutions of sucrose can give an approximate measurement of osmolarity of tissue cells.
7. Explain why diffusion and osmosis are important to cells.
8. Apply principles of osmotic activity to medical, domestic, and environmental activities.

Introduction

Maintaining the steady state of a cell is achieved only through regulated movement of materials through cytoplasm, across organelle membranes, and across the plasma membrane. This regulated movement facilitates communication within the cell and between cytoplasm and the external environment. The cytoplasm and extracellular environment of the cell are aqueous solutions. They are composed of water, which is the **solvent,** or dissolving agent, and numerous organic and inorganic molecules, which are the **solutes,** or dissolved substances. Organelle membranes and the plasma membrane are **selectively permeable,** allowing water to freely pass through but regulating the movement of solutes.

The cell actively moves some dissolved substances across membranes, expending adenosine triphosphate (ATP) (biological energy) to accomplish the movement. Other substances move passively, without expenditure of ATP from the cell, but only if the cell membrane is permeable to those substances. Water and selected solutes move passively through the cell and cell membranes by **diffusion,** a physical process in which molecules move from an area where they are in high concentration to one where their concentration is lower. The energy driving diffusion comes only from the intrinsic kinetic energy in all atoms and molecules. If nothing hinders the movement, a solute will diffuse until it reaches equilibrium.

Osmosis is a type of diffusion; in cells it is the diffusion of water through a selectively permeable membrane from a region where it is highly concentrated to a region where its concentration is lower. The difference in concentration of water occurs if there is an unequal distribution of at least one dissolved substance on either side of a membrane and the membrane is impermeable to that substance. In this situation, the substance is called an **osmotically active substance (OAS).** For example, if a membrane that is impermeable to sucrose separates a solution of sucrose from distilled water, water will move from the distilled water, where it is in higher concentration, through the membrane into the sucrose solution, where it is in lower concentration. In this case, sucrose is the osmotically active substance.

Three terms, **hypertonic, hypotonic,** and **isotonic,** are used when referring to two solutions separated by a selectively permeable membrane (Figure 1). The hypertonic solution (Figure 1a) has a greater concentration of OAS than the solution on the other side of the membrane. It is described, therefore, as having a greater **osmolarity** (solute concentration expressed as molarity). The hypotonic solution (Figure 1b) has a lower concentration of OAS, or a lower osmolarity, than the solution on the other side of the membrane. When the two solutions are in equilibrium, the concentration of OAS being equal on both sides of the membrane, the osmolarities are equal and the substances are said to be isotonic (Figure 1c). The *net flow* of water is from the hypotonic to the hypertonic solution. When the solutions are isotonic, there is no net flow of water across the membrane.

The concept of osmotic pressure must be understood when studying osmosis. The movement of water from a hypotonic solution through the membrane into a hypertonic solution can be prevented by applying force or pressure on the hypertonic side (Figure 2). The force that must be applied to prevent osmotic movement of water from hypotonic to hypertonic, measured in atmospheres, is referred to as **osmotic pressure.** Solutions with greater concentrations of OAS have greater osmotic pressures because greater force is

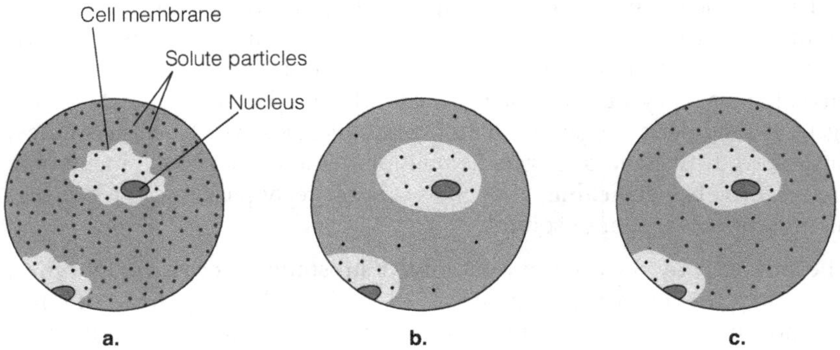

Figure 1.
Diagrammatic representation of cells in (a) hypertonic, (b) hypotonic, and (c) isotonic solutions. The hypertonic solution has a greater concentration of OAS than the solution on the other side of the membrane, the hypotonic solution has a lower concentration of OAS than the solution on the other side of the membrane, and the concentration of OAS is equal on both sides of the membrane in isotonic solutions.

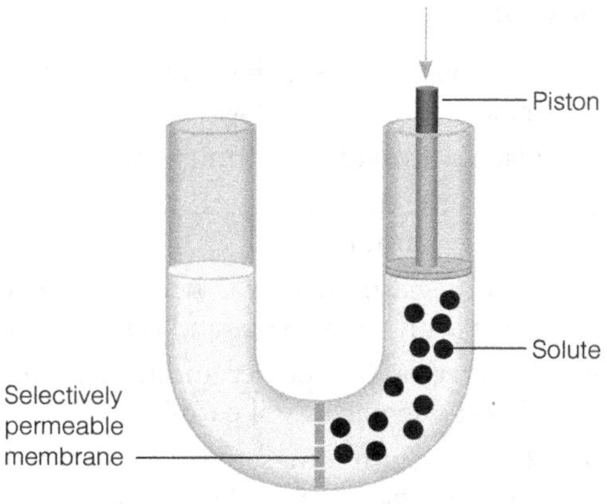

Figure 2.
Applying the correct pressure to the hypertonic side of two osmotically active solutions will prevent water movement into that solution.

required to prevent water movement into them. Distilled water has an osmotic pressure of zero.

EXERCISE 1
Diffusion of Molecules

In this exercise you will investigate characteristics of molecules that facilitate diffusion, factors that influence diffusion rates, and diffusion of solutes through a selectively permeable membrane.

Experiment A. Kinetic Energy of Molecules

Materials

dropper bottle of water
carmine powder
dissecting needle
slide and coverslip
compound microscope

Introduction

Molecules of a liquid or gas are constantly in motion because of the intrinsic kinetic energy in all atoms and molecules. In 1827, Robert Brown, a Scottish botanist, noticed that pollen grains suspended in water on a slide appeared to move by a force that he was unable to explain. In 1905, Albert Einstein, searching for evidence that would prove the existence of atoms and molecules, predicted that the motion observed by Brown must exist, although he did not realize that it had been studied for many years. Only after the kinetic energy of molecules was understood did scientists ask if the motion observed by Brown and predicted by Einstein could be the result of molecular kinetic energy being passed to larger particles. We now know that intrinsic molecular kinetic energy is the driving force of diffusion. In this experiment, you will observe large particles in motion similar to that observed by Brown, traditionally called **Brownian movement.** You will relate the motion observed to the forces that bring about diffusion.

Procedure

Work in pairs. One person should set up the microscope while the other person makes a slide as follows:

1. Place a drop of water on the slide.
2. Touch the tip of a dissecting needle to the drop of water and then into the dry carmine.
3. Add the carmine on the needle to the drop of water on the slide, mix, cover with a coverslip, and observe under the compound microscope.
4. Observe on low power and then high power. Focus as much as possible on one particle of carmine.
5. Record your findings in the Results section, and draw conclusions based on your results in the Discussion section.

Results

Describe the movement of single carmine particles.

1. Is the movement random or directional?
2. Does the movement ever stop?
3. Do smaller particles move more rapidly than larger particles? Other observations?

Discussion

1. Are you actually observing molecular movement? Explain.

2. How can molecular movement bring about diffusion?

3. Speculate about the importance of diffusion in cell metabolism.

Experiment B. Diffusion of Molecules Through a Selectively Permeable Membrane

Materials

string or rubber band	500-mL beaker one-third filled with water
wax pencil	handheld test tube holder
30% glucose solution	3 standard test tubes
starch solution	disposable transfer pipettes
I_2KI solution	2 400-mL beakers to hold dialysis bag
Benedict's reagent	30-cm strip of moist dialysis tubing
hot plate	

Introduction

Dialysis tubing is a membrane made of regenerated cellulose fibers formed into a flat tube. If two solutions containing dissolved substances of different molecular weights are separated by this membrane, some substances may readily pass through the pores of the membrane, but others may be excluded.

Working in teams of four students, you will investigate the selective permeability of dialysis tubing. You will test the permeability of the tubing to the reducing sugar, glucose (molecular weight 180), starch (a variable-length polymer of glucose), and iodine potassium iodide (I_2KI). You will place a solution of glucose and starch into a dialysis tubing bag and then place this bag into a solution of I_2KI. Sketch and label the design of this experiment in the margin of your lab manual to help you develop your hypotheses.

You will use two tests in your experiment:

1. *I_2KI test for presence of starch.* When I_2KI is added to the unknown solution, the solution turns purple or black if starch is present. If no starch is present, the solution remains a pale yellow-amber color.
2. *Benedict's test for reducing sugar.* When Benedict's reagent is added to the unknown solution and the solution is heated, the solution turns green, orange, or orange-red if a reducing sugar is present (the color indicates the sugar concentration). If no reducing sugar is present, the solution remains the color of Benedict's reagent (blue).

Hypothesis

Hypothesize about the selective permeability of dialysis tubing to the substances being tested.

Prediction

Predict the results of the I_2KI and Benedict's tests based on your hypothesis (if/then).

Procedure

1. Prepare the dialysis bag with the initial solutions:
   a. Fold over 3 cm at the end of a 25- to 30-cm piece of dialysis tubing that has been soaking in water for a few minutes, pleat the folded end "accordion style," and close the end of the tube with the string or a rubber band, forming a bag. This procedure must secure the end of the bag so that no solution can seep through.
   b. Roll the opposite end of the bag between your fingers until it opens, and add 4 pipettesful of 30% glucose into the bag. Then add 4 pipettesful of starch solution to the glucose in the bag.
   c. Hold the bag closed and mix its contents. Record its color in Table 1 in the Results section. Carefully rinse the outside of the bag in tap water.
   d. Add 300 mL of water to a 400- to 500-mL beaker. Add several droppersful of I_2KI solution to the water until it is visibly yellow-amber. Record the color of the $H_2O + I_2KI$ solution in Table 1.
   e. Place the bag in the beaker so that the untied end of the bag hangs over the edge of the beaker (Figure 3). *Do not allow the liquid to spill out of the bag!* If the bag is too full, remove some of the liquid and rinse the outside of the bag again. If needed, place a rubber band around the beaker, holding the bag securely in place. If some of the liquid spills into the beaker, dispose of the beaker water, rinse, and fill again.
2. Leave the bag in the beaker for about 30 minutes. (You should go to another lab activity and then return to check your setup periodically.)
3. After 30 minutes, carefully remove the bag and stand it in a dry beaker.
4. Record in Table 1 the final color of the solution in the bag and the final color of the solution in the beaker.
5. Perform the Benedict's test for the presence of sugar in the solutions.
   a. Label three clean test tubes: control, bag, and beaker.
   b. Put 2 pipettesful of water in the control tube.
   c. Put 2 pipettesful of the bag solution in the bag tube.
   d. Put 2 pipettesful of the beaker solution in the beaker tube.
   e. Add 1 dropperful of Benedict's reagent to each tube.
   f. Heat the test tubes in a boiling water bath for about 3 minutes.
   g. Record your results in Table 1.

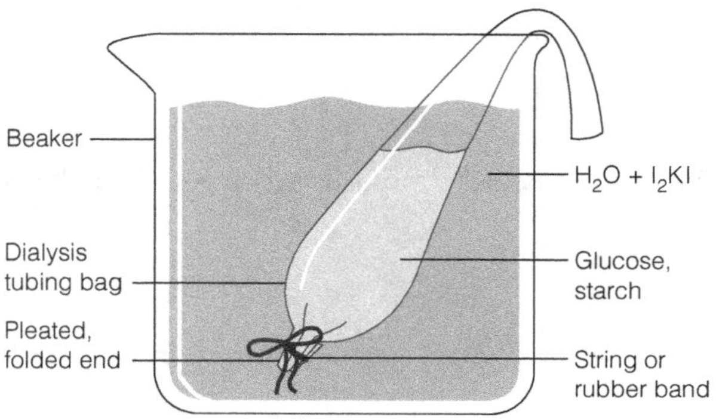

Figure 3.
Setup for Exercise 1, Experiment B. The dialysis tubing bag, securely closed at one end, is placed in the beaker of water and I_2KI. The open end of the bag should drape over the edge of the beaker.

6. Review your results in Table 1 and draw your conclusions in the Discussion section.

Results

Complete Table 1 as you observe the results of Experiment B.

Table 1
Results of Experiment Investigating the Permeability of Dialysis Tubing to Glucose, I_2KI, and Starch

Solution Source	Original Contents	Original Color	Final Color	Color After Benedict's Test
Bag				
Beaker				
Control				

Discussion

1. What is the significance of the final colors and the colors after the Benedict's tests? Did the results support your hypothesis? Explain, giving evidence from the results of your tests.

2. How can you explain your results?

3. From your results, predict the size of I_2KI molecules relative to glucose and starch.

4. What colors would you expect if the experiment started with glucose and I_2KI inside the bag and starch in the beaker? Explain.

EXERCISE 2
Osmotic Activity in Cells

All organisms must maintain an optimum internal osmotic environment. Terrestrial vertebrates must take in and eliminate water using internal regulatory systems to ensure that the environment of tissues and organs remains in osmotic balance. Exchange of waste and nutrients between blood and tissues depends on the maintenance of this condition. Plants and animals living in fresh water must control the osmotic uptake of water into their hypertonic cells.

In this exercise, you will investigate the osmotic behavior of plant and animal cells placed in different molar solutions. What happens to these cells when they are placed in hypotonic or hypertonic solutions? This question will be investigated in the following experiments.

Experiment A. Osmotic Behavior of Animal Cells

Materials

On demonstration:
- test tube rack
- 3 test tubes with screw caps, each containing one of the three solutions of unknown osmolarity
- ox blood
- newspaper or other printed page

For microscopic observations:
- 4 clean microscope slides and coverslips
- wax pencil
- dropper bottle of ox blood
- dropper bottles with three solutions of unknown osmolarity

Introduction

Mature red blood cells (erythrocytes) are little more than packages of hemoglobin bound by a plasma membrane permeable to small molecules, such as oxygen and carbon dioxide, but impermeable to larger molecules, such as proteins, sodium chloride, and sucrose. In mammals these cells even lack nuclei when mature, and as they float in isotonic blood plasma, their shape is flattened and pinched inward into a biconcave disk. Oxygen and carbon dioxide diffuse across the membrane, allowing the cell to carry out its primary function, gas transport, which is enhanced by the increased surface area created by the shape of the cell. When water moves into red blood cells placed in a hypotonic solution, the cells swell and the membranes burst, or undergo **lysis.** When water moves out of red blood cells placed in a hypertonic solution, the cells shrivel and appear bumpy, or **crenate.** In this experiment, you will investigate the behavior of red blood cells when the osmolarity of the environment changes from isotonic to hypertonic or hypotonic.

Hypothesis

Hypothesize about the behavior of red blood cells when they are placed in hypertonic or hypotonic environments.

Prediction

Predict the results of the experiment based on your hypothesis (if/then).

Procedure

1. Observe the three test tubes containing unknown solutions and blood on demonstration. These tubes have been prepared in the following way:

   Test tube 1: 15 mL of unknown solution A

   Test tube 2: 15 mL of unknown solution B

   Test tube 3: 15 mL of unknown solution C

   Your instructor has added 5 drops of ox blood to each test tube.

   Observe the appearance of each test tube. Is it opaque? Is it translucent? Describe your observations in Table 2 in the Results section.
2. Be sure each test tube cap is securely tightened, then hold each test tube flat against the printed newspaper article or page of text.
3. Attempt to read the print. Describe in Table 2 in the Results section.

   Continue your investigation of osmotic behavior of animal cells by performing microscopic observations of cells in the three unknown solutions.

Have your microscope ready, and observe slides immediately after you have prepared them. Do one slide at a time.

---

4. Label four clean microscope slides A, B, C, and D.
5. Place a drop of blood on slide D, cover with a coverslip, and observe the shape of red blood cells with no treatment. Record your observations in Table 2 in the Results section.
6. Put a drop of solution A on slide A and add a coverslip. Place the slide on the microscope stage and carefully add a small drop of blood to the edge of the coverslip. The blood cells will be drawn under the coverslip by capillary action.

7. As you view through the microscope, carefully watch the cells as they come into contact with solution A; record your observations in Table 2.
8. Repeat steps 3 and 4 with solutions B and C.
9. Record your observations in Table 2. Draw your conclusions in the Discussion section.

Results

1. Record your observations of the demonstration test tubes in Table 2.

Table 2
Appearance of Unknown Solutions A, B, and C

	Appearance of the Solution	**Can You Read the Print?**
Test tube 1 (unknown A)		
Test tube 2 (unknown B)		
Test tube 3 (unknown C)		

2. Record your microscopic observations of red blood cell behavior in Table 3.

Table 3
Appearance of Red Blood Cells in Test Solutions

Solution	**Appearance/Condition of Cells**
D (blood only)	
A	
B	
C	

Discussion

Explain your results in terms of your hypothesis.

1. Explain the appearance of the three test tubes on demonstration.

2. Based on the demonstration and your microscopic investigation, which of the three solutions is hypotonic to the red blood cells?

   Hypertonic?

   Isotonic?

   Verify your conclusions with the laboratory instructor.
3. What conditions might lead to results other than those expected?

Experiment B. Osmotic Behavior in Cells with a Cell Wall

Materials

On demonstration: 2 compound microscopes labeled A and B
1 slide of *Elodea* in a hypertonic salt solution
1 slide of *Elodea* in distilled water

Introduction

In their natural environment, cells of freshwater plants and algae are bathed in water with little OAS. The net flow of water is from the surrounding medium into the cells. To understand this process, review the structure of *Elodea* cells.

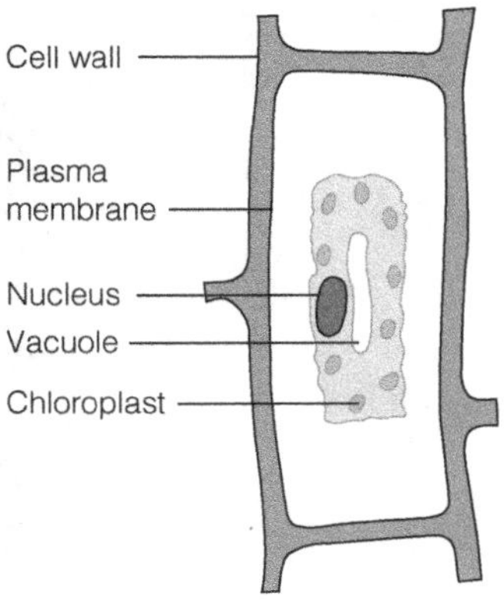

Figure 4.
Plant cell placed in a hypertonic solution. Water leaves the central vacuole and the cytoplasm shrinks, a process called plasmolysis.

The presence of a cell wall and a large fluid-filled central vacuole in a plant or algal cell will affect the cell's response to solutions of differing molarities. When a plant cell is placed in a hypertonic solution, water moves out of the cell; the protoplast shrinks and may pull away from the cell wall. This process is called **plasmolysis,** and the cell is described as **plasmolyzed** (Figure 4). In a hypotonic solution, as water moves into the cell and ultimately into the cell's central vacuole, the cell's **protoplast** (the plant cell exclusive of the cell wall—the cytoplasm enclosed by plasma membrane) expands. The cell wall, however, restricts the expansion, resulting in **turgor pressure** (pressure of the protoplast on the cell wall owing to uptake of water). A high turgor pressure will prevent further movement of water into the cell. This process is a good example of the interaction between pressure and osmolarity in determining the direction of the net movement of water. The hypertonic condition in the cell draws water into the cell until the membrane-enclosed cytoplasm presses against the cell wall. Turgor pressure begins to force water through the membrane and out of the cell, changing the direction of net flow of water (Figure 5).

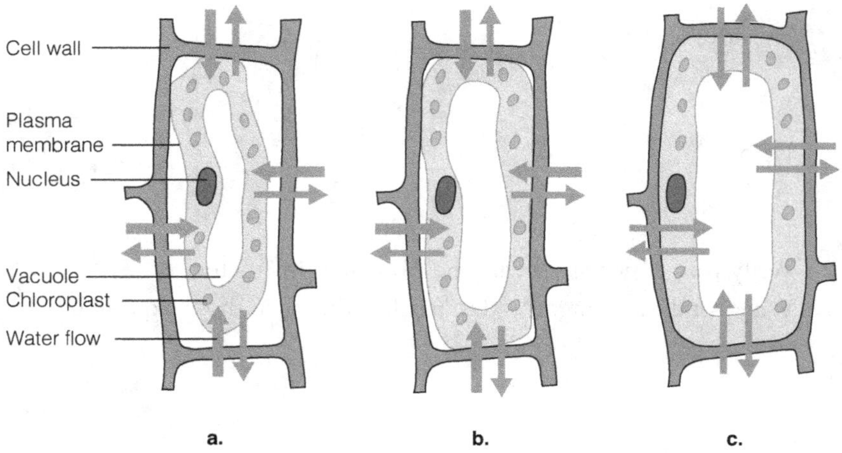

Figure 5.
The effect of turgor pressure on the cell wall and the direction of net flow of water in a plant cell. A plant cell undergoes changes in a hypotonic solution. (a) Low turgor pressure. The net flow of water comes into the cell from the surrounding hypotonic medium. (b) Turgor pressure increases. The protoplast begins to press on the cell wall. (c) Greatest turgor pressure. The tendency to take up water is ultimately restricted by the cell wall, creating a back pressure on the protoplast. Water enters and leaves the cell at the same rate.

Scientists call the combined force created by osmotically active substances (solute concentration) and physical pressure **water potential.** For a detailed explanation of water potential, see a discussion of plant transport mechanisms in your text (e.g., Chapter 36 in Campbell and Reece, 2005). In contrast to an animal cell, the ideal state for a plant cell is turgidity. When a plant cell is turgid, it is not isotonic with its surroundings but is hypertonic, having a higher solute concentration than its surroundings. In this state, the plant cell protoplast presses on the cell wall. The pressure of the protoplast on the cell wall is an important force in plant activity. For example, it may cause young cells to "grow" as the elastic cell wall expands.

For this experiment, two slides have been set up on demonstration microscopes. On each slide, *Elodea* has been placed in a different molar solution: One is hypotonic (distilled water) and one is hypertonic (concentrated salt solution).

Hypothesis

Hypothesize about the movement of water in cells with a cell wall when they are placed in hypertonic or hypotonic environments.

Prediction

Predict the appearance of *Elodea* cells placed in the two solutions (if/then).

Procedure

1. Observe the two demonstration microscopes with *Elodea* in solutions A and B.
2. Record your observations in Table 4 in the Results section, and draw your conclusions in the Discussion section.

Results

Describe the appearance of the *Elodea* cells in Table 4.

Table 4
Appearance of *Elodea* Cells in Unknown Solutions A and B

Solution	Appearance/Condition of Cells
A	
B	

Discussion

1. Based on your predictions and observations, which solution is hypertonic?

   Hypotonic?

2. Which solution has the greatest osmolarity?

3. Would you expect pond water to be isotonic, hypertonic, or hypotonic to *Elodea* cells? Explain.

4. Verify your conclusions with your laboratory instructor.

EXERCISE 3
Investigating Osmolarity of Plant Cells

Knowing the solute concentration of cells has both medical and agricultural applications. In plants, scientists know that for normal activities to take place, the amount of water relative to osmotically active substances in cells must be maintained within a reasonable range. If plant cells have a reduced water content, all vital functions slow down.

In the following experiments, you will estimate the osmolarity of potato tuber cells using two methods, change in weight and change in volume. You will incubate pieces of potato tuber in sucrose solutions of known molarity. The object is to find the molarity at which weight or volume of the potato tuber tissue does not change, indicating that there has been no net loss or gain of water. This molarity is an indirect measure of the solute concentration of the potato tuber. This measure is indirect because water movement in plant cells is also affected by the presence of cell walls (see Figure 5c).

Work in teams of four. Each team will measure either weight change or volume change. Time will be available near the end of the laboratory period for each team to present its results to the class for discussion and conclusions.

Experiment A. Estimating Osmolarity by Change in Weight

Materials

1 large potato tuber
7 250-mL beakers (disposable cups may be substituted)
wax marking pencil
forceps
balance that weighs to the nearest 0.01 g
aluminum foil
petri dish
sucrose solutions: 0.1, 0.2, 0.3, 0.4, 0.5, 0.6 molar (*M*)
razor blade
cork borer
deionized (DI) water (0 molar)
paper towels
metric ruler
calculator

Introduction

In this experiment, you will determine the weight of several potato tuber cylinders and incubate them in a series of sucrose solutions. After the cylinders have incubated, you will weigh them and determine if they have gained or lost weight. This information will enable you to estimate the osmolarity of the potato tuber tissue.

Hypothesis

Hypothesize about the osmolarity of potato tuber tissue in relation to the sucrose solutions.

Prediction

Predict the results of the experiment based on your hypothesis (if/then).

Procedure

1. Obtain 100 mL of DI water and 100 mL of each of the sucrose solutions. Put each solution in a separate, appropriately labeled 250-mL beaker or paper cup.

Cork borers and razor blades can cut! Use them with extreme care! To use the cork borer, hold the potato in such a way that the borer will not push through the potato into your hand.

2. Use a sharp cork borer to obtain seven cylinders of potato. Push the borer through the length of the potato, twisting it back and forth. When the borer is filled, remove from the potato and push the potato cylinder out of the borer. You must have seven complete, undamaged cylinders at least 5 cm long.
3. Line up the potato cylinders and, using a sharp razor blade, cut all cylinders to a uniform length, about 5 cm, removing the peel from the ends.
4. Place all seven potato samples in a petri dish, and keep them covered to prevent their drying out.

In subsequent steps, treat each sample individually. Work quickly. To provide consistency, each person should do one task to all cylinders (one person wipe, another weigh, another slice, another record data).

5. Remove a cylinder from the petri dish, and place it between the folds of a paper towel to blot sides and ends.
6. Weigh it to the nearest 0.01 g on the aluminum sheet on the balance. Record the weight in Table 5 in the Results section.
7. Immediately cut the cylinder lengthwise into two long halves.
8. Transfer potato pieces to the water beaker.
9. Note what time the potato pieces are placed in the water beaker. Time: ___________.
10. Repeat steps 5 to 8 with each cylinder, placing potato pieces in the appropriate incubating solution from 0.1 to 0.6 *M*.

Be sure that the initial weight of the cylinder placed in each test solution is accurately recorded.

11. Incubate 1.5 to 2 hours. (As this takes place, you will be performing other lab activities.)
12. Swirl each beaker every 10 to 15 minutes as the potato pieces incubate.
13. At the end of the incubation period, record the time when the potato pieces are removed. Time: ___________.

    Calculate the approximate incubation time in Table 5.
14. Remove the potato pieces from the first sample. Blot the pieces on a paper towel, removing excess solution only.
15. Weigh the potato pieces and record the final weight in Table 5.
16. Repeat this procedure until all samples have been weighed in the chronological order in which they were initially placed in the test solutions.
17. Record your data in the Results section, and complete the questions in the Discussion section.

Results

1. Complete Table 5. To calculate percentage change in weight, use this formula:

$$\text{Percentage change in weight} = \frac{\text{weight change}}{\text{initial weight}} \times 100$$

   If the sample gained in weight, the value should be positive. If it lost in weight, the value should be negative.

Table 5
Data for Experiment Estimating Osmolarity by Change in Weight

Approximate time in solutions: ___________	Sucrose Molarity						
	0.0	0.1	0.2	0.3	0.4	0.5	0.6
Final weight (g)							
Initial weight (g)							
Weight change (g)							
% change in weight							

2. Plot percentage change in weight as a function of the sucrose molarity in Figure 6.
   a. Place a 0 in the middle of the y axis. Choose appropriate scales.
   b. Label the axes of the graph: Determine dependent and independent variables, and place each on the appropriate axis.

c. Graph your results. Weight increase (positive values) should be above the zero change line on the "percentage change in weight" axis. Weight decrease should be below the zero change line.

d. Construct a curve that best fits the data points. Use this curve to estimate the osmolarity of the potato tuber.

e. Compose an appropriate figure title.

Discussion

1. At what sucrose molarity does the curve cross the zero change line on the graph?

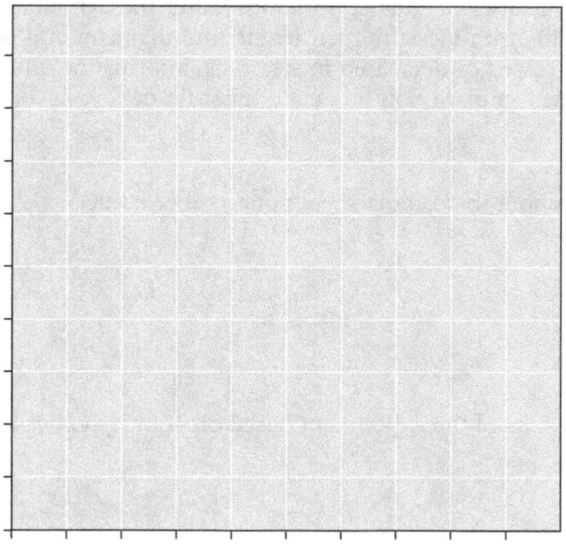

Figure 6.

____

____

____

2. Explain how this information can be used to determine the osmolarity of the potato tuber tissue.

3. In more dilute concentrations of sucrose, the weight of the potato pieces ______ (increases/decreases) after incubation. What forces other than solute concentration will have an impact on the amount of water taken up by the potato pieces (see Figure 5c)?

4. Estimate the osmolarity of the potato tuber tissue.

Experiment B. Estimating Osmolarity by Change in Volume

Materials

1 large potato tuber
vernier caliper
7 250-mL beakers (disposable cups may be substituted)
wax marking pencil
forceps
petri dish
razor blade
cork borer (0.5-cm diameter)
sucrose solutions: 0.1, 0.2, 0.3, 0.4, 0.5, 0.6 *M*
DI water (0 *M*)
metric ruler
paper towels
calculator

Introduction

In this experiment, you will determine the volume of several potato tuber cylinders by measuring the length and diameter of each. You will then incubate them in a series of sucrose solutions. After the cylinders have incubated, you will again measure their length and diameter and determine if they have increased or decreased in size. This information will enable you to estimate the osmolarity of the potato tuber tissue.

Hypothesis

Hypothesize about the osmolarity of potato tuber tissue.

Prediction

Predict the results of the experiment based on your hypothesis (if/then).

Procedure

1. Practice measuring with the vernier caliper (Figure 7a, b).
   a. Identify the following parts of the caliper and add these labels on Figure 7a: *stationary arm, movable arm, ruler, vernier scale.* Notice that the numbers on the bottom ruler scale are centimeters; each graduated line is 1 mm.
   b. Choose a small object (a coin will work) and place it between the two arms, adjusting the movable arm until both arms just touch the object.
   c. Note the 0 mark on the vernier scale (Figure 7b). The graduated line on the ruler just to the left of the 0 mark is the distance between the caliper arms measured in whole millimeters. In Figure 7b, that number is 22 mm. Write that number for your object as the answer in blank (1), on the next page.

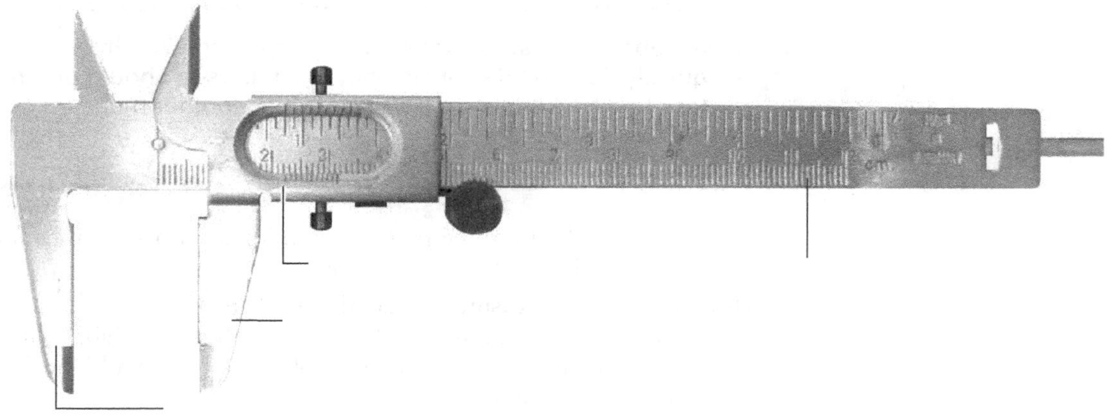

Figure 7a.
Vernier caliper. Identify the stationary arm, movable arm, ruler, and vernier scale.

d. Look at the graduated lines between 0 and 10 on the vernier scale. Note the line on the vernier scale that exactly matches with a line on the ruler. That line on the vernier scale is the measurement in tenths of a millimeter, which should be added to the whole-millimeter reading. In Figure 7b, that number is 4. Write the measurement in tenths of a millimeter for your object as the answer in blank (2) below.

   What is the size of your object?

   (1) ________________

   (2) ________________

   Total measurement: ________________

   When you know how to measure using the caliper, proceed to the next step.

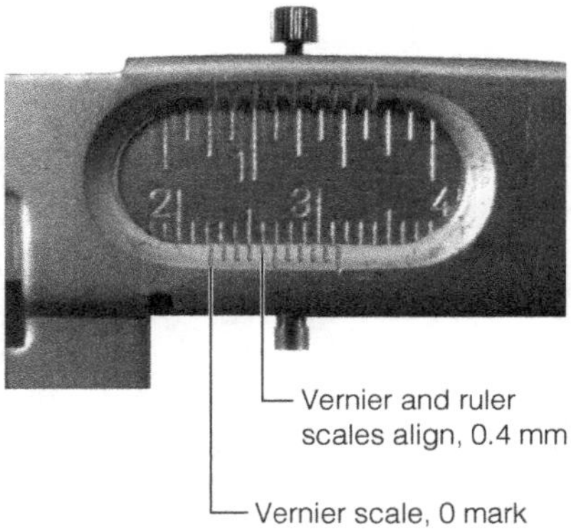

Figure 7b.
Enlarged vernier scale. The correct measurement is 22.4 mm.

2. Obtain 100 mL of DI water and 100 mL of each of the sucrose solutions. Put each solution in a separate, appropriately labeled 250-mL beaker or paper cup.

⚠ **Use cork borers and razor blades with extreme care! To use the cork borer, hold the potato in such a way that the borer will not push through the potato into your hand.**

---

3. Use a sharp cork borer to obtain seven cylinders of potato. Push the borer through the length of the potato, twisting it back and forth. When the borer is filled, remove it from the potato and push the potato cylinder out of the borer. You must have seven complete, undamaged cylinders at least 5 cm long.
4. Line up the potato cylinders and, using a sharp razor blade, cut all cylinders to a uniform length, about 5 cm, removing the peel from the ends.
5. Place all seven potato samples in a petri dish, and keep them covered to prevent their drying out.

In subsequent steps, treat each sample individually. Work quickly. To provide consistency, each person should do one task to all cylinders (one person wipe, another measure, another record data).

6. Remove a cylinder from the petri dish, and place it between the folds of a paper towel to blot sides and ends.
7. Using the caliper, measure the length and diameter of the cylinder to the nearest 0.1 mm, and record these measurements in Table 6 in the Results section. To measure, both arms of the caliper should touch but not compress the cylinder.
8. Transfer the cylinder to the 0 *M* (water) beaker.
9. Note the time the cylinder is placed in the 0 *M* beaker. Time: ___________.
10. Repeat steps 6 to 8 with each cylinder, placing the cylinders in the appropriate incubating solution from 0.1 to 0.6 *M*.

Be sure that the initial length and diameter of the cylinder placed in each test solution are accurately recorded.

11. Incubate from 1.5 to 2 hours. (During this time period, you will be performing other lab activities.)
12. Swirl each beaker every 10 to 15 minutes as the cylinders incubate.
13. At the end of the incubation period, record the time each cylinder is removed from a solution. Time: ___________.

    Calculate the approximate incubation time in Table 6.
14. Remove the cylinders in the chronological order in which they were initially placed in the test solutions.
15. Blot each cylinder as it is removed (sides and ends), and use the vernier caliper to measure the length and diameter to the nearest 0.1 mm.
16. Finish recording your data in the Results section, and answer the questions in the Discussion section.

Results

1. Complete Table 6. To calculate the volume of a cylinder, use this formula:

$$\text{Volume of a cylinder (mm}^3) = \pi(\text{diameter}/2)^2 \times \text{length} \quad (\pi = 3.14)$$

To calculate percentage change in volume, use this formula:

$$\text{Percentage change in volume} = \frac{\text{change in volume}}{\text{initial volume}} \times 100$$

If the sample increases in volume, the value will be positive. If it decreases in volume, the value will be negative.

Table 6
Data for Experiment Estimating Osmolarity by Change in Volume

Approximate time in solutions: ____________							
	Sucrose Molarity						
	0.0	0.1	0.2	0.3	0.4	0.5	0.6
Final diameter (mm)							
Final length (mm)							
Final volume (mm^3)							
Initial diameter (mm)							
Initial length (mm)							
Initial volume (mm^3)							
Change in volume (mm^3)							
% change in volume							

2. Plot percentage change in volume as a function of the sucrose molarity in Figure 8.
   a. Place a 0 in the middle of the *y* axis. Choose appropriate scales.
   b. Label the axes of the graph: Determine dependent and independent variables, and place each on the appropriate axis.
   c. Graph your results. Volume increase should be above the zero change line on the "percentage change in volume" axis. Volume decrease should be below the zero change line.

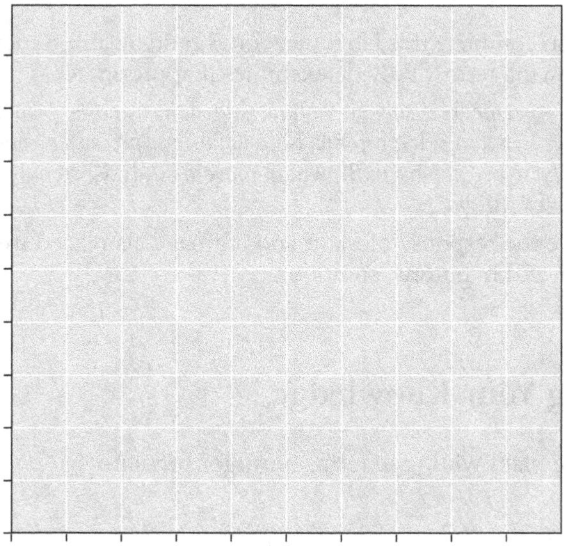

Figure 8.

____

____

____

d. Construct a curve that best fits the data points. Use this curve to estimate the osmolarity of the potato tuber.

e. Compose an appropriate figure title.

Discussion

1. At what sucrose molarity does the curve cross the zero change line on the graph?

2. Explain how this information can be used to determine the osmolarity of the potato tuber tissue.

3. In more dilute concentrations of sucrose, the volume of the potato pieces ______ (increases/decreases) after incubation. What forces other than solute concentration will have an impact on the amount of water taken up by the pieces?

4. Estimate the osmolarity of the potato tuber tissue.

Questions for Review

1. Once you complete this lab topic, you should be able to define and use the following terms. Provide examples if appropriate.

   selectively permeable, solvent, solute, diffusion, osmosis, osmotically active substance, hypotonic, hypertonic, isotonic, turgor pressure, osmotic pressure, osmolarity, water potential, Brownian movement, lysis, crenate, plasmolysis, plasmolyzed, turgid

2. Compare the response of plant and animal cells placed in hypertonic, isotonic, and hypotonic solutions.

Applying Your Knowledge

1. Describe plant wilting in terms of turgor pressure.

2. The emergency room intern, Jim W. Dooley, treated a patient by administering fluids intravenously. The patient died as a result of using the wrong IV fluids. What kind of osmotic solution would have resulted in the patient's death? Why?

3. Tori, an ER volunteer and an amateur botanist, is shocked by the death of Dooley's patient. The next time she waters her flower garden she wonders why applying pure water does not kill plants, but makes them thrive?

4. The pond water samples you observed probably contained a variety of multicellular, colonial, and single-celled organisms. Some of these may have had cell walls, but others were lacking cell walls. What adaptations for osmoregulation are found in single-celled organisms, such as the *Amoeba,* and multicellular organisms that lack cell walls but live in a hypotonic environment?

5. When studying *Trichonympha*, you made a wet mount of these organisms using a drop of saline solution. Why use saline solution rather than water?

6. Shrimp fishing off the coast of Georgia was closed in 2001 due to a drastic reduction in the shrimp population. Captain Forsyth, a local shrimper, suspects that increased salinity has killed the shrimp larvae. Three years of drought and greatly reduced freshwater flow from underground aquifers resulted in increased salinity in the coastal estuaries. These habitats between open ocean and fresh water are the "nurseries" for many marine animals. Design an experiment to determine the range of salt concentration that can be tolerated by shrimp larvae.

7. Water pollution is one of the most serious environmental problems of our time. Using information learned in this lab, predict one impact of pollutants in lakes, ponds, rivers, and streams on the plant and animal inhabitants.

References

Campbell, N. and J. Reece, *Biology,* 7th ed. San Francisco, CA: Benjamin Cummings, 2005.

Lang, F., and S. Waldegger. "Regulating Cell Volume." *American Scientist,* 1997, vol 85, pp. 456–463.

Exercise 1, Experiment A, was adapted from D. R. Helms and S. B. Miller, *Principles of Biology: A Laboratory Manual for Biology 110.* Apex, NC: Contemporary Publishing, 1978. Used by permission.

Macromolecules

Introduction

Living organisms are composed of molecules that come in diverse shapes and sizes and serve a variety of purposes. Some molecules form the structure of an organism's body—for example, the cellulose that makes up the cell walls in plants, the proteins and phospholipids that comprise cell membranes, and the fibers that make up animal muscles.

There is also a wide array of molecules that perform all the functions of life. For example, enzymes catalyze the chemical reactions necessary for biological processes, neurotransmitters convey information from one brain cell to another, and visual pigments absorb light so that you can read the words on this page.

In this laboratory you will study three classes of the largest biological molecules, called **macromolecules:** carbohydrates, lipids, and proteins. A fourth class of macromolecules, the nucleic acids, will not be studied in this laboratory.

Outline

Exercise 1: Carbohydrates
- Activity A: Monosaccharides and Disaccharides
- Activity B: Starch
- Activity C: Hydrolysis of Carbohydrates

Exercise 2: Lipids

Exercise 3: Proteins

Exercise 4: Macromolecules in Food
- Activity A: Separation of Butter
- Activity B: Tests with Food

EXERCISE 1
Carbohydrates

Objectives

After completing this exercise, you should be able to

1. Define monosaccharide, disaccharide, and polysaccharide and give examples of each.
2. Name the monosaccharide components of sucrose and starch.

3. Describe the test that indicates the presence of most small sugars.
4. Describe the test that indicates the presence of starch.
5. Define hydrolysis and give an example of the hydrolysis of carbohydrates.

Most **carbohydrates** contain only carbon (C), oxygen (O), and hydrogen (H). The simplest form of carbohydrate molecules are the **monosaccharides** ("single sugars"). One of the most important monosaccharides is glucose ($C_6H_{12}O_6$), the end product of photosynthesis in plants. It is also the molecule that is metabolized to produce another molecule, ATP, whose energy can be used for cellular work. There are many other common monosaccharides, including fructose, galactose, and ribose.

Some **disaccharides** ("double sugars") are also common. A disaccharide is simply two monosaccharides linked together. For example, maltose consists of two glucose molecules, lactose (milk sugar) consists of glucose and galactose, and sucrose (table sugar) consists of glucose and fructose. Can you discern a rule used in naming sugars?

Carbohydrates are also found in the form of **polysaccharides** ("many sugars"), which are long chains of monosaccharide subunits linked together.

Starch, a polysaccharide composed of only glucose subunits, is an especially abundant component of plants. Most of the carbohydrates we eat are derived from plants. What was the last starch you ate?

Starch is the plant's way of storing the glucose it makes during photosynthesis. When you eat starch, you are consuming food reserves that the plant has stored for its own use. The starch of potatoes and root vegetables, for example, would be used the next spring for the plant's renewed growth after the winter die-back. All perennial plants (those that come up year after year, such as tulips) have some kind of food storage for overwintering. Beans, on the other hand, contain starch in the seeds. Beans are annual plants; they will die at the end of the growing season. So the seeds are stocked with starch to use when they have a chance to germinate the next spring.

Animals store glucose in **glycogen,** which is another form of polysaccharide. Although starch and glycogen are both composed of glucose subunits, the glucose molecules are bonded together in different ways, so these polysaccharides are not identical. Glucose subunits are bonded together a third way in the polysaccharide **cellulose.** While starch and glycogen are meant to be metabolized for energy, cellulose, which is the most abundant carbohydrate in the world, is a structural molecule that is designed *not* to be metabolized. Cellulose makes up the cell walls of plants and is a primary component of dietary fiber. For most animals it is completely indigestible. Those that can digest it, such as termites and cows, do so only with the assistance of organisms such as bacteria, fungi, or protistans.

Most disaccharides and polysaccharides can be broken down into their component monosaccharides by a process called **hydrolysis,** which is accomplished in organisms by digestive enzymes. This process is important in seeds. If the seed's food resource is starch, it must be able to convert the starch to glucose. The glucose is then used to generate ATP, which in turn is used to provide the growing plant embryo with energy for metabolic work. Hydrolysis of starch begins when the seed takes up water and begins to germinate.

Germination of barley seeds is part of the process of brewing beer. When the barley is germinated, the starch-to-sugar conversion begins. In the breakdown of starch, disaccharide maltose molecules are formed before the final product, glucose, is obtained. At a certain point in the germination, the barley is dried so that no further hydrolysis takes place. The maltose sugar is extracted and used in the brewing process. That's the "malt" listed on the beer can as an ingredient. The process of germinating the barley is called malting.

A chemical hydrolysis can be done in the laboratory by heating the molecules with acid in the presence of water. You will perform a chemical hydrolysis in this exercise.

⚠ Wear safety glasses throughout the lab session.

Activity A: Monosaccharides and Disaccharides

You will use **Benedict's reagent** as a general test for small sugars (monosaccharides and disaccharides). When this reagent is mixed with a solution containing single or double sugars and then heated, a colored precipitate (solid material) forms. The precipitate may be yellow, green, orange, or red. If no monosaccharide or disaccharide is present, the reaction mixture remains clear. However, Benedict's reagent does not react with all small sugars. For example, sucrose gives a negative Benedict's reaction.

Glucose will be used in this laboratory to demonstrate a positive Benedict's test (Figure 1). What should be used as a negative control for this test?

Procedure

1. Make a boiling water bath by filling a beaker about half full of water and heating it on a hot plate. Put six or seven boiling chips in the beaker. You will need to use this water bath in several activities.

⚠ Set the hot plate where it will not be in your way as you work. Be careful—it will be very hot!

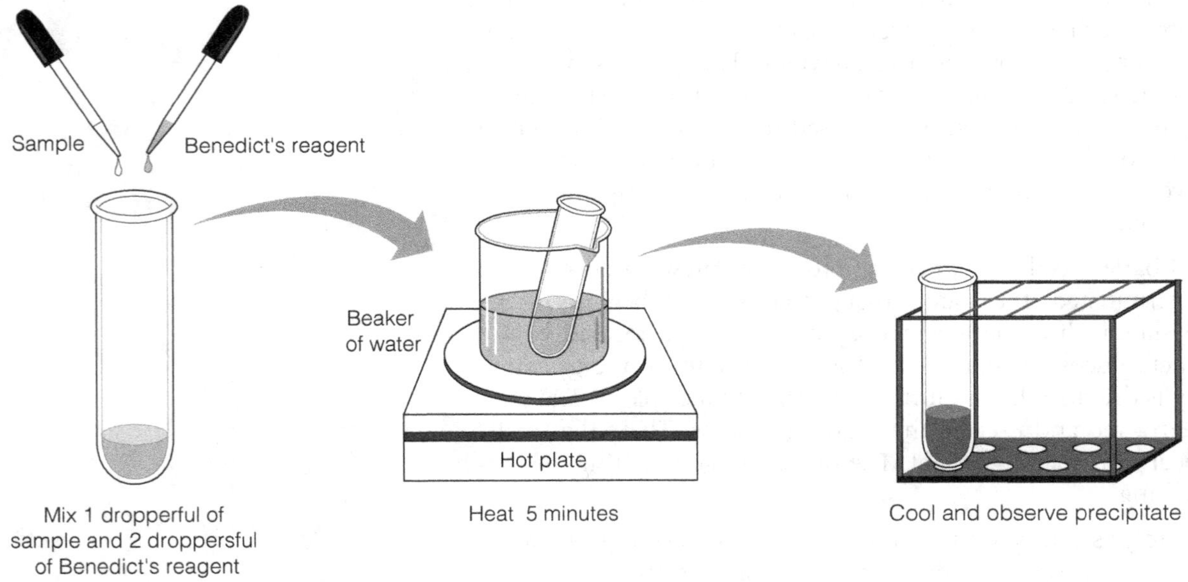

Figure 1.
Benedict's test for detecting small sugars.

2. Get two test tubes and label them 1 and 2 with a wax pencil.

Make heavy marks so that they don't melt off in the water bath.

3. Put 1 dropperful of glucose into Tube 1. Tube 1 is the positive control.
4. Tube 2 is the negative control. What substance goes in it? How much should be used?

5. Add 2 droppersful of Benedict's reagent to each tube.
6. Place the tubes in the boiling water bath and let them heat for 5 minutes.
7. After 5 minutes, remove the tubes from the water bath.

Use a test tube holder to retrieve test tubes from the boiling water.

8. Allow the tubes to cool at room temperature for several minutes in the test tube rack while you go on to the next procedure.

9. Record your observations below.
   Tube 1 (glucose):

   Tube 2 (negative control):

Interpretation of Results

Describe a positive Benedict's test.

What are the limitations of this test?

Activity B: Starch

Starch is tested by using **iodine reagent** (I_2KI—iodine potassium iodide). A dark blue color indicates the presence of starch (Figure 2).

You will use a solution of potato starch to demonstrate a positive test. What negative control should be used for this test?

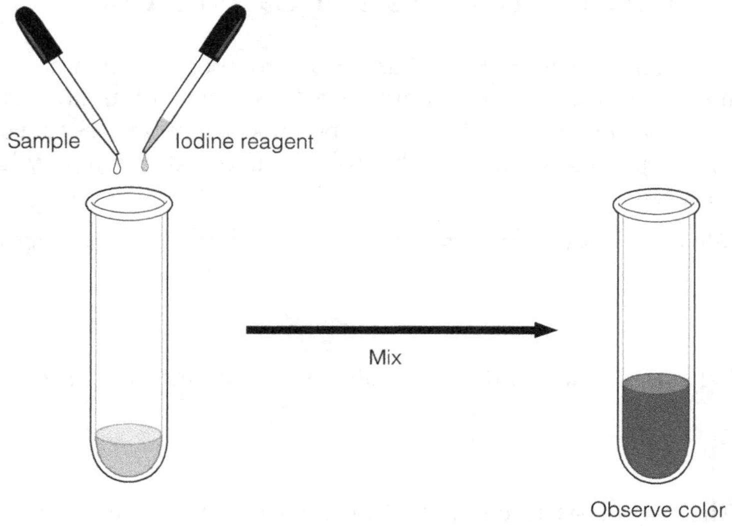

Figure 2. The iodine test for detecting starch.

Procedure

1. Get two test tubes and label them 1 and 2.
2. Put a dropperful of starch solution in Tube 1. This is the positive control.
3. Tube 2 is the negative control. What substance goes in it? How much should be used?
4. Put 3 or 4 drops of iodine reagent into each tube.
5. Record the results below.

   Tube 1 (starch):

   Tube 2 (negative control):

Interpretation of Results

Describe a positive test for starch.

What are the limitations of this test?

Activity C: Hydrolysis of Carbohydrates

As discussed earlier, disaccharides are composed of two monosaccharides linked together. Polysaccharides are long chains of monosaccharides. The bonds joining these subunits can be broken in a process called hydrolysis. In this procedure, you will hydrolyze sucrose and starch by heating them with acid.

What monosaccharides will result from the hydrolysis of sucrose?

What monosaccharide will result from the hydrolysis of starch?

The hydrolysis reactions will be carried out in two large test tubes. As Figure 3 shows, one contains sucrose and hydrochloric acid (HCl) and the

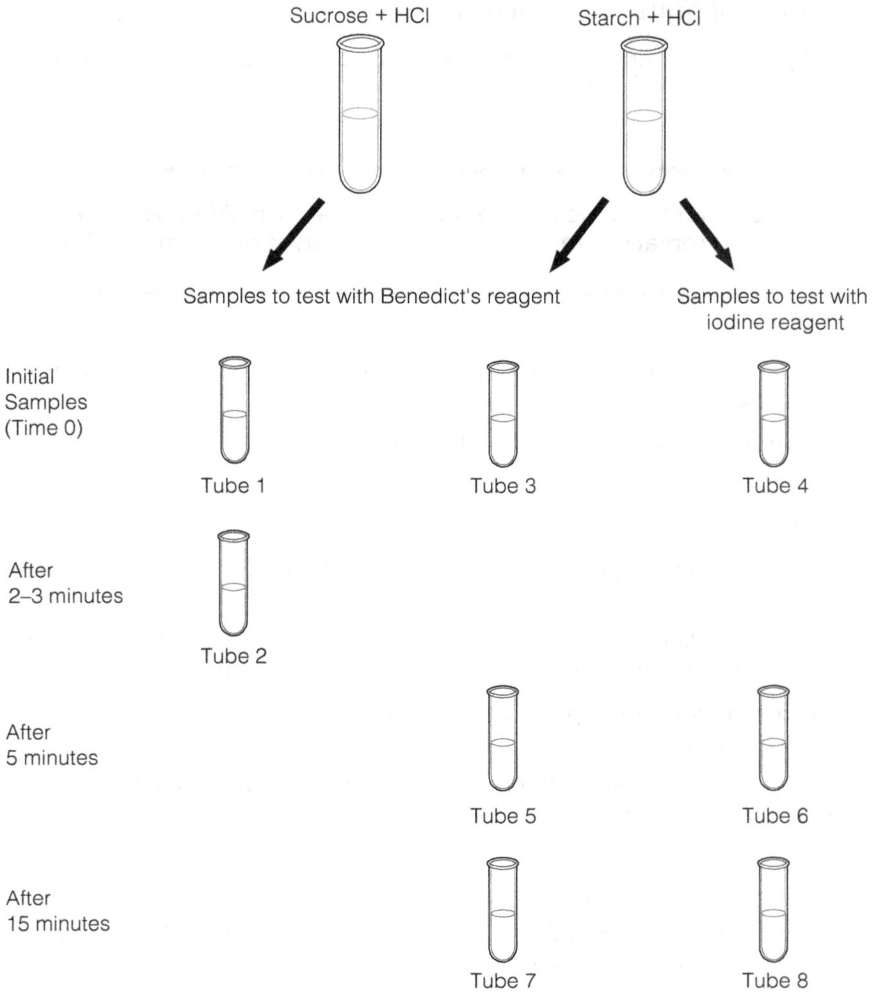

Figure 3.
Sampling hydrolysis products of sucrose and starch.

other contains starch and HCl. You will sample the sucrose tube twice: once before the hydrolysis has begun and again after 3 minutes. You will take six samples from the starch tube: two before the hydrolysis has been done, two after 5 minutes of hydrolysis, and two after 15 minutes. Two samples are needed at each time so that one can be tested for small sugars (Benedict's test) and one can be tested for starch (iodine test).

Procedure

Check your boiling water bath and add water if needed.

1. Get eight test tubes and label them 1 through 8. Line up the test tubes in order in a test tube rack.
2. Get two extra large test tubes and label them starch and sucrose. Use an empty beaker as a test tube holder if the test tubes don't fit in the rack.

Hydrolysis of Starch and Sucrose

3. Pipet 10 mL starch solution and 5 mL 2*N* HCl into the tube labeled starch.

HCl is a strong acid. Handle it with caution. After you use the pipet, replace it in its holder. Do not lay it down on the bench.

4. Pipet 10 mL sucrose solution and 2 mL 2*N* HCl into the tube labeled sucrose.
5. Swirl each tube gently to mix the contents.

Sampling

6. Use a pasteur pipet to draw 1 pipetful of solution from the sucrose tube and put it in Tube 1.
7. Using a *different* pasteur pipet, draw 1 pipetful of solution from the starch tube and put it in Tube 3. (Skip Tube 2 for now.)
8. Draw an additional pipetful of solution from the starch tube and put it in Tube 4.
9. Place the extra-large starch and sucrose tubes in your boiling water bath. Note the time:

   ____

10. After 2 or 3 minutes, draw 1 pipetful of solution from the sucrose tube and put it in Tube 2. You are now finished with the sucrose solution. You may remove it from the water bath.
11. After 5 minutes, draw 1 pipetful of solution from the starch tube and put it in Tube 5.
12. Put a second pipetful of starch solution in Tube 6.
13. Wait 10 more minutes and then repeat steps 11 and 12, putting the solution in Tubes 7 and 8.

Do Exercise 2 during the waiting period.

Testing for Starch and Sugar

14. Add two droppersful of Benedict's reagent to Tubes 1, 2, 3, 5, and 7. Place these tubes in the boiling water bath for 5 minutes.
15. Add 3 or 4 drops of iodine reagent to Tubes 4, 6, and 8. Record the results in Table 1 on the next page.

Table 1

	Tube Number							
	Sucrose		Starch					
	1	2	3	4	5	6	7	8
Time (min)	0	2–3	0	0	5	5	15	15
Benedict's reagent								
Iodine reagent								

16. Remove the tubes from the water bath and wait 5 minutes for them to cool. Record the results in Table 1.

Interpretation of Results

Explain the results you obtained using the Benedict's test on the sucrose solution.

Explain the results you obtained using the iodine reagent test with starch.

Explain the results you obtained using the Benedict's test with starch.

Why does hydrolysis of starch take longer than hydrolysis of sucrose?

EXERCISE 2
Lipids

Objectives

After completing this exercise, you should be able to

1. Define lipid and give examples.
2. Describe the test that indicates the presence of lipids.

Lipids are compounds that contain mostly carbon and hydrogen. They are grouped together solely on the basis of their insolubility in water. The lipids we will consider in this laboratory are fats and oils, which are generally used as storage molecules in both plants and animals. You are no doubt already familiar with the fact that your body converts excess food into fat. This fat is stored in your adipose tissue until your food intake is lower than your metabolic needs, at which time the fat can be metabolized to generate ATP, whose energy can be used for cellular work. Plants, too, can store fats. Seeds are often provisioned with fats that can be metabolized by the developing embryo when germination time comes. Thus we obtain corn oil, peanut oil, sunflower oil, and others by pressing the seeds.

You will use the **paper test** (Figure 4) to indicate the presence of lipids in various foods. Although this test is not very sophisticated, it is quick and convenient.

Figure 4.
Brown paper test for lipids.

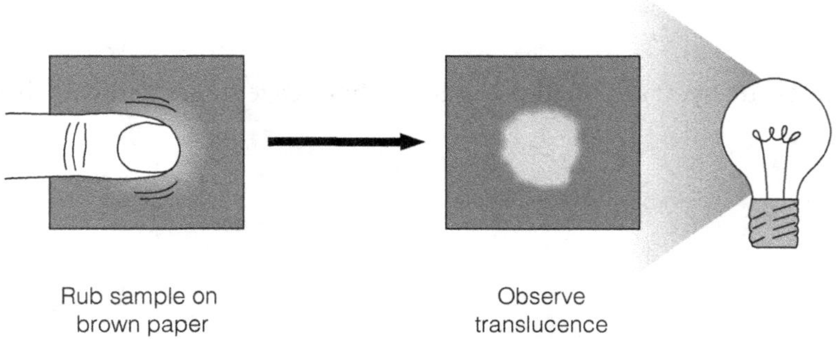

Procedure

1. Get a small square of brown paper. Write "oil" on one half and "water" on the other.
2. Put a tiny drop of salad oil on the half of the paper labeled oil. Rub it gently with your fingertip.
3. As a negative control, put a tiny drop of water on the half of the paper labeled water. Rub it gently with a different fingertip to avoid contamination.
4. Allow the spots to dry. This may take quite a while, so go on to another exercise while you wait.
5. When the spots are dry, hold the paper up to the light.

Interpretation of Results

Describe a positive test for lipids.

What are the limitations of this test?

EXERCISE 3

Proteins

Objectives

After completing this exercise, you should be able to

1. Define protein and give examples.
2. Explain why the structure of a protein is important for its function.
3. Describe the test that indicates the presence of protein.

A **protein's** structure is determined by the amino acid subunits that make up the molecule. Although there are only 20 different naturally occurring amino acids, each protein molecule has a unique sequence. The amino acids are linked by fairly tight bonds, and the side groups that are part of the amino acids also interact with each other to help shape the molecule.

Proteins have a greater diversity of roles than either carbohydrates or lipids. The shape of a protein is key to its purpose: Proteins work by selectively binding to other molecules.

You will use **biuret reagent** as a test for proteins (Figure 5). This reagent, which is blue, reacts with proteins to give a light violet or lavender color.

You will use a solution of egg albumin (a protein extracted from egg whites) to demonstrate a positive biuret test. What negative control should be used for this test?

Procedure

1. Get two test tubes and label them 1 and 2.
2. Put two droppersful of egg albumin into Tube 1.

Figure 5.
Biuret test for protein.

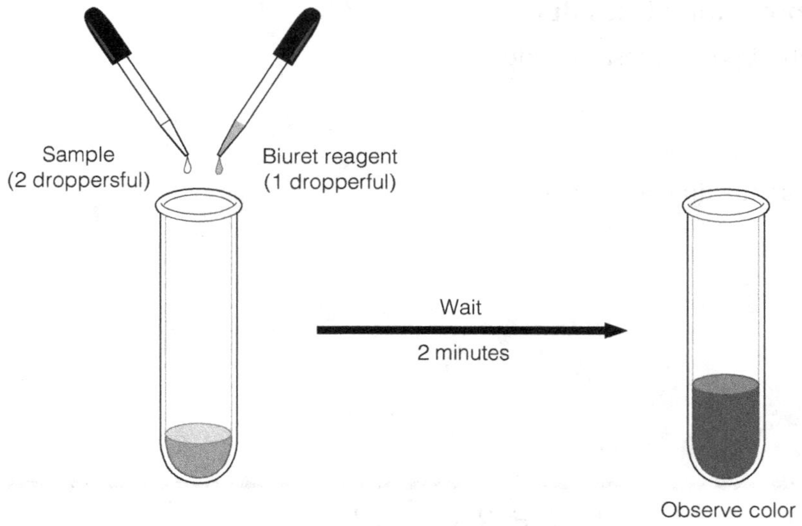

3. Tube 2 is the control. What substance goes in it? How much should be used?

4. Put 1 dropperful of biuret reagent into each tube and swirl gently to mix.
5. After 2 minutes, record the color in each tube.

   Tube 1 (egg albumin):

   Tube 2 (negative control):

Interpretation of Results

Describe a positive biuret test.

What are the limitations of this test?

EXERCISE 4

Macromolecules in Food

Objectives

After completing this exercise, you should be able to

1. Explain how the components of butter are distributed in two fractions by the process of clarification.
2. Interpret the results of tests that indicate the presence of sugar, starch, lipid, and protein in an unknown sample.

We metabolize food in order to release energy to produce the ATP needed for cellular work. We also break down food molecules in order to use their subunits as raw materials for synthesizing our own macromolecules. In this exercise, you will investigate certain foods to learn which macromolecules are present in each.

Activity A: Separation of Butter

Most foods are complex mixtures of substances. Butter, for example, may appear to be solid fat, but it is actually a mixture of proteins, carbohydrates, and lipids. It is an emulsion, which means that the lipids occur in very small droplets dispersed throughout the water-soluble portion.

The lipid can be separated from the water-soluble, protein-containing part of the butter in a process called clarification. Butter is often clarified for use in cooking. Once the water-soluble part has been removed, the lipid that remains can be used to fry at higher temperatures than for whole butter because it is the protein in butter that scorches first. It is also the protein that spoils most readily, so clarified butter keeps longer.

Procedure

1. Fill a 250-mL beaker approximately to the 75-mL mark with water.
2. Put the beaker on a hot plate and let the water come to a boil.
3. Cut approximately 1 tablespoon of butter into smaller chunks and put them in a 50-mL beaker.
4. When the water boils, remove the beaker from the hot plate with a potholder and set it on a paper towel on the lab bench. Choose a spot where it will not be disturbed.
5. Put the 50-mL beaker into the 250-mL beaker (water bath).
6. Leave the butter undisturbed for at least 15 minutes. While you wait, continue with steps 7–9.

7. Get approximately 1 teaspoon of butter from your instructor and put it into a test tube. (A teaspoon is ⅓ of a tablespoon.)
8. Put the test tube in a warm water bath to melt the butter. (You can use the water bath the 50-mL beaker is in, but don't disturb the beaker.)
9. When the butter in the test tube has melted, perform the four tests that were introduced in this laboratory and record your results in Table 2. (The test procedures are reviewed in the next section.)
10. After 15 minutes, gently pick up the 50-mL beaker and set it in ice. Leave it undisturbed for about 10 minutes. Work on Activity B while the lipid (upper) layer solidifies.
11. The upper layer (clarified butter) should now be solid or semisolid. Remove it with a spatula and put it on a paper towel. Pat the bottom of the butter dry with a paper towel to remove any contaminants from the lower layer.
12. Place the clarified butter in a test tube and melt it in a warm water bath.
13. Perform the four tests on the melted clarified butter and record the results in Table 2.
14. Perform the four tests on the lower (liquid) layer of the clarified butter and record the results in Table 2. If you do not have enough liquid to perform all the tests, arrange to share results with another lab group.

Table 2

	Benedict's (sugar)	**Iodine (starch)**	**Paper (lipid)**	**Biuret (protein)**
Whole butter				
Clarified butter, upper layer				
Clarified butter, lower layer				

Interpretation of Results

Describe what happens to butter as a result of the clarification procedure.

Clarified butter lacks the "butter" flavor. What does this tell you about the molecules responsible for the taste of butter?

Some students try this procedure to clarify margarine. They warm the margarine and leave it on ice for 10 minutes as specified in the directions. They find that the margarine has resolidified but there is no liquid lower layer. What does this tell them about the margarine?

Activity B: Tests with Food

Test each of the items in Table 3 for the presence of simple sugars, starch, lipid, and protein. Your instructor may want to modify the list. The procedures for the tests are reviewed below.

Benedict's Test (sugar)

Put 1 pasteur pipetful of sample into a test tube. Add 2 droppersful of Benedict's reagent; mix. Heat in a boiling water bath for 5 minutes. Allow to cool and observe the precipitate.

* Some samples may require extra cooling time, so don't be too hasty in recording results.

Iodine Test (starch)

Put a pipetful of sample into a test tube and add 4 or 5 drops of iodine reagent; mix.

* In some foods, the starch is still contained in granules inside the cells. You may see these dark granules suspended in the yellow solution instead of seeing the entire solution turning blue.

Paper Test (lipid)

If the sample is whole (for example, a peanut), rub a piece of it directly on the paper. If the sample is liquid, put a small drop on the paper.

* **Remember to wait for the paper to dry before you record the results.**

Biuret Test (protein)

Put 1 pipetful of sample into the test tube and add 1 dropperful of biuret reagent; mix.

* **Allow at least 2 minutes for the reaction to occur. Some samples may take 5 minutes to react.**

Some of the foods to be tested are solids. Use a razor blade to mince approximately 1 cm^3 (about the size of a pea) of the sample. Put it in a test tube with 10 mL distilled water. Put your thumb over the top of the test tube and shake it vigorously for 1 minute. Perform the tests using the liquid (except the lipid test). Record your results in Table 3. Be sure to rinse off the razor blade and cutting board between samples to avoid contamination.

Table 3

	Benedict's (sugar)	Iodine (starch)	Paper (lipid)	Biuret (protein)
Banana				
Coconut				
Milk				
Peanut				
Potato				

Interpretation of Results

Which results confirmed your expectations about the composition of foods?

Which results were unexpected?

What factors might result in a false negative test (that is, the food does contain a molecule but the tests results are negative)?

Why might a plant storage organ (such as a fruit or tuber) contain both starch and sugar?

If you have tested foods in addition to the ones listed in Table 3, compare the results from those tests with the results for the foods listed in Table 3.

Questions for Review

1. What subunits make up
   a. Carbohydrates?

   b. Proteins?

2. Why is each test done initially using water as well as a known sample?

3. Why might a substance taste sweet, yet give a negative reaction with the Benedict's test?

   What procedure could you use to check your answer to the previous question?

4. You have been given an unknown solution. Describe how you would test it for the presence of

   a. Starch:

   b. Lipid:

   c. Sugars:

   d. Protein:

5. You have tested an unknown sample with biuret and Benedict's reagents. The solution mixed with biuret reagent is blue. The solution boiled with Benedict's reagent is also blue. What does this tell you about the sample?

6. Whole butter gives only a slightly positive test for protein (and may show no reaction at all). When the same butter is clarified, however, the liquid lower layer is definitely positive for protein. Explain why these different results might have been obtained.

7. Since potatoes have starch in them, why don't they taste sweet after they are boiled?

Acknowledgments

Procedures for the macromolecule tests were adapted from the following sources:

Armstrong, W. D., and C. W. Carr. Physiological Chemistry Laboratory Directions, 3rd ed. Minneapolis: Burgess Publishing, 1963.

Dotti, L. B., and J. M. Orten. Laboratory Instructions in Biochemistry, 8th ed. St. Louis: C. V. Mosby, 1971.

Oser, B. L., ed. *Hawk's Physiological Chemistry*, 14th ed. New York: McGraw-Hill, 1965.

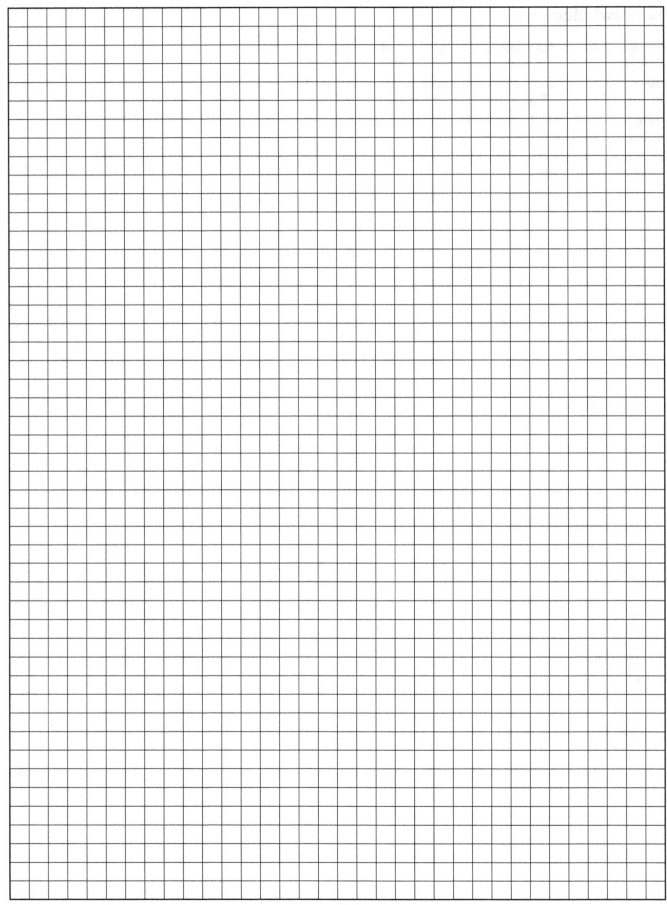

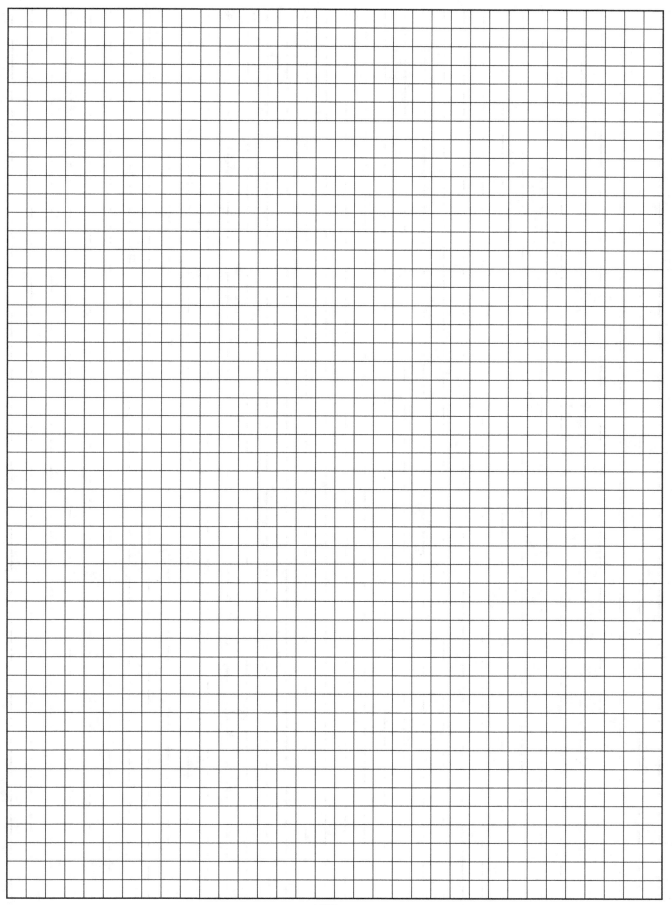

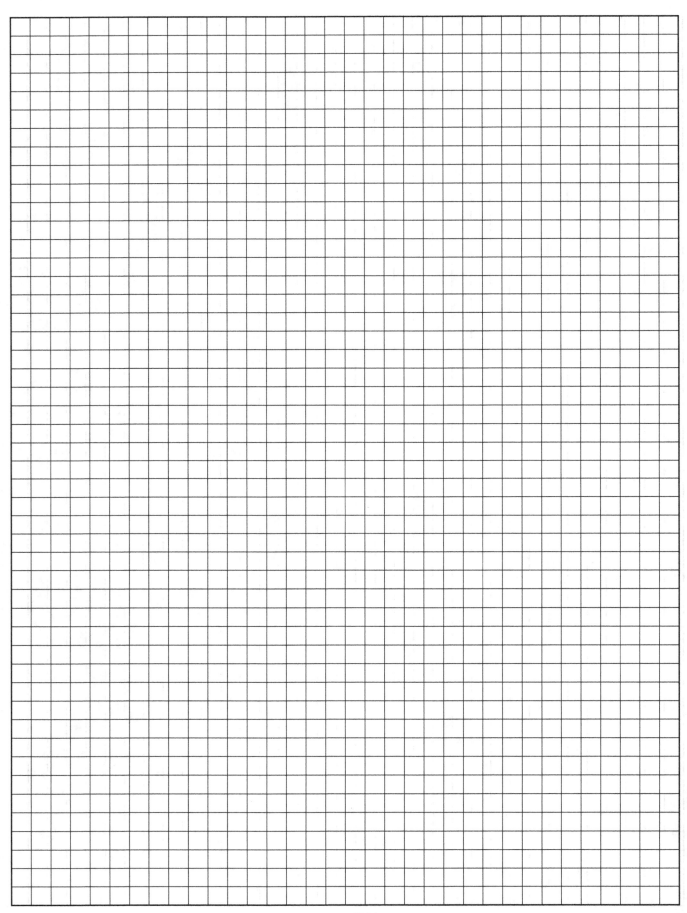

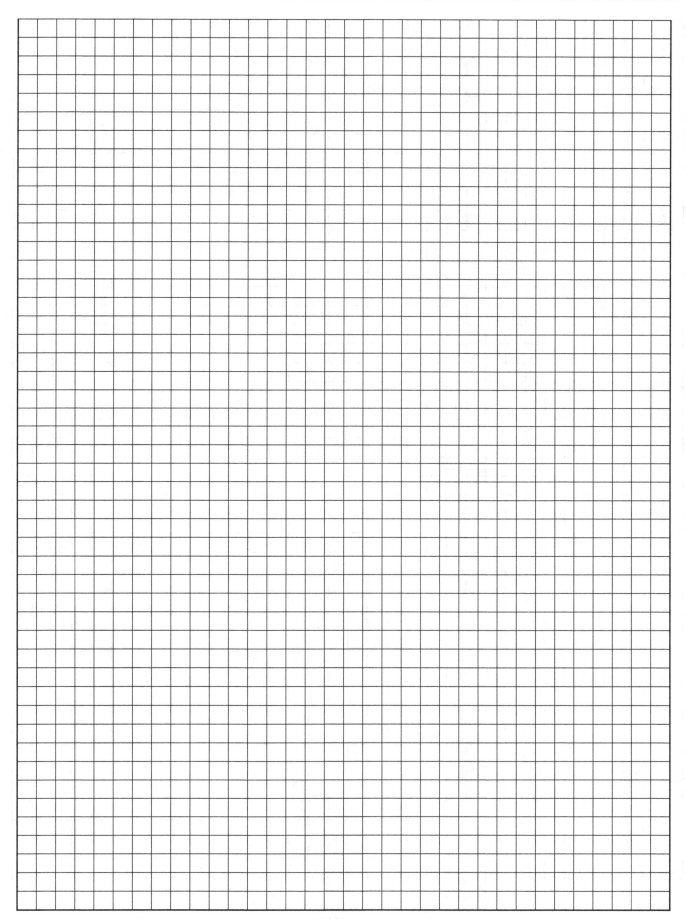

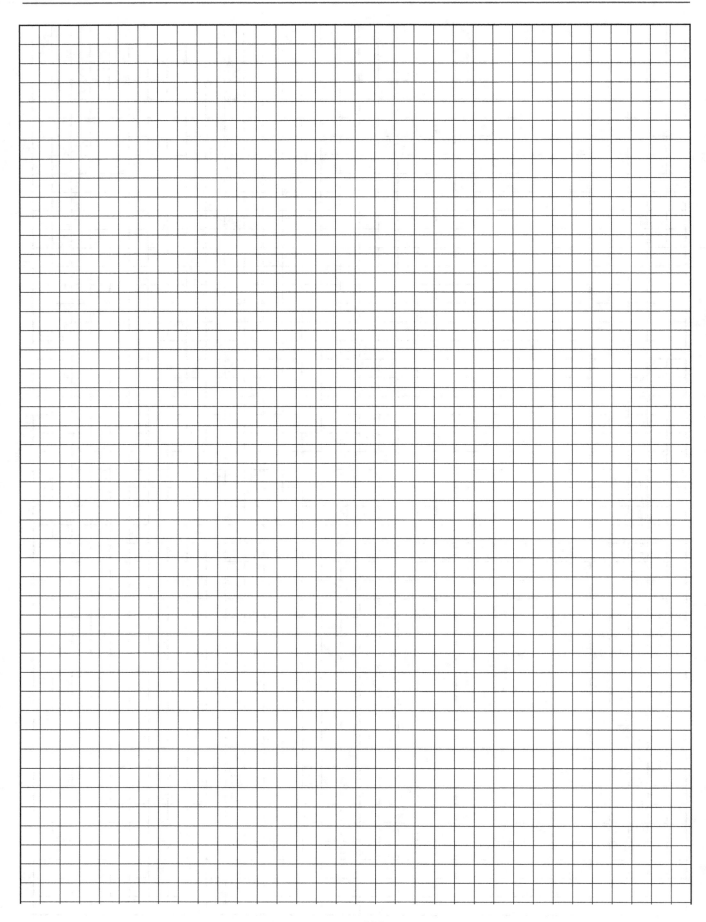

pH and Buffers

Introduction

Molecules that are dissolved in water may separate (ionize) into charged fragments. pH is a measure of the concentration of one of those charged fragments, hydrogen ions (H^+), in solution. A substance that has a high concentration of H^+ is acidic. A substance that has a low concentration of H^+ is basic (alkaline).

The pH scale ranges from 0 (most acidic) to 14 (most basic). There is a tenfold difference between pH units. For example, a solution with a pH value of 6 has a ten-times-greater concentration of hydrogen ions than a solution with a pH value of 7. Some examples are shown in Table 1.

Outline

Exercise 1: Introduction to Acids, Bases, and pH

Exercise 2: Using Red Cabbage Indicator to Measure pH

Activity A: Making a Set of Standards

Activity B: Comparing pH of Beverages and Stomach Medicines

Exercise 3: Using the pH Meter to Determine Buffering Capacity

Exercise 4: Designing an Experiment

Exercise 5: Performing the Experiment and Interpreting the Results

EXERCISE 1
Introduction to Acids, Bases, and pH

Objectives

After completing this introductory exercise, you should be able to

1. Explain what makes a solution acidic or basic.
2. Explain the pH scale.
3. Describe the phenol red test for pH.

An **acid** is a substance that releases or causes the release of H^+ into solution. Solutions that have pH values lower than 7 are considered to be acids. Some common acids are hydrochloric acid, acetic acid, carbonic acid, and sulfuric acid. All of these compounds contain hydrogen. When

Table 1
pH Scale

pH	Relative strength	Examples
0	Strong acid	
1		Battery acid
2		Gastric fluid
3	Moderate acid	Orange juice
4		Tomato juice
5	Weak acid	
6		Rainwater Milk
7	Neutral	Pure water Blood
8		
9	Weak base	Baking soda Milk of Magnesia
10		
11	Moderate base	Household ammonia
12		
13	Strong base	Hair remover
14		Oven cleaner

the compound is dissolved in water, hydrogen ions are released, and the pH of the solution is low. Your instructor will use an indicator called **phenol red** to demonstrate the acidity of hydrochloric acid. Phenol red is red when the solution is basic and turns yellow in acidic solution.

What color is the phenol red solution initially?

What happens when hydrochloric acid is added?

A compound does not have to contain hydrogen ions itself in order to be an acid. Carbon dioxide (CO_2), for example, can combine with water to generate H^+. Your instructor will use phenol red again to demonstrate that CO_2 is an acid. Briefly describe this demonstration.

The reaction of SO_2 (sulfur dioxide) is similar to that of CO_2. The presence of SO_2 in the atmosphere is partially responsible for acid rain.

A **base** is a substance that can remove H^+ from solution, thus lowering the concentration of H^+. Many bases ionize to produce hydroxyl ions (OH^-), which combine with H^+ to make water (H_2O). Some common bases are sodium hydroxide (NaOH), magnesium hydroxide ($Mg(OH)_2$), and potassium hydroxide (KOH).

Mixing an acid with a base can produce a neutral solution by combining the H^+ with the OH^- to make water (H_2O). Pure water, which ionizes to produce equal numbers of H^+ and OH^-, is neutral (pH 7). Don't expect to get a pH of 7 when you measure water in the lab, though. Tap water contains impurities, and its pH varies a great deal. Distilled water is weakly acidic; its pH is usually around 6.

It is important for organisms to maintain a constant internal pH. As you will learn in later laboratories, biological molecules, especially proteins, are sensitive to pH, and they may not function correctly when the pH is changed.

In the following exercises you will make an indicator solution to measure pH and also learn how to use a pH meter. You will determine the pH values of some common substances and investigate how buffer systems work to maintain a constant pH.

Wear safety glasses while performing these exercises. Strong acids and strong bases are corrosive. Inform your instructor immediately if any solution is spilled or comes in contact with your skin or clothing.

EXERCISE 2

Using Red Cabbage Indicator to Measure pH

Objectives

After completing this exercise, you should be able to

1. Explain what a pH indicator is used for.
2. Describe how to measure pH using red cabbage indicator.

Several methods are available for determining pH. Many of these methods rely on the ability of certain chemicals called **indicators** to change color, depending on the pH of the surrounding solution. Papers saturated with indicators, such as litmus paper and alkacid test paper, can also be used.

An indicator can easily be made from a solution of anthocyanins, the pigments responsible for red, blue, and purple colors in flowers, fruits, and autumn leaves. These pigments change color as the pH changes. Red cabbage is loaded with anthocyanins, so we can make a pH indicator by boiling red cabbage to extract the pigments. Your instructor will make the extract at the beginning of class.

The use of standards, a set of known quantities, is an important technique in biological research. By comparing unknowns with the standards, we can determine what we want to know about the unknowns. The color of cabbage extract depends on the pH of the solution it is in. Your set of standards will show the color of the cabbage extract at pH 2, 4, 6, 7, 8, 10, and 12. You will then determine the pH values of various substances by mixing each substance with cabbage extract and comparing its color to the standards.

Activity A: Making a Set of Standards

Your lab team should make a set of standards using the cabbage extract and solutions of known pH according to the following procedure.

Procedure

1. Put seven clean test tubes in a rack and label them 2, 4, 6, 7, 8, 10, and 12.
2. Pipet 5 mL of the appropriate buffer into each tube (pH 2 buffer into the tube labeled 2, and so on).
3. Get a dropping bottle of cabbage extract from your instructor. Add 3 mL of cabbage extract to each tube.
4. Cover the tubes with Parafilm and mix well.
5. Record the color in each tube in Table 2.

Save this set of standards for use throughout the lab period.

Table 2
Color of Standard Solutions for
Red Cabbage Indicator

pH	Color
2	
4	
6	
7	
8	
10	
12	
Record both the initial and final colors at pH 12. The pigments are not stable at this pH.	

Activity B: Comparing pH of Beverages and Stomach Medicines

Look at Table 3 to see what aspect of pH is being investigated in this experiment, and answer the following questions.

Table 3
pH Values of Beverages and Medicines

Beverages	pH	Medicines	pH
White grape juice		Milk of Magnesia ($Mg(OH)_2$)	
7-Up		Sodium bicarbonate ($NaHCO_3$)	
White wine		Maalox	
Seltzer water			

What hypothesis could be tested with this experiment?

What is the independent variable in this experiment?

What is the dependent variable?

What substance could be used as a control for this experiment?

Predict the outcome of the experiment in terms of your hypothesis. What results will support the hypothesis? What results will prove the hypothesis false?

Use the cabbage indicator method to measure the pH of the substances listed in Table 3.

Procedure

1. Put 2 droppersful of the solution to be tested in a clean test tube.
2. Add 1 dropperful of cabbage extract.
3. Swirl the tube gently to mix.
4. Compare the color of the solution to the colors of your cabbage indicator standards.
5. Record the pH value for each substance in Table 3.
6. Measure and record the pH of your control.

   Control: __________

   pH of control: __________

Was your hypothesis proven false or supported by the results? Use data to support your answer.

What components of the beverages you tested might be responsible for the pH values of the beverages?

What components of the medicines you tested might be responsible for the pH values of the medicines?

Explain why stomach medicines should have pH values that are much higher than normal stomach pH, which is around 2. (Hint: Why do people take these medicines?)

EXERCISE 3

Using the pH Meter to Determine Buffering Capacity

Objectives

After completing this exercise, you should be able to

1. Define buffer, and explain why buffers are important to organisms.
2. Describe how to use a pH meter.
3. Interpret a titration curve (graph of pH versus milliliters of HCl and NaOH added) to determine whether a solution has buffering capacity and, if so, over what pH range.
4. Explain why some solutions have buffering capacity and others don't.

In order for normal physiological processes to occur, pH must remain relatively constant. An excess of H^+ or OH^- can interfere with the functioning of biological molecules, especially proteins. In our bodies, for example, blood pH is usually maintained between 7.3 and 7.5. However, blood returning to the heart contains CO_2 picked up from the tissues, which lowers the blood pH. Metabolic reactions in cells may contribute an excess of hydrogen ions. Our diets may also affect blood pH. Several buffering systems keep the pH constant.

A **buffer** is a solution whose pH resists change on addition of small amounts of either an acid or a base. To be a good buffer, a solution should have a component that acts as a base (takes H^+ out of solution) and a component that acts as an acid (puts more H^+ into solution when there is an excess of OH^-).

The buffering capacity of a solution is tested by adding small amounts of acid (for example, HCl) and base (for example, NaOH) and checking the pH after each addition. If the pH changes only slightly, the solution is a good buffer. Eventually its buffering capacity will be exhausted, however, and the pH will change dramatically.

A buffer operates in a specific pH range. The buffering systems in our blood, for example, buffer at around pH 7.4. That is, they maintain the pH at or very close to 7.4. The solutions you used to make up your standards for red cabbage indicator maintain each buffer at a certain pH. The pH 2 buffer maintains pH at 2, the pH 4 buffer maintains pH at 4, and so on. Notice that the purpose of a buffer is *not* to make the pH neutral (7).

Figure 1.
Titration curve for an unknown solution.

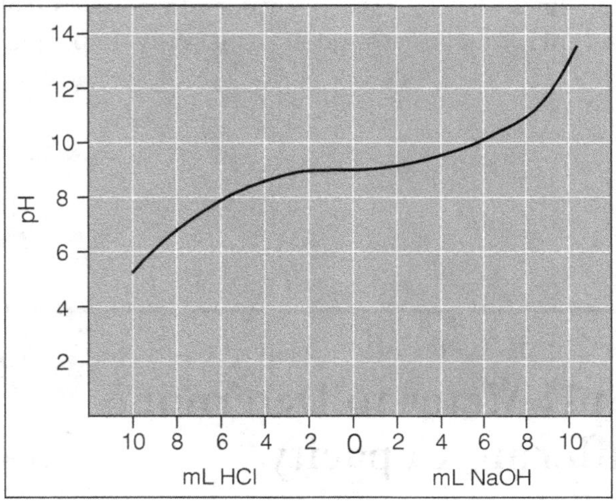

Look at Figure 1. Is this solution a good buffer? Explain how you know.

At what pH does the solution buffer?

Figure 2.
Titration curve for an unknown solution.

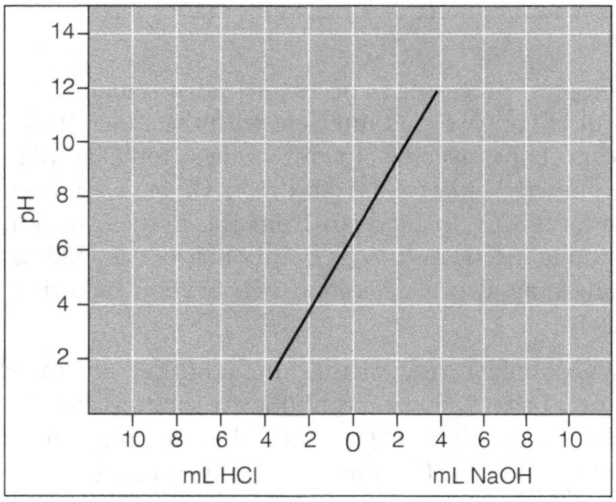

Look at Figure 2. Is this solution a good buffer? Explain how you know.

You will use a pH meter to test buffering capacity in this exercise. The pH meter has a sensitive electrode that measures the H^+ concentration in solution. It can measure in tenths of pH units; some models measure hundredths of pH units.

Most of the control knobs are used only to calibrate the machine (a buffer of known pH is used to standardize the pH meter). Figure 3 illustrates two

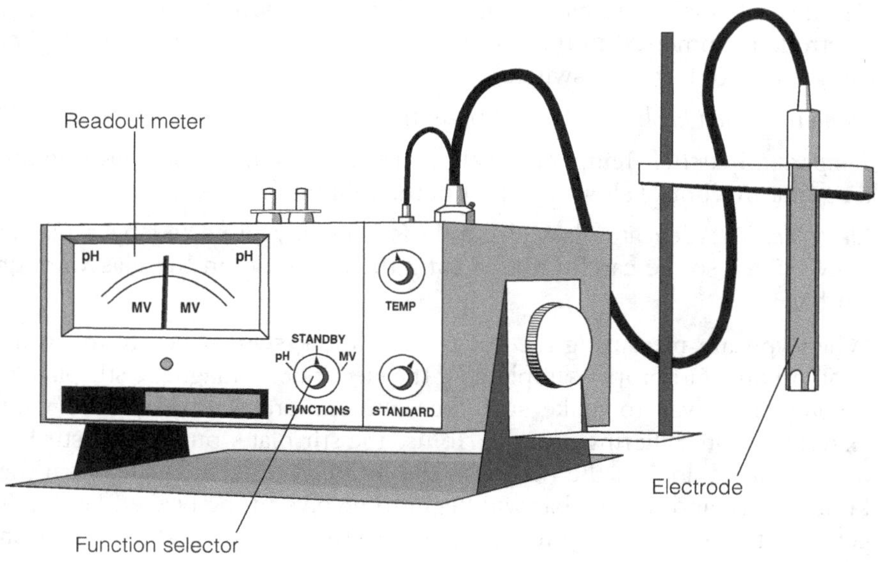

Figure 3a.
Analog pH meter.

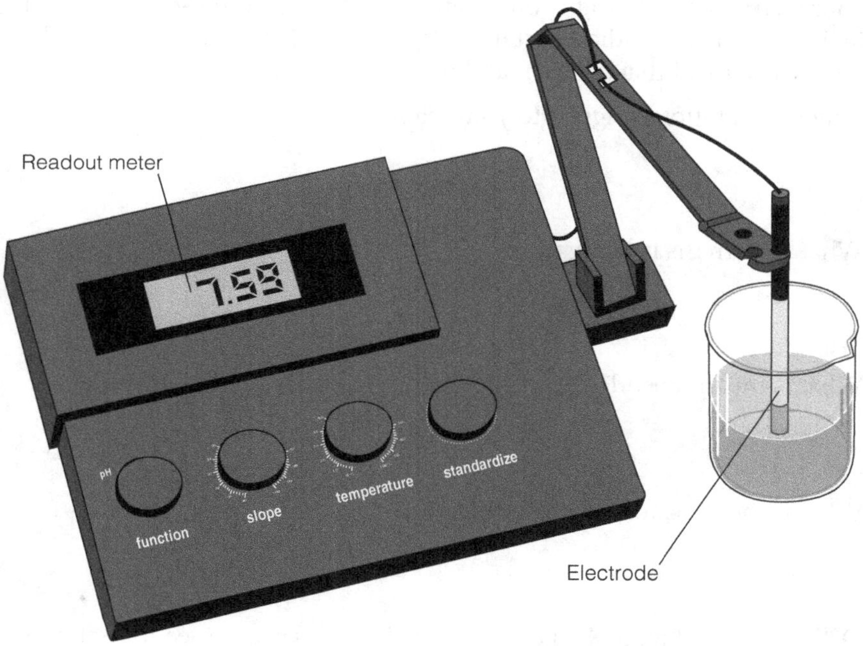

Figure 3b.
Digital pH meter.

commonly used types of pH meters: digital and analog. Your instructor can help you identify the parts you will need to use for the model of pH meter available in your laboratory.

Familiarize yourself with the pH meter in your laboratory by locating the following parts.

Controls

Readout meter: Shows the pH of the solution. On an analog meter, there are usually two scales. One shows pH and the other shows millivolts. You will use the pH scale. (If you are using a digital pH meter, only the number representing the solution's pH will be displayed.)

Function selector (pH/standby switch): Use the pH position only when the electrode is immersed in the solution you want to measure. (Some digital models do not have this switch.)

Standardization knob: Used to calibrate the machine.

Temperature control: Temperature affects pH measurement, so adjusting the temperature control should be part of the calibration procedure.

Electrode: The delicate glass electrode is generally protected by a plastic sleeve. Even so, be careful not to bang the electrode on the glassware or stir bar.

When you are measuring the pH of a solution, swirl it gently to assure good mixing and proper sampling by the electrode. A magnetic stir plate is a convenient way to make sure the solutions are well mixed for your experiment on buffering capacity. To use the stir plate, put a small stir bar in the beaker, and set the beaker in the middle of the stir plate. Turn the knob slowly, and the stir bar will begin to revolve in the beaker. Let it stir gently. If the bar starts to jump around, turn the knob off and then back on again more slowly.

Your instructor will assign your team one of the buffering solutions used to make the cabbage indicator standards in Exercise 2. You will test the buffering capacity of that solution and of water.

Buffering solution assigned to your team:

What hypothesis is being tested?

What is the independent variable in this experiment?

What is the dependent variable?

On the axes of Figure 4, sketch the curve you expect to see for Solution X if your hypothesis is supported. On the same axes, sketch the curve you expect to see if your hypothesis is proven false.

Why should you determine the buffering capacity of water as part of this experiment?

Procedure

1. Pour 40 mL of your assigned solution into a 100-mL beaker. Put a stir bar in the beaker and put it on the magnetic stirrer.

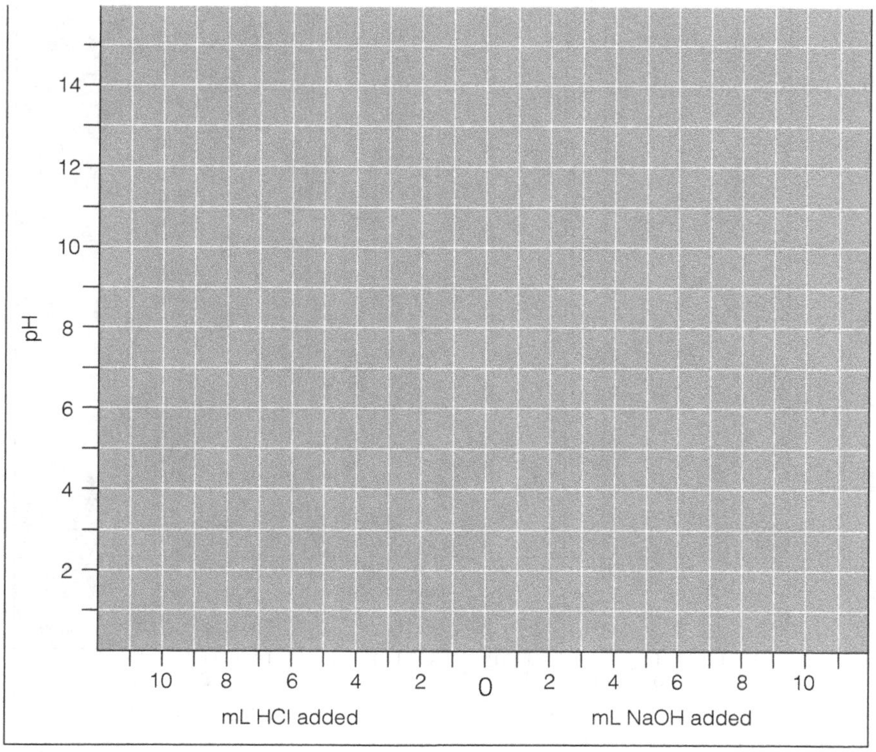

Figure 4.
Predicted results of buffering capacity experiment.

2. Determine the pH of the solution by following steps a–d below.
   a. Raise the electrode out of the soak beaker and rinse it with distilled water from the wash bottle.
   b. Immerse the electrode in the solution you want to measure. Swirl the beaker gently. If you are using a magnetic stir plate, make sure the bar clears the electrode before you turn it on.
   c. If your pH meter has a function switch, change it from standby to pH.
   d. Read the pH value on the readout meter or digital display.
3. Record the pH value at 0 on the x-axis of Figure 5 on the next page.
4. Add 1.0 mL of 0.1*N* HCl. *N* stands for normal, a measure of concentration. (If you're using a magnetic stirrer, you can leave it on with the electrode immersed throughout the procedure. If you must take the electrode out of the beaker to mix, turn the function switch to standby first.)
5. Record the new pH at "1 mL HCl added" on the x-axis of Figure 5.
6. Add another 1 mL of HCl and record the new pH at "2 mL HCl added" on the x-axis of Figure 5.
7. Continue to add 1 mL of HCl at a time and record the pH until you have added 10 mL *or* there is a significant decrease in pH, whichever comes first.
8. If the pH meter has a function switch, turn it back to standby.
9. Raise the electrode out of the solution.

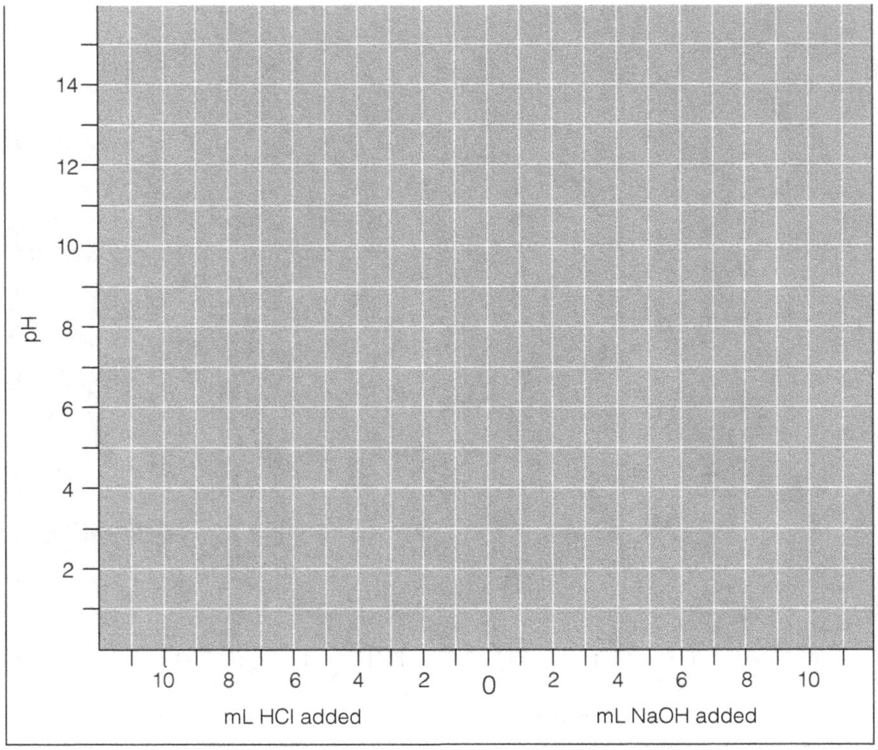

Figure 5.
Results of buffering capacity experiment.

10. Rinse the electrode with distilled water, and wipe it with a cleaning tissue.

Always rinse the electrode with distilled water after use to avoid contamination of solutions.

---

11. Dispose of your solution, and rinse and dry the beaker and stir bar.
12. Put another 40 mL of the same solution into the beaker and repeat the procedure using 0.1*N* NaOH instead of HCl until you have added 10 mL *or* there is a significant increase in pH, whichever comes first. Record the pH values on the "mL NaOH added" side of the x-axis of Figure 5.
13. When you are finished determining the buffering capacity of the solution you were assigned, repeat steps 1–12 to determine the buffering capacity of water. Use the axes in Figure 5 to graph the results.

When you're done with this procedure, leave the electrode immersed in some solution (water or a buffer). It should never be allowed to dry out.

Write a descriptive title for Figure 5.

Review your prediction (Figure 4) about the buffering capacity of the solution you were assigned. Was your prediction correct?

If the solution is a buffer, at what pH does it buffer?

Evaluate your hypothesis. Is it supported or proven false by the results?

Describe the buffering capacity (or lack of it) of this solution.

Describe the buffering capacity (or lack of it) of water.

EXERCISE 4

Designing an Experiment

Objective

After completing this exercise, you should be able to

1. Design an original experiment to investigate some aspect of pH or buffering capacity.

In Exercises 2 and 3 you learned a method of measuring pH and a method of determining buffering capacity. In Exercises 4 and 5, your lab team will design an experiment using one of these methods, perform your experiment, and present and interpret your results.

The following materials will be supplied for your group.

For pH Measurement Using Red Cabbage Indicator

You will already have the standards made up from Exercise 2.

extra test tubes

pasteur pipets and rubber bulbs

For Determining Buffering Capacity

You will use the same materials used in Exercise 3. Your instructor will be able to tell you what additional materials will be available.

Proposed Experiment

If you are considering an experiment using red cabbage indicator, you might want to review Table 1 for ideas. Also, try to think of substances whose function may be pH dependent. For example, you may recall hearing the terms pH, acid, or base used in advertisements. If you are planning an investigation of buffering capacity, consider what substances might be expected to be good buffers.

Describe your experiment below.

Question or Hypothesis

Dependent Variable

Independent Variable

Explain why you think this independent variable will affect pH or buffering capacity.

Control Treatment(s)

Replication

Brief Explanation of Experiment

Predictions (What results would support your hypothesis? What results would prove your hypothesis false?)

Method

Design a Table to Collect Your Data

List Any Additional Materials You Will Require

EXERCISE 5

Performing the Experiment and Interpreting the Results

Objectives

After completing this exercise, you should be able to

1. Perform the experiment your lab team designed.
2. Present and interpret the results of your experiment.

Before you do the experiment, be sure that everyone on your lab team understands the techniques that will be used. You may want to divide up the tasks before you begin work.

Be thorough in collecting data. Don't just write down numbers; record what they mean as well. Don't rely on your memory for information that you need when reporting on your experiment later! If you have any questions, doubts, or problems during the experiment, be sure to write them down, too.

Results

Before you begin to prepare your results for presentation, decide on the best format to use. Remember, you want to give the reader a clear, concise picture of what your experiment showed. If you are drawing graphs, use graph paper. Complete your tables and/or graphs before attempting to interpret your results.

Write a few sentences *describing* the results (don't explain why you got these results or draw conclusions yet).

Discussion

Look back at the hypothesis or question you posed in this experiment. Look at the graphs or tables of your data. Do your results support your hypothesis or prove it false? Explain your answer, using your data for support.

Did your results correspond to the prediction you made? If not, explain how your results are different from your expectations and why this might have occurred.

Describe how your data are supported by information from other sources (for example, textbooks or other lab teams working on the same problem).

If you had any problems with the procedure or questionable results, explain how they might have influenced your conclusion.

If you had an opportunity to repeat and extend this experiment to make your results more convincing, what would you do?

Summarize the conclusion you have drawn from your results.

Questions for Review

1. You have blown air from your lungs into a solution of phenol red and changed its color from red to yellow. Suggest a way to turn the color back to red.

2. Give an example of two substances that, when mixed together, will produce a neutral solution.

3. You measure the pH of your garden soil and find that it is 6. You measure the pH of peat moss and find that it is 4. How much greater is the concentration of hydrogen ions in peat moss than in the garden soil?

4. What's one ingredient that could make soft drinks acidic?

5. Aspirin has a pH of 3. Some people who take large amounts of aspirin (for example, for arthritis) take a pill that combines aspirin with Maalox. What's the purpose of this combination?

6. If you want to do an experiment to measure buffering capacity, why is red cabbage indicator not a good choice of methods?

7. On the graph in Figure 6, which compound is the best buffer? Explain why. Over what pH range does the compound buffer?

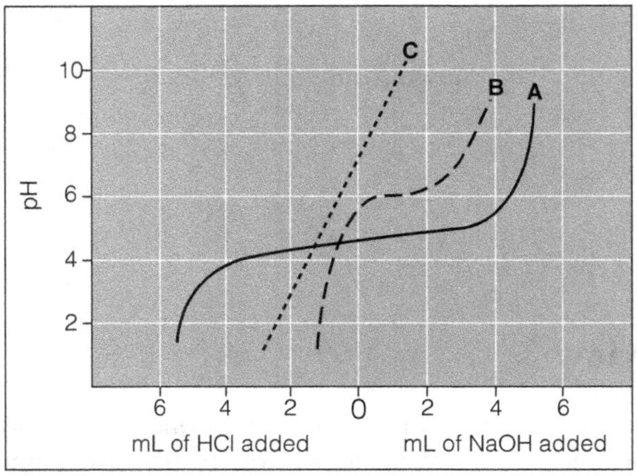

Figure 6.
Graph of buffering activity of three different compounds.

8. Considering that CO_2 is produced as a by-product of cellular metabolism, why is it important for our blood to contain buffers?

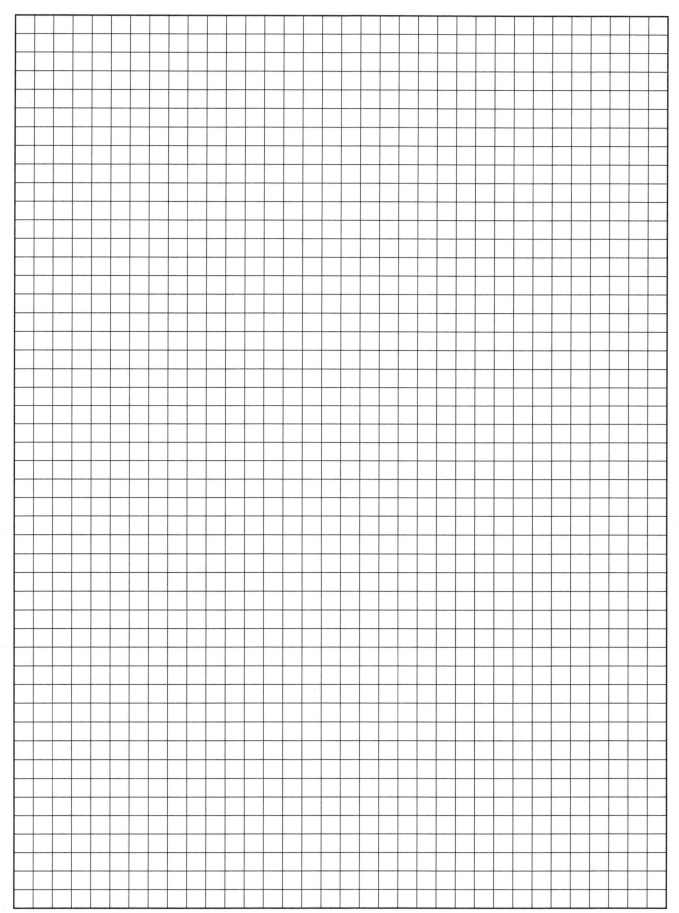

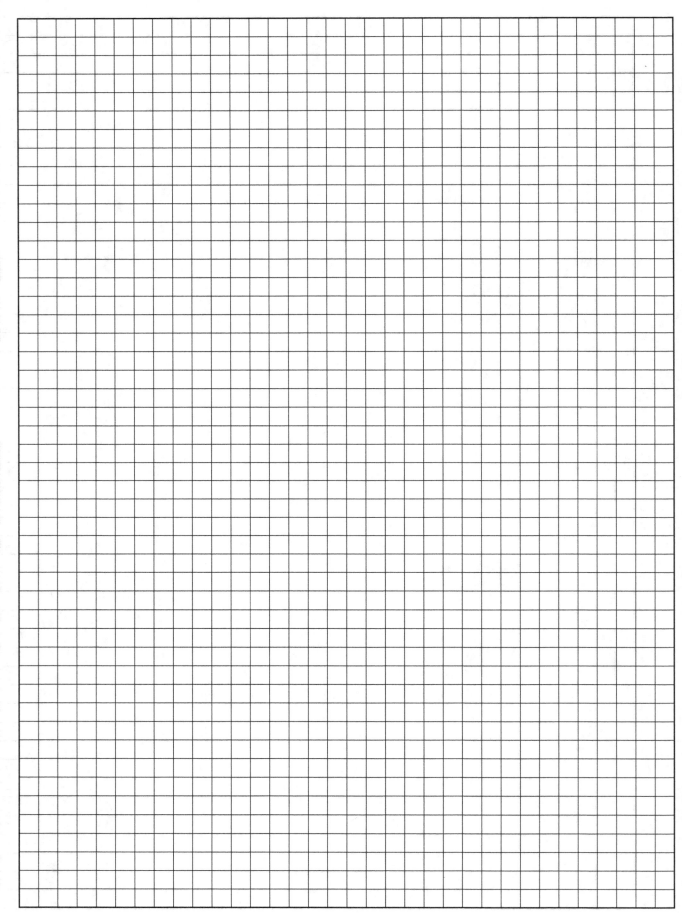

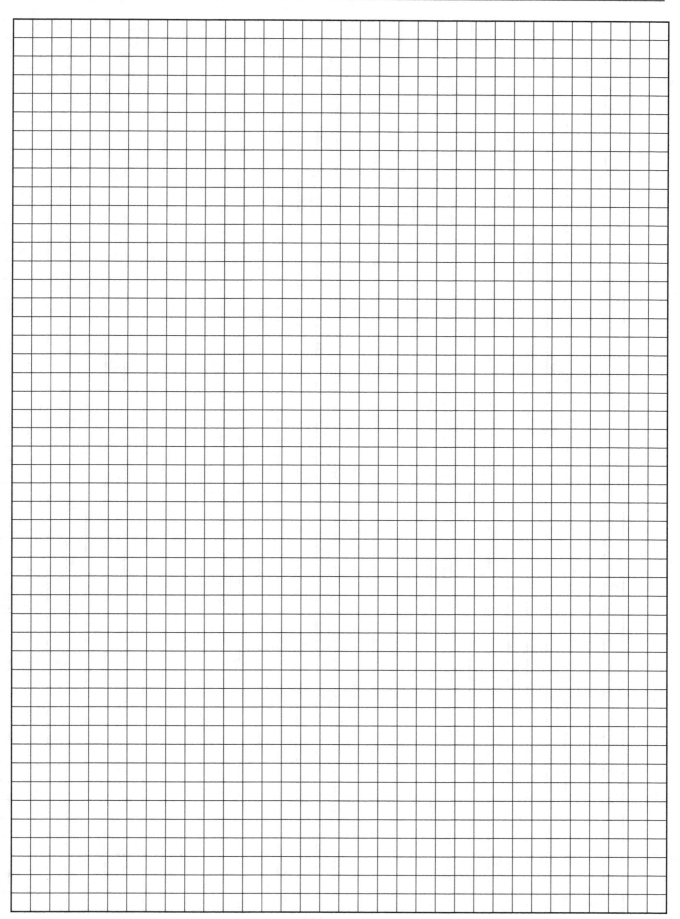

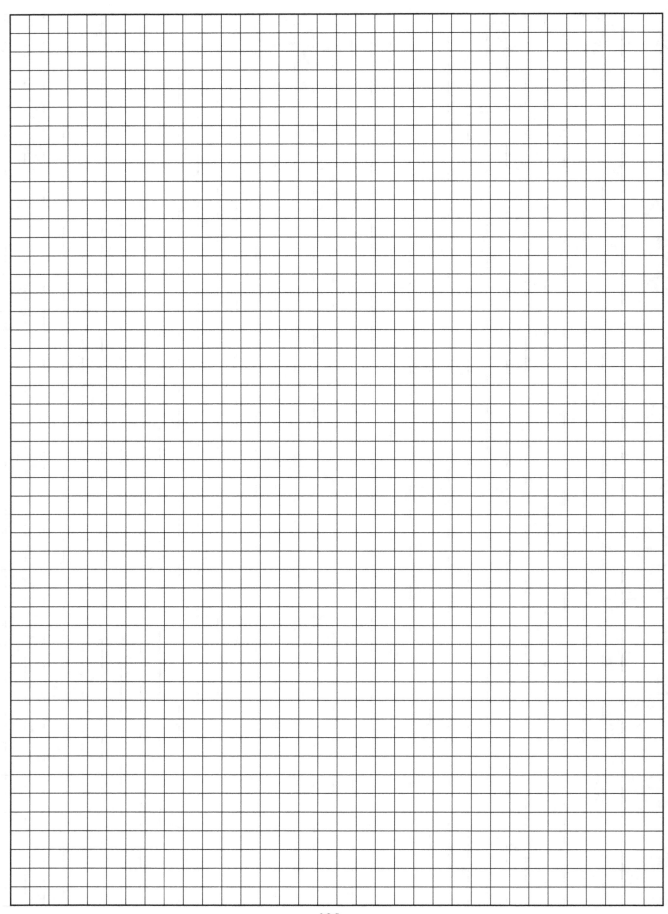

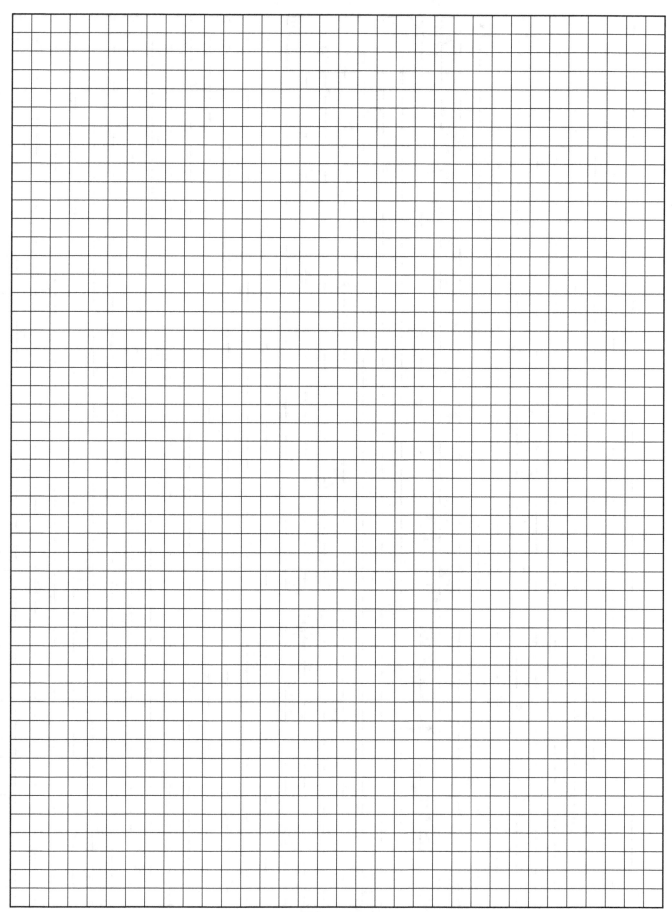

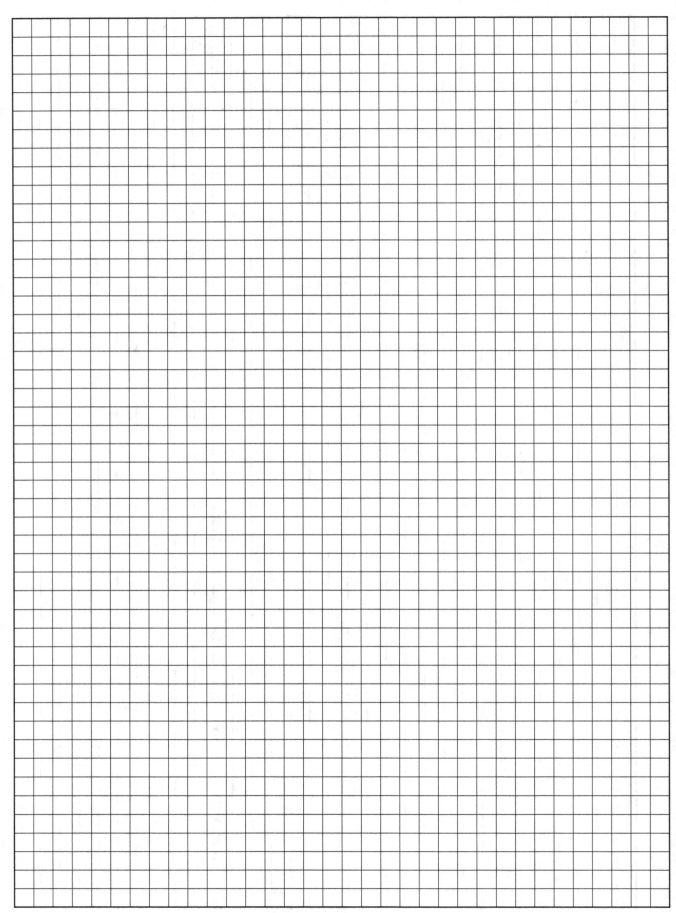

Enzymes

Laboratory Objectives

After completing this lab topic, you should be able to:

1. Define *enzyme* and describe the activity of enzymes in cells.
2. Differentiate competitive and noncompetitive inhibition.
3. Discuss the effects of varying environmental conditions such as pH and temperature on the rate of enzyme activity.
4. Discuss the effects of varying enzyme and substrate concentrations on the rate of enzyme activity.
5. Discuss the scientific process, propose hypotheses, and make predictions based on hypotheses.
6. Practice scientific persuasion and communication by constructing and interpreting graphs of enzyme activity.

Introduction

Living cells perform a multitude of chemical reactions very rapidly because of the participation of enzymes. **Enzymes** are biological **catalysts,** compounds that speed up a chemical reaction without being used up or altered in the reaction. The material with which the catalyst reacts, called the **substrate,** is modified during the reaction to form a new product (see Figure 1). But because the enzyme itself emerges from the reaction unchanged and ready to bind with another substrate molecule, a small amount of enzyme can alter a relatively enormous amount of substrate.

The **active site** of an enzyme will bind with the substrate, forming the **enzyme-substrate complex.** It is here that catalysis takes place, and when it is complete, the complex dissociates into enzyme and product or products.

Enzymes are, in part or in whole, proteins and are highly specific in function. Because enzymes lower the energy of activation needed for reactions to take place, they accelerate the rate of reactions. They do not, however, determine the direction in which a reaction will go or its final equilibrium.

Enzyme activity is influenced by many factors. Varying environmental conditions, such as pH or temperature, may change the three-dimensional shape of an enzyme and alter its rate of activity. Specific chemicals may also bind to an enzyme and modify its shape. Chemicals that must bind for the enzyme

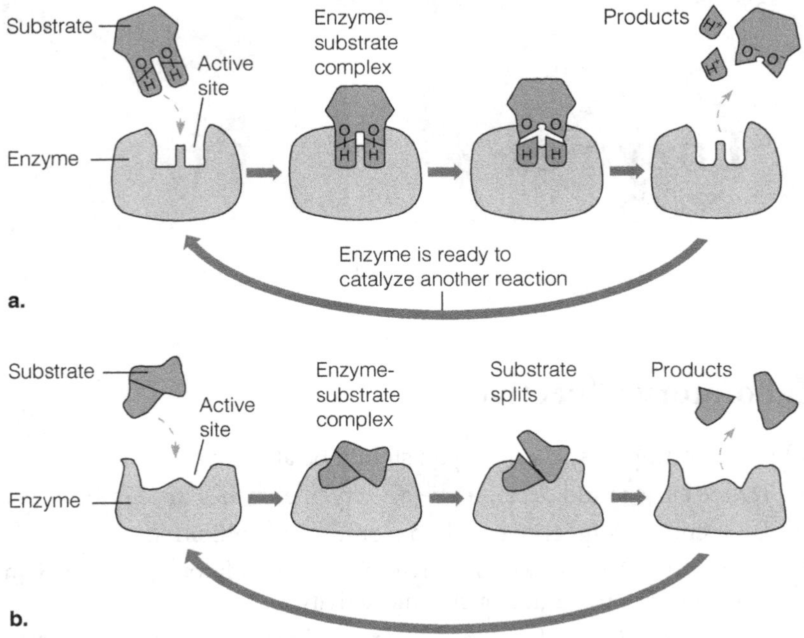

Figure 1.
Enzyme activity. A substrate or substrates bind to the active site of the enzyme, forming the enzyme-substrate complex, which then dissociates into enzyme and product(s). The enzyme may catalyze the addition or removal of a molecule or a portion of a molecule from the substrate to produce the product (a), or the enzyme may catalyze the splitting of a substrate into its component subunits (b).

to be active are called **activators. Cofactors** are nonprotein substances that usually bind to the active site on the enzyme and are essential for the enzyme to work. Organic cofactors are called **coenzymes,** but other cofactors may simply be metal ions. Chemicals that shut off enzyme activity are called **inhibitors,** and their action can be classified as **competitive** or **noncompetitive inhibition.**

Review Figure 1, illustrating enzyme activity. There are two ways to measure enzyme activity: (1) Determine the rate of disappearance of the substrate, and (2) determine the rate of appearance of the product.

In this laboratory, you will use both methods to investigate the activity of two enzymes, **catechol oxidase** and **amylase.** You will use an inhibitor to influence the activity of catechol oxidase and determine if it is a competitive or noncompetitive inhibitor. Additionally, you will investigate the effect of changing environmental conditions on the rate of amylase activity.

EXERCISE 1
Experimental Method and the Action of Catechol Oxidase

Materials

test-tube rack
3 small test tubes
small Parafilm™ squares
calibrated 5-mL pipette
3 calibrated 1-mL pipettes
disposable pasteur pipettes
pipette filler
pipette bulb
distilled or deionized (DI) water
potato extract
catechol
disposable gloves (optional)

Introduction

This exercise will investigate the result of catechol oxidase activity. In the presence of oxygen, catechol oxidase catalyzes the removal of electrons and hydrogens from **catechol,** a phenolic compound found in plant cells. Catechol is converted to benzoquinone, a pigment product. The hydrogens combine with oxygen, forming water (Figure 2). The pigment products are responsible for the darkening of fruits and vegetables, such as apples and potatoes, after exposure to air.

In this exercise you will use an extract of potato tuber to test for the presence of catechol oxidase and to establish the appearance of the products when the reaction takes place.

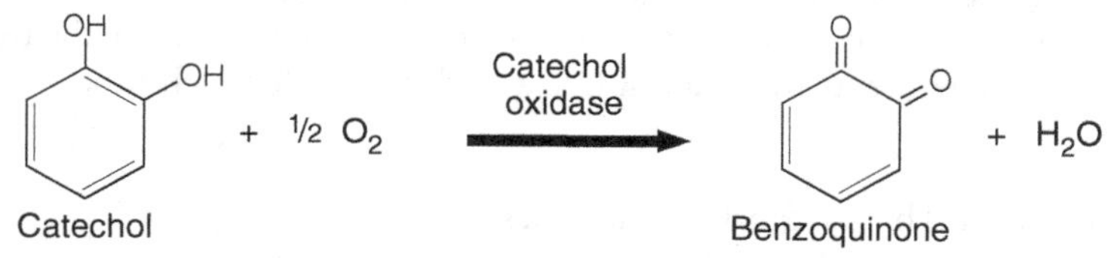

Figure 2.
The oxidation of catechol. In the presence of catechol oxidase, catechol is converted to benzoquinone. Hydrogens removed from catechol combine with oxygen to form water.

Question

Remember that every experiment begins with a question. Review the information given above about the activity of catechol oxidase. You will be performing an experiment using potato extract.

Formulate a question about catechol oxidase and potato extract. The question may be broad, but it must propose an idea that has measurable and controllable elements.

Hypothesis

Construct a hypothesis for the presence or absence of catechol oxidase in potato extract. Remember, the hypothesis must be testable. It is possible for you to propose one or more hypotheses, but all must be testable.

Prediction

Predict the result of the experiment based on your hypothesis. To test for the presence or absence of catechol oxidase in potato extract, your prediction would be what you expect to observe as the result of this experiment (if/then).

Catechol is a poison! Avoid contact with all solutions. Do not pipette any solutions by mouth. Wash hands thoroughly after each experiment. If a spill occurs, notify the instructor. If the instructor is unavailable, wear disposable gloves and use dry paper towels to wipe up the spill. Follow dry towels with towels soaked in soap and water. Dispose of all towels in the trash.

Procedure

1. Using Table 1, prepare the three experimental tubes. Note that all tubes should contain the same total amount of solution. Do not cross-contaminate pipettes! After each tube is prepared, use your finger to hold a Parafilm™ square securely over the tube mouth and then rotate the tube to mix the contents thoroughly. Use a fresh square for each tube.

Table 1
Contents of the Three Experimental Tubes

Tube	Distilled Water	Catechol	Distilled Water	Potato Extract
1	5 ml	0.5 ml (10 drops)	0.5 ml (10 drops)	—
2	5 ml	0.5 ml (10 drops)	—	0.5 ml (10 drops)
3	5 ml	—	0.5 ml (10 drops)	0.5 ml (10 drops)

2. Explain the experimental design: What is the purpose of each of the three test tubes? Which is the control tube? Is more than one control tube necessary? Explain. Which is the experimental tube? Why is an additional 0.5 ml of distilled water added to tubes 1 and 3, but not tube 2?

3. Observe the reactions in the tubes, and record your observations in the Results section below. Explain your conclusions in the Discussion section.

Results

Design a simple table to record results (Table 2).

Table 2
Results of Catechol Oxidation Experiment

Discussion

Explain your results in terms of your hypothesis.

EXERCISE 2
Inhibiting the Action of Catechol Oxidase

Materials

test-tube rack
3 small test tubes
small Parafilm™ squares
calibrated 5-mL pipette
4 calibrated 1-mL pipettes
disposable pasteur pipettes
pipette bulb
distilled water
potato extract
catechol
phenylthiourea (PTU)
disposable gloves (optional)

Introduction

This exercise will investigate the inhibition of enzyme activity by specific chemicals called **inhibitors.** The specific inhibitor used will be **phenylthiourea (PTU).** To be active, catechol oxidase requires copper as a cofactor. PTU is known to combine with the copper in catechol oxidase and inhibit its enzymatic activity.

An inhibitor molecule affects an enzyme in one of two ways. **Competitive inhibition** takes place when a molecule that is structurally similar to the substrate for a particular reaction competes for a position at the active site on the enzyme. This ties up the enzyme so that it is not available to the substrate. Competitive inhibition can be reversed if the concentration of substrate is raised to sufficiently high levels while the concentration of the inhibitor is held constant (Figure 3).

In **noncompetitive inhibition,** the inhibitor binds to a part of the enzyme that is *not* the active site. In so doing, it changes the nature of the enzyme so that its catalytic properties are lost. This can happen in two ways. Either the noncompetitive inhibitor itself physically blocks the access to the active site, or it causes a conformational change in the protein, thus inactivating the active site. In noncompetitive inhibition the inhibitor can become

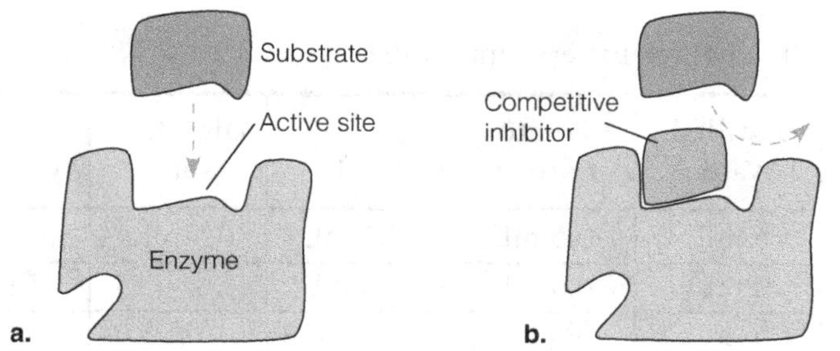

Figure 3.
Action of a competitive inhibitor.
(a) Substrate normally can bind to the active site of an enzyme.
(b) A competitive inhibitor mimics the substrate and competes for the position at the active site on the enzyme.

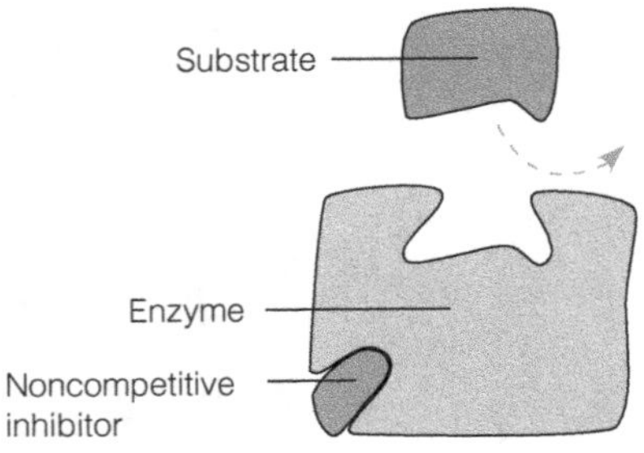

Figure 4.
Action of a noncompetitive inhibitor. The noncompetitive inhibitor binds to the enzyme at a location away from the active site, either blocking access to the active site or changing the conformation of the enzyme, rendering it inactive.

unbound, reversing the inhibition. However, unlike competitive inhibition, adding additional substrate will not reverse the inhibition. (Figure 4.)

In the following experiment, you will determine if PTU is a competitive or noncompetitive inhibitor.

Question

Pose a question about the activity of PTU.

Hypothesis

Hypothesize about the nature of inhibition by PTU.

Prediction

Predict the results of the experiment based on your hypothesis (if/then).

Procedure

PTU and catechol are poisons! Avoid contact with solutions. Do not pipette any solutions by mouth. Wash hands thoroughly after the experiment. If a spill occurs, notify the instructor. If the instructor is unavailable, wear disposable gloves and use dry paper towels to wipe up the spill. Follow dry towels with towels soaked in soap and water. Dispose of all towels in the trash.

1. Using Table 3, prepare three experimental tubes. Be sure to add solutions in the sequence given in the table (water first, potato extract next, PTU next, etc.). Cover each tube with a fresh Parafilm™ square and mix.

Table 3
Contents of the Three Experimental Tubes

Tube	Distilled Water	Potato Extract	PTU	Distilled Water	Catechol
1	5 mL	0.5 mL	0.5 mL	0.5 mL	0.5 mL
2	5 mL	0.5 mL	0.5 mL	—	1 mL
3	5 mL	0.5 mL	—	1 mL	0.5 mL

2. Which test tube is the control?

3. Why was the concentration of catechol increased in test tube 2?

4. Why should the catechol be added to the test tubes last?

5. Record your observations in the Results section, and explain your results in the Discussion section.

Results

Design a table to record your results (Table 4).

Table 4
Results of Inhibition Experiment

Discussion

1. Explain your results in terms of your hypothesis.

2. One member of your team is not convinced that you have adequately tested your hypothesis. How could you expand this experiment to provide additional evidence to strengthen your conclusion?

EXERCISE 3

Influence of Concentration, pH, and Temperature on the Activity of Amylase

Introduction

In the following exercise, you will investigate the influence of enzyme concentration, pH, and temperature on the activity of the enzyme **amylase.** Amylase is found in the **saliva** of many animals, including humans, that utilize **starch** as a source of food. Starch, the principal reserve carbohydrate stores of plants, is a polysaccharide composed of a large number of glucose monomers joined together. Amylase is responsible for the preliminary digestion of starch. In short, amylase breaks up the chains of glucose molecules in starch into maltose, a two-glucose-unit compound. Further digestion of this disaccharide requires other enzymes present in pancreatic and intestinal secretions. To help us follow the digestion of starch into maltose by salivary amylase, we will take advantage of the fact that starch, but not maltose, turns a dark purple color when treated with a solution of I_2KI (this solution is normally yellow-amber in color). Draw equations to help you remember these reactions in the margin of your lab manual.

In the following experiments, the **rate of disappearance** of starch in different amylase concentrations allows a quantitative measurement of reaction rate. Recall that the rate of appearance of the product (in this case, maltose) would give the same information, but the starch test is simpler.

You will be assigned to a team with three or four students. Each team will carry out only one of the experiments. However, each student is responsible for understanding all experiments and results. Be prepared to present your results to the entire class. Your instructor may require you to write a component of a scientific paper.

Experiment A. The Influence of Enzyme Concentration on the Rate of Starch Digestion

Materials

- test-tube rack
- 10 standard test tubes
- wax pencil
- test plate
- flask of distilled or DI water
- beaker of distilled or DI rinse water
- 5-mL graduated cylinder
- 1 calibrated 1-mL pipette
- 2 calibrated 5-mL pipettes
- disposable pasteur pipettes
- pipette bulb
- buffer solution (pH = 6.8)
- I_2KI solution
- 1% starch solution
- 1% amylase solution

Introduction

In this experiment you will vary the concentration of the enzyme amylase to determine what effect the variation will have on the rate of the reaction.

You will make serial dilutions of the amylase resulting in a range of enzyme concentrations. For serial dilutions, you will take an aliquot (sample) of the original enzyme and dilute it with an equal amount of water for a 1:1 dilution (50% of the original concentration). You will then take an aliquot of the resulting 1:1 solution and add an equal amount of water for a 1:3 dilution of the original concentration. You will continue this series of dilutions until you have four different amylase concentrations.

Question

Pose a question about enzyme concentration and reaction rate.

Hypothesis

Hypothesize about the effect of changing enzyme concentration on the rate of reaction.

Prediction

Predict the results of the experiment based on your hypothesis (if/then).

Procedure

1. Prepare the amylase dilution (test tube set 1):
   a. Number five standard test tubes 1 through 5.
   b. Using the 5-mL graduated pipette, add 5 mL distilled water to each test tube.
   c. Make serial dilutions as follows (use the graduated cylinder):

      Tube 1: Add 5 mL amylase and mix by rolling the tube between your hands. (Dilution: 1:1; 0.5% amylase)

      Tube 2: Add 5 mL amylase solution from tube 1 and mix. (Dilution: 1:3; 0.25% amylase)

      Tube 3: Add 5 mL amylase solution from tube 2 and mix. (Dilution: 1:7; 0.125% amylase)

      Tube 4: Add 5 mL amylase solution from tube 3 and mix. (Dilution: 1:15; 0.063% amylase)

      Tube 5: Add 5 mL amylase solution from tube 4 and mix. (Dilution: 1:31; 0.031% amylase)

      Rinse the graduated cylinder thoroughly.
2. Prepare the experimental test tubes (test tube set 2):
   a. Number a second set of five standard test tubes 1 through 5.
   b. Beginning with tube 5 of the first set, transfer 2 mL of this dilution into tube 5 of the second set. Use a 5-mL pipette for the transfer.

Rinse the pipette in distilled water, and repeat the procedure for tubes 4, 3, 2, and 1, transferring 2 mL of tube 4 (first set) into tube 4 (second set), etc. After these transfers have been carried out, test tube set 1 will no longer be used.

c. Add 40 drops of pH 6.8 buffer solution to each of the tubes in the second set. Mix by rolling the tubes between your hands. Set these tubes aside.

d. Add 1 or 2 drops of I_2KI to each compartment of four rows of a test plate. You will use a separate row for each concentration of amylase.

e. Using the second set of tubes, proceed with the tests beginning with tube 5.

(1) Using a clean 1-mL pipette, add 1 mL of the 1% starch solution to tube 5 and mix by rolling the tube between your hands. One team member should immediately record the time. This is time 0.

(2) Quickly remove 1 drop of the mixture with a disposable pasteur pipette, and add it to a drop of I_2KI in the first compartment on the test plate (time 0).

Remember, when the enzyme and substrate are together, the reaction has begun!

(3) Sample the reaction mixture at 10-second intervals, *each time using a new compartment of the test plate.* Continue until a blue color is no longer produced and the I_2KI solution remains yellow-amber (indicating the digestion of all the starch). Record the time required for the digestion of the starch in Table 5.

(4) Repeat steps 1 through 4 for the other four concentrations (tubes 4, 3, 2, and 1 of set 2).

3. Finish recording your findings in the Results section, and state your conclusions in the Discussion section.

Results

1. Complete Table 5 as you determine rates of digestion (time of starch disappearance) in different enzyme concentrations.

Table 5
Time of Starch Disappearance in Different Concentrations of the Enzyme Amylase

Tube	% Amylase	Time of Starch Disappearance (in seconds)
1	0.50	
2	0.25	
3	0.125	
4	0.063	
5	0.031	

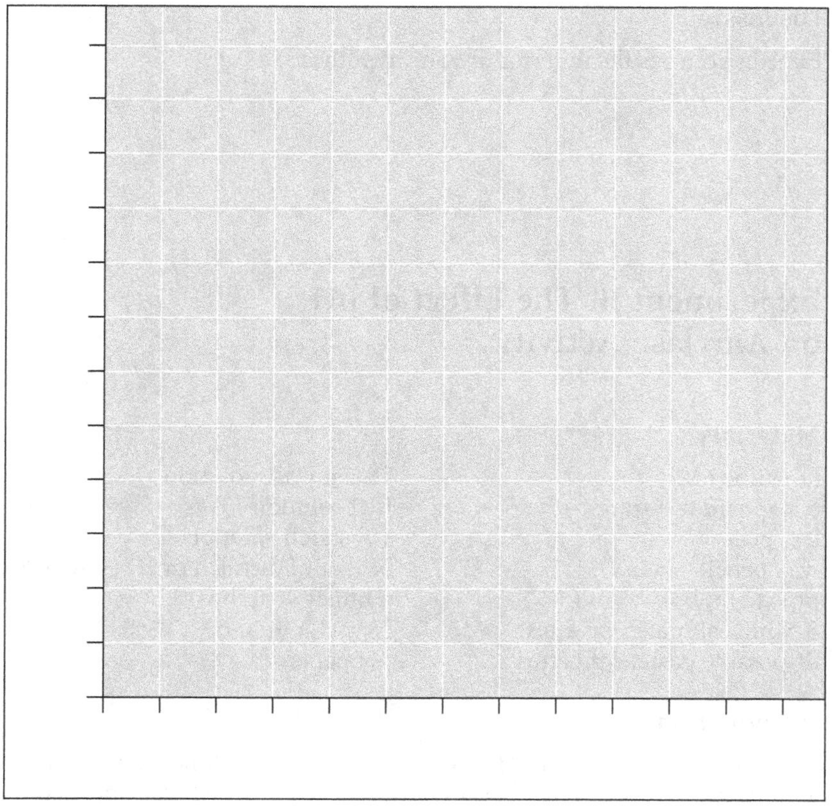

Figure 5.
Enzyme reaction rate (time of starch disappearance) for different concentrations of amylase.

2. Construct a graph (Figure 5) to illustrate your results.
   a. What is the independent variable? Which is the appropriate axis for this variable?

   b. What is the dependent variable? Which is the appropriate axis for this variable?

   c. Label the axes of the graph. Using Table 5, note the maximum number of seconds in your results, and choose an appropriate scale for the dependent variable. Reaction rate, the dependent variable, was measured as time of starch (product) disappearance. The data must, therefore, be graphed in reverse order because the highest values indicate the slowest reaction rate. You should place "0" at the end of the axis and write "fast" by your 0. Place your highest number near the origin (where the *x* and *y* axes cross). Write "slow" near the origin. Choose an appropriate scale for the independent variable (% amylase), and label this axis.

Discussion

Explain your results in terms of your hypothesis.

Experiment B. The Effect of pH on Amylase Activity

Materials

test-tube rack	1% amylase solution
6 standard test tubes	I_2KI solution
test plate	1% starch solution
wax pencil	beaker of distilled or DI rinse water
pipette bulb	6 buffer solutions
3 5-mL calibrated pipettes	(pH = 4, 5, 6, 7, 8, 9)
disposable pasteur pipettes	pH paper

Introduction

The environmental factor pH can influence the three-dimensional shape of an enzyme. Every enzyme has an optimum pH at which it is most active. In this experiment you will determine the optimum pH for the activity of amylase. What was the source of the amylase used in this experiment? (Check the Introduction to this exercise.)

Question

Pose a question about pH and reaction rate.

Hypothesis

Hypothesize about the rate of activity of amylase at various pHs.

Prediction

Predict the results of the experiment based on your hypothesis (if/then).

Procedure

Buffers can burn skin! Avoid contact with all solutions. Do not pipette any solutions by mouth. Wash hands thoroughly after each experiment. If a spill occurs, notify the instructor. If the instructor is unavailable, wear disposable gloves and use dry paper towels to wipe up the spill. Follow dry towels with towels soaked in soap and water. Dispose of all towels in the trash.

1. Using a wax pencil, number six standard test tubes 1 through 6. Beginning with tube 1 and pH 4, mark one tube for each pH of buffer (4, 5, 6, 7, 8, 9). After you mark the test tubes, use a 5-mL graduated pipette to add 5 mL of the appropriate buffer to each test tube (5 mL buffer 4 to tube 1, 5 mL buffer 5 to tube 2, etc.). Rinse the pipette with distilled water after dispensing each buffer.
2. Using a clean 5-mL graduated pipette, add 1.5 mL amylase solution to each tube and mix by rolling the tubes in your hands.
3. Introduce 1 or 2 drops of I_2KI into the compartments of several rows of the test plate.
4. Using only tube 1, add 2.5 mL of the 1% starch solution with a clean 5-mL pipette. Leave the pipette in the starch solution. Mix by rolling the tube in your hands. One team member should immediately record the time. This is time 0. Start testing immediately (next step).

Remember, when the enzyme and substrate are together, the reaction has begun!

5. Using a disposable pasteur pipette, remove a drop of the reaction mixture from tube 1. Add to a drop of I_2KI on the test plate.
6. Sample the reaction mixture at 10-second intervals, *each time using a new compartment of the test plate.* Continue until a blue color is no longer produced and the I_2KI solution remains yellow-amber (indicating the digestion of all the starch).
7. Record the time required for the digestion of the starch in Table 6. If after 7 minutes there is no color change, terminate the experiment with that reaction mixture.
8. Repeat steps 4 through 7 using the other five test tubes. Use separate rows on the test plate for each pH. Rinse the pipette between uses. Record results in Table 6.
9. Graph your observations in the Results section, and explain your results in the Discussion section.

Results

1. Complete Table 6 as rates of digestion (time of starch disappearance) in different pHs are determined.

Table 6
Time of Starch Disappearance in Different pH Environments for the Enzyme Amylase

Tube	pH	Time of Starch Disappearance (in minutes)
1	4	
2	5	
3	6	
4	7	
5	8	
6	9	

2. Construct a graph using Figure 6 to illustrate your results.
   a. What is the independent variable? Which is the appropriate axis for this variable?

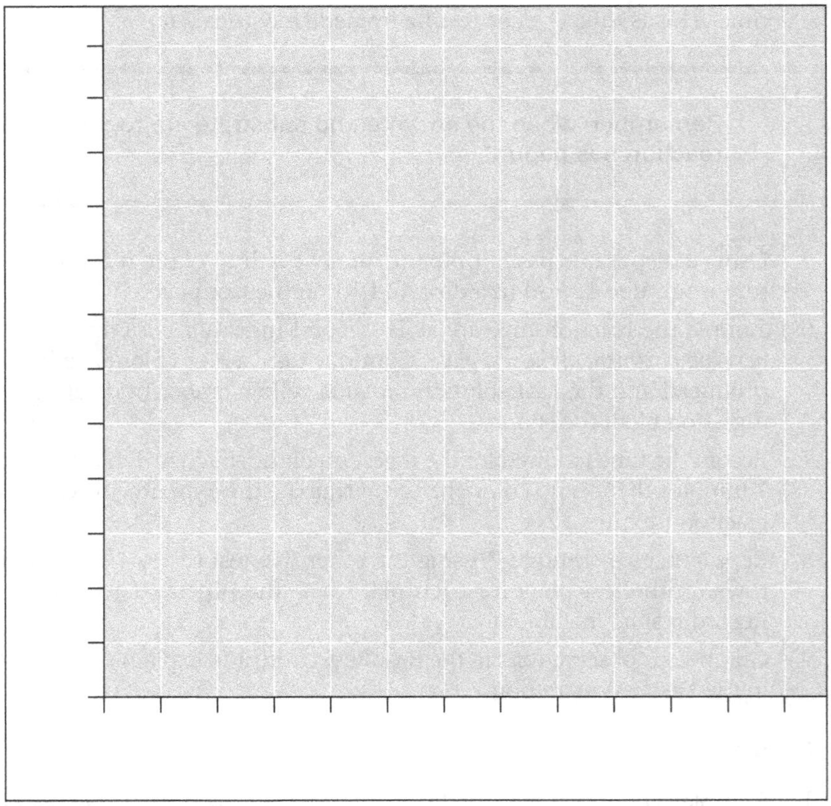

Figure 6.
Reaction rate (time of starch disappearance) of amylase in different pH environments.

b. What is the dependent variable? Which is the appropriate axis for this variable?

c. Label the axes of the graph. Using Table 6, note the maximum number of minutes in your results, and choose an appropriate scale for the dependent variable. Reaction rate, the dependent variable, was measured as time of starch (product) disappearance. The data must, therefore, be graphed in reverse order because the highest values indicate the slowest reaction rate. You should place "0" at the end of the axis and write "fast" by your 0. Place your highest number near the origin (where the *x* and *y* axes cross). Write "slow" near the origin. Choose an appropriate scale for the independent variable (pH) and label the axis.

Discussion

Explain your results in terms of your hypothesis.

Experiment C. The Effect of Temperature on Amylase Activity

Materials

8 standard test tubes
test-tube rack
2 5-mL calibrated pipettes
2 1-mL calibrated pipettes
disposable 7.5-inch pasteur pipettes
pipette bulb
wax pencil
1% starch solution
I_2KI solution
buffer solution (pH = 6.8)
1% amylase solution
flask of DI water
On the demonstration table:
- water bath at 80°C
- water bath at 37°C
- test-tube rack at room temperature
- beaker of crushed ice for ice bath

Introduction

Chemical reactions accelerate as temperature rises, partly because increased temperatures speed up the motion of molecules. This means that substrates collide more frequently with enzyme active sites. Generally, a 10° rise in temperature results in a two- to threefold increase in the rate of a particular reaction. However, at high temperatures, the integrity of proteins can be irreversibly denatured. The activity of enzymes is dependent on the proper tertiary and quaternary structures; the optimum temperature for activity, therefore, may vary, depending on the structure of the enzyme.

What was the source of the amylase used in this experiment? (Check the Introduction to this exercise.)

Question

Pose a question about temperature and reaction rate.

Hypothesis

Hypothesize about the rate of activity of amylase at various temperatures.

Prediction

Predict the results of the experiment based on your hypothesis (if/then).

Procedure

1. Number four standard test tubes 1 through 4.
2. Using the 5-mL calibrated pipette, add 2 mL of the 1% starch solution to each tube.
3. Using a clean 5-mL pipette, add 4 mL DI water to each tube.
4. Add 1 mL of 6.8 buffer to each tube.
5. Place the test tubes as follows:

   Tube 1: 80°C water bath

   Tube 2: 37°C water bath

   Tube 3: test-tube rack (room temperature, or about 22°C)

   Tube 4: beaker of crushed ice (4°C)
6. Number and mark a second set of standard test tubes lA through 4A. Use the 1-mL calibrated pipette to add 1 mL amylase to each tube, and place as follows (do not mix together the solutions in the two sets of tubes until instructed to do so):

   Tube 1A: 80°C water bath

   Tube 2A: 37°C water bath

   Tube 3A: test-tube rack (room temperature, or about 22°C)

   Tube 4A: beaker of crushed ice (4°C)
7. Let all eight tubes sit in the above environments for 10 minutes. You should have one tube of amylase and one of starch at each temperature.
8. Fill several rows of the test plate with 1 or 2 drops of I_2KI per compartment.

Remember, when the enzyme and substrate are together, the reaction has begun!

9. Leaving the tubes in the above environments as they are being tested, mix tubes 1 and 1A, record the time (this is time 0), and use a disposable pipette to immediately add 1 or 2 drops of the mixture to a drop of I_2KI on the test plate.
10. Continue adding mixture drops to *new wells* of I_2KI at 30-second intervals until a blue color is no longer produced and the I_2KI solution remains yellow-amber (indicating that all the starch is digested). If within 10 minutes there is no color change, terminate the experiment with that particular reaction mixture. Record your results in Table 7.
11. Repeat steps 9 and 10 for the other reaction mixtures (mix tubes 2 and 2A and test, mix 3 and 3A and test, etc.).
12. If time permits, transfer tube 4 (in ice, containing the enzyme and substrate) into the 37°C water bath. After 2 minutes, test the contents of the tube at 10-second intervals. Record these results in the margin of your lab manual and refer to them as you answer Discussion Question 2 below.
13. Finish recording and graphing your observations in the Results section, and explain your results in the Discussion section.

Results

1. Complete Table 7 as rates of digestion (time of starch disappearance) in different temperatures are determined.

Table 7
Time of Starch Disappearance in Different Temperatures for the Enzyme Amylase

Tube	Temp. °C	Time of Starch Disappearance (in minutes)
1	80°	
2	37°	
3	22°	
4	4°	

2. Construct a graph using Figure 7 on the next page to illustrate your results.
   a. What is the independent variable? Which is the appropriate axis for this variable?

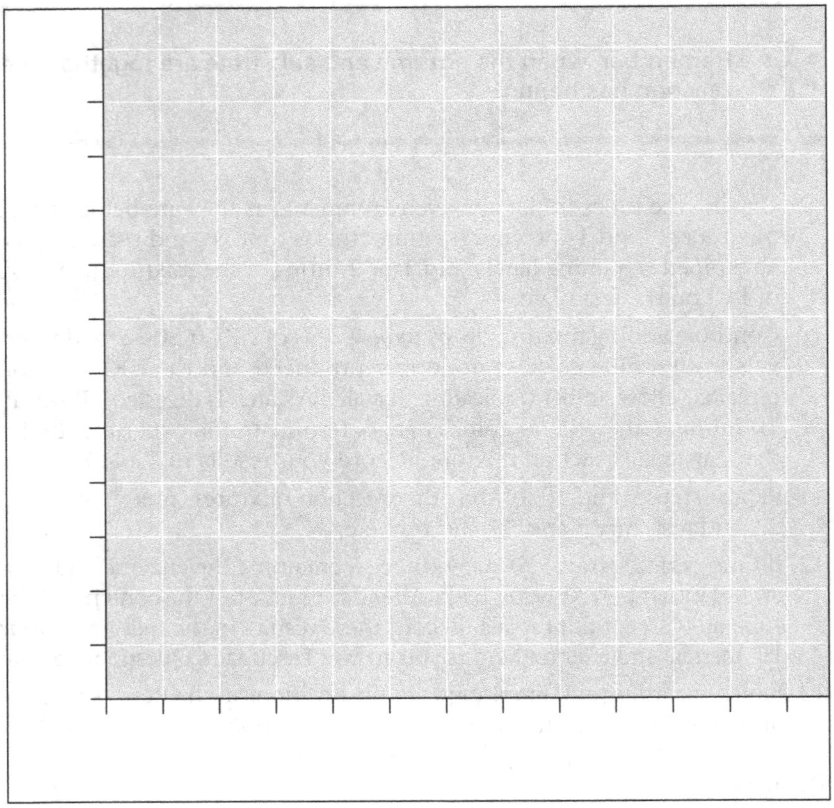

Figure 7.
Reaction rate (time of starch disappearance) of amylase in various temperatures.

b. What is the dependent variable? Which is the appropriate axis for this variable?

c. Label the axes of the graph. Using Table 7, note the maximum number of minutes in your results, and choose an appropriate scale for the dependent variable. Reaction rate, the dependent variable, was measured as the time of starch disappearance. The data must, therefore, be graphed in reverse order because the highest values indicate the slowest reaction rate. You should place "0" at the end of the axis and write "fast" by your 0. Place your highest number near the origin (where the *x* and *y* axes cross). Write "slow" near the origin. Choose an appropriate scale for the independent variable (temperature) and label the axis.

Discussion

1. Explain your results in terms of your hypothesis.

2. What do you think would happen to reaction rate in the tube incubated in ice if this tube, with enzyme and substrate already mixed, were placed in the 37°C water bath?

Explain your answer in terms of the effect of various temperatures on enzyme structure and the rate of enzyme activity.

Questions for Review

1. Define and use the following terms, providing examples if appropriate: *catalyst enzyme, substrate, active site, cofactor, coenzyme, competitive inhibition, noncompetitive inhibition.*
2. a. Compare and contrast competitive and noncompetitive inhibition.

   b. Why does adding additional substrate overcome competitive but not noncompetitive inhibition?

Applying Your Knowledge

1. In the first experiment, the enzyme catechol oxidase was extracted from potato. However, this was not a purified preparation; it contained hundreds of enzymes. What evidence supports the assumption that catechol oxidase was the enzyme studied?

2. Suggest a reason why canned acidic fruits and vegetables (such as tomatoes) have a longer shelf life than those with more neutral pH (such as green beans).

3. The PSA (prostate-specific antigen) test is the most widely used test to detect prostate cancer. The PSA marker is a protease that is manufactured specifically in the prostate gland. Cancer in the prostate gland will cause PSA to be expelled into the bloodstream. How could a researcher devise a test to detect this prostate-specific protease in the lab?

4. Well-preserved mammoths have been found in ice and frozen soil in northern Siberia. Using information about enzyme activity learned in this lab, explain why these animal carcasses have survived all of these years.

5. Ethylene glycol, the main ingredient in antifreeze, is an odorless, colorless, sweet-tasting water-soluble chemical that, when ingested, is a toxic poison. If a pet or human drinks antifreeze the ethylene glycol is rapidly absorbed into the circulatory system and, if not treated, will lead to organ failure and death. If detected immediately, you should induce vomiting in the victim and seek emergency treatment. This treatment will consist of gastric lavage followed by an initial intravenous dose of 10% ethanol and lower maintenance ethanol doses for several hours. Ethylene glycol is metabolized by the enzyme alcohol dehydrogenase (ADH) into four products, and these products are the actual toxic agents. If this reaction can be inhibited, then the kidneys will eliminate the ethylene glycol intact before the toxins are produced. Chemists know that ADH has 100× greater affinity for ethanol than for ethylene glycol.

Given your knowledge of enzyme activity and inhibitors, speculate about the mechanism by which ethanol prevents ethylene glycol poisoning.

6. There is an enzyme that catalyzes the production of the pigment responsible for dark fur color in Siamese cats and Himalayan rabbits. This enzyme is *thermolabile,* meaning that it does not function at higher temperatures. Rabbits raised at 5°C are all black. If raised at 20°C, they are white with black paws, ears, and noses; they are all white when raised at 35°C. Which of the following best represents an activity curve for this enzyme?

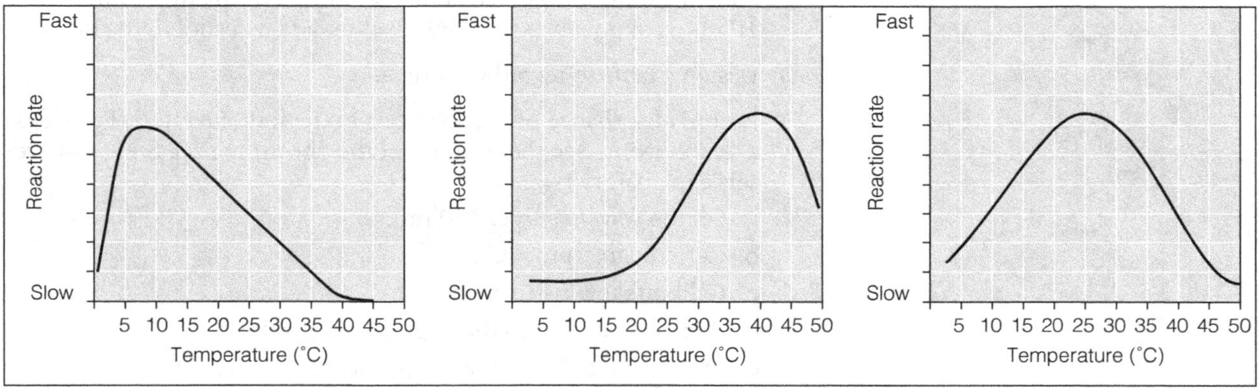

a. **b.** **c.**

7. You are investigating a specific compound known to inhibit the activity of an enzyme. You hypothesize that the compound is a competitive inhibitor of the enzyme's activity. To test your hypothesis, you design an experiment where you add increasing amounts of the enzyme's substrate to a solution containing the enzyme, and then you test the reaction rate. Which of the following graphs represents the predicted results of your experiment, based on your hypothesis?

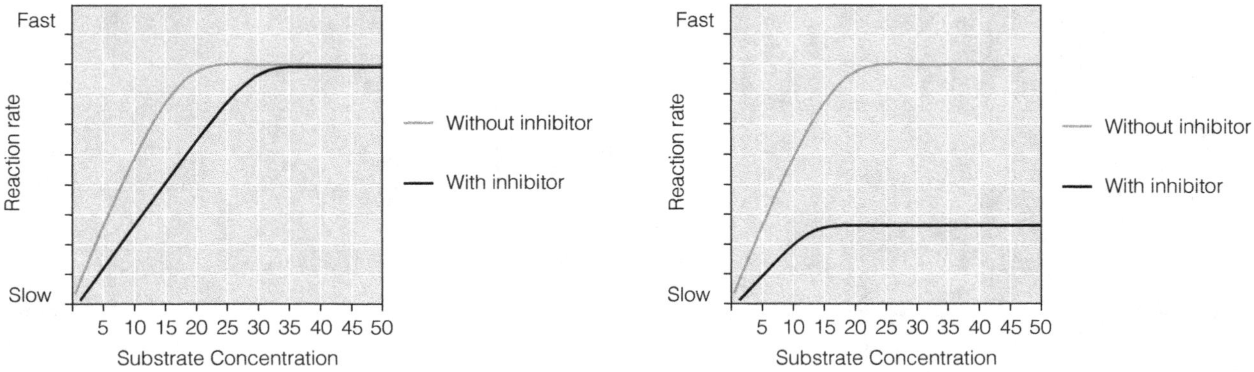

a. **b.**

Investigative Extension

1. Using introductory, microbiology, and biochemistry texts as well as other informational sources, research which antibiotics and chemotherapeutic agents (e.g., penicillins, cephalosporins, sulfonamides) bring about their medicinal effects by interfering with enzyme systems. Determine those that are competitive inhibitors or noncompetitive inhibitors. Describe the mode of action for each agent.
2. The experiments using catechol oxidase may be quantified by measuring results using a Spectronic 20. Modify the instructions in Exercises 1 and 2 according to the following instructions.
   1. Rather than using three experimental tubes, use four cuvettes, and label them B (the blank), 1, 2, and 3.
   2. Prepare the solutions in cuvettes as directed for test tubes 1, 2, and 3, omitting catechol until ready to take the reading. The blank will contain 5 mL of distilled water, 20 drops of distilled water, and 10 drops of potato extract only. Do not add catechol to the blank.
   3. Design a table to record your data.
   4. Record absorbance of the solutions in the four cuvettes. (For steps a–c, following, see the diagram of the Spectronic 20. Steps d–f are self-explanatory.)
      a. Set the wavelength at 540 nm.
      b. Zero the instrument.
      c. Calibrate the instrument.
      d. Add the catechol to the appropriate cuvettes.
      e. Insert cuvette 1 into the sample holder and record absorbance in your data table. Immediately repeat with cuvettes 2 and 3.
      f. Continue to take readings at 5-minute intervals for 30 minutes or an appropriate time.

References

Klabunde, T., C. Eicken, J. Sacchettini, B. Krebs. "Crystal structure of a plant catechol oxidase containing a dicopper center." *Nature Structural Biology,* 1998, vol. 5, #12, pp.1084–1090. Full text available online. Discusses activity of catechol oxidase and the specific mode of inhibition by PTU.

Mathews, C. K., K. G. Ahern. *Biochemistry.* San Francisco: Benjamin Cummings, 2000.

Nelson, D. and M. Cox. *Lehninger Principles of Biochemistry,* 4th ed. New York: Worth Publishers, 2005.

Pommerville, J. C. *Alcamo's Fundamentals of Microbiology,* 7th ed. Boston: Jones and Bartlett Publishers, 2004.

Tortora, G. J., R. F. Berdell. *Microbiology: An Introduction.* San Francisco: Benjamin Cummings, 2004.

Website

Factors Affecting Enzymes. Describes how temperature, pH, and substrate concentration affect enzyme activity: http://ntri.tamuk.edu/cell/enzyme2.html

Photosynthesis

Laboratory Objectives

After completing this lab topic, you should be able to:

1. Describe the roles played by light and pigment in photosynthesis.
2. Name and describe pigments found in photosynthesizing tissues.
3. Explain the separation of pigments by paper chromatography, based on their molecular structure.
4. Demonstrate an understanding of the process of spectrophotometry and the procedure for using the spectrophotometer.

Introduction

Without photosynthesis, there could be no life on Earth as we know it. The Earth is an open system constantly requiring an input of energy to drive the processes of life. All energy entering the biosphere is channeled from the sun into organic molecules via the process of photosynthesis. As the sun's hydrogen is converted to helium, energy in the form of photons is produced. These photons pass to Earth's surface and those with certain wavelengths within the visible light portion of the electromagnetic spectrum are absorbed by pigments in the chloroplasts of plants, initiating the process of photosynthesis.

Photosynthesis ultimately produces glucose and oxygen from carbon dioxide and water. Glucose, a primary source of energy for all cells, may be converted to sucrose and transported or stored in the polymer starch. These organic molecules are building blocks for plant growth and development. Animals consume plants and convert the plant molecules into their own organic molecules and energy sources—the ultimate in recycling. Oxygen, also produced by photosynthesis, is necessary for aerobic respiration in the cells of plants, animals, and other organisms (Figure 1).

In this laboratory, you will investigate cellular and environmental components utilized in the process of photosynthesis. In several experiments, you will determine photosynthetic activity by testing for the production of starch, using iodine potassium iodide (I_2KI), which stains starch purple-black. A change from the yellow-amber color of the iodine solution to a purple-black solution is a positive test for the presence of starch. This is the same test for the presence of starch that you used to study starch digestion by amylase.

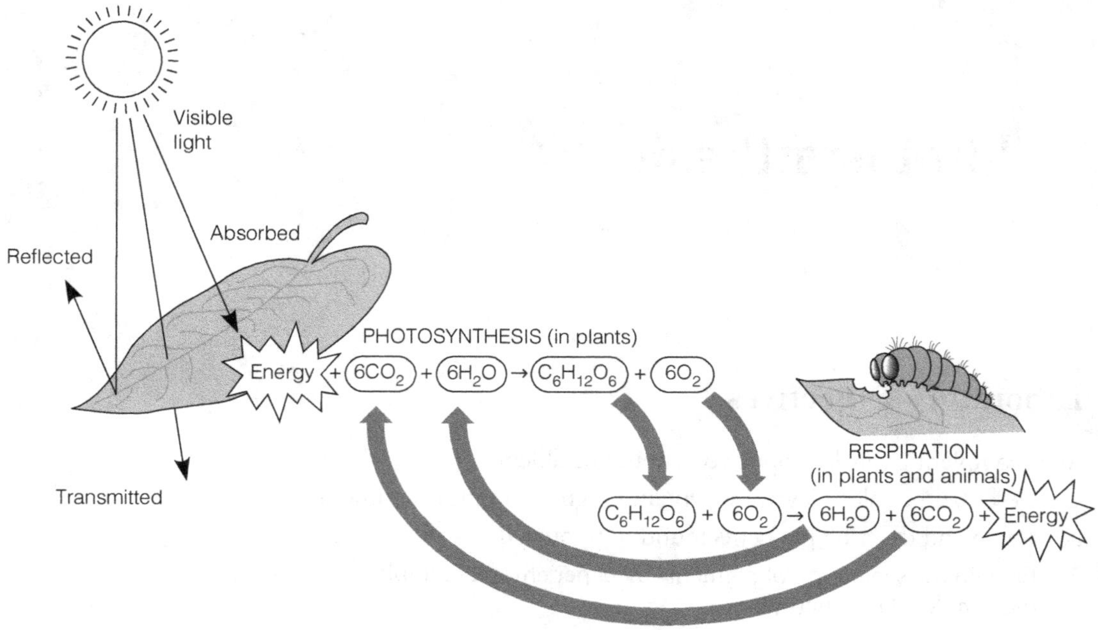

Figure 1.
Energy flow through plants and animals. Energy flows from the sun into the biological systems of Earth, and visible light is reflected, transmitted, or absorbed. Plants absorb light energy and convert it to chemical energy during photosynthesis. In this process, carbon dioxide and water are converted to oxygen and glucose and ultimately to other organic molecules. These organic molecules and the energy stored in them can be utilized by animals and other organisms that consume them. The energy in organic molecules is released during cellular respiration in plants and animals.

EXERCISE 1
The Wavelengths of Light for Photosynthesis

Materials

black construction paper
green, red, and blue plastic filters
paper clips
forceps
hot plate
petri dish
squirt bottle of water
scissors
1 geranium plant with at least 4 good leaves per 8 students
1 1,000-mL beaker filled with 300 mL of water
1 400-mL beaker filled with 200 mL of 80% ethyl alcohol
dropper bottle with concentrated I_2KI solution

Introduction

In this exercise, you will determine if products of photosynthesis are present in leaf tissue that has been exposed to different wavelengths of light for several days. Working with other students in groups of eight, you will cover small portions of different leaves of a geranium plant with pieces of black paper and green, red, and blue plastic filters. Each pair of students will be responsible for one of the four treatments. Later you will determine photosynthetic activity by testing for the presence of starch under the paper or filters.

What wavelength of light will be reflected and transmitted by the black paper and the colored filters? Note that the same wavelengths of light are reflected and transmitted by the filters.

Hypothesis

Hypothesize about photosynthetic activity in cells treated as described.

Prediction

Predict the results of the experiment based on your hypothesis (if/then).

Procedure

1. Four to five days before the experiment is to be carried out, cut a piece from each color of plastic filter and one from the black construction paper. Each piece should be a rectangle approximately 2.5 cm by 5 cm. Double over the strip and slide the edge of a healthy geranium leaf, still attached to the plant, between the folded edges. Carefully slip a slightly sprung paper clip over the paper, securing the paper to the leaf. The paper should be on both sides of the leaf. Follow this procedure with the other colors and the black construction paper, using a different leaf for each strip. Return the plant with treated leaves to bright light. Your instructor may have already carried out this step for you.
2. On the day of the lab, carry the plant with leaves covered to your desk. You will have to be able to recognize each leaf after the paper is removed and the leaf is boiled. To facilitate this, with your teammates devise a way to distinguish each leaf, and write the distinction in the space provided. Differences in size or shape may distinguish different leaves, but it may be necessary to introduce distinguishing features, such as by cutting the petioles to different lengths or cutting out small notches in a

portion of the leaf not covered by the paper. Record below the distinguishing differences for each treatment.

black paper:

green filter:

red filter:

blue filter:

3. After you have distinguished each leaf, sketch the leaf in the Results section, showing the position of the paper or filter on the leaf.
4. Set up the boiling alcohol bath. Place a 1,000-mL beaker containing 300 mL of water on the hot plate. Carefully place the 400-mL beaker containing 200 mL of 80% ethyl alcohol into the larger beaker of water. Turn on the hot plate and bring the nested beakers to a boil. Adjust the temperature to maintain slow boiling. Do not place the beaker of alcohol directly on the hot plate.

Ethyl alcohol is highly flammable! Do not place the beaker of alcohol directly on the hot plate. To bring it to a boil, raise the temperature of the hot plate until the alcohol just boils, and then reduce the temperature to maintain slow boiling. Do not leave boiling alcohol unattended.

5. Remove the paper and filters from each leaf; using forceps, carefully drop all the leaves into the boiling alcohol solution to extract the pigments. Save the plastic filters.
6. When the leaves are almost white, use forceps to remove them from the alcohol. Place them in separate petri dishes, rinse with distilled water, and add enough distilled water to each dish to just cover the leaf. Turn off the hot plate if all teams have completed boiling leaves for this exercise (and Exercise 2).
7. Add drops of I_2KI solution to the water until a pale amber color is obtained. I_2KI reacts with starch to produce a purple-black color.
8. Wait about 5 minutes and sketch each leaf in the Results section, showing which areas of the leaf tested positive for starch.

Results

1. Sketch and label each leaf before boiling, showing the location of the paper or filter.

2. Sketch and label each leaf after staining to show the location of the stain.

Discussion

1. Which treatment allowed the greatest photosynthetic activity? (Explain your results in terms of your hypothesis.)

2. When the red filter is placed on a leaf, what wavelengths of light pass through and reach the leaf cells below?

   Green filter?

   Blue filter?

3. Was starch present under the black construction paper? Explain this in light of the fact that black absorbs all wavelengths of light.

EXERCISE 2

Pigments in Photosynthesis

Materials

Coleus plant with multicolored leaves
forceps
1 1,000-mL beaker filled with 300 mL of water
1 400-mL beaker filled with 200 mL of 80% ethyl alcohol
dropper bottle with concentrated I_2KI solution
hot plate
squirt bottle of water

Introduction

A variety of pigments are found in plants, as anyone who visits a botanical garden in spring or a deciduous forest in autumn well knows. A pigment is a substance that absorbs light. If a pigment absorbs all wavelengths of visible light, it appears black. The black construction paper used in Exercise 1 is colored with such a pigment. Other pigments absorb some wavelengths and reflect others. Yellow pigments, for example, reflect light wavelengths in the yellow portion of the visible light spectrum, green reflects in the green portion, and so on.

Some colors are produced by only one pigment, but an even greater diversity of colors can be produced by the cumulative effects of different pigments in cells. Green colors in plants are produced by the presence of chlorophylls *a* and *b* located in the chloroplasts. Yellow, orange, and bright red colors are produced by carotenoids, also in chloroplasts. Blues, violets, purples, pinks, and dark reds are usually produced by a group of water-soluble pigments, the anthocyanins, that are located in cell vacuoles and do not contribute to photosynthesis. Additional colors may be produced by mixtures of these pigments in cells.

Working with one other student, you will use the I_2KI test for starch as in Exercise 1 to determine which pigment(s) in a *Coleus* leaf support photosynthesis. Before beginning the experiment, examine your *Coleus* leaf and hypothesize about the location of photosynthesis based on the leaf colors.

Hypothesis

Hypothesize about the location of photosynthesis based on the leaf colors.

Prediction

Predict the results of the experiment based on your hypothesis (if/then).

Procedure

1. Remove a multicolored leaf from a *Coleus* plant that has been in strong light for several hours.
2. In Table 1, list the colors of your leaf, predict the pigments present to create that color, and predict the results of the I_2KI starch test in each area of the leaf.
3. Sketch the leaf outline in the Results section, mapping the color distribution before the I_2KI test.
4. Extract the pigments as previously described in Exercise 1, and test the leaf for photosynthetic activity using I_2KI.

Ethyl alcohol is highly flammable! Do not place the beaker of alcohol directly on the hot plate. To bring it to a boil, raise the temperature of the hot plate until the alcohol just boils, and then reduce the temperature to maintain slow boiling. Do not leave boiling alcohol unattended.

5. Sketch the leaf again in the Results section, outlining the areas showing a positive starch test.

Results

1. Record the results of the I_2KI test in Table 1.
2. Compare the sketches of the *Coleus* leaf before and after the I_2KI test.

   Before I_2KI Test: **After I_2KI Test:**

3. Which pigments supported photosynthesis? Record your results in Table 1.

Discussion

Describe and explain your results based on your hypothesis.

Table 1
Predicted and Observed Results for the Presence of Starch in Colored Regions of the *Coleus* Leaf

Color	Pigments	Starch Present (predicted) + or –	Starch Present (actual results) + or –
Green			
Purple			
Pink			
White			
Other			

EXERCISE 3

Separation and Identification of Plant Pigments by Paper Chromatography

Materials

capillary tube
beakers
extractions of leaf pigments in acetone
forceps
scissors
acetone
chromatography paper stapled into a cylinder marked with a pencil line about 1 cm from one end
quart jar with lid, containing solvent of petroleum ether and acetone

Introduction

Your instructor has prepared an extract of chloroplast pigments from fresh green grass or fresh spinach. A blender was used to rupture the cells, and the pigments were then extracted with acetone, an organic solvent. Working with one other student, begin this exercise by separating the pigments extracted using paper chromatography. To do this, you will apply the pigment extract to a cylinder of chromatographic paper. You will then place the cylinder in a jar with the organic solvents petroleum ether and acetone. The solvents will move up the paper and carry the pigments along; the pigments will move at different rates, depending on their different solubilities in the solvents used and the degree of attraction to the paper. The leading edge of the solvent is called the **front.** Discrete pigment bands will be formed from the front back to the point where pigments were added to the paper.

The following information will be helpful to you as you make predictions and interpret results:

1. **Polar molecules** or substances dissolve (or are attracted to) polar molecules.
2. **Nonpolar molecules** are attracted to nonpolar molecules to varying degrees.
3. Chromatography paper (cellulose) is a polar (charged) substance.
4. The solvent, made of petroleum ether and acetone, is relatively nonpolar.
5. The *most nonpolar* substance will dissolve in the nonpolar solvent *first.*
6. The *most polar* substance will be attracted to the polar chromatography paper; therefore, it will move *last.*

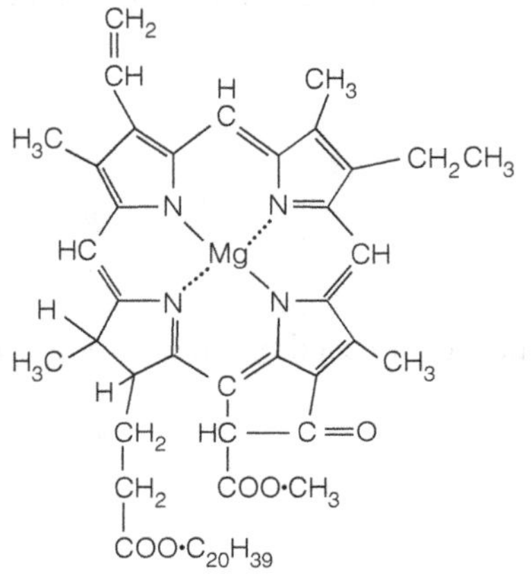

a. Chlorophyll *a*

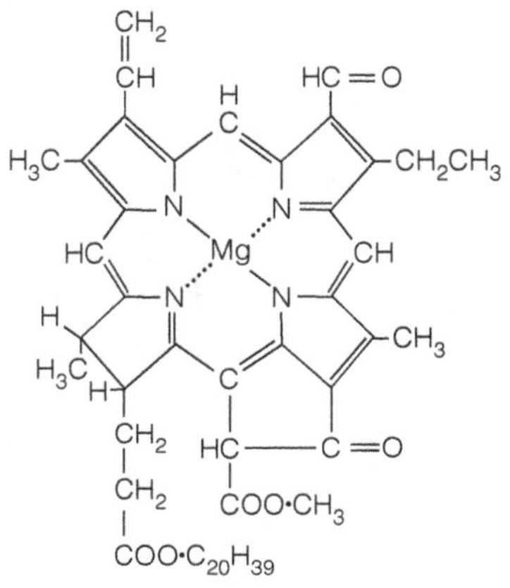

b. Chlorophyll *b*

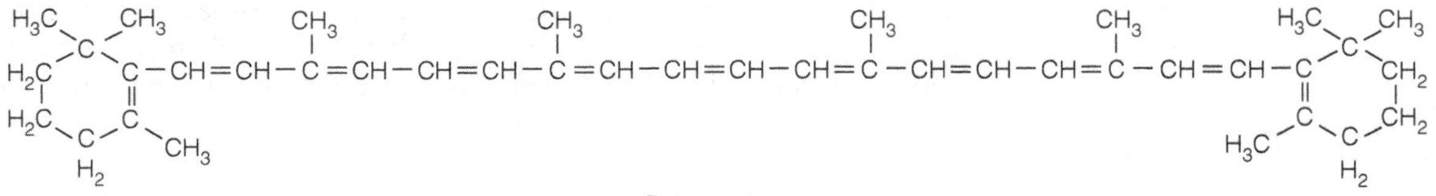

c. Beta carotene

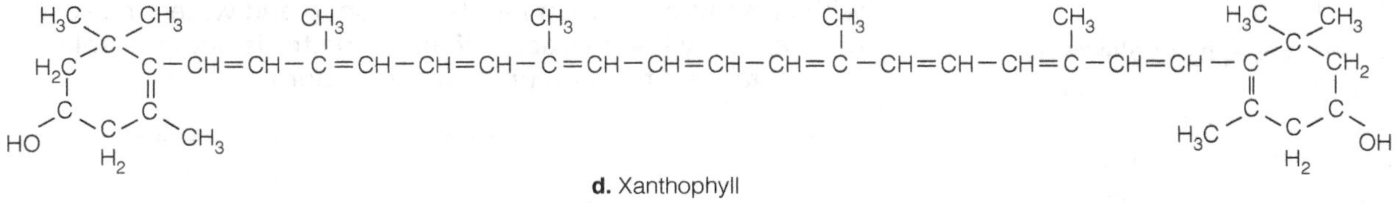

d. Xanthophyll

Figure 2.
Molecular structure of major leaf pigments. The molecular structure of chlorophyll *a*, chlorophyll *b*, carotene, and xanthophyll. To determine polarity, count the number of polar oxygens present in each molecule.

Use this information and the molecular structure of major leaf pigments to predict the relative solubilities and separation patterns for the pigments and to identify the pigment bands. Study the molecular structure of the four common plant pigments in Figure 2. As you study these diagrams, rank the pigments according to polarity in the space provided. To determine polarity, count the number of polar oxygens present in each molecule.

Most polar:

Least polar:

Hypothesis

State a hypothesis relating polarities and solubilities of pigments.

Prediction

Predict the results of the experiment based on your hypothesis (if/then).

Procedure

1. Using a capillary tube, streak the leaf pigment extract on a pencil line previously drawn 1 cm from the edge of the paper cylinder. Allow the chlorophyll to dry. Repeat this step three or four times, allowing the extract to air-dry each time. You should have a band of green pigments along the pencil line. The darker your band of pigments, the better the results of your experiment will be.

Perform the next step in a hood or in a well-ventilated room. Do not inhale the fumes of the solvent. *NO SPARKS!* Acetone and petroleum ether are extremely flammable. Avoid contact with all solutions. Wash hands with soap and water. If a spill occurs, notify the instructor. If an instructor is not available, do not attempt to clean up. Leave the room.

2. Obtain the jar containing the petroleum ether and acetone solvent. Using forceps, carefully lower the loaded paper cylinder into the solvent, and quickly cover the jar tightly with the lid (Figure 3). *Avoid inhaling the solvent.* The jar should now contain a saturated atmosphere of the solvent. Allow the chromatography to proceed until the solvent front has reached to within 3 cm of the top of the cylinder.

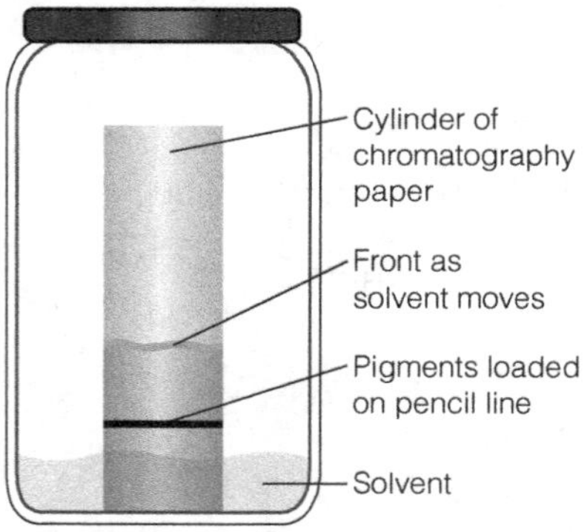

Figure 3.
Paper chromatography of photosynthetic pigments. Add the pigment solution to the paper cylinder along the pencil line. Then carefully place the cylinder into a jar containing a small amount of solvent. Close the lid and watch the pigments separate according to their molecular structures and solubilities.

3. Remove the cylinder from the jar, allow it to dry, and remove the staples.
4. Save your paper with the separated pigments for the next exercise.

Results

Sketch the chromatography paper. Label the color of the various bands. The front, or leading edge of the paper, should be at the top. The pencil line where pigment was added originally should be at the bottom.

Discussion

Based on your hypothesis and predictions, identify the various pigment bands. *The entire class should come to a consensus about the identifications.* Label your drawing in the Results section above, indicating the correct identification of the pigment bands.

EXERCISE 4
Determining the Absorption Spectrum for Leaf Pigments

Materials

spectrophotometer
Kimwipes®
2 cuvettes
20-mL beakers to elute pigments
1 150-mL beaker to hold cuvettes
acetone
cork stoppers for cuvettes

Introduction

In Exercise 1, you applied colored plastic filters and black paper to leaves to determine which wavelengths of light would support photosynthesis. Review your conclusions from that exercise and from Exercise 2 about pigments used in photosynthesis. Which pigments did you conclude support photosynthesis?

In Exercise 4, you will work in teams of four or five students, carrying your investigation a step further by plotting the absorption spectrum of leaf pigments separated by paper chromatography. The **absorption spectrum** is the absorption pattern for a particular pigment, showing relative absorbance at different wavelengths of light. For example, we know that chlorophyll *a* is a green pigment, and we know that it reflects or transmits green wavelengths of light. We do not know, however, the relative proportions of wavelengths of light absorbed by chlorophyll *a*. This information is of interest because it suggests that those wavelengths showing greatest absorbance are important in photosynthesis.

The absorption spectrum can be determined with an instrument called a **spectrophotometer,** or **colorimeter.** A spectrophotometer measures the proportions of light of different wavelengths (colors) absorbed and transmitted by a pigment solution. It does this by passing a beam of light of a particular wavelength (designated by the operator) through the pigment solution being tested. The spectrophotometer then measures the proportion of light transmitted or, conversely, absorbed by that particular pigment and shows the reading on the calibrated scale.

Before measuring the absorption spectrum of the four pigments separated by paper chromatography, consult the diagram of the electromagnetic spectrum, and predict the wavelengths of light at which absorption will be greatest for each pigment. Record your predictions in Table 2.

Table 2
Predicted Wavelengths of Greatest Absorption
for the Photosynthetic Pigments

Pigment	Wavelengths of Greatest Absorption (predicted)
1. Chlorophyll *a*	
2. Chlorophyll *b*	
3. Carotene	
4. Xanthophyll	

Hypothesis

State a hypothesis that describes the general relationship of each of the pigments to the color of light that it absorbs.

Prediction

Predict the results based on your hypothesis (if/then).

Procedure

1. Cut out the pigments you separated by paper chromatography, and distribute the paper strips as follows:

   Team 1: carotene

   Team 2: xanthophyll

   Team 3: chlorophyll *a*

   Team 4: chlorophyll *b*

   Teams 5 and 6: will determine the absorption spectrum of the total pigment solution

Perform the next three steps in a hood or in a well-ventilated room. Do not inhale the fumes of the solvent. *NO SPARKS!* Acetone is extremely flammable. Avoid contact with all solutions. If a spill occurs, notify the instructor. Wash hands with soap and water.

2. *Teams 1 to 4.* Dilute the pigments as follows: Cut up the chromatography paper with your assigned pigment into a small (20-mL) beaker. Add 10 mL of acetone to the beaker and swirl. This solution containing a single pigment will be your solution B, to be used to determine the absorption spectrum for that pigment. Your reference material will be acetone with no pigments, solution A.
3. *Teams 5 and 6.* Add drops of the original chlorophyll extract solution (acetone pigment mixture) to 10 mL of acetone until it looks pale green. This will be your pigment solution for cuvette B. Your reference material will be acetone with no pigment. This will be in cuvette A.
4. Each team should fill two cuvettes two-thirds full, one (B) with the pigment solution, the other (A) with the reference material (acetone only). Wipe both cuvettes with a Kimwipe to remove fingerprints, and handle cuvettes only with Kimwipes as you proceed.

   What is the purpose of the cuvette with reference material only?

5. Measure the absorption spectrum. Record your measurements in Table 3. The instructions that follow are for a Bausch & Lomb Spectronic 20 (Figure 4). Turn on the machine (power switch C) for at least 5 minutes before beginning.
   a. *Select the beginning wavelength* using the wavelength control knob (A). Begin measurements at 400 nanometers (nm).
   b. *Zero the instrument* by adjusting the 0 control knob (same as the power switch C) so that the meter needle reads 0% transmittance. There should be no cuvette in the instrument, and the sample holder cover must be closed.

Figure 4.
The Bausch & Lomb Spectronic 20.
A spectrophotometer measures the proportion of light of different wavelengths absorbed and transmitted by a pigment solution. Inside the spectrophotometer, light is separated into its component wavelengths and passed through a sample. The graph of absorption at different wavelengths for a solution is called an *absorption spectrum.*

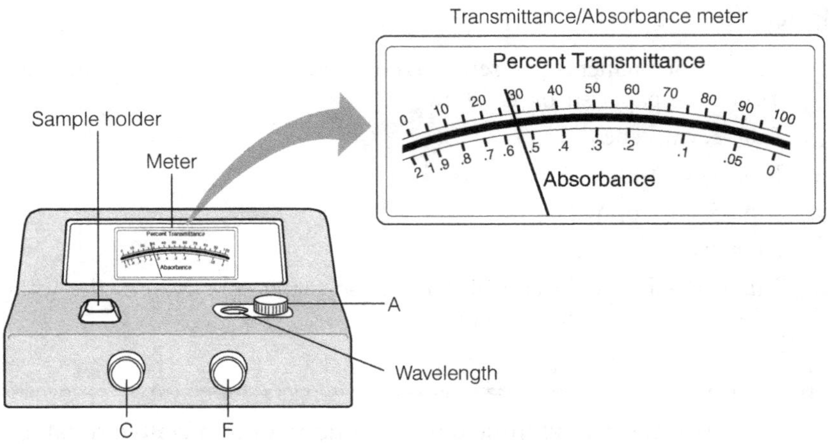

c. *Calibrate the instrument.* Insert cuvette A into the sample holder and close the lid. (Be sure to align the etched mark on the cuvette with the line on the sample holder.) Adjust the light control (F) until the meter reads 100% transmittance, or 0 absorption. You are now ready to make your first reading.

d. *Begin your readings.* Remove cuvette A and insert cuvette B. (Align the etched mark.) Close the cover. Record the reading on the absorbance scale. Remove cuvette B.

e. *Recalibrate the instrument.* Insert cuvette A into the sample holder, and set the wavelength to 420 nm. Again, calibrate the instrument to 100% transmittance (0 absorption) with cuvette A in place, using the light control (F).

f. *Take the second reading.* Remove cuvette A and insert cuvette B. Record absorbance at 420 nm. Remove cuvette B.

g. *Continue your observations,* increasing the wavelength by 20-nm increments until you reach 720 nm. Be sure to recalibrate each time you change the wavelength.

6. Pool data from all teams to complete Table 3.

Results

1. Using the readings recorded in Table 3, plot in Figure 5 the absorption spectrum for each pigment.
2. Choose appropriate scales for the axes, determine dependent and independent variables, and plot data points. Draw smooth curves to fit the values plotted. Label the graph for easy identification of pigments plotted, or prepare a legend and use colored pencils.

Discussion

1. List in the margin or on another page the pigments extracted and the optimum wavelength(s) of light for absorption for each pigment.

Table 3
Absorbance of Photosynthetic Pigments Extracted from Fresh ______________________*

Wavelength	Chlorophyll *a*	Chlorophyll *b*	Xanthophyll	Carotene	Total Pigment
400					
420					
440					
460					
480					
500					
520					
540					
560					
580					
600					
620					
640					
660					
680					
700					
720					

*Complete title with name of plant used for extract, for example, beans.

2. Which pigment is most important in the process of photosynthesis? Support your choice with evidence from your results.

3. Chlorophyll *b* and carotenoids are called *accessory pigments.* Using data from your results, speculate about the roles of these pigments in photosynthesis.

Figure 5.
Absorption spectrum for chlorophyll *a*, chlorophyll *b*, carotene, and xanthophyll. Plot your results from Exercise 4. Label all axes, and draw smooth curves to fit the data. Label the graph for easy identification of pigments.

Questions for Review

1. Using your previous knowledge of photosynthesis and the results from today's exercises, explain the role, origin, or fate of each factor involved in the process of photosynthesis.

2. A pigment solution contains compound A with 4 polar groups and compound B with 2 polar groups. You plan to separate these compounds using paper chromatography with a nonpolar solvent. Predict the location of the two bands relative to the solvent front. Explain your answer.

Applying Your Knowledge

1. Dr. James W. Dooley's students did not get the expected results for their investigation of the effects of different wavelengths of light on photosynthesis in the geranium (Exercise 1). Regardless of the treatment, all their geranium leaves tested positive for the presence of starch. Confused by these results, Dr. Dooley began to look for problems in the preparation of the experiment that could be responsible for the presence of starch under even the black paper. Can you suggest one or more problems that might lead to these results?

2. In response to shortened day length and cool temperatures, many trees begin a period of senescence when the breakdown of chlorophyll exceeds chlorophyll production. The leaves of these trees appear to change to yellow and orange. Using your knowledge of photosynthetic pigments, explain the source of these yellow-orange hues.

3. Land plants and many algae appear green, due to the chlorophyll stored in their chloroplasts. However, the deep-ocean-dwelling red algae, as their name suggests, range in color from pink to red to dark purple, almost black. These red colors are attributed to the photosynthetic pigment phycoerythrin. What color and wavelengths of light do you think phycoerythrin absorbs? Can you suggest how the environmental conditions of red algae might be related to this different pigment system?

4. In a classic experiment in photosynthesis performed in 1883 by the German botanist Thomas Engelmann, he surrounded a filament of algae with oxygen-requiring bacteria. He then exposed the algal strand to the visible-light spectrum along its length. In which wavelengths of light along the algal strand would you expect the bacteria to cluster? Explain.

5. An **action spectrum** is a graph that illustrates the efficacy of different wavelengths of light in promoting photosynthesis. Engelmann's elegant experiment in question #4 is an example of an action spectrum where the efficacy of various wavelengths of light was measured by the production of oxygen and the clustering of bacteria. How does an **action spectrum** differ from the **absorption spectrum** that you created in Exercise 4?

Investigative Extensions

The techniques in this lab can be used to investigate other photosynthetic systems found in algae or photosynthetic bacteria. For procedures for extraction and thin layer chromatography of pigments in brown, red, and green algae and blue-green bacteria, see Motten, 2003.

References

Mauseth, James. *Botany.* Sudbury, MA: Jones and Bartlett, 2003.

Motten, Alex. "Diversity of Photosynthetic Pigments." *Tested Studies for Laboratory Teaching* (Volume 25), Proceedings of the 25th Workshop/Conference of the Association for Biology Laboratory Education (ABLE), Michael A. O'Donnell, Editor, 2003.

Nabors, Murray. *Introduction to Botany.* San Francisco: Benjamin Cummings, 2004.

Nelson, D. and M. Cox. *Lehninger Principles of Biochemistry,* 4th ed. New York: Worth Publishers, 2005.

Taiz, L., and E. Zeigler. *Plant Physiology,* 3rd ed. Sunderland, MA: Sinauer, 2002.

Uno, G., R. Storey, and R. Moore. *Principles of Botany.* Boston, MA: McGraw-Hill, 2001.

Websites

The Photosynthesis Center:
http://photoscience.la.asu.edu/photosyn/default.html

http://photoscience.la.asu.edu/photosyn/education/learn.html

Cellular Respiration and Fermentation

This lab topic gives you another opportunity to practice the scientific process. Be prepared to use this information to design an experiment in fermentation or cellular respiration.

Laboratory Objectives

After completing this lab topic, you should be able to:

1. Describe alcoholic fermentation, naming reactants and products.
2. Describe cellular respiration, naming reactants and products.
3. Explain oxidation/reduction reactions in cellular respiration.
4. Name and describe environmental factors that influence enzymatic activity.
5. Explain spectrophotometry and describe how this process can be used to measure aerobic respiration.
6. Propose hypotheses and make predictions based on them.
7. Design and execute an experiment testing factors that influence fermentation or cellular respiration.
8. Practice scientific persuasion and communication by analyzing and interpreting experimental results.

Introduction

You have been investigating cells and their activities: enzymatic activities, cellular structure and evolution, and movement across cell membranes. This lab topic investigates energy transformations in cells. Photosynthesis is the process of transferring the sun's radiant energy to organic molecules, namely, glucose (Figure 1). This lab topic investigates **fermentation** and **cellular respiration,** cellular processes that transfer the energy in glucose bonds to bonds in **adenosine triphosphate** (ATP). The energy in ATP can then be used to perform cellular work. Fermentation is an anaerobic (without oxygen) process; cellular respiration is aerobic (utilizing oxygen). *All living organisms, including bacteria, protists, plants, and animals, produce ATP in fermentation or cellular respiration and then use ATP in their metabolism.*

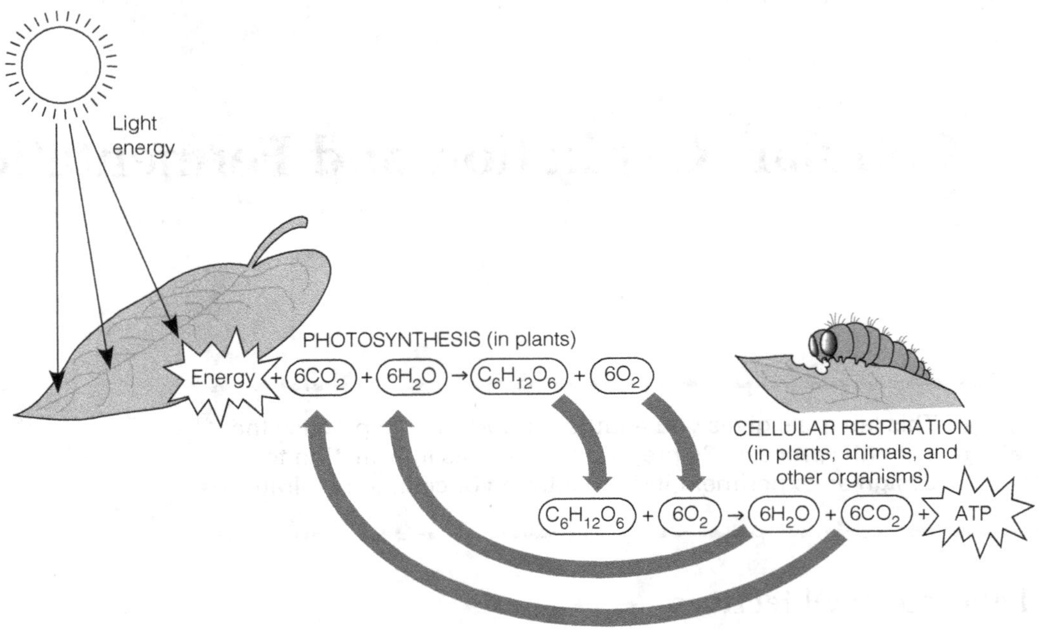

Figure 1.
Energy flow through photosynthesis and cellular respiration. Light energy from the sun is transformed to chemical energy in photosynthesis. Carbon dioxide and water are converted to glucose and oxygen. The energy stored in plant organic molecules—glucose, for example—can be utilized by plants or by consumers. The energy in organic molecules is released during cellular respiration in plants, animals, and other organisms.

Fermentation and cellular respiration involve oxidation-reduction reactions (redox reactions). Redox reactions are always defined in terms of electron transfers, oxidation being the *loss* of electrons and reduction the *gain* of electrons. In cellular respiration, two hydrogen atoms are removed from glucose (oxidation) and transferred to a coenzyme called nicotinamide adenine dinucleotide (**NAD^+**), reducing this compound to **NADH.** Think of these two hydrogen atoms as 2 electrons and 2 protons. NAD^+ is the oxidizing agent that is reduced to NADH by the addition of 2 electrons and one proton. The other proton (H^+) is released into the cell solution. NADH transfers electrons to the electron transport chain. The transfer of electrons from one molecule to another releases energy, and this energy can be used to synthesize ATP.

Cellular respiration is a sequence of three metabolic stages: **glycolysis** in the cytoplasm, and the **Krebs cycle** and the **electron transport chain** in mitochondria (Figure 2). Fermentation involves glycolysis but does not involve the Krebs cycle and the electron transport chain, which are inhibited at low oxygen levels. Two common types of fermentation are **alcoholic fermentation** and **lactic acid fermentation.** Animals, certain fungi, and some bacteria convert pyruvate produced in glycolysis to lactate. Plants and some fungi, yeast in particular, convert pyruvate to ethanol and carbon dioxide. Cellular respiration is much more efficient than fermentation in producing ATP. Cellular respiration can produce a maximum of 38 ATP molecules; fermentation produces only 2 ATP molecules.

Before you begin today's lab topic, refer to the preceding paragraph and Figure 2 as you review major pathways, reactants, and products of fermentation and cellular respiration by answering the following questions:

1. Which processes are anaerobic?

2. Which processes are aerobic?

3. Which processes take place in the cytoplasm of the cell?

4. Which processes take place in mitochondria?

5. What is the initial reactant in cellular respiration?

6. What is (are) the product(s) of the anaerobic processes?

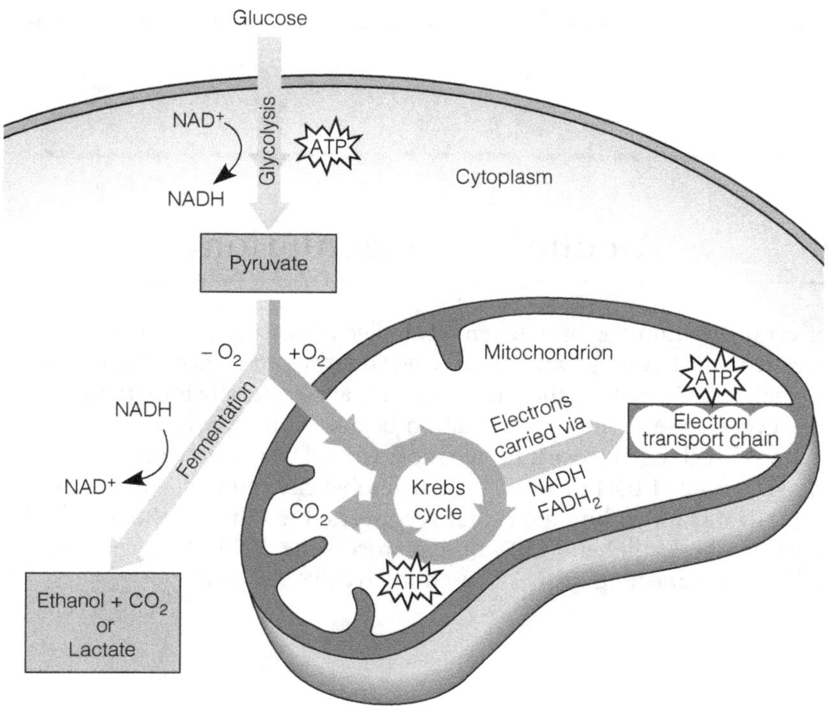

Figure 2.
Stages of cellular respiration and fermentation. Cellular respiration consists of glycolysis, the Krebs cycle, and the electron transport chain. Glycolysis is also a stage in fermentation.

7. What is (are) the product(s) of the aerobic processes?

8. Which gives the greater yield of ATP, alcoholic fermentation or cellular respiration?

In this lab topic you will investigate alcoholic fermentation first and then cellular respiration. Working in teams of two to four students, you will first perform two introductory lab studies (Lab Study A of each exercise). Lab Study B in each exercise provides questions and background to help you propose one or more testable hypotheses based on questions from the lab studies or your prior knowledge. Your team will then design and carry out an independent investigation based on your hypotheses, completing your observations and recording your results in this laboratory period. After discussing the results, your team will prepare an oral presentation in which you will persuade the class that your experimental design is sound and that your results support your conclusions. If required to do so by the lab instructor, *each of you* independently will submit Results and Discussion sections describing the results of your experiment.

First complete Lab Study A in each exercise. Then discuss possible questions for investigation with your research team. Be certain you can pose an interesting question from which to develop a testable hypothesis. Design and perform the experiment today. Prepare to report your results in oral and/or written form.

EXERCISE 1
Alcoholic Fermentation

For centuries, humans have taken advantage of yeast fermentation to produce alcoholic beverages and bread. Consider the products of fermentation and their roles in making these economically and culturally important foods and beverages. Alcoholic fermentation begins with glycolysis, a series of reactions breaking glucose into two molecules of **pyruvate** with a net yield of 2 ATP and 2 NADH molecules. In anaerobic environments, in two steps the pyruvate (a 3-carbon molecule) is converted to ethyl alcohol (ethanol, a 2-carbon molecule) and CO_2. In this process the 2 NADH molecules are oxidized, replenishing the NAD^+ used in glycolysis (Figure 2).

Lab Study A. Alcoholic Fermentation in Yeast

Materials

4 respirometers:
- test tubes, 1-mL graduated pipettes, aquarium tubing, flasks, binder clips

pipette pump
3 5-mL graduated pipettes, labeled "DI water," "yeast," and "glucose"
3-inch donut-shaped metal weights
yeast solution
glucose solution
DI water
water bath
wax pencil

Introduction

In this lab study, you will investigate alcoholic fermentation in a yeast (a single-celled fungus), *Saccharomyces cerevisiae,* or "baker's yeast." When oxygen is low, some fungi, including yeast and most plants, switch from cellular respiration to alcoholic fermentation. In bread making, starch in the flour is converted to glucose and fructose, which then serve as the starting compounds for fermentation. The resulting carbon dioxide is trapped in the dough, causing it to rise. Ethanol is also produced in bread making but evaporates during baking.

In this laboratory experiment, the carbon dioxide (CO_2) produced, being a gas, bubbles out of the solution and can be used as an indication of the relative rate of fermentation taking place. Figure 3 shows the respirometers you will use to collect CO_2. The rate of fermentation, a series of enzymatic reactions, can be affected by several factors, for example, concentration of yeast, concentration of glucose, or temperature. In this lab study you will

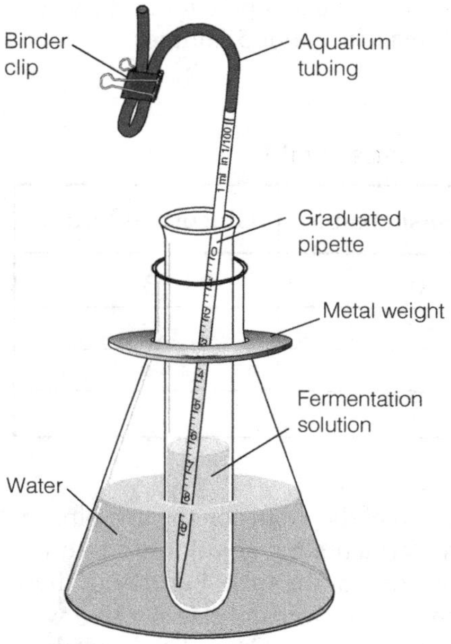

Figure 3.
Respirometer used for yeast fermentation.

investigate *the effects of yeast concentration.* In your independent study you may choose to investigate other independent variables.

Hypothesis

Hypothesize about the effect of different concentrations of yeast on the rate of fermentation.

Prediction

Predict the results of the experiment based on your hypothesis (if/then).

Procedure

1. Obtain four flasks and add enough tap water to keep them from floating in a water bath (fill to about 5 cm from the top of the flask). Label the flasks 1, 2, 3, and 4. To stabilize the flasks, place a 3-inch donut-shaped metal weight over the neck of the flasks.
2. Obtain four test tubes (fermentation tubes) and label them 1, 2, 3, and 4. Add solutions as in Table 1 to the appropriate tubes. Rotate each tube to distribute the yeast evenly in the tube. Place tubes in the corresponding numbered flasks.
3. To each tube, add a 1-mL graduated pipette to which a piece of plastic aquarium tubing has been attached.
4. Place the flasks with the test tubes and graduated pipettes in the water bath at 30°C. Allow them to equilibrate for about 5 minutes.

Table 1
Contents of Fermentation Solutions (volumes in mL)

Tube	DI Water	Yeast Suspension	Glucose Solution
1	4	0	3
2	6	1	0
3	3	1	3
4	1	3	3

5. Attach the pipette pump to the free end of the tubing on the first pipette. Use the pipette pump to draw the fermentation solution up into the pipette. Fill it past the calibrated portion of the tube, but do not draw the solution into the tubing. Fold the tubing over and clamp it shut with the binder clip so the solution does not run out. Open the clip slightly, and allow the solution to drain down to the 0-mL calibration line (or slightly below). If the level is below the zero mark, open the clamp slightly while another student adjusts the level using the pipette pump. Be patient.

This may require a couple attempts! Quickly do the same for the other three pipettes.

6. In Table 2, quickly record your initial readings for each pipette in the "Initial reading" row in each "Actual (A)" column. This will be the *initial* time (I).
7. Two minutes after the initial readings for each pipette, record the actual readings (A) in mL for each pipette in the "Actual (A)" column. Subtract I from A to determine the total amount of CO_2 evolved (A – I). Record this value in the "CO_2 Evolved (A – I)" column. *From now on, you will subtract the initial reading from each actual reading to determine the total amount of CO_2 evolved.*
8. Continue taking readings every 2 minutes for each of the solutions for 20 minutes. Remember, take the actual reading from the pipette and subtract the initial reading to get the total amount of CO_2 evolved in each test tube.
9. Record your results in Table 2.

Results

1. Complete Table 2.

Table 2

Total CO_2 Evolved by Different Concentrations of Yeast. Actual values are the graduated pipette readings. For CO_2 evolved values, subtract the initial reading from the actual reading. This is the amount of CO_2 accumulated over time.

Time (min)	Tube 1		Tube 2		Tube 3		Tube 4	
	Actual (A)	CO_2 Evolved (A – I)	Actual (A)	CO_2 Evolved (A – I)	Actual (A)	CO_2 Evolved (A – I)	Actual (A)	CO_2 Evolved (A – I)
Initial reading (I)		X		X		X		X
2								
4								
6								
8								
10								
12								
14								
16								
18								
20								

2. Using Figure 4, construct a graph to illustrate your results.
   a. What is (are) the independent variable(s)? Which is the appropriate axis for this variable?

   b. What is the dependent variable? Which is the appropriate axis for this variable?

   c. Choose an appropriate scale and label the x and y axes.

   d. Should you use a legend? If so, what would this include?

   e. Compose a figure title.

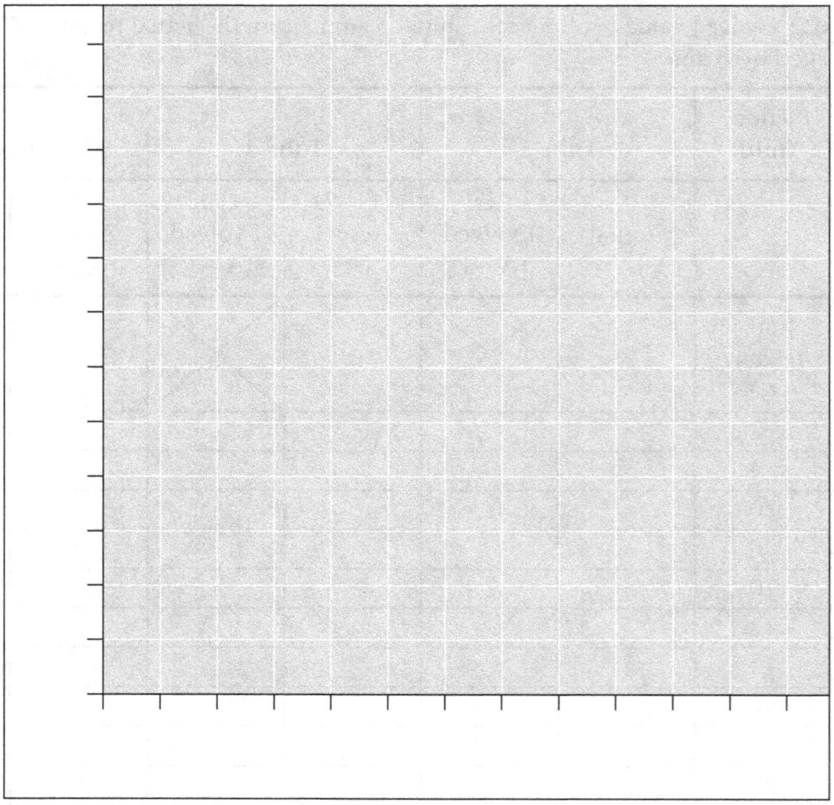

Figure 4.

Discussion

1. Explain the experimental design. What is the purpose of each test tube? Which is (are) the control tube(s)?

2. Which test tube had the highest rate of fermentation? Explain why.

3. Which test tube had the lowest rate of fermentation? Explain why.

4. Why were different amounts of water added to each fermentation solution?

Lab Study B. Additional Investigations of Alcoholic Fermentation

Materials

all materials from Lab Study A
beakers
graduated pipettes of various sizes
different substrates: sucrose, saccharin, Nutrasweet™, Splenda™, fructose, starch, glycogen, honey, corn syrup, pyruvate
different types of yeast: dry active, quick rise, Pasteur champagne (for wine making)
various fermentation inhibitors: sodium fluoride, ethyl alcohol, Na benzoate
various salt solutions
various pH buffers
spices: ground cinnamon, cloves, caraway, ginger, cardamom, nutmeg, mace, thyme, dry mustard, chili powder, cayenne pepper
disposable gloves
additional glassware

Introduction

If your team chooses to study alcoholic fermentation for your independent investigation and report, design a simple experiment to investigate some factor that affects alcoholic fermentation. Use the available materials or ask your instructor about the availability of additional materials.

Procedure

1. Collaborating with your research team, read the following potential questions, and choose a question to investigate using this list or an idea from your prior knowledge. You may want to check your text and other sources for supporting information. You should be able to explain the rationale behind your choice of question. For example, if you choose to investigate *starch* as a substrate, you should be able to explain that the yeast must first digest starch before the glucose can be used in alcoholic fermentation and the impact this might have on the experiment.
   a. Would other substrates be as effective as glucose in alcoholic fermentation? Possible substrates:
      sucrose (table sugar—glucose and fructose disaccharide)
      honey (mainly glucose and fructose)
      corn syrup (fructose and sucrose)
      starch (glucose polymer in plants)
      saccharin, Equal™, Splenda™
      fructose
      pyruvate
   b. Would fermentation rates change with different types of yeasts?
   c. What environmental conditions are optimum for alcoholic fermentation?
      What temperature ranges?
      What pH ranges?
   d. What is the maximum amount of ethyl alcohol that can be tolerated by yeast cells?

If you select toxins or fermentation inhibitors for your investigation, ask the instructor about safety procedures. Post safety precautions and follow safety protocol, including wearing gloves and protective eyewear. Notify the instructor of any spills.

   e. Sodium fluoride, commonly used to prevent tooth decay, inhibits an enzyme in glycolysis. At what concentration is it most effective?
   f. Would adding $MgSO_4$ enhance glycolysis? $MgSO_4$ provides Mg^{++}, a cofactor necessary to activate some enzymes in glycolysis.
   g. Does a high concentration of sucrose inhibit fermentation?
   h. An old German baker's wisdom says, "A pinch of ginger will make your yeast work better." Some spices enhance yeast activity while others inhibit it (Corriher, 1997). What effect do spices have on yeast activity? Try ginger, ground cardamom, caraway, cinnamon, mace, nutmeg, thyme, dry mustard, cayenne pepper or others.
   i. Salt is often used as a food preservative to prevent bacterial and fungal growth (for example, in country ham). But salt is also important to enhance the flavor of bread when added in small amounts. At what concentration does salt begin to inhibit yeast fermentation?
   j. Does the food preservative Na benzoate inhibit cellular respiration?

2. Design your experiment, proposing hypotheses, making predictions, and determining procedures as instructed in Exercise 3.

EXERCISE 2
Cellular Respiration

Most organisms produce ATP using cellular respiration, a process that involves glycolysis, the Krebs cycle, and the electron transport chain. In cellular respiration, many more ATP molecules are produced than were produced in alcoholic fermentation (potentially 38 compared to 2), and water, unlike ethanol, is not toxic to the cells. After the series of reactions in the cytoplasm (glycolysis), pyruvate enters the mitochondria, where enzymes for the Krebs cycle and the electron transport chain are located. The Krebs cycle is a series of eight steps, each catalyzed by a specific enzyme. As one compound is converted to another, CO_2 is given off and hydrogen ions and electrons are removed. The electrons and hydrogen ions are passed to NAD^+ and another electron carrier, FAD (flavin adenine dinucleotide). NADH and $FADH_2$ carry the electrons to the electron transport chain, where the electrons pass along the chain to the final electron acceptor, oxygen. In the process, ATP molecules are produced (Figure 2).

Lab Study A. Oxidation-Reduction Reactions in a Mitochondrial Suspension

Materials

mitochondrial suspension
succinate
buffer
DPIP solution
1-mL graduated pipette
pipette pump
4 cuvettes or small test tubes
Parafilm® squares
Kimwipes®
spectrophotometer
wax pencil

Introduction

In this lab study, you will investigate cellular respiration in isolated mitochondria. Your instructor has prepared a mitochondrial suspension from pulverized lima beans. The suspension has been kept on ice to prevent enzyme degradation, and the Krebs cycle will continue in the mitochondria as in intact cells. Sucrose has been added to the mitochondrial suspension to maintain an osmotic balance.

One step in the Krebs cycle is the enzyme-catalyzed conversion of succinate to fumarate in a redox reaction. In intact cells, succinate loses hydrogen ions and electrons to FAD, and, in the process, fumarate is formed (Figure 5).

We will utilize this step in the Krebs cycle to study the rate of cellular respiration under different conditions. To perform this study, we will add a substance called DPIP (di-chlorophenol-indophenol), an electron acceptor that

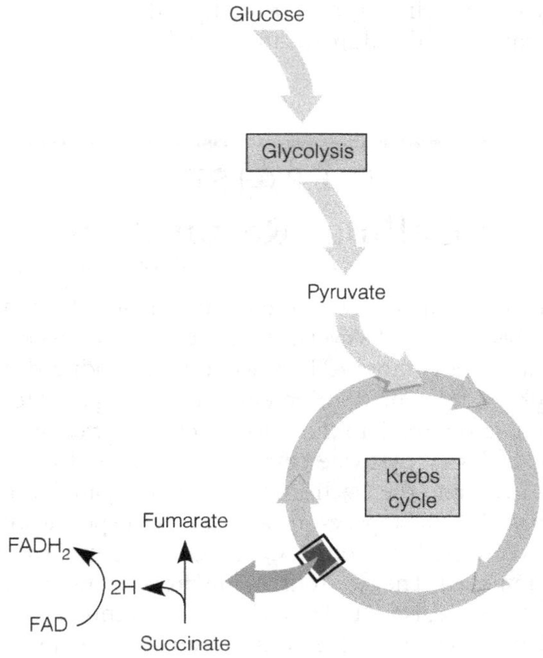

Figure 5.
At one point in the Krebs cycle, succinate is converted to fumarate. Hydrogens from succinate pass to FAD, reducing it to $FADH_2$.

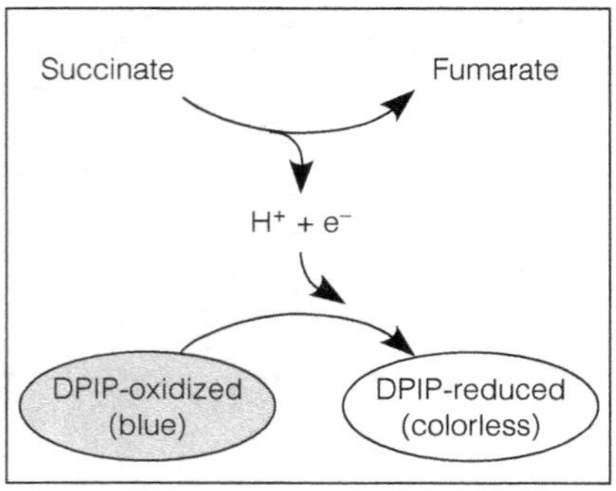

Figure 6.
DPIP intercepts the hydrogen ions and electrons as succinate is converted to fumarate. DPIP changes from blue to colorless.

intercepts the hydrogen ions and electrons released from succinate, changing the DPIP from an oxidized to a reduced state. DPIP is *blue* in its oxidized state but changes from blue to *colorless* as it is reduced (Figure 6).

We can use this color change to measure the respiration rate. To do this, however, we must have some quantitative means of measuring color change. An instrument called a **spectrophotometer** will allow us to do this. A spectrophotometer measures the amount of light absorbed by a pigment. In the spectrophotometer, a specific wavelength of light (chosen by the operator) passes through the pigment solution being tested—in this case, the blue DPIP. The spectrophotometer then measures the proportion of light *transmitted* or, conversely, *absorbed* by the DPIP and shows a reading on a calibrated scale. As the DPIP changes from blue to clear, it will absorb less light and more light will pass through (be transmitted through) the solution. The change in transmittance will be read by the spectrophotometer. As more light passes through the solution, the transmittance reading goes up. As aerobic respiration takes place, what should happen to the percent transmittance of light through the DPIP?

Our experiment will involve using succinate as the substrate and investigating the effect that *changing the amount of succinate will have on the cellular respiration rate*.

Hypothesis

Hypothesize about the effect of an increased amount of substrate on the rate of cellular respiration.

Prediction

Predict the results of the experiment based on your hypothesis (if/then).

Procedure

1. Prepare the spectrophotometer.

   The instructions that follow are for a Bausch & Lomb Spectronic 20 (Figure 7). Turn on the machine (power switch C) at least 5 minutes before beginning.

   a. Using the wavelength control knob (A), select the wavelength: 600 nm. Your instructor has previously determined that this wavelength is absorbed by DPIP.

   b. Zero the instrument by adjusting the control knob (the same as power switch C) so that the meter needle reads 0% transmittance. There should be no cuvette in the instrument, and the sample holder cover must be closed. Once it is set, do not change this setting.

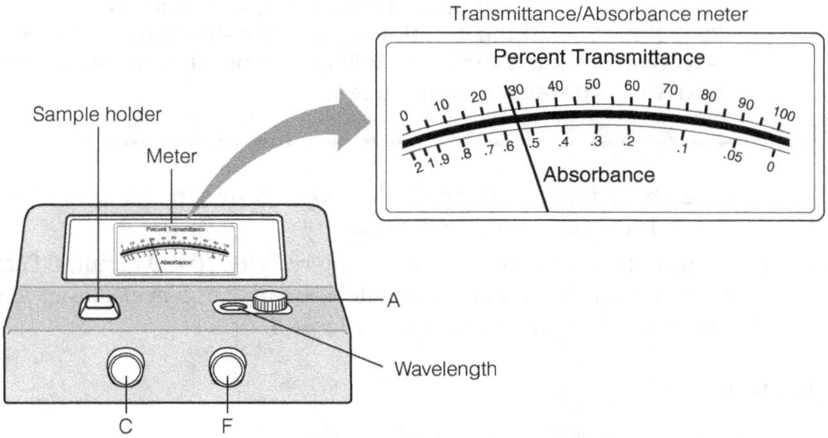

Figure 7.
The Bausch & Lomb Spectronic 20. A spectrophotometer measures the proportion of light of different wavelengths absorbed and transmitted by a pigment solution. Inside the spectrophotometer, light is separated into its component wavelengths and passed through a sample. Transmittance or absorbance can be read on a calibrated scale.

2. Obtain four cuvettes and label them B, 1, 2, and 3. The B will be the blank.
3. Prepare the blank first by measuring 4.6 mL buffer, 0.3 mL mitochondrial suspension, and 0.1 mL succinate into the B cuvette. Cover the cuvette tightly with Parafilm and invert it to mix the reactants thoroughly.
4. Calibrate the spectrophotometer as follows: Wipe cuvette B with a Kimwipe and insert it into the sample holder. Be sure you align the etched mark on the cuvette with the line on the sample holder. Close the cover. Adjust the light control (F) until the meter reads 100% transmittance, or 0 absorption. Remove cuvette B. You are now ready to prepare the experimental cuvettes. The blank corrects for differences in transmittance due to the mitochondrial solution.
5. Measure the buffer, DPIP, and mitochondrial suspension into cuvettes 1, 2, and 3 as specified in Table 3.

   Do not add the succinate yet!

Table 3
Contents of Experimental Tubes (volumes in mL)

Tube	Buffer	DPIP	Mitochondrial Suspension	Succinate (add last)
1	4.4	0.3	0.3	0
2	4.3	0.3	0.3	0.1
3	4.2	0.3	0.3	0.2

6. Perform the next two steps as *quickly* as possible. First, add the succinate to each cuvette.
7. Cover tube 1 with Parafilm, wipe it with a Kimwipe, insert it into the sample holder, and record the percent transmittance in Table 4 in the Results section. Repeat this step for tubes 2 and 3.

If the initial reading is higher than 30%, tell your instructor immediately. You may need to add another drop of DPIP to each tube and repeat step 7. The reading must be low enough (the solution dark enough) to give readings for 20–30 minutes. If the solution is too light (the transmittance is above 30%), the reactions will go to completion too quickly to detect differences in the tubes.

---

8. Before each reading, insert the blank, cuvette B, into the sample holder. Adjust to 100% transmittance if necessary.
9. Continue to take readings at 5-minute intervals for 20–30 minutes. *Each time, before you take a reading, cover the tube with Parafilm and invert it to mix the contents.* Record the results in Table 4.

Results

1. Complete Table 4. Compose a title for the table.

Table 4

	Time (min)						
Tube	0	5	10	15	20	25	30
1							
2							
3							

2. Using Figure 8, construct a graph to illustrate your results.
   a. What is (are) the independent variable(s)? Which is the appropriate axis for this variable?

   b. What is the dependent variable? Which is the appropriate axis for this variable?

   c. Choose an appropriate scale and label the *x* and *y* axes.
   d. Should you use a legend? If so, what would this include?

   e. Compose a figure title.

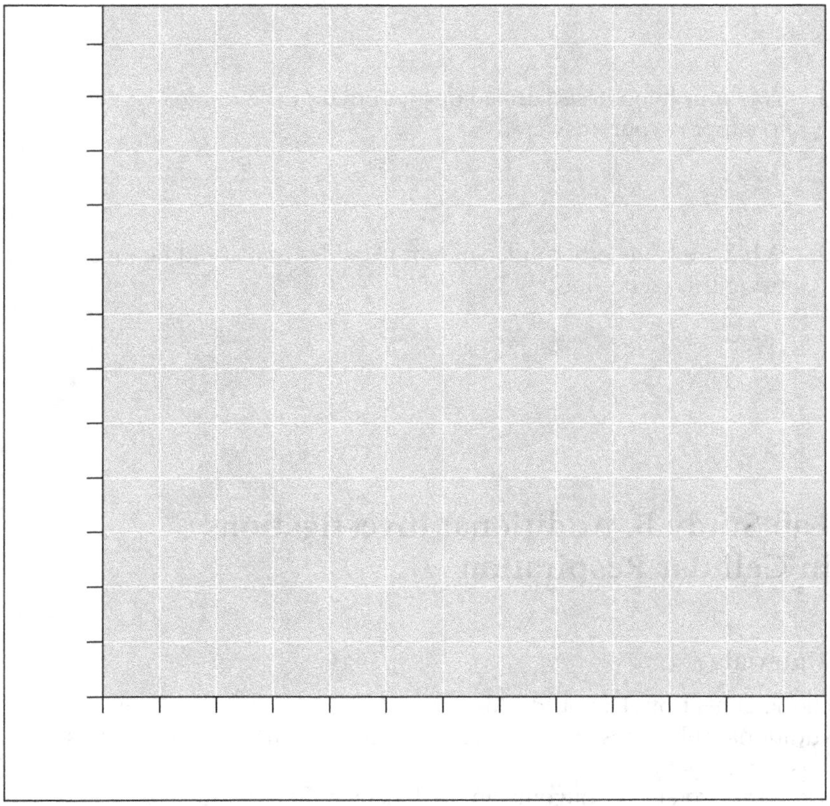

Figure 8.

Discussion

1. Explain the experimental design. What is the role of each of the components of the experimental mixtures?

2. Which experimental tube is the control?

3. In which experimental tube did transmittance increase more rapidly? Explain.

4. Why should the succinate be added to the reaction tubes last?

5. Was your hypothesis falsified or supported by the results? Use your data to support your answer.

6. What are some other independent variables that could be investigated using this technique?

Lab Study B. Additional Investigations in Cellular Respiration

Materials

all materials from Lab Study A
additional substrates: glucose, fructose, maltose, artificial sweeteners, starch, glycogen
inhibitors: rotenone, oligomycin, malonate, antimycin A
different pH buffers
ice bath
water bath
disposable gloves

Introduction

If your team chooses to study cellular respiration for your independent investigation and report, design a simple experiment to investigate some factor that affects cellular respiration. Use the available materials, or ask your instructor about the availability of additional materials.

If you select toxins or respiratory inhibitors for your investigation, ask the instructor about safety procedures. Post safety precautions and follow safety protocol, including wearing gloves and protective eyewear. Notify the instructor of any spills.

Procedure

1. Collaborating with your research team, read the following potential questions, and choose a question to investigate using this list or an idea from your prior knowledge. You may want to check your text and other sources for supporting information.
   a. Would other substrates be as effective as succinate in cellular respiration? Possible substrates:

      glucose

      sucrose (table sugar—glucose and fructose disaccharide)

      starch (glucose polymer in plants)

      saccharin, Nutrasweet™, Splenda™, or other artificial sweeteners

      fructose

   b. What environmental conditions are optimum for cellular respiration?

      What temperature ranges?

      What pH ranges?

   c. What inhibitors of cellular respiration are most effective? Consider the following list:

      Rotenone, an insecticide, inhibits electron flow in the electron transport chain.

      Oligomycin, an antibiotic, inhibits ATP synthesis.

      Malonate blocks the conversion of succinate to malate. How would you determine if this is competitive or noncompetitive inhibition?

      Antimycin is an antibiotic that inhibits the transfer of electrons to oxygen.

      Crushed peach seeds contain cyanide, a respiratory inhibitor.

2. Design your experiment, proposing hypotheses, making predictions, and determining procedures as instructed in Exercise 3.

EXERCISE 3

Designing and Performing Your Independent Investigation

Materials

See each Lab Study B materials list in Exercises 1 and 2.

Introduction

Now that you have completed both introductory investigations, your research team should decide if you will investigate fermentation or cellular respiration. Use Lab Topic 1 as a reference for designing and performing a scientific investigation. Be ready to assign tasks to members of your lab team. Be sure that everyone understands the techniques that will be used. Your experiment will be successful only if you plan carefully, cooperate with your team members, perform lab techniques accurately and systematically, and record and report data accurately.

Procedure

1. **Decide on one or more questions to investigate.**

   Question:

2. **Formulate a testable hypothesis.**

   Hypothesis:

3. **Summarize the experiment.** (Use separate paper.)
4. **Predict the results of your experiment based on your hypothesis.**
   Prediction: (If/then)

5. **Outline the procedures used in the experiment.**
   a. On a separate sheet of paper, list each step in your procedure in numerical order.
   b. Remember to include the number of repetitions (usually a minimum of five), levels of treatment, appropriate time intervals, and controls for each procedure.

c. If you have an idea for an experiment that requires materials other than those provided, ask your laboratory instructor about their availability. If possible, additional supplies will be made available.

d. When carrying out an experiment, remember to quantify your measurements when possible.

6. **Perform the experiment,** making observations and collecting data for analysis.

If your experiment involves the use of toxins or respiration inhibitors, use them only in liquid form as provided by the instructor. Wear protective gloves and eyewear. Ask your instructor about proper disposal procedures. If a spill occurs, notify your instructor immediately for proper cleanup.

---

7. **Record observations and data** on a separate sheet of paper. Design tables and graphs, at least one of each. Be thorough when collecting data. Do not just write down numbers, but record what they mean as well. Do not rely on your memory for information that you will need when reporting your results.

8. **Prepare your discussion.** Discuss your results in light of your hypothesis.

a. Review your hypothesis. Review your results (tables and graphs). Do your results support or falsify your hypothesis? Explain your answer, using your data for support.

b. Review your prediction. Did your results correspond to the prediction you made? If not, explain how your results are different from your predictions, and why this might have occurred.

c. If you had problems with the procedure or questionable results, explain how they might have influenced your conclusion.

d. If you had an opportunity to repeat and expand this experiment to make your results more convincing, what would you do?

e. Summarize the conclusion you have drawn from your results.

9. **Be prepared to report your results to the class.** Prepare to persuade your fellow scientists that your experimental design is sound and that your results support your conclusions.

10. If your instructor requires it, **submit Results and Discussion sections** of a scientific paper. Keep in mind that although you have performed the experiments as a team, you must turn in a lab report of *your original writing*. Your tables and figures may be similar to those of your team members, but your Results and Discussion sections must be the product of your own literature search and creative thinking.

Questions for Review

1. Having completed this lab topic, you should be able to define, describe, and use the following terms: *aerobic, anaerobic, substrate, reactants, products, spectrophotometer, respirometer,* NAD^+, *NADH, FAD,* $FADH_2$, *ATP.*

2. State the beginning reactants and the end products of glycolysis, alcoholic fermentation, the Krebs cycle, and the electron transport chain. Describe where these processes take place in the cell and the conditions under which they operate (aerobic or anaerobic).

   glycolysis:

   alcoholic fermentation:

   Krebs cycle:

   electron transport chain:

3. Suppose you do another experiment using DPIP to study cellular respiration in isolated mitochondria, and the results using the spectrophotometer show a final percent transmittance reading of 42% in tube 1 and 78% in tube 2. Both tubes had an initial reading of 30%. In which tube did the greater amount of cellular respiration occur? Explain your answer in terms of the changes that take place in DPIP.

4. How do you know that the electrons causing the change in color of DPIP are involved in the succinate–fumarate step?

Applying Your Knowledge

1. Your mother has been making yeast bread all afternoon, and she has just put two loaves in the oven. You open the oven door to see what is baking. Your mother yells, "Don't slam the door!" Why?

2. Two characteristics of natural wines are that they have a maximum alcohol content of 14% and are "sparkling" wines. Apply your understanding of alcoholic fermentation to explain these characteristics.

3. Cassava is a major food crop for over 500 million people in tropical countries. You may have eaten tapioca pudding, which is made from cassava root. Cassava varieties are described as bitter or sweet depending on the concentration of toxic compounds called cyanogenic glycosides, which are enzymatically converted to hydrocyanic acid (HCN), a respiratory inhibitor. The bitter forms must be detoxified by boiling, grating, and/or fermenting before they can be eaten. Design an experiment using mitochondria to test the relative concentrations of toxins in varieties of sweet and bitter cassava.

4. Skunk cabbage is a plant that is able to generate heat and regulate its body temperature, like a warm-blooded animal. Botanists have suggested that the ability to produce heat is important in these plants because it provides a warm environment for pollinators. The heat may also help to dissipate the carrion-like scent produced by some skunk cabbage flowers. Clearly, these plants must have a high respiratory rate to produce temperatures as high as 37°C. How could you determine if the temperature is the result of cellular respiration? What features of the plant surface and cell structure might be present if respiration is actively occurring in the flowers?

References

Campbell, N. and J. Reece. *Biology,* 7th ed. San Francisco, CA: Benjamin Cummings, 2005.

Corriher, S. O. *Cookwise: The Hows and Whys of Successful Cooking.* New York: William Morrow, 1997.

Lehninger, A. L., D. L. Nelson, and M. M. Cox. *Principles of Biochemistry*, 3rd ed. New York: Worth Publishers, 2000.

Seymour, R. S. "Plants That Warm Themselves." *Scientific American,* 1997, vol. 276, pp. 104–107.

Simpson, B. B. and M. Conner-Ogorzaly. *Economic Botany,* 2nd ed. New York: McGraw-Hill, 1995. Includes information on spices, medicinal plants, toxins, and other possible choices for independent investigations.

Some procedures and many ideas in this lab topic were based on an exercise written by Jean Dickey, published in J. Dickey, *Laboratory Investigations for Biology*. Menlo Park, CA: Addison Wesley Longman, 1995.

The procedure used to assay mitochondrial activity was based on a procedure from "Succinic Acid Dehydrogenase Activity of Plant Mitochondria," in F. Witham, D. Blaydes, and R. Devlin, *Exercises in Plant Physiology*. Boston, MA: Prindle, Weber & Schmidt, 1971.

Websites

http://www.ruf.rice.edu/~bioslabs/studies/mitochondria/mitopoisons.html

Cornell University Poisonous Plants Page http://www.ansci.cornell.edu/plants/index.html

Mitosis and Meiosis

Laboratory Objectives

After completing this lab topic, you should be able to:

1. Describe the activities of chromosomes, centrioles, and microtubules in the cell cycle, including all phases of mitosis and meiosis.
2. Recognize human chromosomes in leukocytes.
3. Identify the phases of mitosis in root tip and whitefish blastula cells.
4. Describe differences in mitosis and cytokinesis in plant and animal cells.
5. Describe differences in mitosis and meiosis.
6. Explain crossing over, and describe how this can bring about particular arrangements of ascospores in the fungus *Sordaria*.

Introduction

The nuclei in cells of eukaryotic organisms contain chromosomes with clusters of **genes**, discrete units of hereditary information consisting of duplicated deoxyribonucleic acid (DNA). Structural proteins in the chromosomes organize the DNA and participate in DNA folding and condensation. When cells divide, chromosomes and genes are duplicated and passed on to daughter cells. Single-celled organisms divide for reproduction. Multicellular organisms have reproductive cells (eggs or sperm), but they also have somatic (body) cells that divide for growth or replacement.

In somatic cells and single-celled organisms, the nucleus divides by **mitosis** into two daughter nuclei, which have the same number of chromosomes and the same genes as the parent cell. In multicellular organisms, in preparation for sexual reproduction, a type of nuclear division called **meiosis** takes place. In meiosis, nuclei of certain cells in ovaries or testes (or sporangia in plants) divide twice, but the chromosomes replicate only once. This process results in four daughter nuclei with differing alleles on the chromosomes. Eggs or sperm (or spores in plants) are eventually formed. Generally, in both mitosis and meiosis, after nuclear division the cytoplasm divides, a process called **cytokinesis.**

Events from the beginning of one cell division to the beginning of the next are collectively called the **cell cycle.** The cell cycle is divided into two major phases: interphase and mitotic phase (M). The M phase represents the division of the nucleus and cytoplasm (Figure 1).

Figure 1.
The cell cycle. In interphase (G_1, S, G_2), DNA replication and most of the cell's growth and biochemical activity take place. In the M phase, the nucleus divides in mitosis, and the cytoplasm divides in cytokinesis.

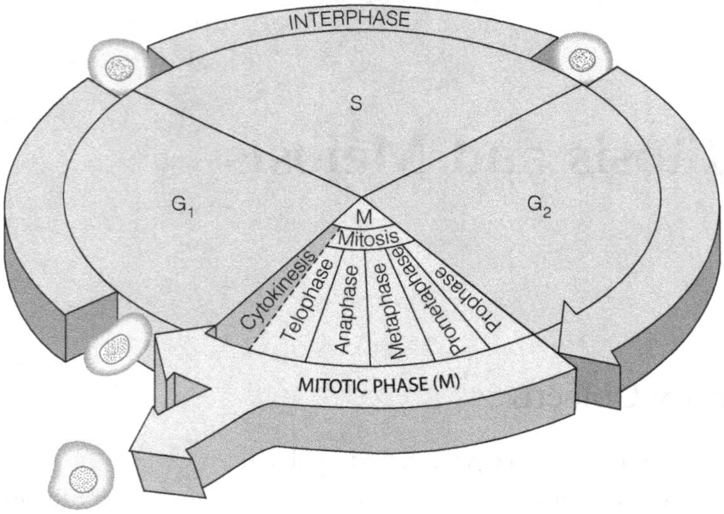

EXERCISE 1
Modeling the Cell Cycle and Mitosis in an Animal Cell

Materials

60 pop beads of one color
60 pop beads of another color
4 magnetic centromeres
4 centrioles

Introduction

Scientists use models to represent natural structures and processes that are too small, too large, or too complex to investigate directly. Scientists develop their models from observations and experimental data, usually accumulated from a variety of sources. Building a model can represent the culmination of a body of scientific work, but most models represent a well-developed hypothesis that can then be tested against the natural system and modified.

Linus Pauling's novel and successful technique of building a physical model of hemoglobin was based on available chemical data. This technique was later adopted by Francis Crick and James Watson to elucidate the nature of the hereditary material, DNA. Watson and Crick built a wire model utilizing evidence collected by many scientists. They presented their conclusions about the structure of the DNA helix in the journal *Nature* in April 1953 and were awarded the Nobel Prize for their discovery in 1962.

Today in lab you will work with a partner to build models of cell division: mitosis and meiosis. Using these models will enhance your understanding of the behavior of chromosomes, centrioles, membranes, and microtubules during the cell cycle. After completing your model, you will consider ways in which it is and is not an appropriate model for the cell cycle. You and your partner should discuss activities in each stage of the cell cycle as you build your model. After going through the exercise once together, you will demonstrate the model to each other to reinforce your understanding.

In the model of mitosis that you will build, your cell will be a **diploid** cell (2*n*) with four chromosomes. This means that you will have two homologous pairs of chromosomes. In diploid cells, **homologous chromosomes** are the same length, have the same centromere position, and contain genes for the same characters. One pair will be long chromosomes, the other pair, short chromosomes. (**Haploid** cells have only one of each homologous pair of chromosomes, denoted *n*.)

Lab Study A. Interphase

During interphase, a cell performs its specific functions: Liver cells produce bile; intestinal cells absorb nutrients; pancreatic cells secrete enzymes; skin cells produce keratin. Interphase consists of three subphases, G_1, S, and G_2, which begin as a cell division ends. As interphase begins, there is approximately half as much cytoplasm in each cell as there was before division. Each new cell has a nucleus that is surrounded by a **nuclear envelope** and that contains chromosomes in an uncoiled, or decondensed, state. In this uncoiled state, the mass of DNA and protein is called **chromatin.** Located outside the nucleus is the **centrosome,** a granular region that contains a pair of **centrioles** in animal cells. The centrosome is the organizing center for microtubules. (See Figure 2.)

Procedure

1. Build a homologous pair of single chromosomes using 10 beads of one color for one member of the long pair and 10 beads of the other color for the other member of the pair. Place the magnetic centromere at any position in the chromosome, but note that it must be in the same position on homologous chromosomes. The centromere appears as a constricted region when chromosomes are condensed. Build the short pair with the same two different colors, but use fewer beads. You should have enough beads left over to duplicate each chromosome.
2. Model **interphase** of the cell cycle:
   a. Pile all the assembled chromosomes in the center of your work area to represent the decondensed chromosomes as a mass of chromatin in **G_1 (gap 1).**
   b. Position two centrioles as a pair just outside your nucleus. Have the two members of the centriole pair at right angles to each other. (Recall, however, that most plant cells do not have centrioles.)

   In the G_1 phase, the cytoplasmic mass increases and will continue to do so throughout interphase. Proteins are synthesized, new organelles are formed, and some organelles such as mitochondria and chloroplasts grow and divide in two. Throughout interphase one or more dark, round bodies, called **nucleoli** (singular, **nucleolus**), are visible in the nucleus.

   c. Duplicate the centrioles: Add a second pair of centrioles to your model; again, have the two centrioles at right angles to each other.

   Centriole duplication begins in late G_1 or early S phase.

   d. Duplicate the chromosomes in your model cell to represent DNA replication in the **S (synthesis) phase:** Make a second strand that is identical to the first strand of each chromosome. In duplicating

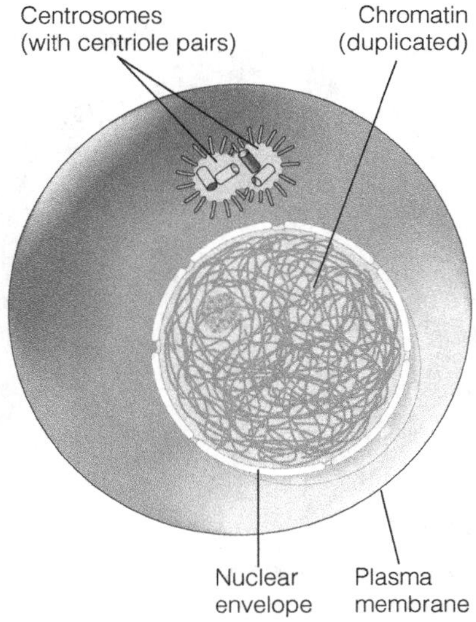

Figure 2. Interphase.

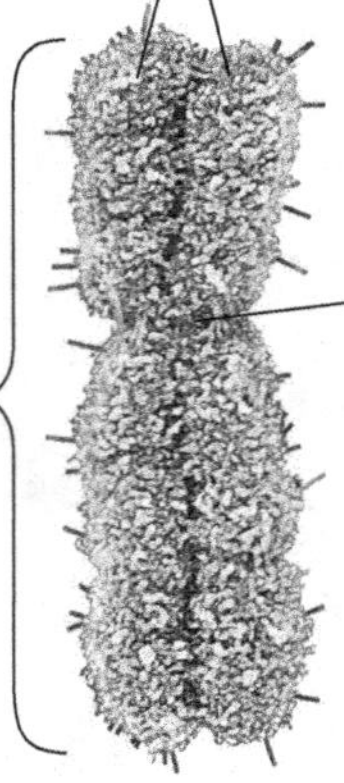

Figure 3.
Duplicated chromosome composed of two sister chromatids held together at the centromere; condensed as in prometaphase.

chromosomes, you will use two magnets to form the new centromere. In the living cell, the centromere in a cell is a single unit until it splits in metaphase. In your model, consider the pair of magnets to be the single centromere.

Unique activities taking place during the S phase of the cell cycle are the replication of chromosomal DNA and the synthesis of chromosomal proteins. DNA synthesis continues until chromosomes have been duplicated. Each strand of a duplicated chromosome is called a **sister chromatid.** Sister chromatids are identical to each other and are held together tightly at the centromere (Figure 3).

e. Do not disturb the chromosomes to represent **G_2 (gap 2).**

During the G_2 phase, in addition to continuing cell activities, cells prepare for mitosis. Enzymes and other proteins necessary for cell division are synthesized during this phase.

f. Separate your centriole pairs, moving them toward opposite poles of the nucleus to represent that the G_2 phase is coming to an end and mitosis is about to begin.

How many pairs of homologous chromosomes are present in your cell during this stage of the cell cycle?

Lab Study B. M Phase (Mitosis and Cytokinesis)

In the M phase, the nucleus and cytoplasm divide. Nuclear division is called *mitosis*. Cytoplasmic division is called *cytokinesis*. Mitosis is divided into five subphases: prophase, prometaphase, metaphase, anaphase, and telophase.

Procedure

1. To represent **prophase,** leave the chromosomes piled in the center of the work area.

   Prophase begins when chromosomes begin to coil and condense. At this time they become visible in the light microscope. Centrioles continue to move to opposite poles of the nucleus, and as they do so, a fibrous, rounded structure tapering toward each end, called a **spindle,** begins to form between them. Nucleoli begin to disappear (Figure 4).

   What structures make up the fibers of the spindle? (Check text if necessary.)

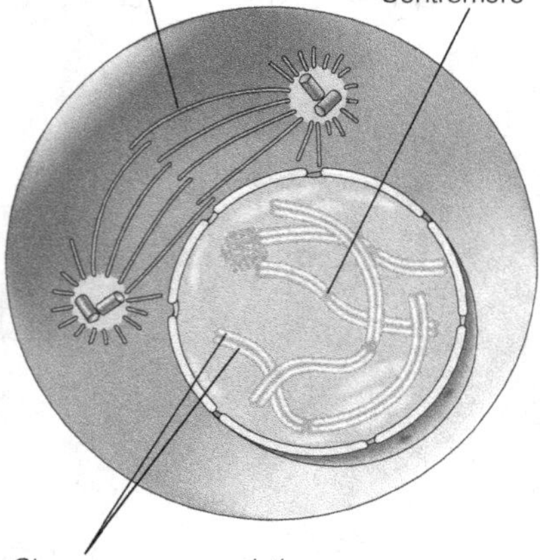

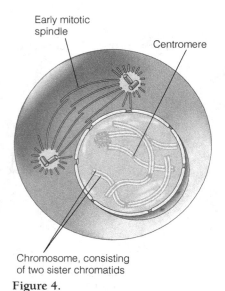

Figure 4.
Prophase mitosis.

2. At **prometaphase,** the centrioles are at the poles of the cell. To represent the actions in prometaphase, move the centromeres of your chromosomes to lie on an imaginary plane (the equator) midway between the two poles established by the centrioles.

   During prometaphase chromosomes continue to condense (Figure 3). The nuclear envelope breaks down as the spindle continues to form. Some spindle fibers become associated with chromosomes at protein structures called kinetochores. Each sister chromatid has a **kinetochore** at the centromere. These spindle microtubules now extend from the chromosomes to the centrosomes at the poles. The push and pull of spindle fibers on the chromosomes ultimately leads to their movement to the equator. When the centromeres lie on the equator, prometaphase ends and the next phase begins (Figure 5).

How many duplicated chromosomes are present in your prometaphase nucleus?

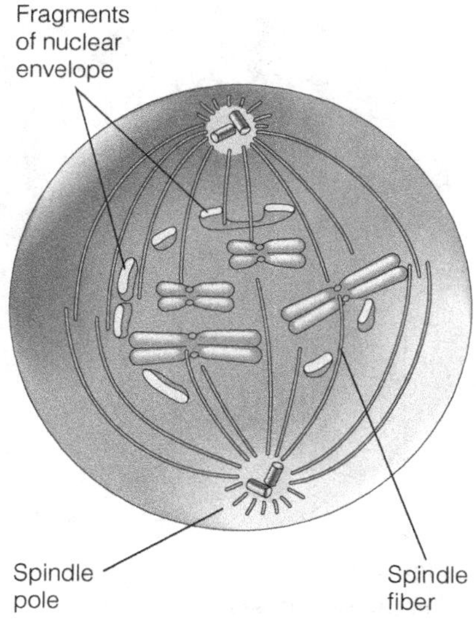

Figure 5.
Prometaphase mitosis.

Students often find it confusing to distinguish between chromosome number and chromatid number. To simplify this problem, count the number of centromeres. The number of centromeres represents the number of chromosomes. In your model, the pair of joined magnets represents one centromere.

3. To represent **metaphase,** a relatively static phase, leave the chromosomes with centromeres lying on the equator.

   In metaphase, duplicated chromosomes lie on the equator (also called the metaphase plate). The two sister chromatids are held together at the centromere. Metaphase ends as the centromere splits.

   Label Figure 6 with *chromosome, sister chromatids, spindle fibers, centrosome, centrioles, kinetochore, equator.*

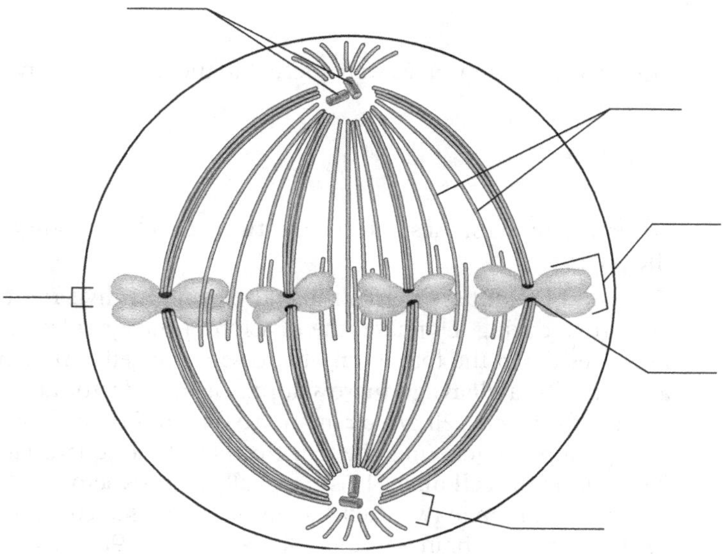

Figure 6.
The mitotic spindle at metaphase.

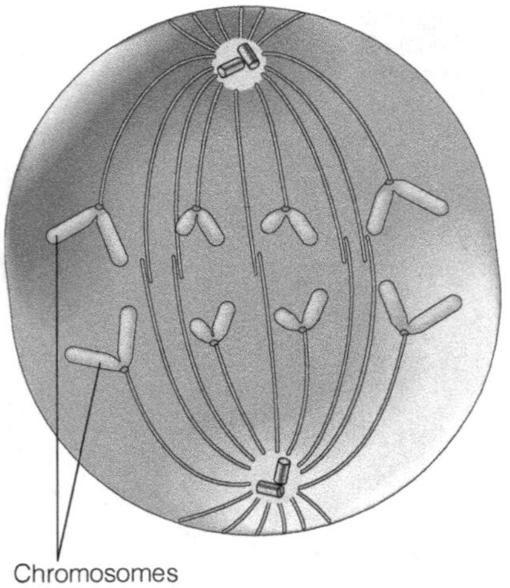

Figure 7.
Anaphase mitosis.

4. Holding on to the centromeres, pull the magnetic centromeres apart and move them toward opposite poles. This action represents **anaphase.**

   After the centromere splits, sister chromatids separate and begin to move toward opposite poles. Chromatids are now called **chromosomes.** Anaphase ends as the chromosomes reach the poles (Figure 7).

   Describe the movement of the chromosome arms as you move the centromeres to the poles.

   Certain biologists are currently investigating the role played by spindle fibers in chromosome movement toward the poles. Check your text for a discussion of one hypothesis, and briefly summarize it here.

5. Pile your chromosomes at the poles to represent **telophase.**

   As chromosomes reach the poles, anaphase ends and telophase begins. The spindle begins to break down. Chromosomes begin to uncoil, and nucleoli reappear. A nuclear envelope forms around each new cluster of chromosomes. Telophase ends when the nuclear envelopes are complete (Figure 8).

   How many chromosomes are in each new nucleus?

   How many chromosomes were present in the nucleus when the process began?

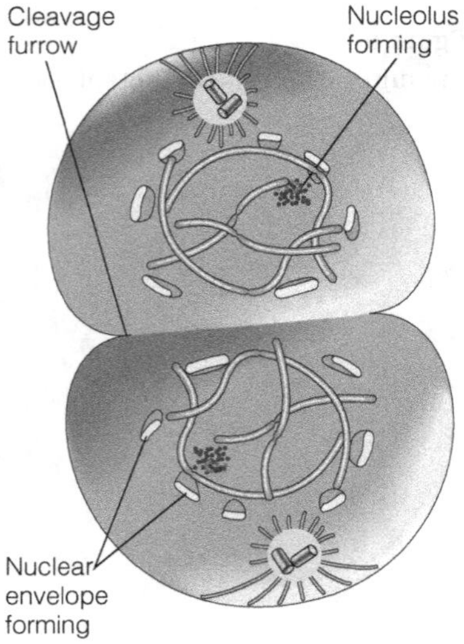

Figure 8.
Telophase mitosis.

6. To represent cytokinesis, leave the two new chromosome masses at the poles.

   The end of telophase marks the end of nuclear division, or mitosis. Sometime during telophase, the division of the cytoplasm, or cytokinesis, results in the formation of two separate cells. In cytokinesis in animal cells, a **cleavage furrow** forms at the equator and eventually pinches the parent cell cytoplasm in two (Figure 9a). In plant cells membrane-bound vesicles migrate to the center of the equatorial plane and fuse to form the **cell plate.** This eventually extends across the cell, dividing the cytoplasm in two. Cell wall materials are secreted into the space between the membranes of the cell plate (Figure 9b, c).

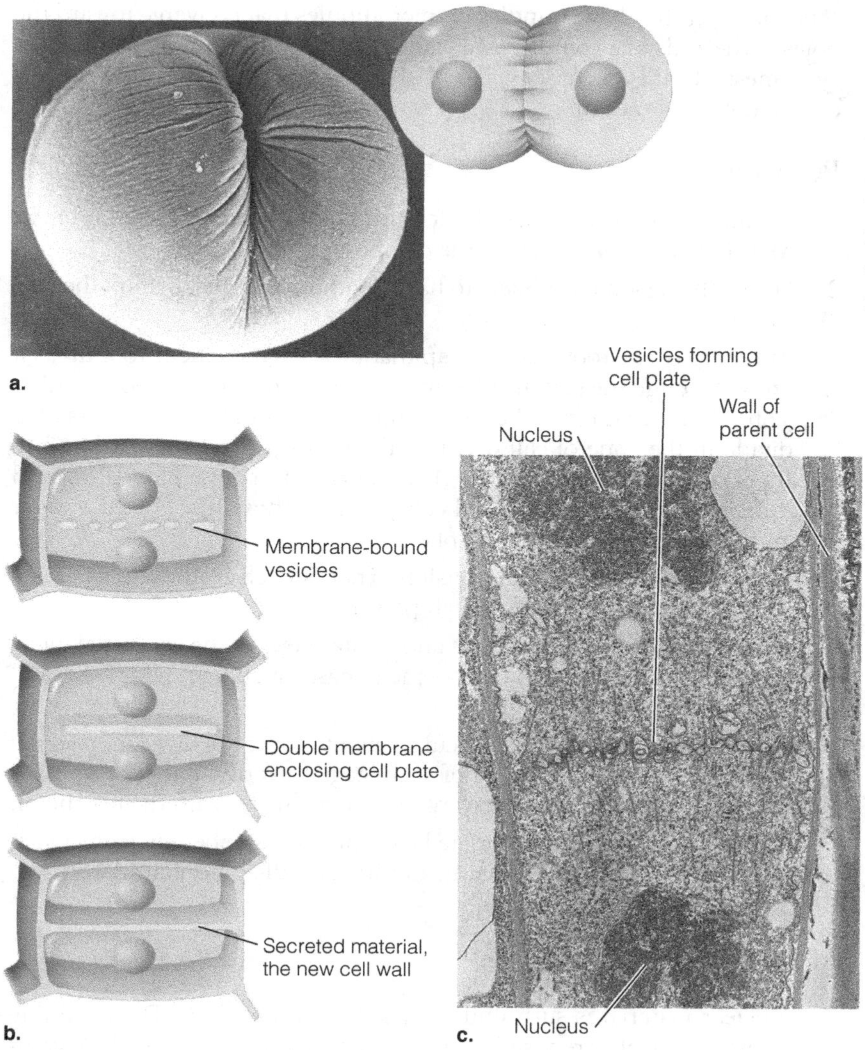

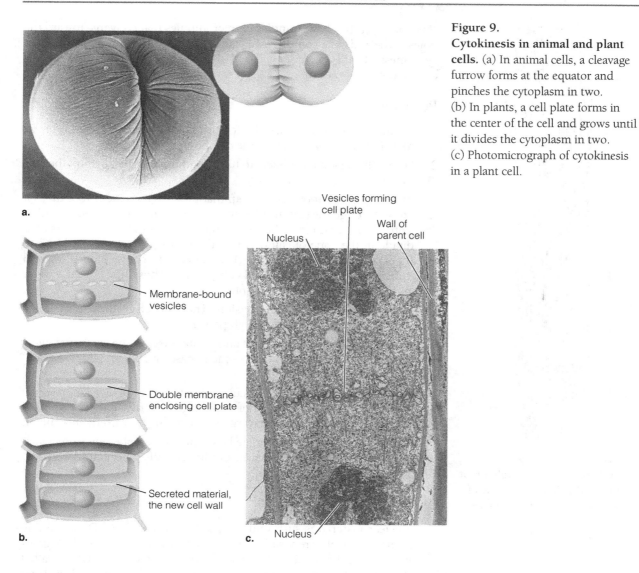

Figure 9.
Cytokinesis in animal and plant cells. (a) In animal cells, a cleavage furrow forms at the equator and pinches the cytoplasm in two.
(b) In plants, a cell plate forms in the center of the cell and grows until it divides the cytoplasm in two.
(c) Photomicrograph of cytokinesis in a plant cell.

EXERCISE 2

Observing Mitosis and Cytokinesis in Plant Cells

Materials

prepared slide of onion root tip
compound microscope

Introduction

The behavior of chromosomes during the cell cycle is similar in animal and plant cells. However, differences in cell division do exist. Plant cells have no

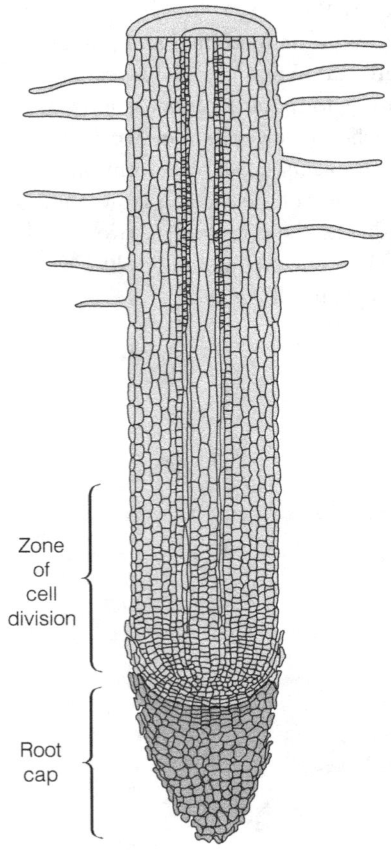

Figure 10.
Longitudinal section through a root tip. Cells are dividing in the zone of cell division just behind the root cap.

centrioles, yet they have bundles of microtubules that converge toward the poles at the ends of a spindle. Cell walls in plant cells dictate differences in cytokinesis. In this exercise, you will observe dividing cells in the zone of cell division of a root tip.

Procedure

1. Examine a prepared slide of a longitudinal section through an onion root tip using low power on the compound microscope.
2. Locate the region most likely to have dividing cells, just behind the root cap (Figure 10).

   At the tip of the root is a root cap that protects the tender root tip as it grows through the soil. Just behind the root cap is the zone of cell division. Notice that rows of cells extend upward from this zone. As cells divide in the zone of cell division, the root tip is pushed farther into the soil. Cells produced by division begin to mature, elongating and differentiating into specialized cells, such as those that conduct water and nutrients throughout the plant.
3. Focus on the zone of cell division. Then switch to the intermediate power, focus, and switch to high power.
4. Survey the zone of cell division and locate stages of the cell cycle: interphase, prophase, prometaphase, metaphase, anaphase, telophase, and cytokinesis.
5. As you find a dividing cell, speculate about its stage of division, read the following descriptions given of each stage to verify that your guess is correct, and, if necessary, confirm your conclusion with the instructor.
6. Draw the cell in the appropriate boxes provided. Label nucleus, nucleolus, chromosome, chromatin, mitotic spindle, and cell plate when appropriate.

Interphase (G_1, S, G_2)

Nuclear material is surrounded by a nuclear envelope. Dark-staining bodies, nucleoli, are visible. Chromosomes appear only as dark granules within the nucleus. Collectively, the chromosome mass is called *chromatin.* The chromosomes are not individually distinguishable because they are uncoiled into long, thin strands. Chromosomes are replicated during this phase.

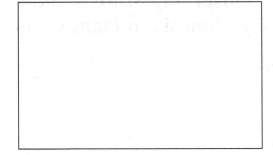

Prophase

Chromosomes begin to coil and become distinguishable thin, thread-like structures, widely dispersed in the nucleus during prophase. Although there are no centrioles in plant cells, a spindle begins to form. Nucleoli begin to disappear. The nuclear envelope is still intact.

Prometaphase

By prometaphase, the chromosomes are thick and short. Each chromosome is duplicated consisting of two chromatids held together by a centromere. The nuclear membrane breaks down in prometaphase. Chromosomes move toward the equator.

Metaphase

Metaphase begins when the centromeres of the chromosomes lie on the equator of the cell. The arms of the chromatids extend randomly in all directions. A spindle may be apparent. Spindle fibers are attached to centromeres and extend to the poles of the cell. As metaphase ends and anaphase begins, the centromeres split.

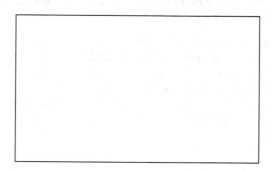

Anaphase

The splitting of centromeres marks the beginning of anaphase. Each former chromatid is now a new single chromosome. These chromosomes are drawn apart toward opposite poles of the cell. Anaphase ends when the migrating chromosomes reach their respective poles.

Telophase and Cytokinesis

Chromosomes have now reached the poles. The nuclear envelope re-forms around each compact mass of chromosomes. Nucleoli reappear. Chromosomes begin to uncoil and become indistinct. Cytokinesis is accomplished by the formation of a cell plate that begins in the center of the equatorial plane and grows outward to the cell wall.

EXERCISE 3

Observing Chromosomes, Mitosis, and Cytokinesis in Animal Cells

In this exercise, you will look at the general shape and form of human chromosomes and observe chromosomes and the stages of mitotic division in the whitefish. You will also compare these chromosomes with the plant chromosomes studied in Exercise 2. Chromosome structure in animals and plants is basically the same in that both have centromeres and arms. However, plant chromosomes are generally larger than animal chromosomes.

Lab Study A. Mitosis in Whitefish Blastula Cells

Materials

prepared slide of sections of whitefish blastulas
compound microscope

Introduction

The most convenient source of actively dividing cells in animals is the early embryo, where cells are large and divide rapidly with a short interphase. In blastulas (an early embryonic stage), a large percentage of cells will be dividing at any given time. By examining cross sections of whitefish blastulas, you should be able to locate many dividing cells in various stages of mitosis and cytokinesis.

Procedure

1. Examine a prepared slide of whitefish blastula cross sections. Find a blastula section on the lowest power, focus, switch to intermediate power, focus, and switch to high power.
2. As you locate a dividing cell, identify the stage of mitosis. *Be able to recognize all stages of mitosis in these cells.*
3. Identify the following in several cells:

   nucleus, nuclear envelope, and **nucleolus**

   chromosomes

   mitotic spindle

   asters—an array of microtubules surrounding each centriole pair at the poles of the spindle

   centrioles—small dots seen at the poles around which the microtubules of the spindle and asters appear to radiate

   cleavage furrow

Results

1. List several major differences you have observed between mitosis in animal cells and mitosis in plant cells:

2. Locate, draw, and label in the space provided a blastula cell in metaphase and a cell in telophase/cytokinesis to illustrate these differences.

Metaphase	Telophase/Cytokinesis

Lab Study B. Human Chromosomes in Dividing Leukocytes

Materials

slides of human leukocytes (white blood cells) on demonstration with compound microscopes

Introduction

Cytogeneticists examining dividing cells of humans can frequently detect chromosome abnormalities that lead to severe mental retardation. To examine human chromosomes, leukocytes are isolated from a small sample of the patient's blood and cultured in a medium that inhibits spindle formation during mitosis. As cells begin mitosis, chromosomes condense and become distinct, but in the absence of a spindle they cannot move to the poles in anaphase. You will observe a slide in which many cells have chromosomes condensed as in prometaphase or metaphase, but they are not aligned on a spindle equator.

Procedure

1. Attempt to count the chromosomes in one cell in the field of view. Normally, humans have 46 chromosomes. Persons with trisomy 21 (three copies of chromosome 21), or Down syndrome, have 47 chromosomes. Are the cells on this slide from a person with a normal chromosome number?

2. Notice that each chromosome is duplicated, being made up of two sister chromatids held together by a single centromere. In very high magnifications, bands can be seen on the chromosomes. Abnormalities in banding patterns can also be an indication of severe mental retardation.

EXERCISE 4

Modeling Meiosis

Materials

60 pop beads of one color
60 pop beads of another color
8 magnetic centromeres
4 centrioles
letters *B*, *D*, *b*, and *d* printed on mailing labels

Introduction

Meiosis takes place in all organisms that reproduce sexually. In animals, meiosis occurs in special cells of the gonads; in plants, in special cells of the sporangia. Meiosis consists of *two* nuclear divisions, **meiosis I** and **II**, with an atypical interphase between the divisions during which cells do not grow and synthesis of DNA does not take place. This means that meiosis I and II result in four cells from each parent cell, each containing half the number of chromosomes, one from each homologous pair. Recall that cells with only one of each homologous pair of chromosomes are haploid (n) cells. The parent cells, with pairs of homologous chromosomes, are diploid ($2n$). The haploid cells become sperm (in males), eggs (in females), or spores (in plants). One advantage of meiosis in sexually reproducing organisms is that it prevents the chromosome number from doubling with every generation when fertilization occurs.

What would be the consequences in successive generations of offspring if the chromosome number were not reduced during meiosis?

Lab Study A. Interphase

Working with another student, you will build a model of the nucleus of a cell in interphase before meiosis. Nuclear and chromosome activities are similar to those in mitosis. You and your partner should discuss activities in the nucleus and chromosomes in each stage. Go through the exercise once together, and then demonstrate the model to each other to reinforce your understanding. Compare activities in meiosis with those in mitosis as you build your model.

Procedure

1. Build the premeiotic interphase nucleus much as you did the mitotic interphase nucleus. Have two pairs of chromosomes ($2n = 4$) of distinctly different sizes and different centromere positions. Have one member of each pair of homologues be one color, the other, a different color.
2. To represent G_1 (gap 1), pile your four chromosomes in the center of your work area. The chromosomes are decondensed.

   Cell activities in G_1 are similar to those activities in G_1 of the interphase before mitosis.

   In G_1, are chromosomes single or duplicated?

3. Duplicate the chromosomes to represent DNA duplication in the S (synthesis) phase. Recall that in living cells, the centromeres remain single, but in your model you must use two magnets. What color should the sister chromatids be for each pair?

4. Duplicate the centriole pair.
5. Leave the chromosomes piled in the center of the work area to represent G_2 (gap 2).

   As in mitosis, in G_2 the cell prepares for meiosis by synthesizing proteins and enzymes necessary for nuclear division.

Lab Study B. Meiosis I

Meiosis consists of two consecutive nuclear divisions, called *meiosis I* and *meiosis II.* As the first division begins, the chromosomes coil and condense, as in mitosis. Meiosis I is radically different from mitosis, however, and the differences immediately become apparent. In your modeling, as you detect the differences, make notes in the margin of your lab manual.

Procedure

1. Meiosis I begins with the chromosomes piled in the center of your work area.

   As chromosomes begin to coil and condense, prophase I begins. Each chromosome is duplicated, made up of two sister chromatids. Two pairs of centrioles are located outside the nucleus.
2. Separate the two centriole pairs and move them to opposite poles of the nucleus.

   The nuclear envelope breaks down and the spindle begins to form as in mitosis.
3. Move each homologous chromosome to pair with its partner. You should have four strands together.

   Early in prophase I, each chromosome finds its homologue and pairs in a tight association. The process of pairing is called **synapsis.** Because the chromosomes are duplicated, this means that each paired duplicated chromosome complex is made of four strands. This complex is called a **tetrad.**

   How many tetrad complexes do you have in your cell, which is $2n = 4$?
4. Represent the phenomenon of **crossing over** by detaching and exchanging identical segments of any two nonsister chromatids in a tetrad.

   Crossing over takes place between nonsister chromatids in the tetrad. In this process, a segment from one chromatid will break and exchange with the exact same segment on a nonsister chromatid in the tetrad. The crossover site forms a **chiasma** (plural, **chiasmata**).
5. Return the exchanged segments of chromosome to their original chromosomes before performing the crossing-over activity in the next step.

   Genes (traits) are often expressed in different forms. For example, when the gene for seed color is expressed in pea plants, the seed may be green or yellow. Alternative forms of genes are called **alleles.** Green and yellow are alleles of the seed-color gene. It is significant that crossing over produces new allelic combinations among genes along a chromatid. To see how new allelic combinations are produced, proceed to step 6.

6. Using the letters printed on mailing labels, label one bead (gene locus) on each chromatid of one chromosome *B* for brown hair color. Label the beads in the same position on the two chromatids of the other member of the homologous pair *b* for blond hair color.

   The *B* and *b* represent alleles, or alternate forms of the gene for hair color.

   On the chromatids with the *B* allele, label another gene *D* for dark eye color. On the other member of the homologous pair of chromosomes, label the same gene *d* for pale eyes. In other words, one chromosome will have *BD*, the other chromosome, *bd* (Figure 11).

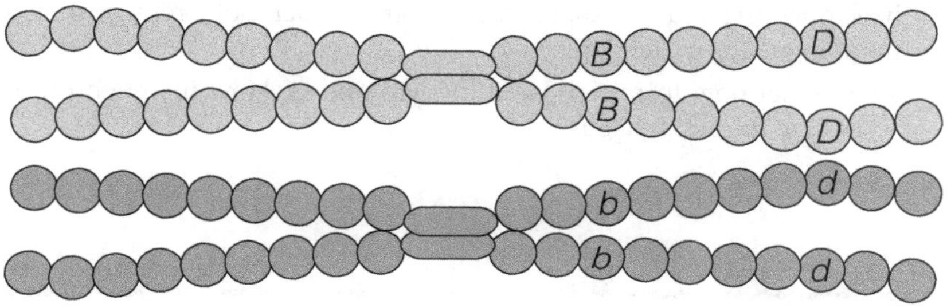

Figure 11.
Arrangement of alleles *B*, *b*, *D*, and *d* on chromosome models. One duplicated homologous chromosome has *B* alleles and *D* alleles on each chromatid. The other has *b* and *d* alleles on each chromatid.

7. Have a single crossover take place involving only two of the four chromatids between the loci for hair color and eye color. Remember, the crossover must take place between nonsister chromatids.

   What combinations of alleles are now present on the chromatids?

8. Confirm your results with your laboratory instructor.

If you are having difficulty envisioning the activities of chromosomes in prophase I and understanding their significance, discuss these events with your lab partner and, if needed, ask questions of your lab instructor before proceeding to the next stage of meiosis I.

---

9. Move your tetrads to the equator, midway between the two poles.

   Late in prophase I, tetrads move to the equator.

10. To represent metaphase I, leave the tetrads lying at the equator.

    During this phase, tetrads lie on the equatorial plane. *Centromeres do not split as they do in mitosis.*

11. To represent anaphase I, separate each duplicated chromosome from its homologue, and move one homologue toward each pole. In our model, the two magnets in sister chromatids represent one centromere holding together the two sister chromatids of the chromosome.

    How does the structure of chromosomes in anaphase I differ from that in anaphase in mitosis?

12. To represent telophase I, place the chromosomes at the poles. You should have one long and one short chromosome at each pole, representing a homologue from each pair.

    Two nuclei now form, followed by cytokinesis. How many chromosomes are in each nucleus?

The number of chromosomes is equal to the number of centromeres. In this model, two magnets represent one centromere in duplicated chromosomes.

Would you describe the new nuclei as being diploid ($2n$) or haploid (n)?

How has crossing over changed the combination of alleles in the new nuclei?

Are both red chromosomes in the same nucleus? Compare your results with others.

13. To represent meiotic interphase, leave the chromosomes in the two piles formed at the end of meiosis I.

    The interphase between meiosis I and meiosis II is usually short. There is little cell growth and no synthesis of DNA. All the machinery for a second nuclear division is synthesized, however.

14. Duplicate the centriole pairs.

Lab Study C. Meiosis II

The events that take place in meiosis II are similar to the events of mitosis. Meiosis I results in two nuclei with half the number of chromosomes as the parent cell, but the chromosomes are duplicated (made of two chromatids), just as they are at the beginning of mitosis. The events in meiosis II must change duplicated chromosomes into single chromosomes. As meiosis II begins, two new spindles begin to form, establishing the axes for the dispersal of chromosomes to each new nucleus.

Procedure

1. To represent prophase II, separate the centrioles and set up the axes of the two new spindles. Pile the chromosomes in the center of each spindle.

   The events that take place in each of the nuclei in prophase II are similar to those of a mitosis prophase. In each new cell the centrioles move to the poles, nucleoli break down, the nuclear envelope breaks down, and a new spindle forms. The new spindle forms at a right angle to the axis of the spindle in meiosis I.
2. Align the chromosomes at the equator of their respective spindles.

   As the chromosomes reach the equator, prophase II ends and metaphase II begins.
3. Leave the chromosomes on the equator to represent metaphase II.
4. Pull the two magnets of each duplicated chromosome apart.

   As metaphase II ends, the centromeres finally split and anaphase II begins.
5. Separate sister chromatids (now chromosomes) and move them to opposite poles.

   In anaphase II, single chromosomes move to the poles.
6. Pile the chromosomes at the poles.

   As telophase II begins, chromosomes arrive at the poles. Spindles break down. Nucleoli reappear. Nuclear envelopes form around each bunch of chromosomes as the chromosomes uncoil. Cytokinesis follows meiosis II.

   a. What is the total number of nuclei and cells now present?

   b. How many chromosomes are in each?

   c. How many cells were present when the entire process began?

   d. How many chromosomes were present per cell when the entire process began?

e. How many of the cells formed by the meiotic division just modeled are genetically identical? (Assume that alternate forms of genes exist on homologues.)

f. Explain your results in terms of independent assortment and crossing over. (Refer to your textbook.)

Results

Summarize the major differences between mitosis and meiosis in Table 1.

Table 1
Comparing Nuclear and Chromosomal Activities in Mitosis and Meiosis

	Mitosis	**Meiosis**
Synapsis		
Crossing over		
When centromeres split		
Chromosome structure and movement during anaphase		
No. of divisions		
No. of cells resulting		
No. of chromosomes in daughter cells		
Genetic similarity of daughter cells to parent cells		

EXERCISE 5
Meiosis in *Sordaria fimicola:* A Study of Crossing Over

Materials

petri dish containing mycelia resulting from a cross between *Sordaria* with black and tan spores
slides and coverslips
dropper bottles of water
matches
wire bacterial transfer loop
alcohol lamp

Introduction

In the study of meiosis, you demonstrated that genetic recombination may occur as a result of the exchange of genetic material between homologous chromosomes in the process of crossing over. Crossing over occurs during prophase I, when homologous chromosomes synapse. While they are joined in this complex, nonsister chromatids may break at corresponding points and exchange parts. A point at which they appear temporarily joined as a result of this exchange is called a **chiasma** (Figure 12).

Sordaria fimicola is a fungus that spends most of its life as a haploid **mycelium,** a mass of cells arranged in filaments. When conditions are favorable, cells of filaments from two different mating types fuse (see Figures 13a and b); ultimately, the nuclei fuse (Figure 13c) and $2n$ zygotes are produced, each inside a structure called an **ascus** (plural, **asci**) (Figure 13d). Asci are protected within a **perithecium.** Each $2n$ zygote undergoes meiosis, and the resulting cells (ascospores) remain aligned, the position of an ascospore within the ascus depending on the orientation of separating chromosomes on the equatorial plane of meiosis I. After meiosis, each resulting ascospore divides once by mitosis (Figure 13e), resulting in eight ascospores per ascus (Figure 13f). This unique sequence of events means that it is easy to detect the occurrence of crossing over involving chromatids carrying alleles that encode for color of spores and mycelia.

If two mating types of *Sordaria,* one with black spores and the other with tan spores, are grown on the same petri dish, mycelia from the two may

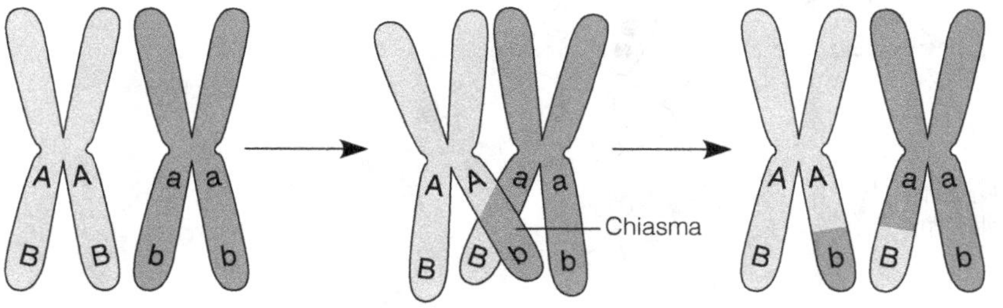

Figure 12.
Crossing over. Chromatid arms break and rejoin with a nonsister member of the tetrad, forming a chiasma between nonsister chromatids. This process results in the exchange of genetic material.

Figure 13.
Abbreviated diagram of the life cycle of *Sordaria fimicola.*
(a) Cells from filaments of two different mating types fuse.
(b) One cell with two nuclei is formed.
(c) The two nuclei fuse, forming a 2*n* zygote. (d) The zygote nucleus begins meiosis, and an ascus begins to form in a perithecium. (e) Meiosis continues, followed by mitosis.
(f) The mature ascus contains eight ascospores. (g) Micrograph of crushed perithecium with asci containing ascospores.

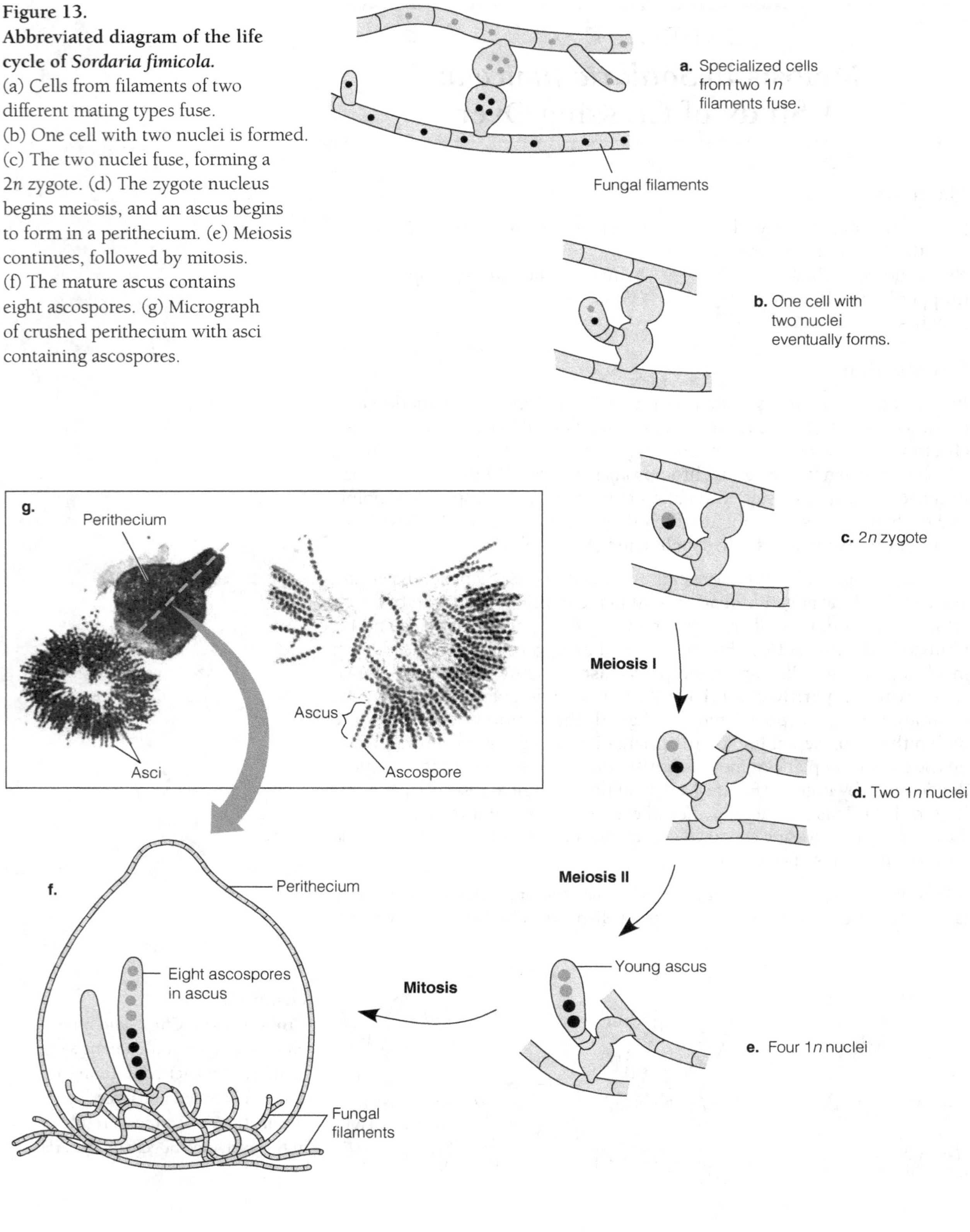

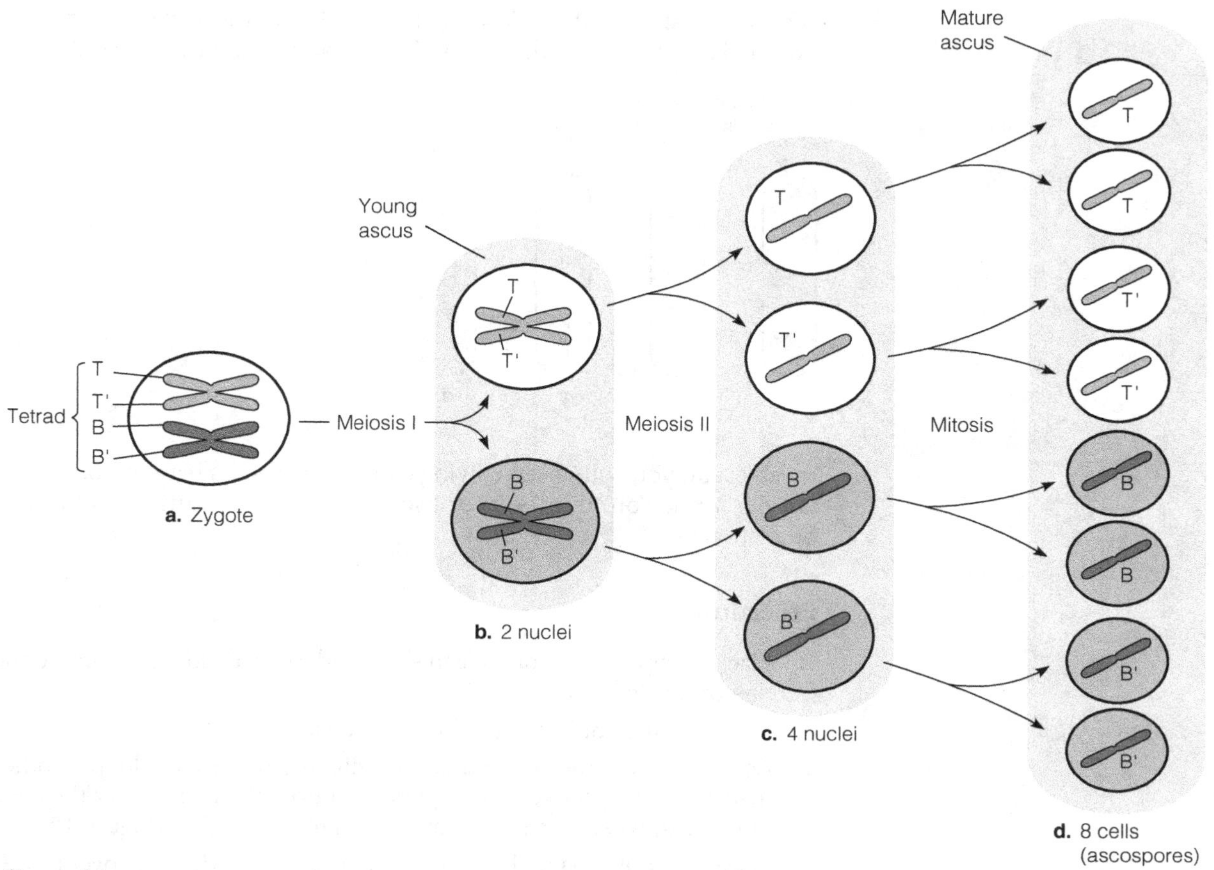

Figure 14.
Arrangement of spores in asci resulting from a cross between fungi with black spores and fungi with tan spores when no crossing over takes place. (a) In the zygote nucleus, the light homologous chromosome has chromatids labeled T and T′. Each chromatid has identical tan alleles for spore color. The dark homologous chromosome (chromatids labeled B and B′) has black alleles. (b) During meiosis I, the two homologous chromosomes separate into two different nuclei retained in one developing ascus. (c) Meiosis II produces four nuclei, two containing a chromosome with the tan allele and two containing a chromosome with the black allele, still within the one ascus. (d) Now each nucleus divides by mitosis, followed by cytokinesis, resulting in eight cells, called ascospores. The ascus now contains eight ascospores. Four of the spores have the tan allele in their nuclei and appear tan-colored. Four ascospores have the black allele and appear black.

grow together, and certain cells may fuse. Nuclei from two fused cells then fuse, and the resulting zygote contains one chromosome carrying the allele for black spores and another carrying the allele for tan spores. After meiosis takes place, one mitosis follows, and the result is eight ascospores in one ascus: four black spores and four tan spores. If no crossing over has taken place, the arrangement of spores will appear as in Figure 14.

If crossing over does take place, the arrangement of spores will differ. In the spaces provided, using Figure 14 as a reference, draw diagrams that illustrate the *predicted* arrangement of spores in the ascus when crossing over takes place between the following chromatids and the alleles for color are exchanged: (a) T and B, (b) T and B′, (c) T′ and B, and (d) T′ and B′.

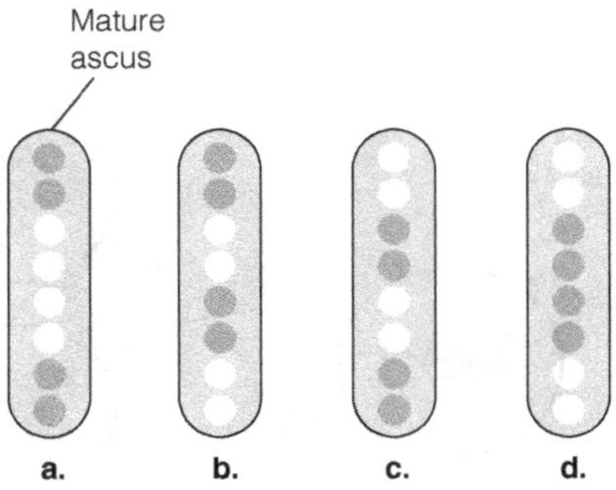

In lab today, you will observe living cultures of crosses between black and tan *Sordaria*. You will look for asci with spores arranged as in your predictions.

Procedure

1. Place a drop of water on a clean slide, and carry it and a coverslip to the demonstration table.
2. Light the alcohol lamp and flame a transfer loop.
3. Open the lid of the *Sordaria* culture slightly, and use the loop or other instrument to remove several perithecia from the region near the edge of the dish where the two strains have grown together (Figure 15).
4. Place the perithecia in the drop of water on your slide, and cover it with the coverslip.
5. Return to your work area.
6. Using the eraser end of a pencil, tap lightly on the coverslip to break open and flatten out the perithecia.
7. Systematically scan back and forth across the slide using the intermediate power of the compound microscope. When you locate clusters of asci, focus, switch to high power, count the asci, and determine if crossing over has taken place. Record your numbers in Table 2.

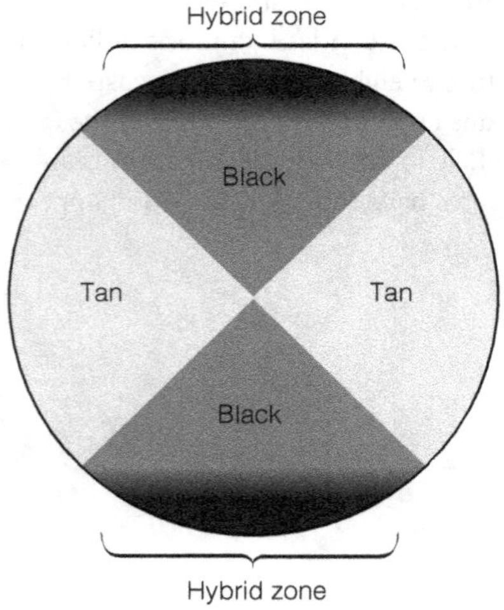

Figure 15.
Most likely location for perithecia containing asci with hybrid spores. Following the procedure, collect dark, round perithecia from zones of hybridization along the petri dish perimeter as indicated.

Results

In Table 2, record the numbers of asci with (a) spores all of one color (indicating that the zygote was formed by fusion of cells of the same strain), (b) black and tan spores with no crossover, and (c) black and tan spores with a crossover.

Table 2
Numbers of Asci in Each Category

Spores all one color	
Crossover absent	
Crossover present	

Discussion

1. What percentage of asci observed resulted from the fusion of cells from different strains?

2. What percentage of those asci resulting from the fusion of different strains demonstrates crossovers?

Questions for Review

1. Define the following terms and use each in a meaningful sentence. Give examples when appropriate.

   mitosis, meiosis, cytokinesis, chromosome, chromatin, centromere, centriole, centrosome, kinetochore, spindle, aster, homologous chromosome, synaptonemal complex, synapsis, tetrad, chiasma, sister chromatid, nucleolus, cell plate, cleavage furrow, diploid, haploid, crossing over, mycelium, perithecium, ascus

2. Describe the activity of chromosomes in each stage of mitosis.

3. In the photomicrograph of dividing root cells at right, identify interphase and the following phases of mitosis: prophase, metaphase, anaphase, telophase, and cytokinesis.

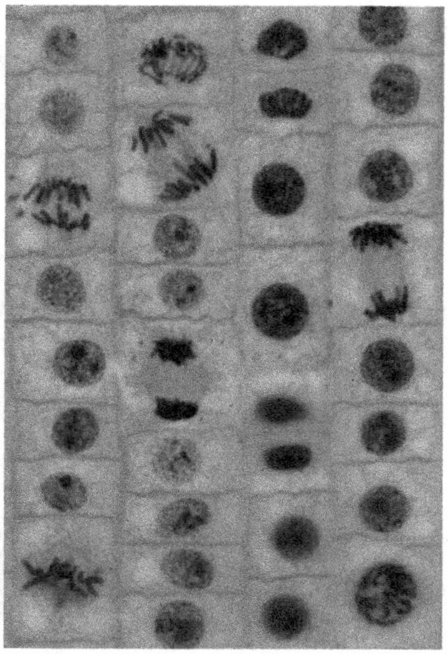

4. Describe the activity of chromosomes in each stage of meiosis I and meiosis II.

5. Observe the drawing of several phases of meiosis below.
   a. Using the designated letters, list the phases of meiosis in sequence.

   b. Label each stage (include I or II).
   c. At what stage would crossing over occur?
   d. What is the diploid number for this organism?

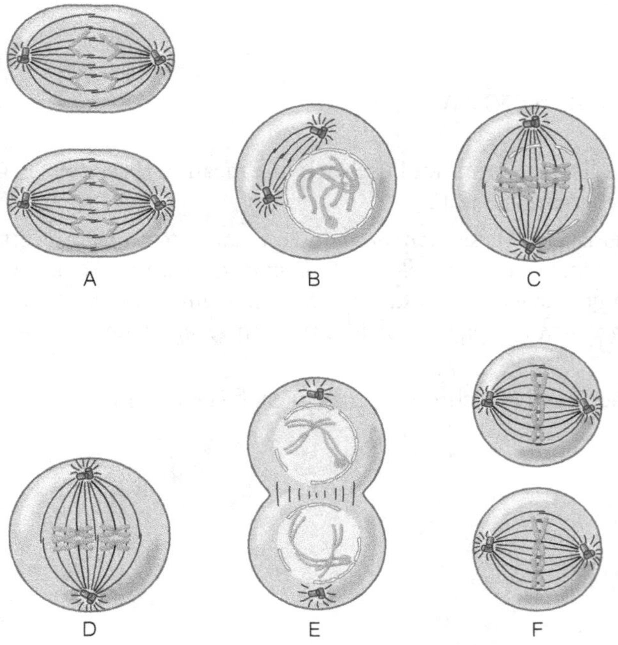

6. Provide examples of specific plant and animal cells that typically undergo mitosis. Provide examples for meiosis.

Applying Your Knowledge

1. What advantage does the process of crossing over bring to reproduction?

2. Can you think of any way in which new gene combinations resulting from crossovers might be disadvantageous?

3. Explain why models are important to scientific study of biological systems. Provide two examples of models other than those described in the exercises.

4. Why would the method of cytokinesis in animal cells not work in plant cells?

5. Two natural plant products, vinblastine from the rosy periwinkle and paclitaxel (taxol) from the Pacific yew, have been used successfully in the treatment of a wide range of cancers. These chemicals work by interfering with mitosis but by different methods. Vinblastine inhibits mitosis by preventing the assembly of the spindle. Paclitaxel promotes microtubule synthesis and binds to the microtubles preventing the depolymerization (disassembly) of the spindle during mitosis. Based on your knowledge of mitosis, at what phase do you expect cell division to be interrupted by each of these cancer-fighting compounds? Explain your answer based on the activities occurring at the mitotic stage.

6. In 1998, Dr. Patricia Hunt recognized a striking increase in the number of abnormal chromosomes in the mice eggs she was studying. The lab animals generally have an abnormality rate of only 1–2%. Dr. Hunt found that in 40% of the eggs in her mice, the chromosomes failed to attach to the spindle. The apparent cause was a chemical—bisphenol A (BPA)—that leached from the plastic animal cages after they were washed with an alkaline detergent. Based on your understanding of meiosis, what do you think would be the effect of this chemical on the number of chromosomes in the egg cells?

7. Identical twins Jan and Fran were very close sisters. So, when Jan died suddenly, Fran moved in to help take care of Jan's daughter (her niece),

Millie. Some time later Fran married her brother-in-law and became Millie's stepmother. When Fran announced that she was pregnant, poor Millie became confused and curious. "So," Millie asked, "who is this baby? Will she be my twin? Will she be my sister, my stepsister, my cousin?" Can you answer her questions? What is the genetic relationship between Millie and the baby? What processes are involved in the formation of gametes and how do they affect genetic variation?

Investigative Extensions

Additional investigations of cell reproduction can be pursued online at the University of Arizona Biology Project web site. "Online Onion Root Tips," is an investigation of onion root tip mitosis. Using digitized photomicrographs students determine relative durations of phases of the cell cycle. Available at http://www.biology.arizona.edu/cell_bio/activities/cell_cycle/cell_cycle.html

"Karyotyping Activity" uses photomicrographs of actual human chromosomes to develop Karyotypes and investigate human disorders. Available at http://www.biology.arizona.edu/human_bio/activities/karyotyping/karyotyping.html

References

Becker, W. M., L. Kleinsmith, and J. Hardin. *The World of the Cell*, 5th ed. Redwood City, CA: Benjamin Cummings, 2003.

Bold, H. C., C. J. Alexopoulos, and T. Delevoryas. *Morphology of Plants and Fungi.* New York: Harper & Row, 1980.

Costello, M. and K. Kellmel. "Medical Attributes of *Taxus brevifolia*—The Pacific Yew" [online] available at http://wilkesl.wilkes.edu/~kklemow/Taxus.html, 2003.

Hunt, P. A., K. E. Koehler, M. Susiarjo, C. A. Hodges, A.Ilagan, R. C. Voigt, S. Thomas, B. F. Thomas, and T. Hassold. "Bisphenol A Exposure Causes Meiotic Aneuploidy in the Female Mouse." *Current Biology*, 2003, 13:546–553.

Olive, L. S. "Genetics of *Sordaria fimicola*. I. Ascospore color mutants." *American Journal of Botany* 43:97, 1956.

Snyder, Lucy. "Pharmacology of Vinblastine, Vincristine Vindesine and Vinorelbine." *Cyberbotanica.* [online] available at http://biotech.icmb.utexas.edu/botany/vvv.html, 2004.

Websites

Additional resources for the cell cycle and mitosis:

http://www.cellsalive.com/cellcycle.html
http://www.cellsalive.com/mitosis.html

Animation of meiosis and independent assortment:

http://www.csuchico.edu/~Bio/207/animations/assortment.html

Description of the cell cycle and mitosis, relating these processes to cancer:

http://cancerquest.emory.edu

Experiment

Genetics

Supplies ▶ Materials Needed

Compound Microscope

Lens paper

Glass slides

Cover slips

Toothpicks

Fixative (10% formalin in 100% alcohol; final formalin in concentration = 4%)

Giemsa stain (stock solution; Harelco #620)

Coplin jars

Nutrient culture media—Bacto phytohemagglutinin M & P

Phenistix

PTC (phenylthiocarbamide) paper

PTT (phenylthiourea) solution—5%

Genetic corn—Carolina Biological Supply Company

Stilling or Ishihara color charts

Introduction ▶

Genetics (je-NET-iks) is the branch of biology that studies inheritance. ***Inheritance*** is the passage of hereditary traits from one generation to another. It is through the passage of hereditary traits that you acquired your characteristics from your parents and will transmit your characteristics to your children. If all individuals were brown-eyed, we could learn nothing of the hereditary basis of eye color. However, because some people are blue-eyed and marry brown-eyed people, we can gain some knowledge of how hereditary traits are transmitted. We constantly analyze the genetic bases of the *differences* between individuals. Some of these differences occur normally, such as differences in eye color, blood groups, or ability to taste PTC (phenylthiocarbamide). Other differences are abnormal, such as physical abnormalities and abnormalities in the processes of metabolism.

Genotype and Phenotype

▶ The vast majority of human cells, except gametes, contain 23 pairs of chromosomes (diploid number) in their nuclei. One chromosome from each pair comes from the mother, and the other comes from the father. The two chromosomes that belong to a pair are called ***homologous*** (hō-MOL-ō-gus) ***chromosomes***, and these homologues contain genes that control the same traits. The homologue of a chromosome that contains a gene for height also contains a gene for height.

Figure 1 Inheritance of phenylketonuria (PKU).

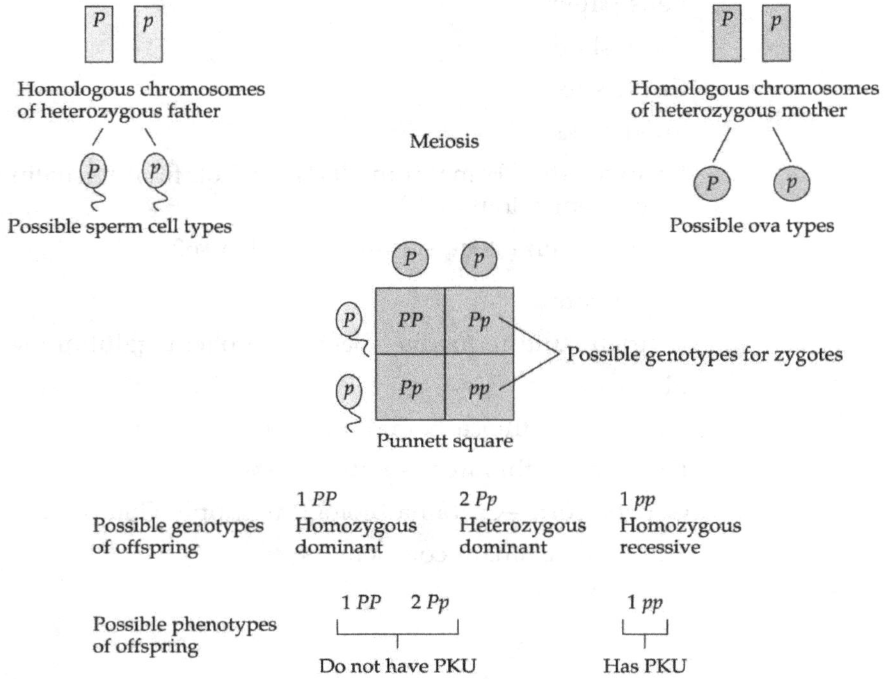

The relationship of genes to heredity can be illustrated by the disorder called ***phenylketonuria***, or ***PKU*** (see Figure 1). People with PKU are unable to manufacture the enzyme phenylalanine hydroxylase. Current belief is that PKU results from the presence of an abnormal gene symbolized as *p*. The normal gene is symbolized as *P*. *P* and *p* are said to be alleles. An ***allele*** is one of many alternative forms of a gene, occupying the same ***locus*** (position of a gene on a chromosome) inhomologous chromosomes. The chromosome that has the gene that directs phenylalanine hydroxylase production will have either *p* or *P* on it. Its homologue will also have either *p* or *P*. Thus every individual will have one of the following genetic makeups, or ***genotypes*** (JĒ-nō-tīps): *PP*, *Pp*, or *pp*. Although people

Table 1 Selected Hereditary Traits in Humans

Dominant	Recessive
Coarse body hair	Fine body hair
Male pattern baldness	Baldness
Normal skin pigmentation	Albinism
Freckles	Absence of freckles
Astigmatism	Normal vision
Near- or farsightedness	Normal vision
Normal hearing	Deafness
Broad lips	Thin lips
Tongue roller	Inability to roll tongue into a U shape
PTC taster	PTC nontaster
Large eyes	Small eyes
Polydactylism (extra digits)	Normal digits
Brachydactylism (short digits)	Normal digits
Syndactylism (webbed digits)	Normal digits
Feet with normal arches	Flat feet
Hypertension	Normal blood pressure
Diabetes insipidus	Normal excretion
Huntington's chorea	Normal nervous system
Normal mentality	Schizophrenia
Migraine headaches	Normal
Widow's peak	Straight hairline
Curved (hyperextended) thumb	Straight thumb
Normal Cl^- transport	Cystic fibrosis
Hypercholesterolemia (familial)	Normal cholesterol level

with genotypes of *Pp* have the abnormal gene, only those with genotype *pp* suffer from the disorder because the normal gene masks the abnormal one. A gene that masks the expression of its allele is called the ***dominant gene***, and the trait expressed is said to be a dominant trait. The homologous gene that is masked is called the ***recessive gene***. The trait expressed when two recessive genes are present is called the recessive trait. Several dominant and recessive traits inherited in human beings are listed in Table 1.

Traditionally, the dominant gene is symbolized with a capital letter and the recessive one with a lowercase letter. When the same genes appear on homologous chromosomes, as in *PP* or *pp*, the person is said to be ***homozygous*** for a trait. When the genes on homologous chromosomes are different, however, as in *Pp*, the person is said to be ***heterozygous*** for the trait. ***Phenotype*** (FĒ-nō-tīp; *pheno* = showing) refers to how the genetic composition is expressed in the body. An individual with *Pp* has a different genotype from one with *PP*, but both have the same phenotype—which in this case is normal production of phenylalanine hydroxylase.

Punnett Squares

To determine how gametes containing haploid chromosomes unite to form diploid fertilized eggs, special charts called ***Punnett squares*** are used. The Punnett square is merely a device that helps one visualize all the possible combinations of male and female gametes, and is invaluable as a learning exercise in genetics. Usually, the possible paternal alleles in sperm cells are placed at the side of the chart and the possible maternal alleles in secondary oocytes are placed at the top (Figure 1). The spaces in the chart represent the possible genotypes for that trait in fertilized ova formed by the union of the male and female gametes. Possible combinations are determined simply by dropping the female gamete on the left into the two boxes below it and dropping the female gamete on the right into the two spaces under it. The upper male gamete is then moved across to the two spaces in line with it, and the lower male gamete is moved across to the two spaces in line with it.

Sex Inheritance

Lining up human chromosomes in pairs reveals that the last pair (the twenty-third pair) differs in males and in females (Figure 2). In females, the pair consists of two rod-shaped chromosomes designated as X chromosomes. One X chromosome is also present in males, but its mate is hook-shaped and called a Y chromosome. The XX pair in the female and the XY pair in the male are called the ***sex chromosomes***, and all other pairs of chromosomes are called ***autosomes***.

Figure 2 Inheritance of sex. Note the sex chromosomes, X and Y. Human male chromosomes

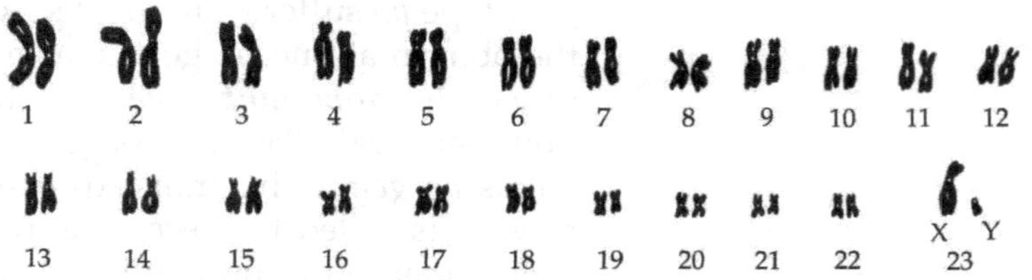

The sex of an individual is determined by the sex chromosomes (Figure 3). When a spermatocyte undergoes meiosis to reduce its chromosome number from diploid to haploid, one daughter cell will contain the X chromosome and the other will contain the Y chromosome. When the secondary oocyte is fertilized by an X-bearing sperm, the offspring normally will be a female (XX). Fertilization by a Y sperm cell normally produces a male (XY).

Figure 3 Inheritance of sex. Sex determination

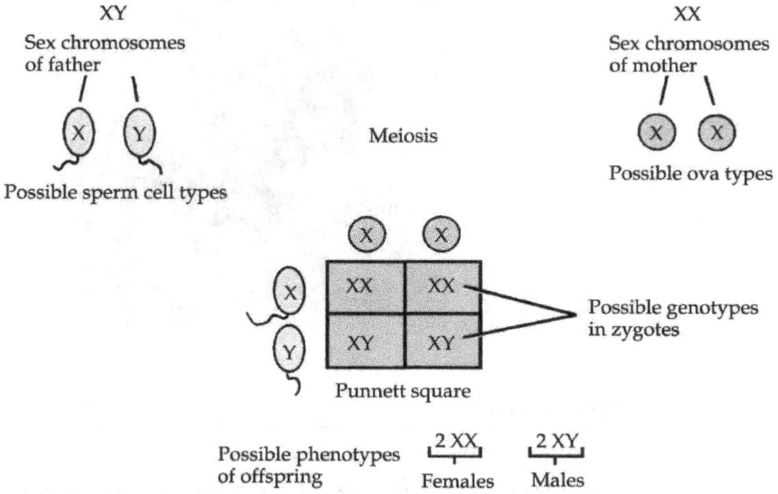

Sometimes chromosomes fail to move toward opposite poles of a cell in meiotic anaphase. This is called ***nondisjunction*** and results in one sex cell having two members of a chromosome pair while the other receives none. Thus, eggs can contain two X's or no X (symbolized as 0), and sperm cells may contain both an X and a Y chromosome, two X's or two Y's, or no sex chromosomes at all.

Because the X chromosome contains so many genes unrelated to sex that are necessary for development, a zygote must contain at least one X chromosome to survive. Thus, Y0 and YY zygotes do not develop. However, other zygotes with sex chromosome anomalies do develop. Examples are Turner's syndrome (the presence of only one X chromosome, X0) and Kleinfelter's syndrome (an extra Y chromosome, XYY).

"Extra" X chromosomes (more than two in the female and more than one in the male) have a surprisingly minor effect on the individual, compared with the significant effect of other additional chromosomes. Studies show that only one X chromosome is active in any cell. Any additional X chromosomes are randomly inactivated early in development and do not express the genes contained on them.

These inactivated X chromosomes remain tightly coiled against the cell membrane and can be seen as what are called ***Barr bodies*** (Figure 4). Since XY males do not have inactivated X chromosomes, no Barr bodies will be seen in normal male cells.

Figure 4 Barr body in cell from buccal mucosa of human female. Feulgen stain; magnification ×300.

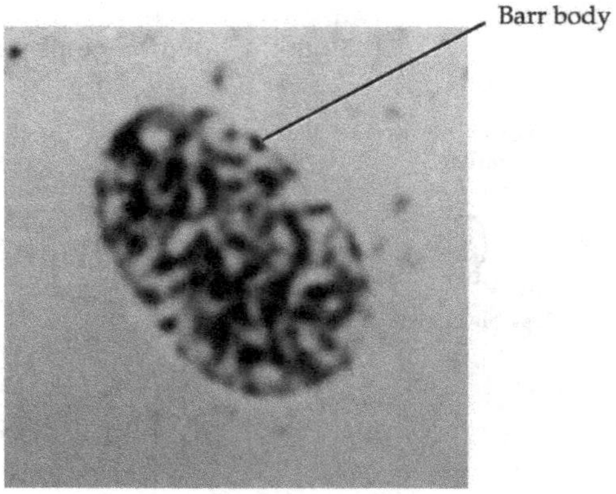

Procedure

1. Make a buccal smear by *gently* scraping the inside of your cheek with the flat end of a toothpick. Discard the toothpick and *gently* scrape the same area again. This will produce more live cells from a deeper layer of the epithelium of the mucous membrane.
2. Spread the material over a clean glass slide.
3. Promptly place the slide in a Coplin jar filled with fixative for 1 min.
4. Remove the slide and wash gently under running tap water.
5. Place the slide in a Coplin jar filled with Giemsa stain for 10 to 20 min. Fresh solutions of stain prepared within 2 hr require 10 min; older stains require a longer time.
6. Wash the slide *gently* under running water and air-dry.
7. Examine the slide under high power and look for interphase nuclei. Identify Barr bodies, small disc-shaped chromatin bodies lying against the nuclear membrane (see Figure 4). Depending on the position of the nuclei and the staining technique, Barr bodies should be seen in 30 to 70% of the cells of a normal female.
8. Examine a slide prepared from the buccal epithelium of a class member not of your sex.
9. Draw a cell containing a Barr body in the space provided.

Barr body

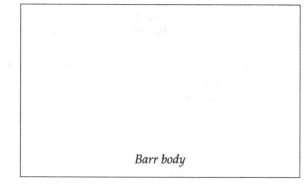

Sex-Linked Inheritance

▶ As do the other 22 pairs of chromosomes, the sex chromosomes contain genes that are responsible for the transmission of a number of nonsexual traits. Genes for these traits appear on X chromosomes, but many of these genes are absent from Y chromosomes. Traits transmitted by genes on the X chromosome are called ***sex-linked traits***. This pattern of heredity is different from the pattern described earlier. About 150 sex-linked traits are known in humans. Examples of sex-linked traits are red–green color blindness and hemophilia.

Red–Green Color Blindness

Let us consider the most common type of color blindness, called red–green color blindness. In this condition, there is a deficiency in either red or green cones and red and green are seen as the same color, either red or green, depending on which cone is present. The gene for ***red–green color blindness*** is a recessive one designated *c*. Normal color vision, designated *C*, dominates. The *C*/*c* genes are located on the X chromosome. The Y chromosome does not contain these genes. Thus the ability to see colors depends entirely on the X chromosomes. The possible combinations are:

Genotype	**Phenotype**
X^CX^C	Normal female
X^CX^c	Normal female (carrying the recessive gene)
X^cX^c	Red–green color-blind female
X^C Y	Normal male
X^cY	Red–green color-blind male

Only females who have two X^c genes are red–green color-blind. This rare situation can result only from the mating of a color-blind male and a color-blind or carrier female. In X^CX^c females, the trait is masked by the normal, dominant gene. Males, on the other hand, do not have a second X chromosome that would mask the trait.

Therefore all males with an X^c gene will be red–green color blind. The inheritance of red–green color blindness is illustrated in Figure 5.

Figure 5 Inheritance of red–green color blindness.

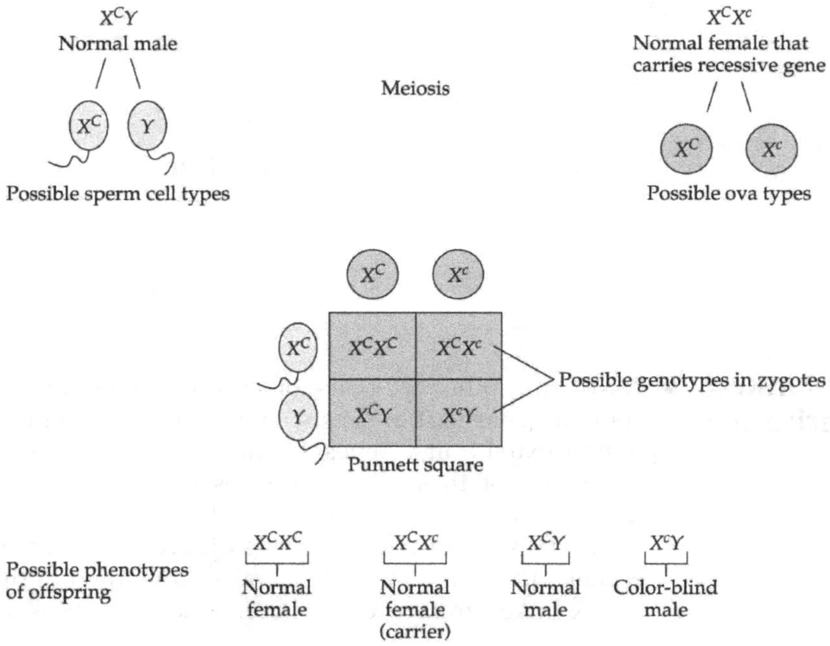

Hemophilia

Hemophilia is a condition in which the blood fails to clot or clots very slowly after an injury. Hemophilia is a much more serious defect than color blindness because individuals with severe hemophilia can bleed to death from even a small cut. Hemophilia is caused by a recessive gene as is color blindness. If *H* represents normal clotting and *h* represents abnormal clotting, X^hX^h females will be hemophiliacs. Males with X^HY will be normal and males with X^hY will be hemophiliacs. Other sex-linked traits in humans are fragile X syndrome, nonfunctional sweat glands, certain forms of diabetes, some types of deafness, uncontrollable rolling of the eyeballs, absence of central incisors, night blindness, one form of cataract, juvenile glaucoma, and juvenile muscular dystrophy.

Mendelian Laws

▶ In any genetic cross, all the offspring in the first (that is, the parental, or P_1) generation are symbolized as F_1. The F is from the Latin word *filial,* which means progeny. The second generation is symbolized as F_2, the third as F_3, and continues that way. The recognized "father" of genetics is Gregor Mendel, whose basic experiments were performed on garden peas. As a result of his tests, Gregor Mendel postulated what are now called ***Mendelian Laws***, or ***Mendelian Principles***. The ***First Mendelian Law***, or the ***Law of Segregation***, asserts that, in cells of individuals, genes occur in pairs, and that when those individuals produce germ cells, each germ cell receives only one member of the pair.

This law applies equally to pollen grains (or sperm) and to ova. The genetic cross is represented as follows:

Yellow parent × **Green parent**

YY *yy*

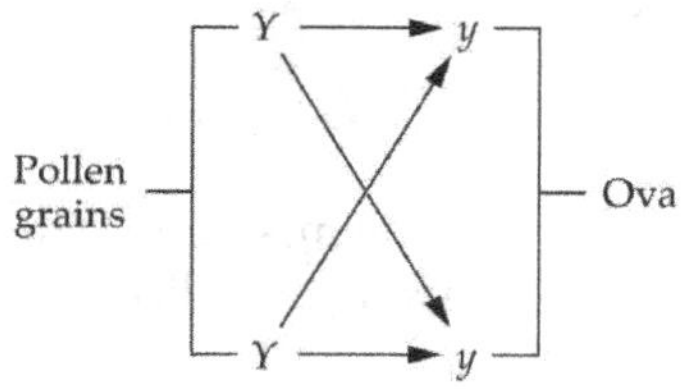

or

	Y	Y
y	Yy	Yy
y	Yy	Yy

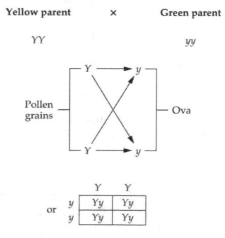

All possible combinations of pollen grains and ova are indicated by the arrows. Notice that all combinations yield the genotype *Yy*. All these F_1 seeds were yellow, yellow being dominant to green, or, in genetic terms, *Y* being dominant to *y*. These F_1 individuals resembled the yellow parent in phenotype (being yellow) but not in genotype (*Yy* as opposed to *YY*). Both parents were homozygous. Both members of that pair of alleles were the same. The yellow parent was homozygous for *Y* and the green parent for *y*. The F_1 individuals were heterozygous, having one *Y* and one *y*.

When the F_1 plants were self-fertilized, the F_2 seeds appeared in the ratio of 3 yellow/1 green. Mendel found similar 3:1 ratios for the other traits he studied, and this type of result has been reported in many species of animals and plants for a variety of traits. Not only does the recessive trait reappear in the F_2, but also in a definite proportion of the individuals, one-fourth of the total. If the sample is small, the ratio may deviate considerably from 3:1, but as the progeny or sampling numbers get larger, the ratio usually comes closer and closer to an exact 3:1 ratio. The reason is that the ratio depends on the random union of gametes. The result is a 3:1 phenotypic ratio, or a 1:2:1 genotypic ratio.

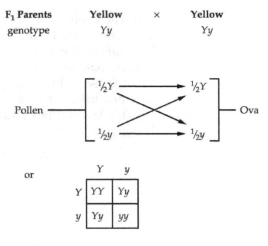

F_1 Parents	**Yellow**	×	**Yellow**
genotype	*Yy*		*Yy*

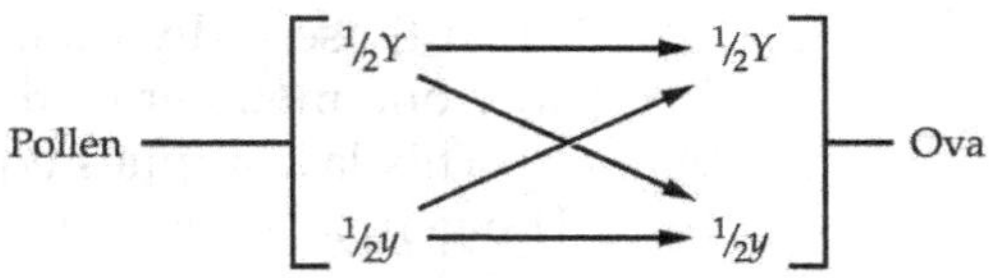

or

	Y	*y*
Y	*YY*	*Yy*
y	*Yy*	*yy*

Thus, the four combinations of pollen and ova are expected to occur as follows:

1/4*YY*	= yellow 3/4
1/4*Yy*	= yellow 3/4
1/4*Yy*	= yellow 3/4
1/4*yy*	= green 1/4

It is important to realize that these fractions depend on the operation of the laws of probability. A model using coins will emphasize the point. This model consists of two coins, a nickel and a penny, tossed at the same time. The penny may represent the pollen (male parent). At any given toss, the chances are equal that the penny will come up "heads" or that it will come up "tails." Similarly, at any given fertilization the chances are equal that a *Y*-bearing pollen grain or that a *y*-bearing one will be transmitted. The nickel represents the ovum. Again, the chances are equal for "heads" or "tails," just as the chances are equal that in any fertilization a *Y*-bearing or a *y*-bearing ovum will take part. If we toss the two coins together and do it many times, we will obtain approximately the following:

1/4 nickel heads; penny heads	(= *YY*)
1/4 nickel heads; penny tails	(= *Yy*)
1/4 nickel tails; penny heads	(= *yY*)
1/4 nickel tails; penny tails	(= *yy*)

If we assume "heads" as dominant, we find that three-fourths of the time there is at least one "head" and one-fourth of the time no "heads" (both coins "tails"). Hence this gives us a model of the 3:1 ratio dependent on the laws of probability.

The genetic cross just demonstrated considers only one pair of alleles (yellow versus green or "heads" versus "tails") and is therefore called a ***monohybrid cross***. Mendel's second principle applies to genetic crosses in which two traits or two pairs of alleles are considered. These ***dihybrid crosses*** enabled him to postulate his second principle, the ***Principle of Independent Assortment***. This principle states that the segregation of one pair of traits occurs independently of the segregation of a second pair of traits. This is the case only if the traits are caused by genes located on nonhomologous chromosomes.

When Mendel crossed garden peas with round yellow seeds with garden peas with wrinkled green seeds, his F_1 generation showed that yellow and round were dominant. If self-fertilization then occurred, the F_2 generation resulted as follows:

Round yellow	$3/4 \times 3/4 = 9/16$
Round green	$3/4 \times 1/4 = 3/16$
Wrinkled yellow	$1/4 \times 3/4 = 3/16$
Wrinkled green	$1/4 \times 1/4 = 1/16$

Therefore, in a dihybrid cross, the expected phenotypic ratio was 9:3:3:1, with 9/16 of the F_2 being doubly dominant, and only 1/16 being doubly recessive.

Multiple Alleles

▶ In the genetics examples we have considered to this point, we have discussed only two alleles of each gene. However, many, and possibly all genes, have ***multiple alleles***; that is, they exist in more than two allelic forms even though a diploid cell cannot carry more than two alleles.

One example of multiple alleles in humans involves ABO blood groups. The four basic blood types (phenotypes) of the ABO system are determined by three alleles: I^A, I^B, and i. Alleles I^A and I^B are not dominant over each other. Rather, they are ***codominant***; that is, both genes are expressed equally. Both I^A and I^B alleles, however, are dominant over allele i. These three alleles can give rise to six genotypes, as follows:

Genotype	Phenotype (blood type)
I^AI^A or I^Ai	A
I^BI^B or I^Bi	B
I^AI^B	AB
ii	O

Given this information, is it possible for a child with type O blood to have a mother with type O blood and a father with type AB blood? Explain ____________________

____

____

If two children in a family have type O blood, the mother has type B blood and the father has type A blood, what is the genotype of the father?____________________

What is the genotype of the mother?____________________

Genetics Exercises ▶

Karyotyping

A group of cytogeneticists meeting in Denver, Colorado, in 1960 adopted a system for classifying and identifying human chromosomes. Chromosome ***length*** and ***centromere position*** were the bases for classification. The Denver classification has become a standard for human chromosome studies. By the early 1970s, most human chromosomes could be identified microscopically.

Every chromosome pair could not be identified consistently until chromosome ***banding techniques*** finally distinguished all 46 human chromosomes. Bands are defined as parts of chromosomes that appear lighter or darker than adjacent regions with particular staining methods.

A ***karyotype*** is a chart made from a photograph of the chromosomes in metaphase. The chromosomes are cut out and arranged in matched pairs according to length (see Figure 2). Their comparative size, shape, and morphology are then examined to determine if they are normal.

Karyotyping helps scientists to visualize chromosomal abnormalities. For example, individuals with Down syndrome typically have 47 chromosomes, instead of the usual 46, with chromosome 21 being represented three times rather than only twice. The syndrome is characterized by mental retardation, retarded physical development, and distinctive facial features (round head, broad skull, slanting eyes, and large tongue). With chronic myelogenous leukemia, part of the long arm of a chromosome 22 is missing, resulting in the blood disease. The chromosome is referred to as the Philadelphia chromosome, named for the city where it was first detected.

PKU Screening

Phenylketonuria (PKU), an inherited metabolic disorder that occurs in approximately 1 in 16,000 births, is transmitted by an autosomal recessive gene (see Figure 1). Individuals with this condition do not have the enzyme phenylalanine hydroxylase, which converts the amino acid phenylalanine to tyrosine. As a result, phenylalanine and phenylpyruvic acid accumulate in the blood and urine. These substances are toxic to the central nervous system and can produce irreversible brain damage. Most states in the United States require routine screening for this disorder at birth. The test is accomplished by a simple color change in treated urine.

The procedure for testing for PKU is as follows.

1. A Phenistix® test strip is made specifically for testing urine for phenylpyruvic acid. Dip this test strip in freshly voided urine.
2. Compare the color change with the color chart on the Phenistix® bottle. The test is based on the reaction of ferric ions with phenylpyruvic acid to produce a gray–green color.
3. Record your results in the LABORATORY REPORT RESULTS at the end of the exercise.

PTC Inheritance

The ability to taste the chemical compound known as phenylthiocarbamide, commonly called PTC, is inherited. On the average, 7 out of 10 people, on chewing a small piece of paper treated with PTC, detect a definite bitter or sweet taste. Others do not taste anything.

Individuals who can taste something (bitter or sweet) are called "tasters" and have the dominant allele *T*, either as *TT* or *Tt*. A nontaster is a homozygous recessive and is designated as *tt*.

Determine your phenotype for tasting PTC and record your results in the LABORATORY REPORT RESULTS at the end of the exercise.

Note: If PTC paper is not available, a 0.5% solution of phenylthiourea (PTT) can be substituted because the capacity to taste PTT is also inherited as a dominant.

Corn Genetics

Genetic corn may be purchased and used in this exercise. Each ear of corn represents a family of offspring. Mark a starting row with a pin to avoid repetition. Count the kernels (individuals) for each trait (color, wrinkled, or smooth). Record your results in the LABORATORY REPORT RESULTS at the end of the exercise.

Develop a ratio by using your lowest number as "1" and dividing it into the others to determine what multiples of it they are. See how close you come to Mendel's ratios. Figure out the probable genotype and phenotype of the parent plants if you can. Monohybrid crosses, test crosses, dihybrid crosses, and trihybrid crosses are available.

Color Blindness

Using either Stilling or Ishihara test charts, test the entire class for red–green color blindness. Tests for color blindness depend on the person's ability to distinguish various colors from one another and also on his or her ability to judge correctly the degree of contrast between colors.

Of all men, 2% are color-blind to red and 6% to green, so 8% of all men are red–green color-blind. Red–green color blindness is rare in the female, occurring in only 1 of every 250 women. Record your results in the LABORATORY REPORT RESULTS at the end of the exercise.

Mendelian Laws of Inheritance

Follow the procedure outlined in the explanation of the Mendelian Law of Segregation, tossing a nickel and a penny simultaneously to prove the law and determine ratios.

1. Toss the nickel and the penny together 10 times to get the genotypes of a family of 10. Repeat this procedure for a total of five times to obtain five families of 10 offspring. Record all of the results on the chart in the LABORATORY REPORT RESULTS at the end of the exercise.

Note: Use the following symbols for the following exercises.

G =	gene for yellow
g =	gene for green
GG =	the genotype of an individual pure (homozygous) for yellow
gg =	the genotype of an individual pure (homozygous) for green
Gg =	the genotype of the hybrid (heterozygous) individual, phenotypically yellow
♀ =	symbol for female
♂ =	symbol for male

2. Obeying the Mendelian Law of Segregation and using the Punnett square shown in the LABORATORY REPORT RESULTS at the end of the exercise, cross yellow garden peas with green garden peas (a monohybrid cross). Show the P_1, F_1, and F_2 generations and all the different phenotypes and genotypes.

3. Obeying the Mendelian Law of Independent Assortment and using the Punnett square shown in the LABORATORY REPORT RESULTS at the end of the exercise, cross the round yellow seeds with the wrinkled green seeds (a dihybrid cross). Show the P_1, F_1, and F_2 generations and all the different phenotypes and genotypes. The F_2 generation can be generated from a Punnett square comparable to that for the monohybrid cross, but with 16 rather than 4 squares.

Observing Phenotypes

The pattern of inheritance of many human traits is complex and involves many genes; the inheritance of other traits is controlled by single genes. You are asked to record your phenotype and your genotype, if it can be determined, for several traits controlled by single genes. For example, if you have the phenotypically dominant trait *A*, your genotype will be *A*−, indicating that the allele symbolized as "−" is not known, since you could be homozygous dominant (*AA*) or heterozygous (*Aa*) for the trait. If you have the recessive trait *a*−, your genotype will be *aa*. Record your phenotype and genotype for the following traits in the LABORATORY REPORT RESULTS at the end of theexercise.

1. ***Attached earlobes*** The dominant gene *E* causes earlobes that develop free from the neck; *ee* results in adherent earlobes connected to the cervical skin.
2. ***Tongue rolling*** The dominant gene *R* causes the development of muscles that allow the tongue to be rolled into a U shape. The *rr* genotype prohibits such rolling.
3. ***Hair whorl direction*** The dominant gene *W* causes the hair whorl on the cranial surface of the scalp to turn in a clockwise direction; the genotype *ww* determines a counterclockwise whorl.
4. ***Little-finger bending*** The dominant gene *B* causes the distal segment of the little finger to bend laterally. The genotype *bb* results in a straight distal segment.
5. ***Double-jointed thumbs*** The dominant gene *J* results in loose ligaments that allow the thumb to be bent out of the constricted orientation caused by the recessive genotype *jj*.
6. ***Widow's peak*** The dominant gene *W* causes the hairline to extend caudally in the midline of the forehead. The recessive genotype *ww* results in a straight hairline.

7. ***Rh factor*** A dominant gene *Rh* results in the presence of the Rh antigen on red blood cells. This antigen is not present with the recessive genotype *rhrh*. Use the results obtained in to determine your phenotype.

What additional information would you need to determine your complete genotype if you have the dominant phenotype for these traits? ______________________________

____

____

LABORATORY REPORT

Name: ______________________ ID No.: ______________________

Instructor: ______________________ Course/Section: ______________________

Partner's Name (if applicable): ______________________ Date: ______________________

Genetics Exercises

PKU Screening

1. ____________ negative—cream color

____________ 15 mg%—light green

____________ 40 mg%—medium green

____________ 100 mg%—dark green

PTC Inheritance

2. ____________ bitter taste

____________ sweet taste

____________ negative (no taste)

Corn genetics

3. Ratio ____________ monohybrid cross

Ratio ____________ test cross

Ratio ____________ dihybrid cross

Ratio ____________ trihybrid cross

Color Blindness

4.

	Male students	Female students
Red color-blind	____________	____________
Green color-blind	____________	____________

Mendelian Laws of Inheritance

5. Record the results of tossing a nickel and a penny together 10 times.

	Female (nickel)	Male (penny)	1	2	3	4	5	Total	Class total
Dominant offspring	A Heads	A Heads							
	A Heads	a Tails							
	a Tails	A Heads							
Recessive offspring	a Tails	a Tails							
Ratio dominant to recessive									

6. Complete the following monohybrid cross. Fill in genotypes (within circles) and phenotypes (under circles).

Monohybrid cross in the garden pea (*Pisum sativum*). G = allele for yellow, g = allele for green, P_1 = parental generation, F_1 = first filial generation, F_2 = second filial generation.

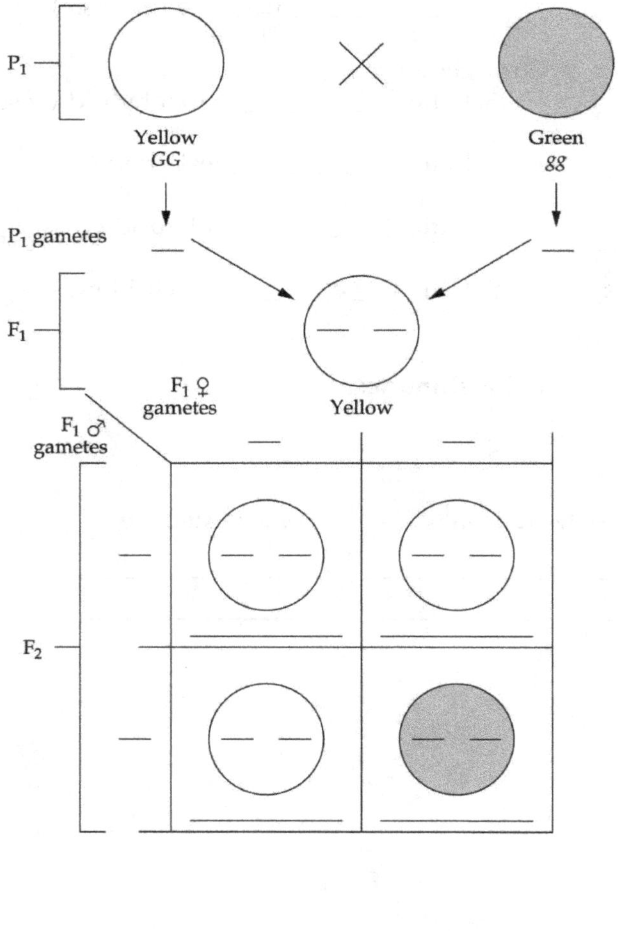

7. What is the phenotype ratio of the F_2 generation?__________ yellow/__________ green.

8. Complete the following dihybrid cross. Fill in genotypes (within circles) and phenotypes (under circles).

Dihybrid cross in the garden pea (*Pisum sativum*). *W* allele for round, *w* = allele for wrinkled, *G* = allele for yellow, *g* = allele for green.

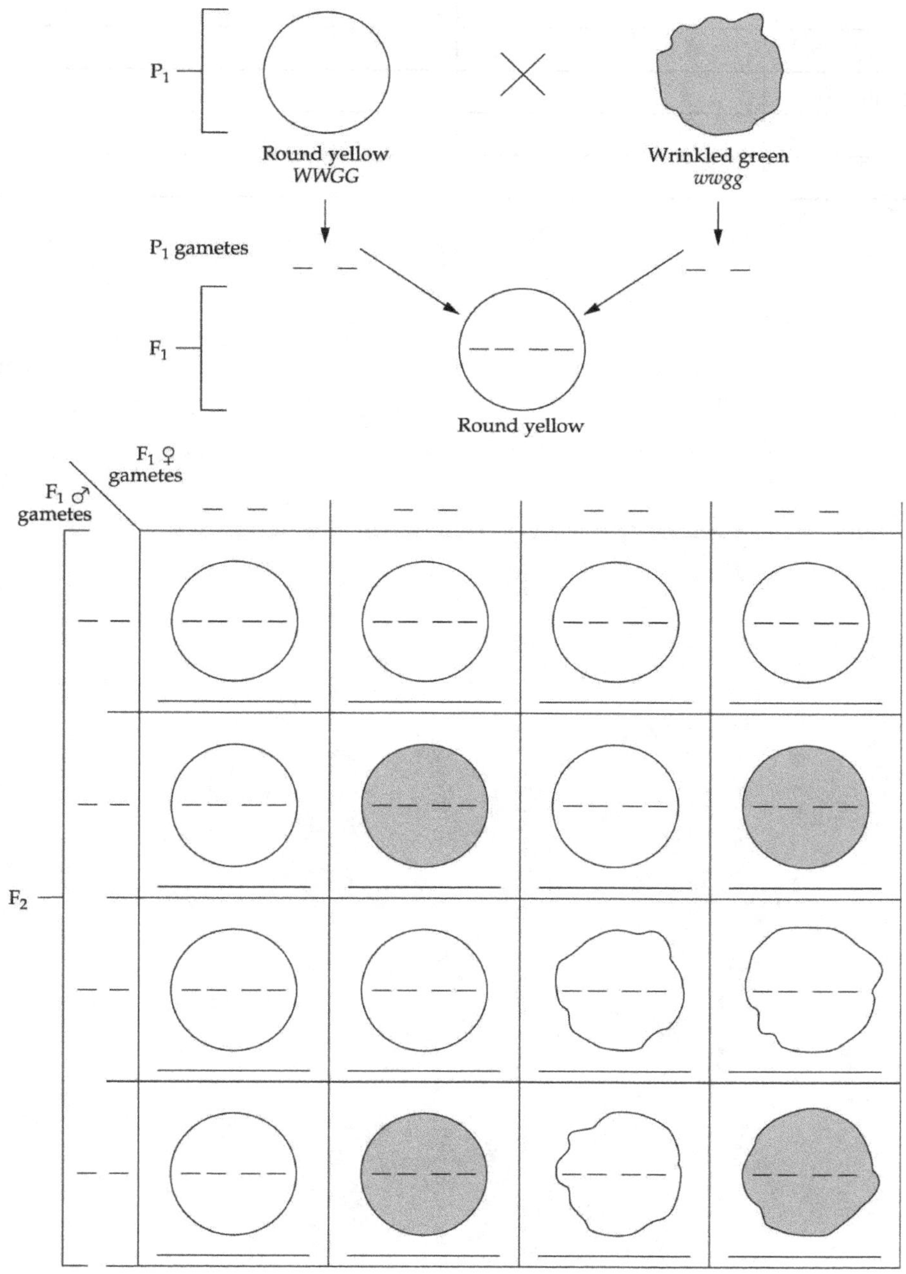

9. What is the phenotype ratio of the F_2 generation?

____________ round yellow/____________ wrinkled yellow/
____________ round green/____________ wrinkled green.

10. Observe phenotypes.

Trait	Phenotype	Genotype
Earlobes		
Tongue rolling		
Hair whorl		
Double-jointed thumbs		
Window's peak		
Rh factor		

Name: ______________________________ Date: ______________________________

Multiple Choice

1. Using the symbols *Aa* to represent genes, which of the following is true?

   a. the trait is homozygous for the dominant characteristic

   b. the trait is homozygous for the recessive characteristic

   c. the trait is heterozygous

   d. sex-linked inheritance is in operation

2. Which statement concerning the normal inheritance of sex is correct?

   a. all zygotes contain a Y chromosome

   b. some ova contain a Y chromosome

   c. all ova and all sperm cells contain an X chromosome

   d. all ova have an X chromosome, some sperm cells have an X chromosome, and some sperm cells have a Y chromosome

3. The genotype that will express characteristics associated with hemophilia (assume that *H* represents the gene for normal blood) is

   a. $X^{H}X^{h}$

   b. $X^{h}Y$

   c. $X^{H}X^{H}$

   d. $X^{H}Y$

4. The exact position of a gene on a chromosome is called the

   a. homologue

   b. locus

   c. triad

   d. allele

Name: ______________________________ Date: ______________________

Completion

1. When the same genes appear on homologous chromosomes, as in *PP* or *pp*, the individual is said to be __________ for the trait.

2. If different genes appear on homologous chromosomes, as in *Pp*, the individual is __________ for the trait.

3. Genetic composition expressed in the body or morphologically is called the body's __________.

4. The device that helps one visualize all the possible combinations of male and female gametes is called the __________.

5. The twenty-third pair of human chromosomes are the sex chromosomes. All of the other pairs of chromosomes are called __________.

6. Red–green color blindness is an inherited trait that is specifically called a(n) __________ trait.

7. The recognized "father" of genetics is __________.

8. A genetic cross that involves only one pair of alleles (or traits) is called a(n) __________ cross.

9. Passage of hereditary traits from one generation to another is called __________.

10. The genetic makeup of an individual is called the person's __________.

11. One of the many alternative forms of a gene is called its __________.

12. Two chromosomes that belong to a pair are called __________ chromosomes.

13. A gene that masks the expression of its allele is called a(n)__________ gene.

14. Failure of chromosomes to move to opposite poles of a cell during meiotic prophase is called __________.

15. A normal female who carries the recessive gene for red–green color blindness would have the following genotype: __________.

16. Genes that are expressed equally are said to be __________.

Molecular Biology

Laboratory Objectives

After completing this lab topic, you should be able to:

1. Describe the function of restriction enzymes.
2. Discuss the basic principles of electrophoresis in general and for DNA specifically.
3. Construct a tentative map of DNA molecules based on restriction fragments.
4. Explain the use of enzymes to map DNA molecules, and discuss the importance of mapping.
5. Use gel results to estimate DNA fragment sizes.
6. Discuss the universality of the genetic code.
7. Describe ways in which the technology of molecular biology is being used in industry, medicine, criminal justice, agriculture, and basic research.

Introduction

Although a German scientist, Friedrich Miescher, isolated **DNA (deoxyribonucleic acid)** in 1869, it took nearly a century to recognize this chemical as the genetic material for all living cells. In 1953, James Watson and Francis Crick determined that DNA structure is a **double helix,** and in the following decade the essence of the genetic code was solidly established. Scientists developed DNA technology in the 1980s, and the importance and applications of this achievement were soon realized. In 1980, Paul Berg was awarded the Nobel Prize for his 1972 work developing recombinant DNA technology to clone a DNA sequence. In the 1980s, Kary Mullis developed the polymerase chain reaction, a technique for rapidly cloning small segments of DNA outside the organism. In the 1990s, the first breast cancer gene was cloned and the Human Genome Project was initiated. A sheep named Dolly was the first animal cloned from adult cells using DNA technology. Scientists are now applying recombinant DNA technology in hopes of curing cancer, Alzheimer's disease, heart disease, and many other hereditary diseases. DNA technology is important in areas other than medical applications. These include the genetic manipulation of corn for high yield and enhanced flavor (Figure 1) and the genetic manipulation of tomatoes for slower ripening. What's more, the criminal justice system is now using DNA fingerprinting to identify criminals in cases of rape and murder.

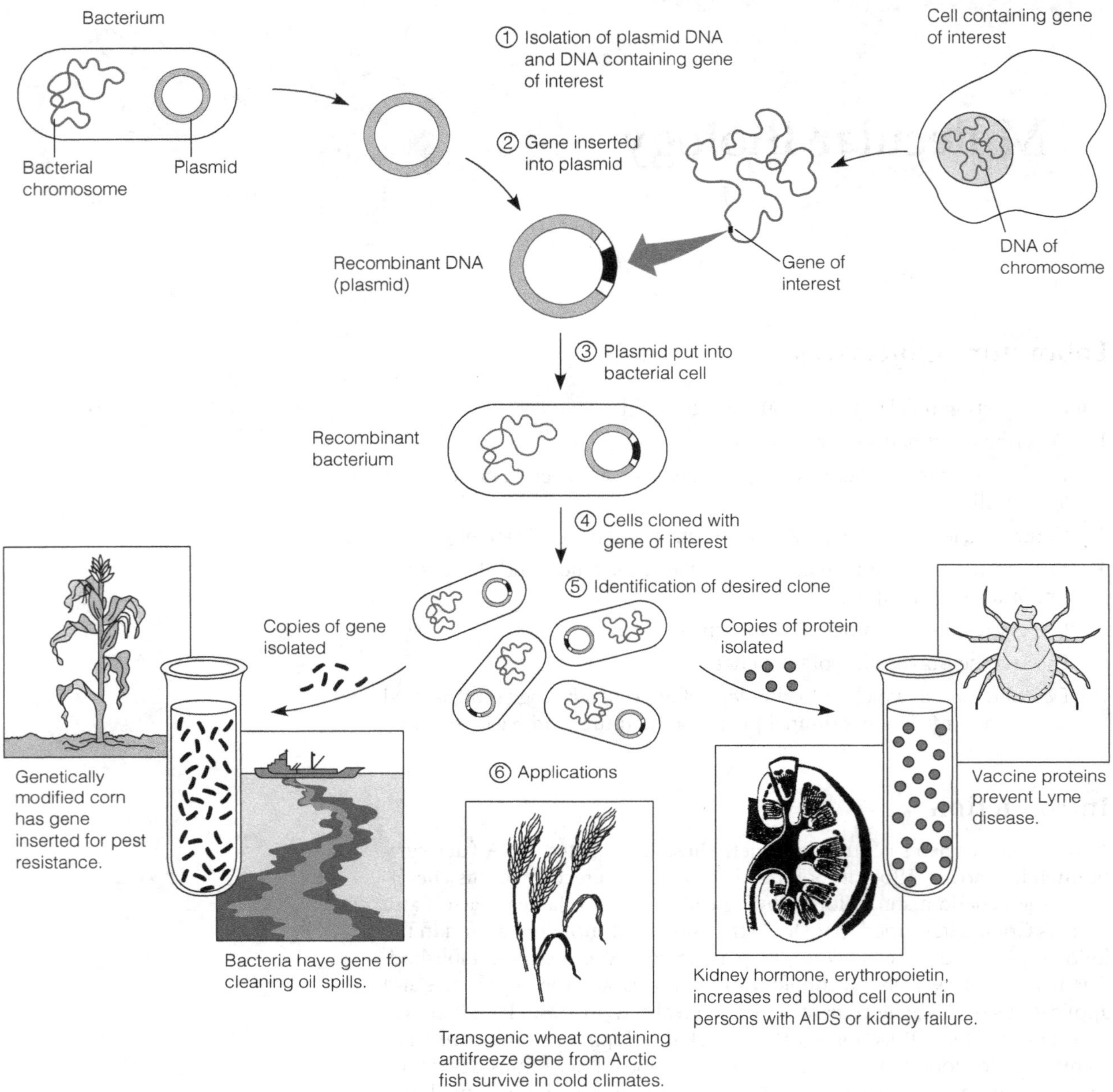
Bacterium
Bacterial chromosome
Plasmid
① Isolation of plasmid DNA and DNA containing gene of interest
Cell containing gene of interest
② Gene inserted into plasmid
Recombinant DNA (plasmid)
Gene of interest
DNA of chromosome
③ Plasmid put into bacterial cell
Recombinant bacterium
④ Cells cloned with gene of interest
⑤ Identification of desired clone
Copies of gene isolated
Copies of protein isolated
⑥ Applications
Genetically modified corn has gene inserted for pest resistance.
Bacteria have gene for cleaning oil spills.
Transgenic wheat containing antifreeze gene from Arctic fish survive in cold climates.
Kidney hormone, erythropoietin, increases red blood cell count in persons with AIDS or kidney failure.
Vaccine proteins prevent Lyme disease.

Figure 1.

Overview of recombinant DNA technology. 1. The genetic engineer isolates plasmid DNA from bacteria and purifies DNA containing the gene of interest from another cell. **2.** A piece of DNA containing the gene is inserted into the plasmid, producing recombinant DNA. **3.** The plasmid is put back into a bacterial cell. **4.** This genetically engineered bacterium is then grown in culture. The bacterial culture now contains many copies of the gene (one per cell in this example). **5.** The cell clone carrying the gene of interest is isolated. **6.** The bottom of the figure illustrates a few of the current applications of genetically engineered bacteria.

In 2000, DNA research reached another milestone when scientists announced that essentially all the human genome had been sequenced. Although scientists still must determine even basic information such as how many genes make up the human genome, what proteins they produce in the body, and how these proteins interact, knowing the 3 billion or so letters is a remarkable achievement. In addition to humans, the complete genome sequences are known for a wide variety of organisms including *Drosophila, E. coli, C. elegans* (a roundworm), and the flowering plant, *Arabadopsis.*

Not only does an understanding of DNA and how it works have medical and agricultural applications, understanding the universality of the genetic code has applications in studies of evolution. The similarity in structure and function of many of the protein products determined by this code in organisms as diverse as viruses, mosses, birds, and human beings provides some of the most convincing evidence supporting the theory of evolution. For example, cytochrome *c*, an important electron carrier in the respiratory pathway, is found in all aerobic eukaryotes. Although mutations have occurred over time, the structure of cytochrome *c* is similar in all members of this diverse group of organisms. This universality has allowed information gleaned from the study of organisms such as yeasts and flies to be applied to human beings. Molecular biology is one powerful tool that has been used successfully to explore the evolutionary relationships among living organisms on Earth.

In the following exercise, you will employ some of the basic molecular techniques used in laboratories worldwide to study everything from the virus that causes AIDS to DNA extracted from mummies. Following the procedures outlined in Exercise 1, you will use enzymes to cut the DNA and propose a tentative map of the location of genetic material. Then you will be asked to answer a series of questions that will lead you through a process of analyzing your results and constructing a restriction map.

EXERCISE 1

Mapping DNA Using Restriction Enzymes and Electrophoresis

Materials

gel electrophoresis apparatus:
- gel plates
- comb to make wells
- chamber for electrophoresis
- chamber cover

power supply with electrodes
heat-resistant gloves
250-mL Erlenmeyer flask
100-mL graduated cylinders
microwave or hot plate
deionized water
agarose
pUC 19 (plasmid) DNA
ice
restriction enzymes:
- *Ava* II, *Pvu* II

restriction buffers
molecular weight markers (λ DNA)
gel loading dye (bromophenol blue)
plastic wrap
15 1.5-mL microtubes (various colors)
thermometer
metric rulers

TBE (Tris base; boric acid; ethylenediaminetetraacetic acid, or EDTA; NaOH), 10× to be diluted in lab to 1×
microcentrifuge (helpful, not necessary)
micropipettors and tips or microcapillary pipettes and plunger (various sizes from 1 to 100 µL)
37°C incubator or water bath
55°C water bath for agarose
portable freezer box or ice chest
Polaroid camera with Polaroid 667 film

methylene blue stain:	alternative stain: ethidium bromide
0.025% methylene blue	ethidium bromide
staining trays	UV-protective goggles
light box	UV light box
deionized water	disposable gloves

Introduction

The first step in any refined DNA analysis, such as DNA sequencing or expressing a gene in another organism, is to construct a map of the molecule. Scientists use naturally occurring enzymes to cut large DNA molecules into smaller pieces. These fragments are sorted and separated by size using a technique called *electrophoresis*. The results are then used to reconstruct the DNA molecule. This initial process of DNA analysis is called **mapping.**

Molecular biologists use some of nature's own tools to do this mapping. In this experiment, you will use **restriction endonucleases** to help manipulate DNA molecules. Restriction endonucleases are enzymes that have been purified from different species of bacteria. Restriction enzymes recognize a specific DNA sequence wherever it occurs in a DNA molecule (Figure 2) and cut the DNA at or near that site; thus, the name: *Restriction* refers to cutting, *endo* to inside a molecule (as opposed to *exo,* which refers to the ends of a molecule), and *nuclease* to the digestion of a nucleic acid such as DNA. Each restriction enzyme is named for the species of bacteria from which it is isolated. For example, *Eco* RI was discovered in *Escherichia coli,* strain R, Roman numeral "I."

Cutting (also called **restricting,** or **digesting**) requires energy in the form of adenosine triphosphate (ATP) and involves a physical cleaving of chemical bonds. The specific recognition sites where the cuts occur are often **palindromic;** that is, the sequences of the complementary strands read the same backward and forward (Figure 3). (The phrase *race car* is an example of a palindrome. Can you think of others?) In nature, bacteria use restriction enzymes to recognize and metabolize foreign DNA. This constitutes a primitive immune system, since it recognizes and rids the organism of an invader.

In this exercise, you will use restriction endonucleases in conjunction with gel electrophoresis to map the 2,686-**base-pair** (bp) pUC 19 **plasmid.** A plasmid is a relatively small extrachromosomal and circular molecule of DNA found in bacteria and yeasts. pUC 19, a plasmid found in *E. coli,* is one of the most significant cloning tools used in molecular biology labs. Because of its size and DNA sequence, it is an excellent system to study.

Once you have cut pUC 19 into discrete fragments, you will need a method of detecting the digested products. Agarose gel electrophoresis is commonly used to separate these fragments (Figure 4). The DNA fragments are placed in the gel, and an electric current runs through the matrix of the gel-like

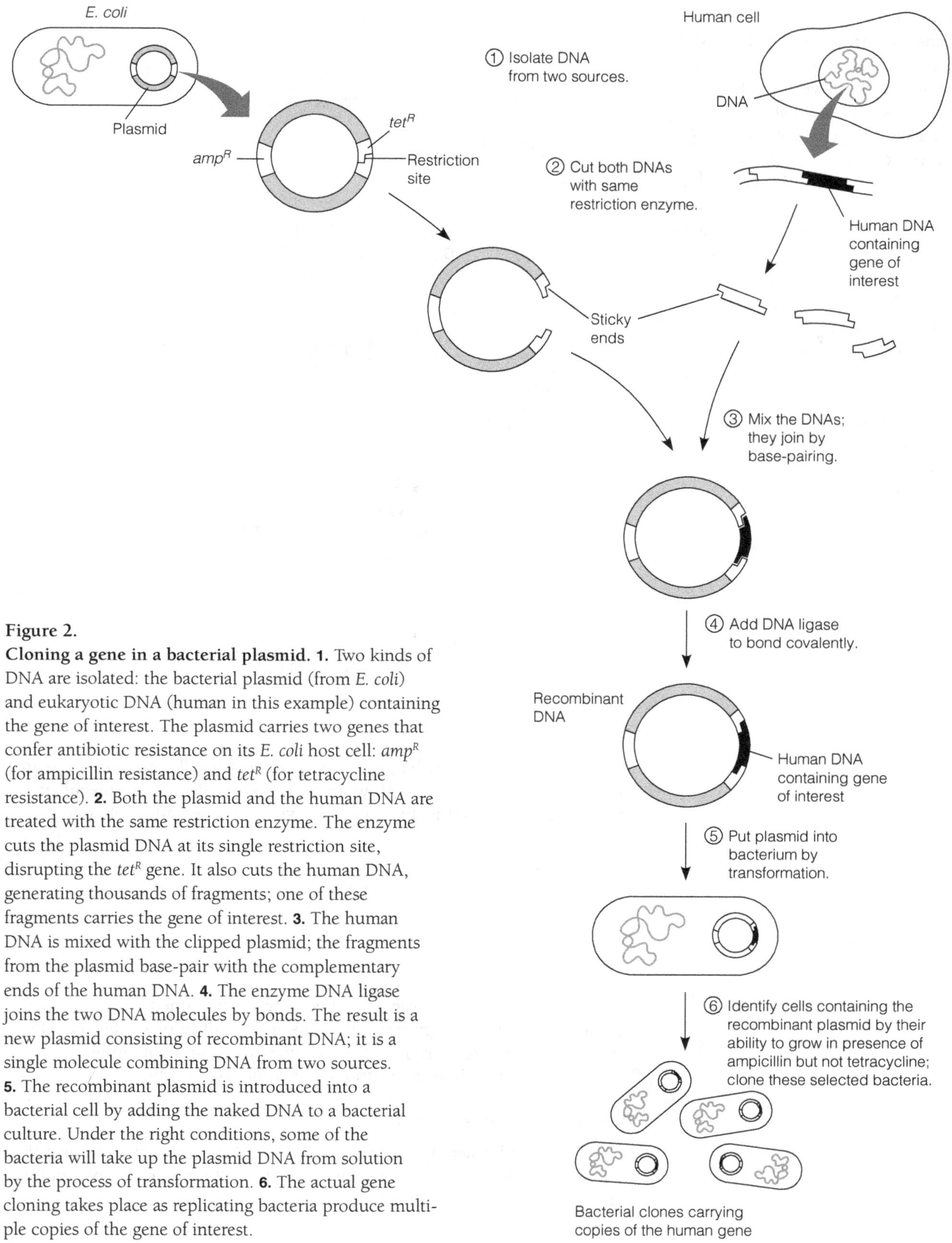
E. coli
Plasmid
Human cell
DNA
① Isolate DNA from two sources.
ampR
tetR
Restriction site
② Cut both DNAs with same restriction enzyme.
Human DNA containing gene of interest
Sticky ends
③ Mix the DNAs; they join by base-pairing.
④ Add DNA ligase to bond covalently.
Recombinant DNA
Human DNA containing gene of interest
⑤ Put plasmid into bacterium by transformation.
⑥ Identify cells containing the recombinant plasmid by their ability to grow in presence of ampicillin but not tetracycline; clone these selected bacteria.
Bacterial clones carrying copies of the human gene

Figure 2.
Cloning a gene in a bacterial plasmid. **1.** Two kinds of DNA are isolated: the bacterial plasmid (from *E. coli*) and eukaryotic DNA (human in this example) containing the gene of interest. The plasmid carries two genes that confer antibiotic resistance on its *E. coli* host cell: amp^R (for ampicillin resistance) and tet^R (for tetracycline resistance). **2.** Both the plasmid and the human DNA are treated with the same restriction enzyme. The enzyme cuts the plasmid DNA at its single restriction site, disrupting the tet^R gene. It also cuts the human DNA, generating thousands of fragments; one of these fragments carries the gene of interest. **3.** The human DNA is mixed with the clipped plasmid; the fragments from the plasmid base-pair with the complementary ends of the human DNA. **4.** The enzyme DNA ligase joins the two DNA molecules by bonds. The result is a new plasmid consisting of recombinant DNA; it is a single molecule combining DNA from two sources. **5.** The recombinant plasmid is introduced into a bacterial cell by adding the naked DNA to a bacterial culture. Under the right conditions, some of the bacteria will take up the plasmid DNA from solution by the process of transformation. **6.** The actual gene cloning takes place as replicating bacteria produce multiple copies of the gene of interest.

Figure 3.
Using a restriction enzyme and DNA ligase to make recombinant DNA. The restriction enzyme (*Eco* RI) recognizes a six-base-pair sequence and makes staggered cuts in the sugar-phosphate backbone within this sequence. Notice that the recognition sequence along one DNA strand is the exact reverse of the sequence along the complementary strand (that is, they are palindromic). Complementary ends will stick to each other by hydrogen bonding, rejoining fragments in their original combinations or in new recombinant combinations. The enzyme DNA ligase can then catalyze the formation of bonds joining the fragment ends. If the fragments are from two different sources, the result is recombinant DNA.

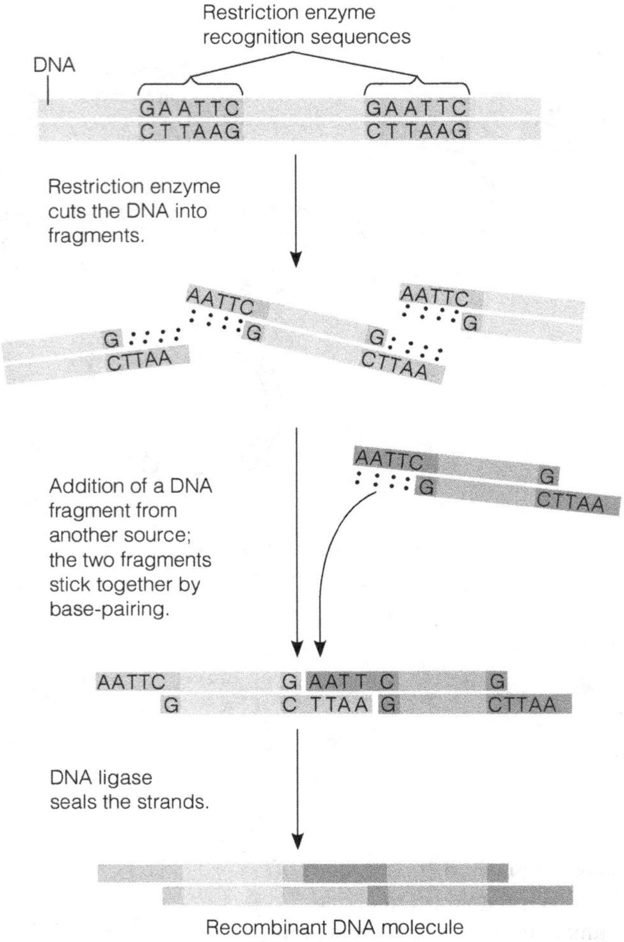

agarose. The fragments will move through the gel at different rates, depending on their charge and size. How does the charge of a DNA molecule vary with its size? How is this different from what you see with proteins?

After running the DNA samples in a gel, the gel is stained with methylene blue and viewed on a light box, allowing the visualization of discrete DNA bands on the gel. Alternatively, the gel is stained with ethidium bromide, which binds the DNA and fluoresces under ultraviolet (UV) light.

Preliminary Questions

Based on your knowledge of the structure and function of DNA and the technique of gel electrophoresis, answer the following questions before beginning your investigation.

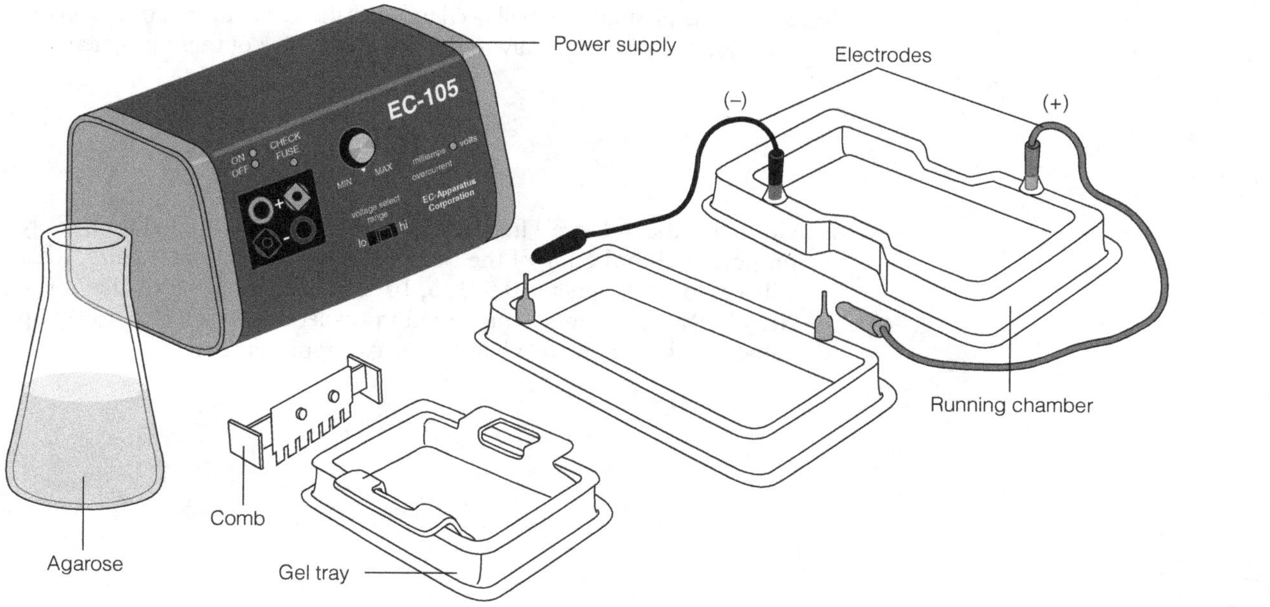

Figure 4.
Electrophoresis apparatus. The apparatus should include the gel tray, comb, agarose, running chamber with electrodes, and power supply.

1. DNA will move through the gel along the electric current, its direction depending in part on the molecule's charge. In which direction, positive to negative or vice versa, will DNA move in the electric field? Why?

2. Given that all DNA molecules have similar charge-to-mass ratios, what property do you think is most important in determining migration within the gel? Why?

3. To map the plasmid, you will need to know the size of the fragments on the gel. Can you suggest a way to determine the size of these fragments?

4. Given that the distance a fragment of DNA moves into the gel is inversely proportional to the log of the size of the fragment in base pairs, what will a graph of fragments 0.5, 1, 5, 10, and 20 kilobases look like? (The size of DNA fragments is measured in nucleotide bases, and 1,000 bp equals 1 kilobase, Kb.) What do the axes represent?

Hypothesis

Based on your understanding of restriction enzymes and electrophoresis, state a hypothesis concerning the migration of DNA fragments.

Prediction

Predict the banding patterns you will observe in the gel based on your hypothesis.

Procedure

1. Practice pipetting and loading a gel

If you have not used a micropipettor or microcapillary pipette before, practice the technique. You may want to have your instructor check your technique because errors as small as one-half microliter can result in inappropriate digests. Although a microliter (μL) seems very small, it can be an amazing amount in molecular biology. For example, 1 μL might contain the amount of DNA in all the genes in a human cell!

a. Set the micropipettor to 20 μL.

b. Attach the pipette tip.

c. Using the practice mixture of water, glycerin, and a blue dye, practice drawing the liquid into the pipette tip. Micropipettors usually have two stop positions. Depress the pipette plunger to the *first position* and place the tip in the solution. Release the plunger while keeping the tip in the liquid to withdraw the correct amount into the pipette. To expel the liquid, the pipette should be depressed to the *second position,* which ensures that no liquid remains in the pipette. *Do not withdraw liquids by fully depressing the pipette*. You would withdraw an unknown volume.

d. Practice loading a gel. Your instructor has prepared practice gels in a petri dish. The gel should be covered with water. Draw 20 μL of the blue practice mixture into the pipette tip and hold the micropipettor with two hands—one hand to deliver the sample and the other to stabilize the end. Be sure that the sample is all the way down in the tip of the pipette and that there is no air between the sample and the tip. Carefully place the tip just inside the well but not piercing the side or bottom of the well. Slowly release the liquid into the well. All students should practice this procedure several times.

In all cases, a fresh, unused pipette tip or microcapillary pipette should be used every time a pipetting task is performed. This is true even if you are pipetting repeatedly from the same solution, especially in the case of enzymes, which are easily contaminated.

2. *Prepare the digestions*

a. Your instructor has already prepared three color-coded microtubes containing deionized (DI) water and an appropriate buffer. Obtain these three microtubes and label them **A** (for *Ava* II), **P** (for *Pvu* II), and **AP** (for both). Be sure that your labels correspond to the color key provided by the instructor. Write that color in the appropriate cell in the first column of Table 1. When prompted, you will add the amounts of each substance indicated in Table 1 to these microtubes. Read and understand steps b–d before you prepare your microtubes. *Do not begin to prepare your microtubes until step e.*

b. The buffers added by your instructor are endonuclease buffers for the respective restriction enzymes. They contain a Tris buffer to maintain the pH and salts such as NaCl to maintain optimal ionic strength and $MgCl_2$ required by the enzymes for catalytic activity.

c. The concentration of pUC 19 DNA solution in Table 1 has been prepared by your instructor to contain 1 μg/2 μL of DNA (or 0.5 μg/μL). This DNA will be cut into smaller pieces by the restriction enzymes.

d. You will use restriction enzymes *Ava* II (found in *Anabena variabilis*) and *Pvu* II (found in *Proteus vulgaris*). Enzymes are assigned units based on the amount required to digest 1 μg of DNA in 1 hour. Thus, 5 μg of DNA requires 5 units of enzyme to completely digest the DNA in 1 hour. Given that we will be digesting 1 μg of DNA, at the appropriate time, you will add 1 μL of the appropriate enzyme to each microtube.

Table 1
Contents of the Three Tubes

Write the appropriate color for each tube, A, P, and AP. These tubes will be incubated in a 37°C water bath for at least 30 minutes. Some items in the tube have already been added by the instructor. Students will add the DNA and enzyme. Note that each tube should have a total of 30 μL of solution.

Tube Label/Color	Instructor Adds	Student Adds Before Incubating Tube
A/ ____________	24 μL DI water 3 μL *Ava* II buffer	2 μL pUC 19 DNA 1 μL *Ava* II enzyme
P/ ____________	24 μL DI water 3 μL *Pvu* II buffer	2 μL pUC 19 DNA 1 μL *Pvu* II enzyme
AP/ ____________	23 μL DI water 3 μL *Ava* II* buffer	2 μL pUC 19 DNA 1 μL *Ava* II enzyme 1 μL *Pvu* II enzyme

*Use the *Ava II* buffer only.

The restriction endonucleases must be added last to the mixture. Adding the enzyme early will result in immediate and inappropriate digestion of the DNA!

Once you understand each component added to the microtubes, proceed with step e.

e. Add 2 μL of pUC 19 DNA to each tube. Tap the bottom of the tube on the lab bench to move the DNA to the bottom of the tube. Return the stock supply of DNA to the cold box.

f. Add the appropriate enzyme(s) to each tube. Tap the bottom of the tube on the lab bench. Be sure all 20 μL of the reaction mix is together at the bottom of the tube. If it is not, gently tap the bottom of the tube on the lab bench until all the liquid accumulates at the bottom. Return stock supplies of enzymes to the cold box.

g. Place the tubes at 37°C in a water bath or incubator for at least 45 minutes but preferably 1 hour.

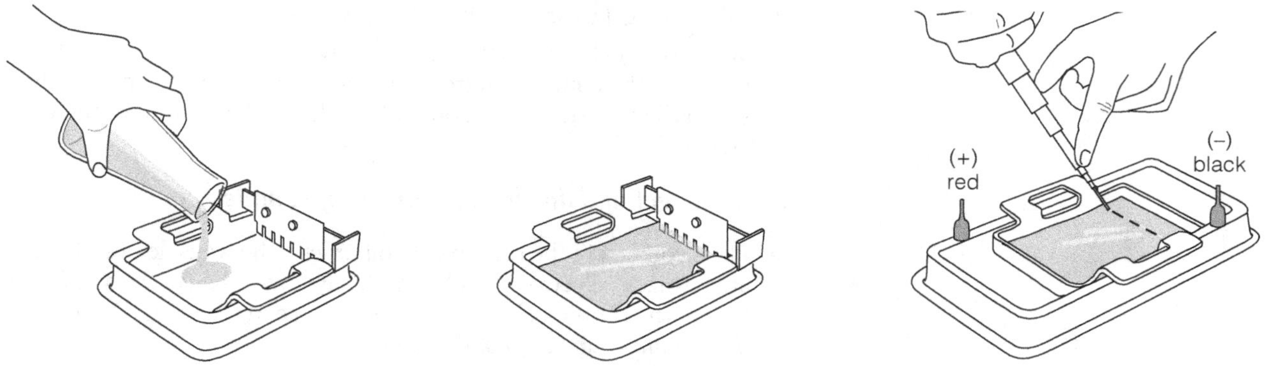

a. Pour gel with comb in position

b. Gel covers half of comb teeth

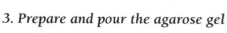

c. Load samples

Figure 5.

Preparing, loading, and running the gel. (a) Pouring the gel into the gel tray. Note position of comb. (b) The gel is poured so that it covers approximately half the height of the comb teeth. The comb will be removed before the samples are loaded. (c) Loading samples and dye using a micropipettor. (d) Gel running with electrodes attached. Note that the dye bands are moving through the gel.

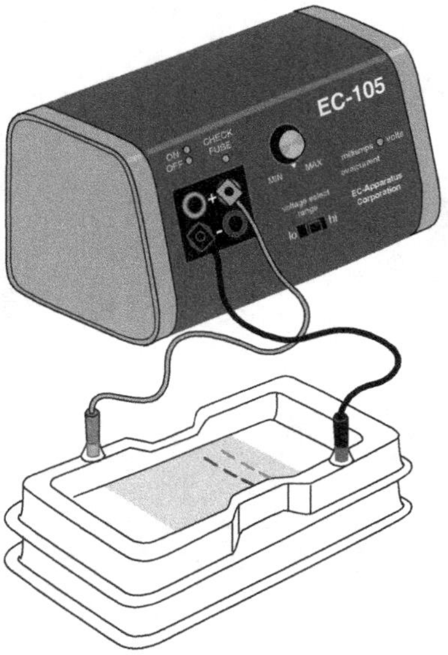

d. Gel running—note loading dye moving on gels

3. *Prepare and pour the agarose gel*

While the DNA digestions are incubating, your instructor will demonstrate how to make a gel, or you will make your own gel. Refer to Figure 5 as you make and pour your gel. Your instructor may have already performed steps a–c. If so, skip to step d.

a. Put 0.8 g of agarose in a 250-mL Erlenmeyer flask and add 100 mL of 1X Tris-borate-EDTA, or TBE (if the TBE is 10X, be sure to dilute tenfold with deionized water).

b. Cover the flask loosely with plastic wrap, and place it in a microwave oven for 2–3 minutes or on a hot plate until the solution boils. In either case, swirl the solution intermittently while wearing a protective glove. Continue until the solution is clear, indicating that all of the agarose is in solution.

Watch closely to ensure that the solution does not boil over!

c. Allow the gel solution to cool to about 50°C. This process can be expedited by carefully swirling the flask under cool water from the sink. Be careful not to let the gel solidify in the flask.

d. Set the comb over the gel plate so that the teeth rest just above the plate (Figure 5a).

e. Slowly pour the gel onto the plate until the solution covers about one-half the height of the comb's teeth (Figure 5a, b). Avoid creating bubbles. If any form, quickly and carefully pop them with a sharp object, such as a micropipette tip. (Why would bubbles be a problem?) If the gel is too thin, it will fall apart; if it is too thick, it will take too long to run.

f. Allow the gel to solidify. It will become opaque.

g. When the gel has hardened, squirt some water around the comb and then pull the comb teeth from the gel slowly, carefully, and evenly. If you pull too fast, the suction will break out the bottom of the wells created by the comb.

4. *Load the gel and do electrophoresis of samples*

a. Place your gel in the running chamber with the wells nearest the negative (black) electrode, and completely cover the gel with 1X TBE. Orient the running chamber so you can see in the wells. *Do not move the running chamber from this point on.*

b. Before you load the gel, you must assemble three additional samples. Obtain these tubes from the instructor. One sample (labeled l) is for loading dye only. A second sample (labeled 2) contains **molecular weight markers,** and the third (labeled 6) is for uncut pUC 19 DNA. Your instructor will give you the key for tube colors. Write the color for each of these tubes below. These tubes contain the following, already added by your instructor:

1 (color ____________): 20 μL of DI water

2 (color ____________): 2 μL of λ DNA, 18 μL of DI water (the molecular weight markers)*

6 (color ____________): 18 μL of DI water

*The molecular weight markers (tube 2) are used to determine the size of a DNA fragment. These markers, purchased commercially, are of known sizes with which you can compare your results. You will analyze these markers simultaneously in the same gel with your fragments of unknown size.

c. Assemble the six microtubes with respective solutions that you will load on your gel and arrange in this order in a microtube rack:

(1) Tube 1 from step b (DI water)

(2) Tube 2 from step b (molecular weight markers)

(3) Digestion sample A (*Ava* II digest)

(4) Digestion sample P (*Pvu* II digest)

(5) Digestion sample AP (*Ava* II and *Pvu* II digest)

(6) Tube 6 from step b (DI water)

d. Add 2 μL of loading dye to each of the six tubes. Tap the end of each tube on the table to mix.

e. Add 2 μL of pUC 19 DNA that has not been digested (uncut DNA) to tube 6. Tap the tube on the table. What is the purpose of the uncut or undigested DNA in tube 6?

f. Carefully load each of the six samples into their corresponding wells in your gel, as shown in Figure 6. Tube 1 will be in well 1, tube 2 in well 2, the *Ava* II digest in well 3, the *Pvu* II digest in well 4, the *Ava* II/*Pvu* II digest in well 5, and the uncut DNA in well 6. *Set your micropipettor to 20 μL.* Load 20 μL of each sample.

Hold the micropipettor with two hands, one hand to deliver the sample and the other to stabilize the end. Be sure that the sample is all

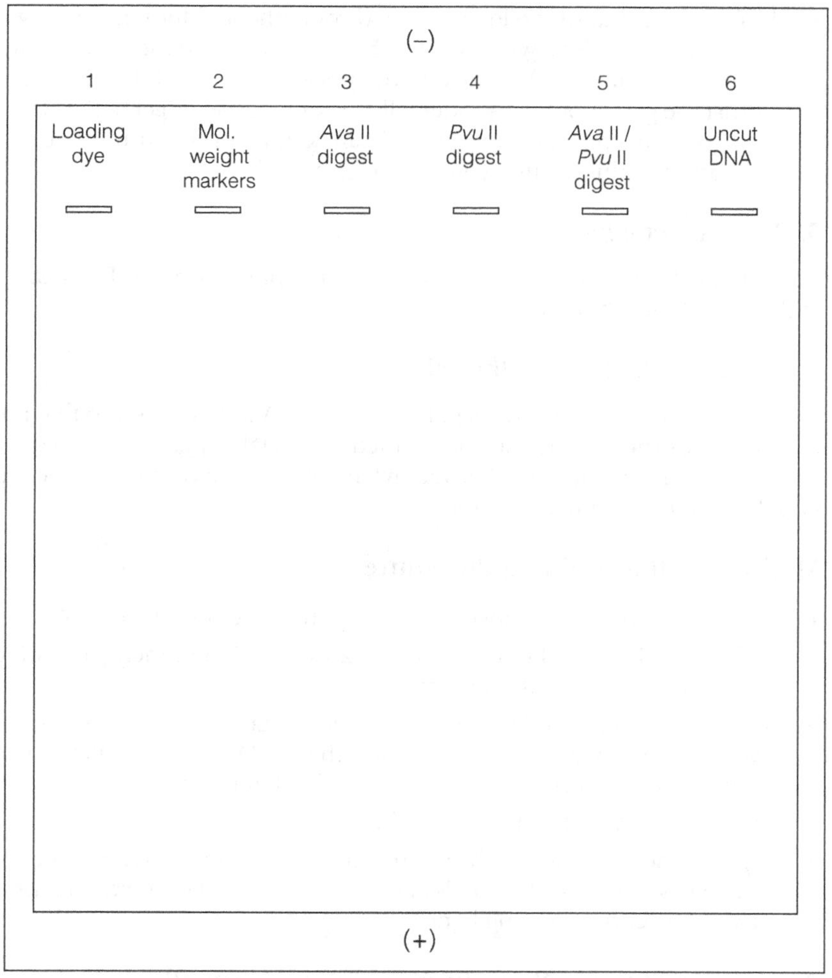

Figure 6.
Wells for loading the gel. Well 1 is used only to practice loading dye. Refer to this figure to ensure that the correct sample is loaded into the appropriate well. Write the appropriate microtube color above each well.

the way down in the tip of the pipette and that no air is between the sample and the tip. Place the tip of the pipette below the surface of the buffer and just into the well. Be careful not to puncture the well bottom. Slowly release the sample into the well. The density of the dye will help it sink into the well (Figure 5c).

g. Carefully attach positive (red) and negative (black) electrodes to the corresponding terminals (red into red, black into black) on the power supply and on the gel box (Figure 5d).

h. Turn the power on to about 100 volts, and make sure that small bubbles arise from the electrodes in the gel buffer, verifying current flow. Check the loading dye to make sure that the samples are running in the correct direction, toward the positive electrode (see Figure 5d).

Turn off the power to the gel before making any adjustments to the electrophoresis setup.

i. Run the gel until the loading dye (bromophenol blue) moves down the gel 10 cm (this will take 60–75 minutes). Watch the gel carefully. After 10 minutes, first turn off the power; then check to make sure that the gel is not hot. Accidentally making the gel or gel buffers from the wrong concentration of TBE can result in gel and buffer overheating. If this occurs, your experiment will fail.

5. Practice mapping

While the gel is running, work the practice mapping problem (Exercise 2) at the end of the lab topic.

6. Visualize the DNA in the gel

The dye you see on the gel does not stain the DNA but is added so that the movement of the current can be verified. The DNA must be stained by another means, by adding either methylene blue or ethidium bromide. To visualize the DNA, proceed as follows.

Methylene Blue Staining Procedure

1. Turn off the power. Remove the gel tray from the running chamber.
2. Slide the gel out of the tray into a 0.025% solution of methylene blue in a staining tray for 30 minutes.
3. Transfer the gel to a destaining tray and destain for several hours or overnight in enough water to just cover the gel. DNA bands will become visible when the gel is viewed over a visible light box.
4. Photograph the gel using a Polaroid camera.
5. If you do not photograph the gel, measure the distance traveled for each band on the gel, sketch the bands in Figure 7, and record your measurements next to the corresponding bands.

Alternative Staining Procedure—Ethidium Bromide

Ethidium bromide is carcinogenic and should be handled with gloves that are thrown away immediately after use. Ethidium bromide should be used only in a confined area, and all lab equipment that comes in contact with the ethidium should be treated with bleach. Once ethidium bromide is added to the gel, you must wear gloves and avoid handling the gel.

1. Turn off the power. Wear disposable gloves.
2. Remove the gel tray from the running chamber. Slide the gel out of the tray onto a piece of plastic wrap. Using a disposable pipette, moisten the gel with a small amount of buffer.
3. Place the ethidium bromide staining paper on the gel with the unprinted surface down. Firmly smooth the entire surface of the paper onto the gel. Repeat the smoothing step several times. Place a small beaker on top of the gel to assure good contact between the stain and the gel.

4. After 2 minutes, remove the stain card. Discard the card in the receptacle provided by your instructor. Carefully lift the plastic wrap to move the gel to the UV light source in a darkroom. Wear protective goggles! Observe the DNA bands with the darkroom lights off.

UV-safe goggles must be worn at all times when viewing gels on the UV box.

5. Photograph the gel using a camera with shields for UV photography. This will minimize exposure to the UV light and provide a permanent record of your gel.
6. Using the photograph, measure the distance traveled for each band on the gel, sketch the bands in Figure 7, and record your measurements next to the corresponding bands.

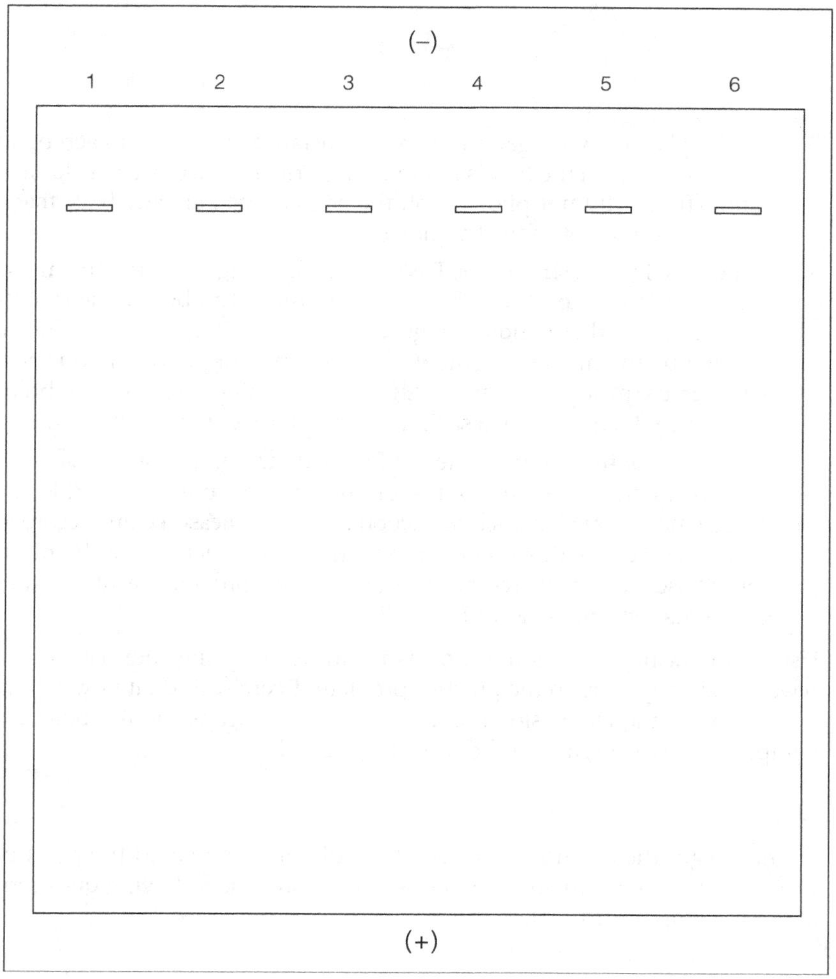

Figure 7.
Results of gel electrophoresis.
Sketch the bands seen on your gel. Record next to each band the distance traveled, as measured on the photograph, and the size of each fragment, determined from the molecular weight marker standards.

Results

1. What are the "controls" in the gel you ran?

2. In the wells where uncut DNA is run, you will see more than one band. Hypothesize: What types of DNA molecules might be represented in the different bands? How could you test your ideas? (*Hint:* Remember that the agarose gel is a matrix and consider if your uncut pUC 19 is linear or circular.)

3. On the photo of your gel, measure the distance traveled for each band on the gel. Sketch the bands in Figure 7. Write the distance beside each band. (If you did not photograph the gel, you will already have made these measurements and sketches.)
4. Obtain the known sizes of the DNA molecular weight marker fragments from your instructor. Write these sizes (in bp or Kb) beside the molecular weight marker bands in Figure 7. In Figure 8, graph the distance traveled by the marker fragments (bands) on your gel (in cm on the x axis) versus the log of the size of the corresponding fragments (in bp or Kb on the y axis). Draw a best-fit line through these points on the graph.
5. Using the graph you constructed in Figure 8, determine the size of every other band on the gel. To do this, on the line drawn in Figure 8, locate the distance traveled by each restriction fragment (measured and recorded in step 3). Follow this point over to the y axis to determine the number of base pairs in the restriction fragment. Record your results next to the corresponding band in Figure 7.

Use the following Discussion section as a guide to analyzing your data. If you have not already worked the practice problem, Exercise 2, do it now, before continuing to the Discussion section. Your final analysis should include a complete restriction map of the pUC 19 plasmid.

Discussion

Do not begin the discussion questions until you understand the practice problem. Then refer to your results as you answer the following questions about the map of pUC 19.

1. How many Kb is pUC 19?

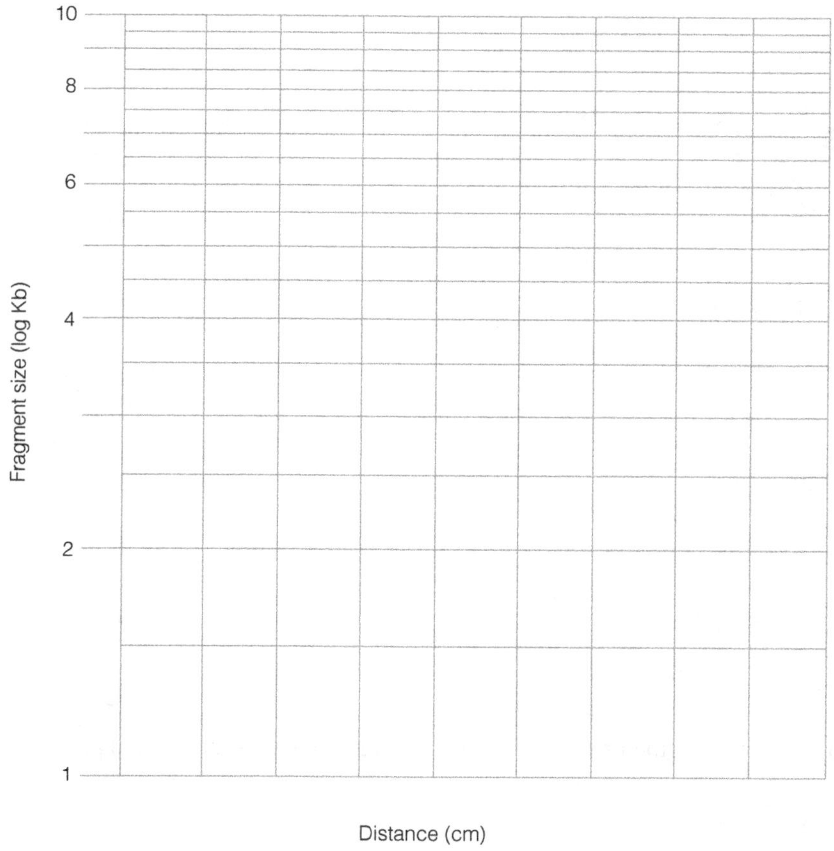

Figure 8.
Relationship of distance traveled (cm) and the size of the restriction fragment (log Kb) for known DNA molecular weight markers. Note the distances traveled for each marker, and choose and add an appropriate scale for the *x* axis. Obtain the known marker sizes from your instructor, and graph them with the corresponding distances from your gel.

2. How many DNA fragments were produced by the enzyme digestions?
   By *Ava* II?

   By *Pvu* II?

   By the double digest with *Ava* II and *Pvu* II?

3. Note that both the small fragments generated in the single digest are still present in the double digest. What does this mean?

4. Draw the two restriction fragments for *Ava* II in the space provided. Label the two ends "*Ava* II." Indicate the size of the fragments that were produced in the double digest, and place the *Pvu* II sites on the large *Ava* II fragment. Refer to the practice problem for assistance.

5. Join the fragments you have drawn above to re-create the original plasmid.

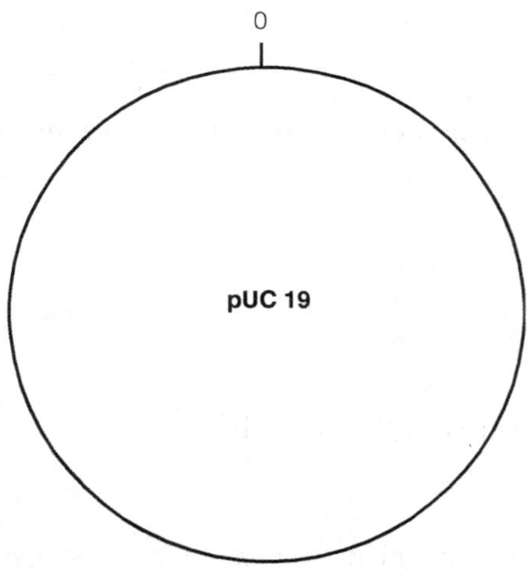

6. Now that you have mapped some DNA fragments, what could you do to further characterize the DNA you have isolated? Refer back to the introduction to this lab topic.

EXERCISE 2
Practice Problem for Mapping DNA

Mapping and sequencing genomes of organisms has led to a new field of genetics called **genomics.** One approach to determining the gene sequence is mapping the DNA fragments produced by restriction enzymes. These restriction sites can serve as markers to align the DNA. An example of a DNA map is shown in Figure 9 for a small plasmid similar to pUC 19, LITMUS 28i. The numerous restriction sites are indicated by the abbreviations around the perimeter of the circle. Can you find a restriction site for *Pvu* II? The location of each enzyme's restriction site was determined using a process similar to the one you will be using today. Fortunately, you are working with only two enzymes!

The construction of a DNA map is really a logic puzzle. You must compare results for the single digests with those of the double digests (those cut with two enzymes) to correctly orient the sites on the DNA molecule. As with anything else, the process becomes easier with practice. The experience you will gain as you solve the following problem will help prepare you to analyze your exercise results.

You are investigating the pathogenic organism *Bacillus anthrax*, which has recently been isolated from infected individuals. It is known that this organism contains a plasmid, and because these genetic elements often contain antibiotic resistance genes, you decide to begin your investigation with the plasmid. Initial studies indicate that the DNA molecule is 4,000 bp (4 Kb) long.

Procedure

1. Inspect the gel diagrammed in Figure 10. The restriction pattern shown in the gel diagram was produced by digestion of the bacterial plasmid with two restriction enzymes, *A* and *B*.

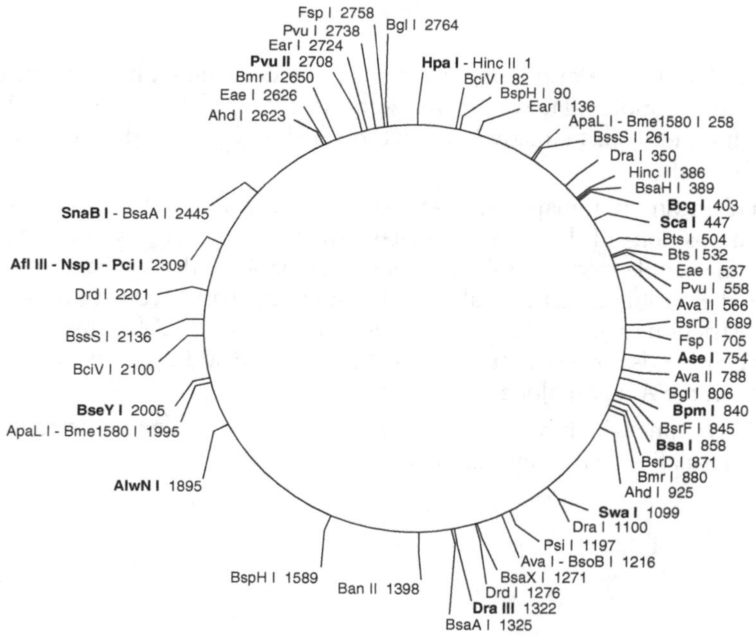

Figure 9.
Restriction enzyme map of LITMUS 28i, a small *E. coli* plasmid.

Figure 10.
Restriction pattern generated by restriction digest of the *Bacillus anthrax* plasmid. Note the position of the origin and the molecular weight markers.

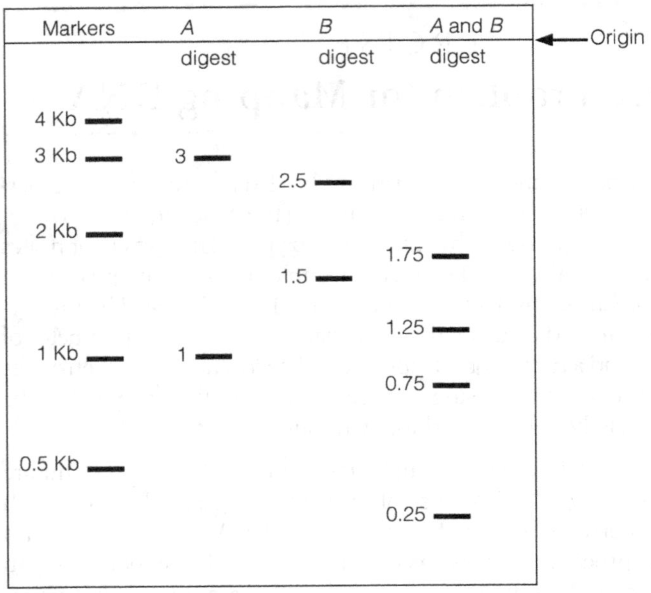

2. Determine the number of fragments produced by each enzyme, and determine the number of fragments produced by the double digest.

   How does the number of fragments correlate with the number of restriction sites in the DNA molecule? Remember that plasmids are circular.

3. Note that the size of the fragments has to be determined by comparison to the molecular weight markers. In this problem, the size of the fragments has already been determined and is recorded next to each band.
4. Make a restriction map of the isolated plasmid by determining the relative positions of the restriction sites. The best approach is to realize that the double digest is really an extension of the single digests. For example, the double digest is analogous to taking the bands you see in the *A* restriction digest and digesting these bands with the *B* enzyme. The smaller bands you see in the double digest should add up to the bands seen in the *A* digest alone.
   a. Determine which bands of the double digest come together to form the small *A* restriction fragment.

b. Determine which bands of the double digest make up the large *A* fragment.

c. Draw the two *A* restriction fragments in the space provided, and indicate where the *B* restriction sites fall on the fragments. Indicate the size of the fragments that are produced in the double digest.

d. Do the same analysis on the *B* fragments. Compare the double digest with the single *B* digest.

e. Draw the *B* restriction fragments in the space provided, and indicate where the *A* restriction sites fall on the fragments. Indicate the size of the fragments that are produced in the double digest.

f. Align the fragments from the preceding analysis. You will notice from your drawings that there are double digest fragments of the same size. These fragments are the key to solving our puzzle because they represent overlap. If we align the large *B* fragment and the large *A* fragment, we find that we can match up restriction sites (Figure 11).

g. Continue to align fragments. As shown in Figure 11, the alignment is used to draw out one longer fragment. By continuing to align fragments, it is possible to re-create the entire restriction map. Which fragments would you try to line up next?

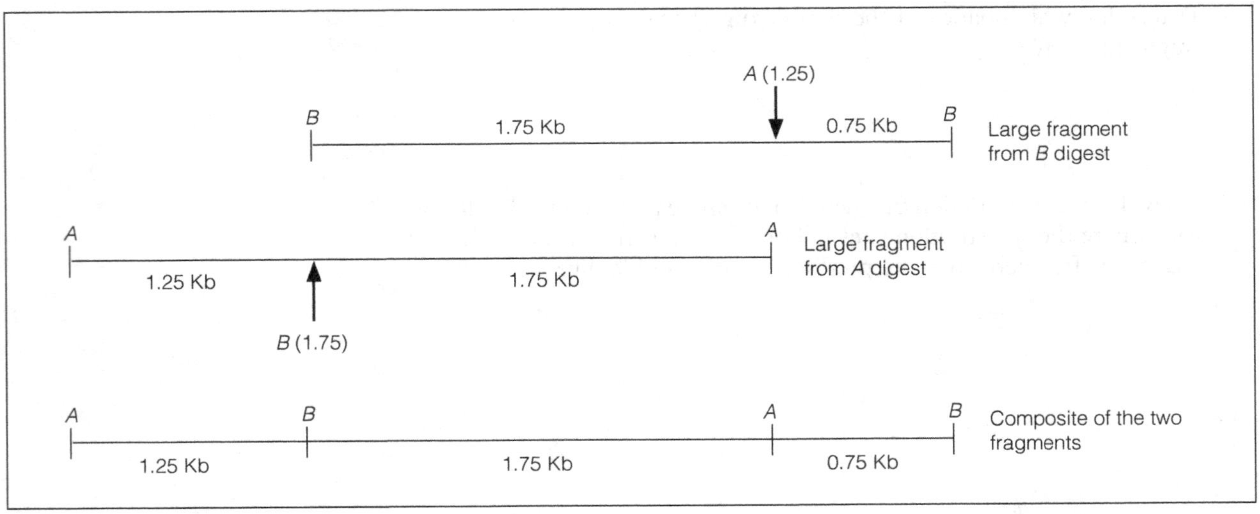

Figure 11.
Alignment of the large fragments from single digests. The large fragments from both single digests can be aligned so that one longer fragment is drawn.

Since we are working with a circular DNA molecule, would you expect to eventually repeat yourself?

h. Continue to align fragments until you have finished your complete map.
i. Draw the map in the space provided. *Hint:* Arbitrarily place one of the *A* sites at position 0 (the very top of your circle) and use that as your reference site.

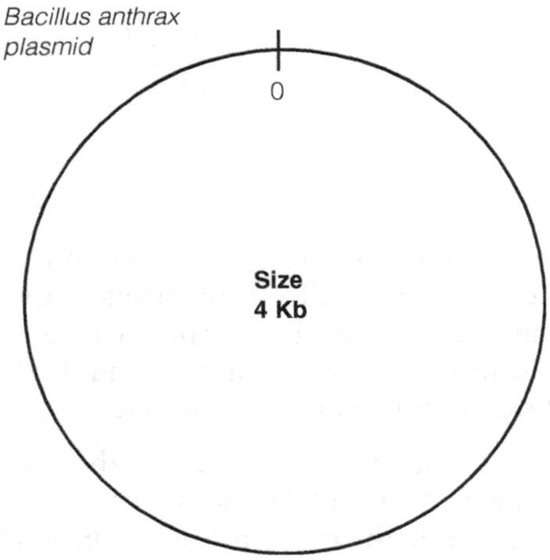

After completing the practice problem, resume your work to complete Exercise 1.

Questions for Review

1. Hypothesize about why restriction enzyme digestions are performed at 37°C.

2. Restriction endonucleases are enzymes. What type of macromolecule are endonucleases? Think of a general way that these enzymes might go about the business of cutting DNA.

Applying Your Knowledge

1. Scientists are developing genetically engineered foods that are insect-resistant, are more nutritious than traditional foods, and can grow in poorer soils. Many scientists believe that genetically modified (GM) foods will become essential as human populations continue to grow. Other scientists fear, however, that GM foods can pose serious threats to humans, wildlife, and the environment. Using resources from the Web, the library, and your text, write a short essay answering the following about GM foods.
   a. How are they produced?
   b. Give specific examples of benefits derived from GM foods.
   c. Give examples of concerns that these foods may be harmful; for example, why do some fear that insects such as monarch butterflies may be harmed?
2. More and more, in cases of rape or murder, forensic scientists are using DNA fingerprinting as evidence for the guilt or innocence of a suspect. In this process, a few selected portions of DNA from small amounts of blood or semen from the crime scene can be analyzed and compared with DNA from a suspect. If gel electrophoresis shows that two samples match, the probability that the two samples are *not* from the same person can be anywhere from one chance in 100,000 to one in 1 billion, depending on how the test was performed. And yet, even with compelling DNA evidence to the contrary, suspects are sometimes found "not guilty." What problems with this type of evidence can arise to create doubt about the guilt of the person?

3. The map for pUC 19 is available online at New England Biolabs, www.neb.com; in the search window type "pUC 19 map." Compare your map using *Pvu* II and *Ava* II with that published on the Web.

   Locate the restriction sites for *Pvu* I and *Acl* I. How many restriction sites are present for each enzyme?

   How many fragments would be produced from digestions of pUC 19 using these two enzymes?

References

Arri Eisen and Alex Escobar, Biology Department, Emory University, contributed significantly to the writing of this lab topic.

Bloom, M. V., G. A. Freyer, and D. A. Micklos. *Laboratory DNA Science*. Menlo Park, CA: Benjamin Cummings, 1996.

Brown, K. "Seeds of Concern." *Scientific American*, 2001, vol. 284, (4), pp. 52–57.

Hopkin, K. "The Risks on the Table." *Scientific American*, 2001, vol. 284, (4), pp. 60–61.

Russell, P. J. *iGenetics*. San Francisco, Benjamin Cummings, 2002.

Websites

An introduction to the concepts of molecular genetics:
http://www.bis.med.jhmi.edu/Dan/DOE/intro.html

Describes the technology of cloning the insulin gene including the action of restriction enzyme EcoRI:
http://esg-www.mit.edu:8001/esgbio/rdna/cloning.html

Population Genetics I: The Hardy-Weinberg Theorem

Laboratory Objectives

After completing this lab topic, you should be able to:

1. Explain Hardy-Weinberg equilibrium in terms of allelic and genotypic frequencies and relate these to the expression $(p + q)^2 = p^2 + 2pq + q^2 = 1$.
2. Describe the conditions necessary to maintain Hardy-Weinberg equilibrium.
3. Use the bead model to demonstrate conditions for evolution.
4. Test hypotheses concerning the effects of evolutionary change (migration, mutation, genetic drift by either bottleneck or founder effect, and natural selection) using a computer model.

Introduction

Charles Darwin's unique contribution to biology was not that he "discovered evolution" but, rather, that he proposed a mechanism for evolutionary change—**natural selection,** the differential survival and reproduction of individuals in a population. In *On the Origin of Species,* published in 1859, Darwin described natural selection and provided abundant and convincing evidence in support of **evolution,** the change in the genetic structure of populations over time. Evolution was accepted as a theory with great explanatory power supported by a large and diverse body of evidence. However, at the turn of the century, geneticists and naturalists still disagreed about the role of natural selection and the importance of small variations in natural populations. How could these variations provide a selective advantage that would result in evolutionary change? It was not until evolution and genetics became reconciled with the advent of population genetics that natural selection became widely accepted.

Ayala (1982) defines evolution as "changes in the genetic constitution of populations." A **population** is defined as a group of organisms of the same species that occur in the same area and interbreed or share a common **gene pool,** all the alleles at all gene loci of all individuals in the population. The population is considered the basic unit of evolution. The small scale changes in the genetic structure of populations from generation to generation is

---

called **microevolution.** *Populations evolve, not individuals.* Can you explain this statement in terms of the process of natural selection?

In 1908, English mathematician G. H. Hardy and German physician W. Weinberg independently developed models of population genetics that showed that the process of heredity by itself did not affect the genetic structure of a population. The **Hardy-Weinberg theorem** states that the frequency of alleles in the population will remain the same regardless of the starting frequencies. Furthermore, the equilibrium genotypic frequencies will be established after one generation of random mating. This theorem is valid only if certain conditions are met:

1. The population is very large.
2. Matings are random.
3. There are no net changes in the gene pool due to mutation; that is, mutation from A to a must be equal to mutation from a to A.
4. There is no migration of individuals into and out of the population.
5. There is no selection; all genotypes are equal in reproductive success.

It is estimated, for example, that at the beginning of the 19th century in Great Britain, more than 95% of the peppered moths were light colored, while less than 5% were dark. Only one or two of the dark forms were seen in collections before mid century. Under Hardy-Weinberg equilibrium, these proportions would be maintained in each generation for large, random-breeding populations with no change in the mutation rate and migration rate, as long as the environment was relatively stable. The process of heredity would not change the frequency of the two forms of the moth. Later in this laboratory, you will investigate what happened to these moths as the environment changed following the Industrial Revolution.

Basically, the Hardy-Weinberg theorem provides a baseline model in which gene frequencies do not change and *evolution does not occur.* By testing the fundamental hypothesis of the Hardy-Weinberg theorem, evolutionists have investigated the roles of mutation, migration, population size, nonrandom mating, and natural selection in effecting evolutionary change in natural populations. Although some populations maintain genetic equilibrium, the exceptions are intriguing to scientists.

Use of the Hardy-Weinberg Theorem

The Hardy-Weinberg theorem provides a mathematical formula for calculating the frequencies of alleles and genotypes in populations. If we begin with a population with two alleles at a single gene locus—a dominant allele, A, and a recessive allele, a—then the frequency of the dominant allele is p, and the frequency of the recessive allele is q. Therefore, $p + q = 1$. If the frequency of one allele, p, is known for a population, the frequency of the other allele, q, can be determined by using the formula $q = 1 - p$.

During sexual reproduction, the frequency of each type of gamete produced is equal to the frequency of the alleles in the population. If the gametes combine at random, then the probability of AA in the next generation is p^2, and the probability of aa is q^2. The heterozygote can be obtained two ways, with either parent providing a dominant allele, so the probability would be $2pq$. These genotypic frequencies can be obtained by multiplying $p + q$ by $p + q$. The general equation then becomes

$$(p + q)^2 = p^2 + 2pq + q^2 = 1$$

To summarize:

$$p^2 = \text{frequency of } AA$$
$$2pq = \text{frequency of } Aa$$
$$q^2 = \text{frequency of } aa$$

Follow the steps in this example.

1. If alternate alleles of a gene, *A* and *a*, occur at equal frequencies, *p* and *q*, then during sexual reproduction, 0.5 of all gametes will carry *A* and 0.5 will carry *a*.
2. Then $p = q = 0.5$.
3. Once allelic frequencies are known for a population, the genotypic makeup of the next generation can be predicted from the general equation. In this case,

$$(0.5A + 0.5a)^2 = 0.25AA + 0.5Aa + 0.25aa = 1$$
$$(p + q)^2 = p^2 + 2pq + q^2 = 1$$

This represents the results of random mating as shown in Figure 1.

4. The genotypic frequencies in the population are specifically

$$p^2 = \text{frequency of } AA = 0.25$$
$$2pq = \text{frequency of } Aa = 0.50$$
$$q^2 = \text{frequency of } aa = 0.25$$

5. The allelic frequencies remain $p = q = 0.5$.

		Eggs	
		A egg $p = 0.5$	*a* egg $q = 0.5$
Sperm	*A* sperm $p = 0.5$	*AA* $p^2 = 0.25$	*Aa* $pq = 0.25$
	a sperm $q = 0.5$	*aA* $pq = 0.25$	*aa* $q^2 = 0.25$

Figure 1.
Random mating in a population at Hardy-Weinberg equilibrium. The combination of alleles in randomly mating gametes maintains the allelic and genotypic frequency generation after generation. The gene pool of the population remains constant, and the populations do not evolve.

In actual populations the frequencies of alleles are not usually equal. For example, in a population of jimsonweed 4% of the population might be white (a recessive trait), and the frequency of the white allele could be calculated as the square root of 0.04.

1. White individuals = $q^2 = 0.04$ (genotypic frequency); therefore, $q = \sqrt{0.04} = 0.2$ (allelic frequency).
2. Since $p + q = 1$, the frequency of *p* is $(1 - q)$, or 0.8. So 4% of the population are white, and 20% of the alleles in the gene pool are for white flowers and the other 80% are for purple flowers. (Note that you could not determine the frequency of *A* by taking the square root of the frequency of all individuals with purple flowers because you cannot distinguish the heterozygote and the homozygote for this trait.)
3. The genotypic frequencies of the next generation now can be predicted from the general Hardy-Weinberg theorem. First determine the results of random mating by completing Figure 2.
4. What will be the genotypic frequencies from generation to generation, provided that alleles *p* and *q* remain in genetic equilibrium?

AA =
Aa =
aa =

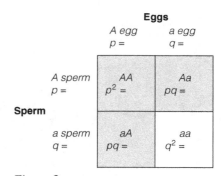

		Eggs	
		A egg $p =$	*a* egg $q =$
Sperm	*A* sperm $p =$	*AA* $p^2 =$	*Aa* $pq =$
	a sperm $q =$	*aA* $pq =$	*aa* $q^2 =$

Figure 2.
Random mating for a population at Hardy-Weinberg equilibrium. Complete the mating combinations for albinism and normal pigmentation.

The genetic equilibrium will continue indefinitely if the conditions of the Hardy-Weinberg theorem are met. How often in nature do you think these conditions are met? Although natural populations may seldom meet all the conditions, Hardy-Weinberg equilibrium serves as a valuable model from which we can predict genetic changes in populations as a result of natural selection or other factors. This allows us to understand quantitatively and in genetic language how evolution operates at the population level.

Note: using the square root to obtain the allelic frequency (step 1 above) is only valid if the population is in Hardy-Weinberg equilibrium. Later in the exercise you will use a counting method to calculate allelic frequencies.

EXERCISE 1

Testing Hardy-Weinberg Equilibrium Using a Bead Model

Materials

plastic or paper bag containing 100 beads of two colors

Introduction

Working in pairs, you will test Hardy-Weinberg equilibrium by simulating a population using colored beads. The bag of beads represents the gene pool for the population. Each bead should be regarded as a single gamete, the two colors representing different alleles of a single gene. Each bag should contain 100 beads of the two colors in the proportions specified by the instructor. Record in the space provided below the color of the beads and the initial frequencies for your gene pool.

A = ______________ color ____________ allelic frequency

a = ______________ color ____________ allelic frequency

1. How many diploid individuals are represented in this population?

2. What would be the color of the beads for a homozygous dominant individual?

3. What would be the color of the beads for a homozygous recessive individual?

4. What would be the color of the beads for a heterozygous individual?

Hypothesis

State the Hardy-Weinberg theorem in the space provided. This will be your hypothesis.

Predictions

Predict the genotypic frequencies of the population in future generations (if/then).

Procedure

1. Without looking, randomly remove two beads from the bag. These two beads represent one diploid individual in the next generation. Record in the margin of your lab manual the diploid genotype (*AA, Aa,* or *aa*) of the individual formed from these two gametes.
2. *Return the beads to the bag* and shake the bag to reinstate the gene pool. By replacing the beads each time, the size of the gene pool remains constant, and the probability of selecting any allele should remain equal to its frequency. This procedure is called **sampling with replacement.**
3. Repeat steps 1 and 2 (select two beads, record the genotype of the new individual, and return the beads to the bag) until you have recorded the genotypes for 50 individuals who will form the next generation of the population.

Results

1. *Before calculating the results of your experiment,* determine the *expected* frequencies of genotypes and alleles for the population. To do this, use the original allelic frequencies for the population provided by the instructor. (Recall that the frequency of $A = p$, and the frequency of $a = q$.) Calculate the expected genotypic frequencies using the Hardy-Weinberg equation $p^2 + 2pq + q^2 = 1$. The number of individuals expected for each genotype can be calculated by multiplying 50 (total population size) by the expected frequencies. Record these results in Table 1.

Table 1
Expected Genotypic and Allelic Frequencies for the Next Generation Produced by the Bead Model

Parent Populations		New Populations				
Allelic Frequency		Genotypic Number (and Frequency)			Allelic Frequency	
A	*a*	*AA* ( )	*Aa* ( )	*aa* ( )	*A*	*a*

2. Next, *using the results of your experiment,* calculate the *observed* frequencies in the new population created as you removed beads from the bag. Record the number of diploid individuals for each genotype in Table 2, and calculate the frequencies for the three genotypes (*AA, Aa, aa*). Add the

numbers of each allele, and calculate the allelic frequencies for *A* and *a*. These values are the observed frequencies in the new population. Genotypic frequencies and allelic frequencies should each equal 1.

Table 2
Observed Genotypic and Allelic Frequencies for the Next Generation Produced by the Bead Model

Parent Populations		**New Populations**				
Allelic Frequency		**Genotypic Number (and Frequency)**			**Allelic Frequency**	
A	*a*	*AA* ( )	*Aa* ( )	*aa* ( )	*A*	*a*

3. To compare your observed results with those expected, you can use the statistical test, chi-square. Table 3 will assist in the calculation of the chi-square test. *Note: to calculate chi-square you must use the actual number of individuals for each genotype, not the frequencies.*

Table 3
Chi-Square of Results from the Bead Model

	AA	*Aa*	*aa*
Observed value (*o*)			
Expected value (*e*)			
Deviation $(o - e) = d$			
d^2			
d^2/e			
Chi-square $(\chi^2) = \Sigma d^2/e$			

Degrees of freedom =
Level of significance, $p < 0.05$

4. Is your calculated χ^2 value greater or smaller than the given χ^2 value for the degrees of freedom and *p* value for this problem?

Discussion

1. What proportion of the population was homozygous dominant?

   Homozygous recessive?

   Heterozygous?

2. Were your observed results consistent with the expected results based on your statistical analysis? If not, can you suggest an explanation?

3. Compare your results with those of other students. How variable are the results for each team?

4. Do your results match your predictions for a population at Hardy-Weinberg equilibrium?

   What would you expect to happen to the frequencies if you continued this simulation for 25 generations?

   Is this population evolving?

   Explain your response.

5. Consider each of the conditions for the Hardy-Weinberg model. Does this model meet each of those conditions?

EXERCISE 2

Simulation of Evolutionary Change Using the Bead Model

Under the conditions specified by the Hardy-Weinberg model (random mating in a large population, no mutation, no migration, and no selection), the genetic frequencies should not change, and evolution should not occur. In this exercise, the class will modify each of the conditions and determine the effect on genetic frequencies in subsequent generations. You will simulate the evolutionary changes that occur when these conditions are not met.

Working in teams of two or three students, you will simulate two of the experimental scenarios presented and, using the bead model, determine the changes in genetic frequencies over several generations. The scenarios include the migration of individuals between two populations, also called **gene flow**; the effects of small population size, called **genetic drift**; and examples of **natural selection.** The effects of mutation take longer to simulate with the bead model, so you will use computer simulation to consider these in Exercise 3. *All teams will begin by simulating the effect of genetic drift, specifically, the bottleneck effect. For the second simulation, you can choose to investigate migration, one of two examples of natural selection, or the founder effect—another example of genetic drift.*

The procedure for investigating each of the conditions will follow the general procedures described as follows. Before beginning one of the simulation experiments, be sure you understand the procedures to be used.

Procedure

1. Sampling with Replacement

Unless otherwise instructed, the gene pool size will be 100 beads. Each new generation will be formed by randomly choosing 50 diploid individuals represented by pairs of beads. After removing each pair of beads (representing the genotype of one individual) from the bag, replace the pair before removing the next set, *sampling with replacement.* Continue your simulations for several generations. For example, if the starting population has 50 beads each of *A* and *a* (allelic frequency of 0.5), then in the next generation you might produce the following results:

Number of individuals: 14*AA*, 24*Aa*, 12*aa*
Number of alleles (beads): 28*A* + 24*A*, 24*a* + 24*a*
Total number of alleles: 100

Frequency of *A*: $28 + 24 = \frac{52}{100} = 0.52$

Frequency of *a*: $24 + 24 = \frac{48}{100} = 0.48$

In this example, the frequency should continue to approximate 0.5 for *A* and *a*.

2. Reestablishing a Population with New Allelic Frequencies

In some cases, the number of individuals will decrease as a result of the simulation. In those cases, return the population to 100 but reestablish the population with new allelic frequencies. For example, if you eliminate by selection all homozygous recessive (*aa*) individuals in your simulation, then the resulting frequencies would be:

Number of individuals: 14*AA*, 24*Aa*, 0*aa*
Number of alleles (beads): 28*A* + 24*A*, 24*a*
Total number of alleles: 76

Frequency of A: $28 + 24 = \frac{52}{76} = 0.68$

Frequency of a: $24 = \frac{24}{76} = 0.32$

To reestablish a population of 100, then, the number of beads should reflect these new frequencies. *Adjust the number of beads* so that A is now $^{68}/_{100}$ and a is $^{32}/_{100}$. Then continue the next round of the simulation.

If this information is not clear to you, ask for assistance before beginning your simulations.

Experiment A. Simulation of Genetic Drift

Materials

plastic or paper bag containing 100 beads, 50 each of two colors
additional beads as needed

Introduction

Genetic drift is the change in allelic frequencies in small populations as a result of chance alone. In a small population, combinations of gametes may not be random, owing to sampling error. (If you toss a coin 500 times, you expect about a 50:50 ratio of heads to tails; but if you toss the coin only 10 times, the ratio may deviate greatly in a small sample owing to chance alone.) **Genetic fixation,** the loss of all but one possible allele at a gene locus in a population, is a common result of genetic drift in small natural populations. Genetic drift is a significant evolutionary force in situations known as the **bottleneck effect** and the **founder effect.** *All teams will investigate the bottleneck effect. You may choose the founder effect (pp. 283–284) for your second simulation.*

1. Bottleneck Effect

A **bottleneck** occurs when a population undergoes a drastic reduction in size as a result of chance events (not differential selection), such as a volcanic eruption or hurricane. (Bad luck, not bad genes!) In Figure 3, the beads pass through a bottleneck, which results in an unpredictable combination of beads that pass to the other side. These beads would constitute the beginning of the next generation.

Hypothesis

As your hypothesis, either propose a hypothesis that addresses the bottleneck effect specifically or state the Hardy-Weinberg theorem.

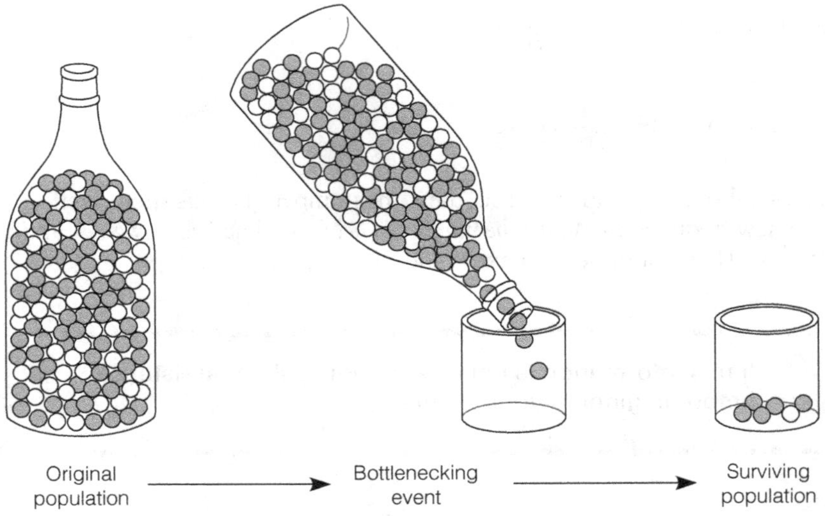

Figure 3.
The bottleneck effect. The gene pool can drift by chance when the population is drastically reduced by factors that act unselectively. Bad luck, not bad genes! The resulting population will have unpredictable combinations of genes. What has happened to the amount of variation?

Prediction

Either predict equilibrium values as a result of Hardy-Weinberg or predict the type of change that you expect to occur in a small population (if/then).

Procedure

1. To investigate the bottleneck effect, establish a starting population containing 50 individuals (how many beads?) with a frequency of 0.5 for each allele (Generation 0).
2. *Without replacement,* randomly select 5 individuals (10% of the population), two alleles at a time. This represents a drastic reduction in population size. On a separate sheet of paper, record the genotypes and the number of *A* and *a* alleles for the new population.
3. Count the numbers of each genotype and the numbers of each allele. Using these numbers, determine the genotypic frequencies for *AA, Aa,* and *aa* and the new allelic frequencies for *A* (p) and *a* (q) for the surviving 5 individuals. These are your *observed* frequencies. Enter these frequencies in Table 4, Generation 1.
4. Using the new observed allelic frequencies, calculate the *expected* genotypic frequencies (p^2, $2pq$, q^2). Record these frequencies in Table 4, Generation 1.

5. Reestablish the population to 50 individuals using the new allelic frequencies. Repeat steps 2, 3, and 4. Record your results in the appropriate generation in Table 4.
6. Reestablish the gene pool with new frequencies after each generation until one of the alleles becomes fixed in the population for several generations.
7. Summarize your results in the Discussion section.

Results

1. How many generations did you simulate?
2. Using the graph paper at the end of the lab topic, sketch a graph of the change in p and q over time. You should have two lines, one for each allele.
3. Did one allele go to fixation in that time period? Which allele?

   Remember, genetic fixation occurs when the gene pool is composed of only one allele. The others have been eliminated. Did the other allele ever appear to be going to fixation?

Table 4
Changes in Allelic and Genotypic Frequencies for Simulations of the Bottleneck Effect, an Example of Genetic Drift. First, record frequencies based on the observed numbers in your experiment. Then, using the observed allelic frequencies, calculate the expected genotypic frequencies.

	Genotypic Frequency Observed			**Allelic Frequency Observed**		**Genotypic Frequency Expected**		
Generation	*AA*	*Aa*	*aa*	*A* (p)	*a* (q)	p^2	$2pq$	q^2
0	—	—	—	0.5	0.5	0.25	0.50	0.25
1								
2								
3								
4								
5								
6								
7								
8								
9								
10								

4. Did any of the expected genotypic frequencies go to fixation? If none did, why not?

5. Compare results with other teams. Did the same allele go to fixation for all teams? If not, how many became fixed for *A* and how many for *a*?

Discussion

1. Compare the pattern of change for p and q. Is there a consistent trend or do the changes suggest chance events? Look at the graphs of other teams before deciding.

2. Explain your observations of genetic fixation for the replicate simulations completed by the class. What would you expect if you simulated the bottleneck effect 100 times?

3. How might your results have differed if you had started with different allelic frequencies, for example, $p = 0.2$ and $q = 0.8$?

4. Since only chance events—that is, the effect of small population size—are responsible for the change in gene frequencies, would you say that evolution has occurred? Explain.

On completion of this simulation, choose one or two of the remaining scenarios to investigate. All scenarios should be completed by at least one team in the laboratory.

2. *Founder Effect*

When a small group of individuals becomes separated from the larger parent population, the allelic frequencies in this small gene pool may be different from those of the original population as a result of chance alone. This occurs when a group of migrants becomes established in a new area not currently inhabited by the species—for instance, the colonization of an island—and is therefore referred to as the **founder effect.**

Hypothesis

As your hypothesis, either propose a hypothesis that addresses founder effect specifically or state the Hardy-Weinberg theorem.

Prediction

Either predict equilibrium values as a result of Hardy-Weinberg or predict the type of change that you expect to occur in a small population (if/then).

Procedure

1. To investigate the founder effect, establish a starting population with 50 individuals with starting allelic frequencies of your choice. Record the frequencies you have selected for Generation 0 in Table 5 in the Results section at the end of this exercise.
2. *Without replacement,* randomly select 5 individuals, two alleles at a time, to establish a new founder population. On a separate sheet of paper, record the genotypes and the number of *A* and *a* alleles for the new population.
3. Calculate the new frequencies for *A* (p) and *a* (q) and the genotypic frequencies for *AA* (p^2), *Aa* ($2pq$), and *aa* (q^2) for the *founder population,* and record this information as Generation 1 in Table 5.
4. Reestablish the population to 50 diploid individuals using the new allelic frequencies.

5. Follow the founder population through several generations in the new population. From this point forward, each new generation will be produced by *sampling 50 individuals with replacement.* After each generation, reestablish the new population based on the new allelic frequencies. Continue until you have sufficient evidence to discuss your results with the class.
6. Summarize your results in the Discussion section at the end of this exercise. You will want to compare the founder population with the original population and compare equilibrium frequencies if appropriate. Each group will present its results to the class at the end of the laboratory.

Experiment B. Simulation of Migration: Gene Flow

Materials

2 plastic or paper bags, each containing 100 beads of two colors
additional beads as needed

Introduction

The migration of individuals between populations results in gene flow. In a natural population, gene flow can be the result of the immigration and emigration of individuals or gametes (for example, pollen movement). The rate and direction of migration and the starting allelic frequencies for the two populations can affect the rate of genetic change. In this example, the migration rate is equal in the two populations, and the starting allelic frequencies differ for the two. Work in teams of four students.

Hypothesis

As your hypothesis, either propose a hypothesis that addresses migration specifically or state the Hardy-Weinberg theorem.

Prediction

Either predict equilibrium values as a result of Hardy-Weinberg or predict the type of change that you expect to observe as a result of migration (if/then).

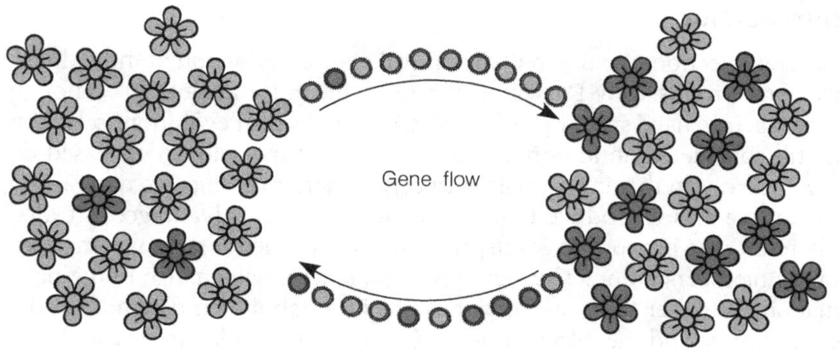

Figure 4.
Migration. Migration rates are constant between two populations that differ for starting allelic frequencies.

Procedure

1. To investigate the effects of gene flow on population genetics, establish two populations of 100 beads each. Choose different starting allelic frequencies for *A* and *a* for each population. For example, in Figure 4, population 1 might start with 90*A* and 10*a* while population 2 might have 50 of each allele initially. For comparison, you might choose one population with the same starting frequencies as your population in Exercise 1. Record the allelic frequencies for each starting population, Generation 0, in Table 5 in the Results section at the end of this exercise.
2. Select 10 individuals (how many alleles?) from each population, and allow them to migrate to the other population by exchanging beads. Do not sample with replacement in this step.
3. Select 50 individuals from each of these new populations, *sampling with replacement.* On a separate sheet of paper, record the genotypes and the number of *A* and *a* alleles for population 1 and population 2.
4. Calculate the new allelic and genotypic frequencies in the two populations following migration. Record your results in Table 5 in the Results section. Reestablish each bag based on the new allelic frequencies.
5. Repeat this procedure (steps 2 to 4) for several generations. In doing this, you are allowing migration to take place with each generation. Continue until you have a sufficient number to allow you to discuss your results in class successfully.
6. Summarize your results in the Discussion section at the end of this exercise. Each group will present its results to the class at the end of the laboratory.

Experiment C. Simulation of Natural Selection

Materials

plastic or paper bag containing 100 beads of two colors
additional beads as needed

Introduction

Natural selection, the differential survival and reproduction of individuals, was first proposed by Darwin as the mechanism for evolution. Although other factors have since been found to be involved in evolution, selection is still considered an important mechanism. Natural selection is based on the observation that individuals with certain heritable traits are more likely to survive and reproduce than those lacking these advantageous traits. Therefore, the proportion of offspring with advantageous traits will increase in the next generation. The genotypic frequencies will change in the population. Whether traits are advantageous in a population depends on the environment and the selective agents (which can include physical and biological factors). Choose one of the following evolutionary scenarios to model natural selection in population genetics.

1. Industrial Melanism

The peppered moth, *Biston betularia,* is a speckled moth that sometimes rests on tree trunks during the day, where it avoids predation by blending with the bark of trees (an example of cryptic coloration). At the beginning of the 19th century, moth collectors in Great Britain collected almost entirely light forms of this moth (light with dark speckles) and only occasionally recorded rare dark forms (Figure 5). With the advent of the Industrial Revolution and increased pollution the tree bark darkened, lichens died, and the frequency of the dark moth increased dramatically in industrialized areas. However, in rural areas, the light moth continued to occur in high frequencies. (This is an example of the relative nature of selective advantage, depending on the environment.)

Color is controlled by a single gene with two allelic forms, dark and light. Pigment production is dominant (*A*), and the lack of pigment is recessive (*a*). The light moth would be *aa,* but the dark form could be either *AA* or *Aa*.

a. b.

Figure 5.
Two color forms of the peppered moth. The dark and light forms of the moth are present in both photographs. Lichens are absent in (a) but present in (b). In which situation would the dark moth have a selective advantage?

Hypothesis

As your hypothesis, either propose a hypothesis that addresses natural selection occurring in polluted environments specifically or state the Hardy-Weinberg theorem.

Prediction

Either predict equilibrium values as a result of the Hardy-Weinberg theorem or predict the type of change that you expect to observe as a result of natural selection in the polluted environment (if/then).

Procedure

1. To investigate the effect of natural selection on the frequency of light and dark moths, establish a population of 50 individuals with allelic frequencies of light (a) = 0.9 and dark (A) = 0.1. Record the frequencies of the starting population, Generation 0, in Table 5 in the Results section at the end of this exercise.
2. Determine the genotypes and phenotypes of the population by selecting 50 individuals, two alleles at a time, by sampling with replacement. On a separate sheet of paper, record the genotypes and phenotypes of each individual.

   Now, assume that pollution has become a significant factor and that in this new population 50% of the light moths but only 10% of the dark moths are eaten. How many light moths must you eliminate from your starting population of 50 individuals? How many dark moths? Can selection distinguish dark moths with *AA* and *Aa* genotypes? How will you decide which dark moths to remove? Remove the appropriate number of individuals of each phenotype.
3. Calculate new allelic frequencies for the remaining population. Reestablish the population with these new allelic frequencies for the 100 alleles. Record the new frequencies in Table 5 in the Results section.
4. Continue the selection procedure, recording the frequencies, for several generations until you have sufficient evidence to discuss your results with the class.
5. Summarize your results in the Discussion section at the end of this exercise. Each group will present its results to the class at the end of the laboratory.

Figure 6.
Effects of the sickle-cell allele.
(a) Normal red blood cells are disk-shaped. (b) The jagged shape of sickled cells causes them to pile up and clog small blood vessels.
(c) The results include damage to a large number of organs. In the homozygous condition, sickle-cell disease can be fatal.

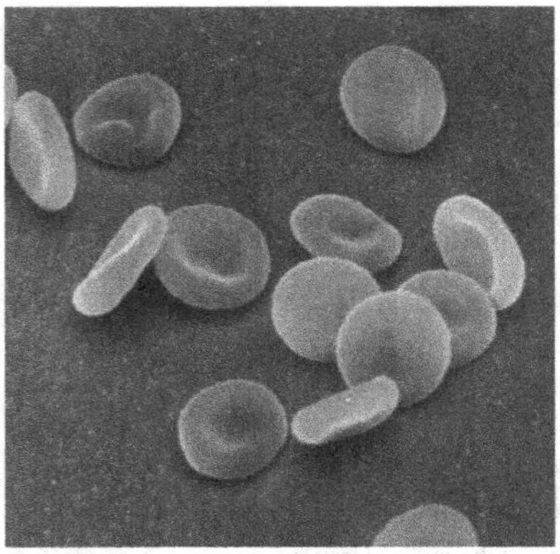

a.

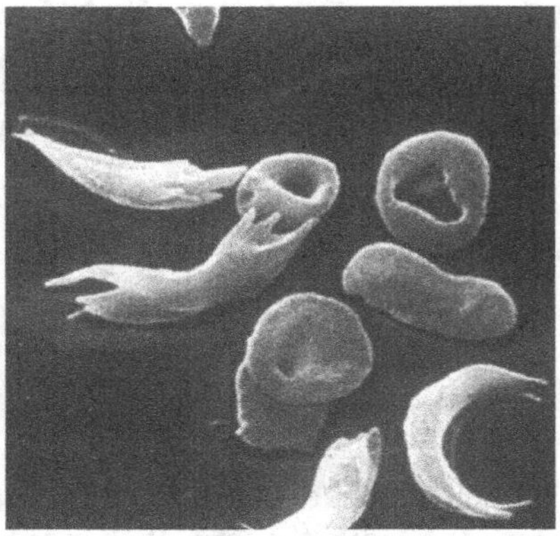

b.

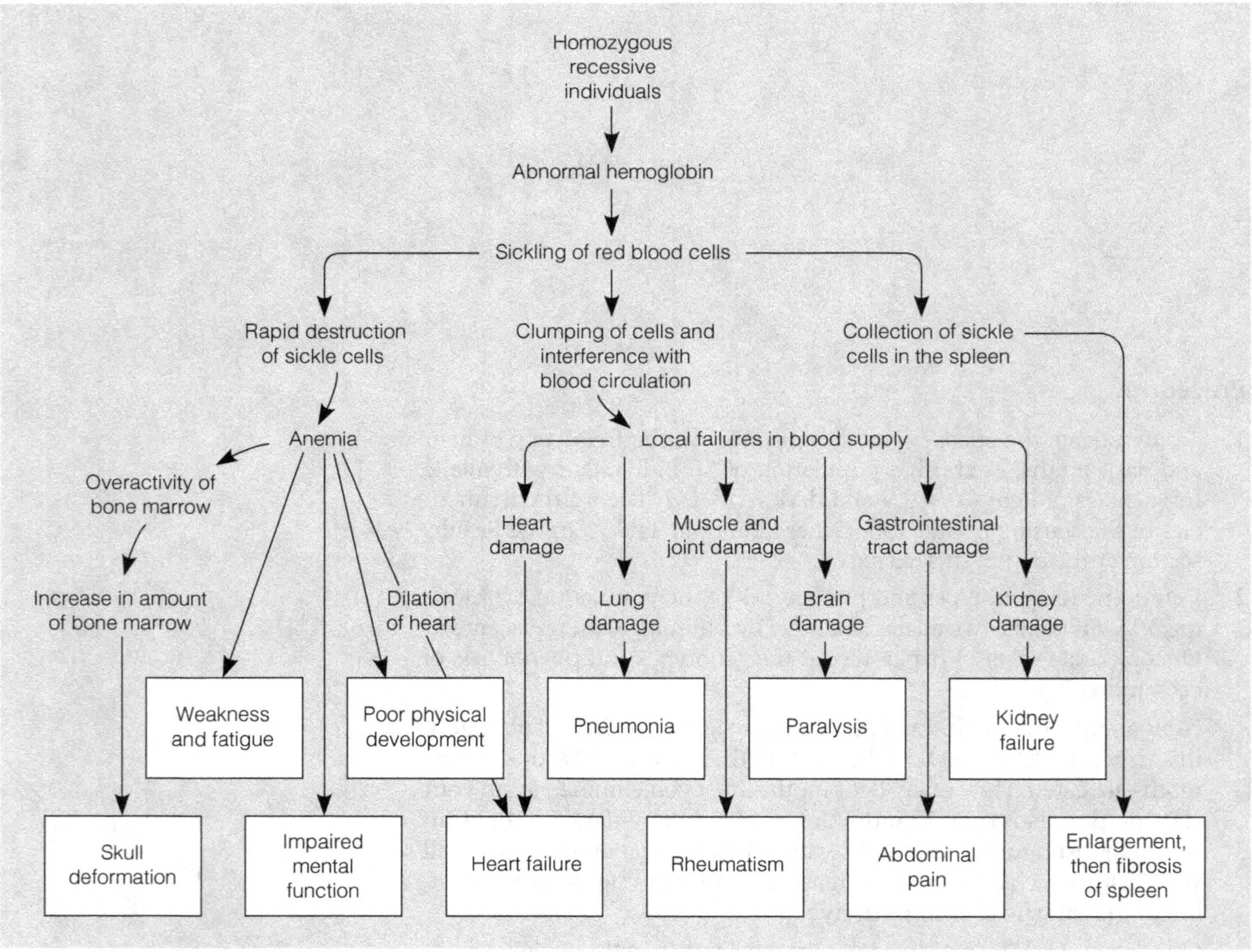

c.

2. *Sickle-Cell Disease*

Sickle-cell disease is caused by a mutant allele (Hb^-), which, in the homozygous condition, in the past was often fatal to people at quite young ages. The mutation causes the formation of abnormal, sickle-shaped red blood cells that clog vessels, cause organ damage, and are inefficient transporters of oxygen (Figure 6). Individuals who are heterozygous (Hb^+Hb^-) have the sickle-cell trait (a mild form of the disease), which is not fatal. Scientists were surprised to find a high frequency of the Hb^- allele in populations in Africa until they determined that heterozygous individuals have a *selective advantage* in resisting malaria. Although the homozygous condition may be lethal, the heterozygotes are under both a positive and a negative selection force. In malarial countries in tropical Africa, the heterozygotes are at an advantage compared to either homozygote.

Hypothesis

As your hypothesis, either propose a hypothesis that addresses natural selection in tropical Africa specifically or state the Hardy-Weinberg theorem.

Prediction

Either predict equilibrium values as a result of the Hardy-Weinberg theorem or predict the type of change that you expect to observe as a result of natural selection in tropical Africa (if/then).

Procedure

1. To investigate the role of selection under conditions of heterozygote advantage, establish a population of 50 individuals with allelic frequencies of 0.5 for both alleles. Record the frequencies of the starting population, Generation 0, in Table 5 in the Results section at the end of this exercise.

   For our model, assume that the selection force on each genotype is

   Hb^+Hb^+: 30% die of malaria
   Hb^+Hb^-: 10% die of malaria
   Hb^-Hb^-: 100% die of sickle-cell disease

2. Determine the genotypes and phenotypes of the population by selecting 50 individuals, two alleles at a time, by *sampling with replacement*. On a separate sheet of paper, record the 50 individuals. Select against each genotype by eliminating individuals according to the percent mortality shown above. How many Hb^+Hb^+ must be removed? How many Hb^+Hb^-? How many Hb^-Hb^-? Remove the appropriate number of beads for each color.

3. Calculate new allelic and genotypic frequencies based on the survivors, and reestablish the population using these new frequencies. Record your new frequencies in Table 5 in the Results section.
4. Continue the selection procedure, recording frequencies, for several generations, until you have sufficient evidence for your discussion in class.
5. Summarize your results in the Discussion section. Each group will present its results to the class at the end of the laboratory.

Results and Discussion for Selected Simulation

Results

Each team will record the results of its chosen experiment in Table 5. Modify the table to match the information you need to record for your simulation. Use the margins to expand the table or make additional notes.

Discussion

In preparation for presenting your results to the class, answer the following questions about your chosen simulation. Choose one team member to make the presentation, which should be organized in the format of a scientific paper.

1. Which of the conditions that are necessary for Hardy-Weinberg equilibrium were met?

2. Which condition was changed?

3. Briefly describe the scenario that your team simulated.

4. What were your predicted results?

5. How many generations did you simulate?

Table 5
Changes in Allelic and Genotypic Frequencies for Simulations Selected in Exercise 2.
Calculate expected frequencies based on the actual observed numbers in your experiment.

Experiment ____________ **Simulation of** ____________					
	Allelic Frequency		**Genotypic Frequency**		
Generation	p	q	p^2	$2pq$	q^2
0					
1					
2					
3					
4					
5					
6					
7					
8					
9					
10					

6. Sketch a graph of the change in p and q over time. You should have two lines, one for each frequency.

7. Describe the changes in allelic frequencies p and q over time. Did your results match your predictions? Explain.

8. Describe the changes in the genotypic frequencies.

9. Compare your final allelic and genotypic frequencies with those of the starting population.

10. If you can, formulate a general summary statement or conclusion.

11. Would you expect your results to be the same if you had chosen different starting allelic frequencies? Explain.

12. Critique your experimental design and outline your next simulation.

Be prepared to take notes, sketch graphs, and ask questions during the student presentations. You are responsible for understanding and answering questions for all conditions simulated in the laboratory.

EXERCISE 3
Investigating the Evolution of Populations Using Computer Simulations

Simulations involving only a few generations are fairly easy with the bead model, but this model is too cumbersome to obtain information about long-term changes or to combine two or more factors. Computer simulations will allow you to model 50 or 100 generations quickly or to do a series of simulations changing one factor and comparing the results. As with any scientific investigation, design your experiment to test a hypothesis and make predictions before you begin.

Several computer simulation programs are available; the instructor will demonstrate the software. From the following suggestions or your own ideas, pursue one of the factors in more detail or several in combination. Consult with your instructor before beginning your simulations. Be prepared to present your results in the next lab period in either oral or written form. Follow the procedures provided with the simulation program.

Mutation

Evolution can occur only when there is variation in a population, and the ultimate source for that variation is mutation. The mutation rate at most gene loci is actually very small (1×10^{-5} per gamete per generation), and the forward and backward rates of mutation are seldom at equilibrium. Evolutionary change as a result of mutation alone would occur very slowly, thus requiring many generations of simulation. Changes in this condition are best considered using a computer simulation that easily handles the lengthy process. *Do not simulate this condition using the bead model.*

Other Suggestions for Computer Simulations

1. The migration between natural populations seldom occurs at the same rate in both directions. Devise a model to simulate different migration rates between two populations. Compare your results with the bead model.

2. How does the probability of genetic fixation differ for populations that have different starting allelic frequencies? Simulate genetic drift using a variety of allelic frequencies.
3. How large must a population be to avoid genetic drift?
4. Devise a model to simulate selection for recessive lethals. Then, using the same starting allelic frequencies, select against the dominant lethals. Compare rate of change of allelic frequency as a result of lethality for dominant and recessive traits.
5. Mutation alone has only small effects on evolution over long periods of time. Using realistic rates of mutation, compare the evolutionary change for mutation alone with simulations that combine mutation and natural selection.
6. Combine factors (usually two at a time). For example, combine mutation and natural selection, using realistic estimates of mutation rates. Combine genetic drift and migration. Compare your results to simulations of each condition alone.

Questions for Review

1. Define and provide examples of the following terms: *evolution, population, gene pool, gene flow, genetic drift, bottleneck effect, founder effect, natural selection, genetic fixation, genotypic frequency, allelic frequency,* and *model.*
2. State the five conditions necessary for Hardy-Weinberg equilibrium.

3. Describe how gene flow, genetic drift, and natural selection bring about evolution.

4. In a population of 100 rock pink plants, 84 individuals have red flowers while 16 have white flowers. Assume that white petals are inherited as a recessive trait (a) and red petals as a dominant trait (A). What are the frequencies p and q? In the next generation, what will be the equilibrium genotypic frequencies?

5. Explain the difference between evolution and natural selection. Use an example to illustrate your answer.

Applying Your Knowledge

1. Red blood cells deficient in the enzyme NADH diaphorase cannot reduce the iron in methemoglobin to reform hemoglobin. As a result, individuals with this mutation (*bb*) appear blue. Individuals who are heterozygous (*Bb*) have reduced enzyme activity and their lips and fingers appear blue in the cold. Although the blue coloration is startling, the condition does not seem to affect the general health of individuals with the allele. The *b* allele is generally found in a low frequency in the population, however doctors were surprised to find a high frequency of "blue" people (compared to the larger U.S. population) in an isolated settlement in Alaska. Which of the factors investigated in this Lab Topic are most likely responsible for the high frequency of "blue" people.

2. Migration occurs at a constant rate between two populations of field mice. In one population, 65% of the population are white; in the other population, only 15% are white. What would you expect to happen to the allelic frequencies of these two populations over time?

3. Cystic fibrosis (CF) is caused by a genetic mutation resulting in defective proteins in secretory cells, mainly in the epithelial lining of the respiratory tract. The one in every 2,000 Caucasian babies who has the disease is homozygous for the recessive mutant. Although medical treatment is becoming more effective, in the past most children with CF died before their teens. About 20 Caucasians in 2,000 are carriers of the trait, having one mutant and one normal allele, but they do not develop the disease. According to rules of population genetics, the frequency of the homozygous recessive genotype should be rarer than it is. What is one possible explanation for the unusually high frequency of this allele in Caucasian populations?

4. The northern right whale that has its calving ground off the coast of Georgia is the most endangered large whale in the world. Although now protected from hunting, at one time this whale was widely sought by harpooners, and the present population is estimated to be fewer than 400 individuals. This drastic population reduction is an example of which evolutionary force studied in this lab topic?

   What might you predict has happened to frequencies of many alleles as a result of this event?

5. In the figure below, the frequency of dark forms of the peppered moth are shown for populations in northwestern England. Describe the changes in dark moth frequency from 1970 to 2000.

   Do these populations appear to be in Hardy-Weinberg equilibrium? Explain.

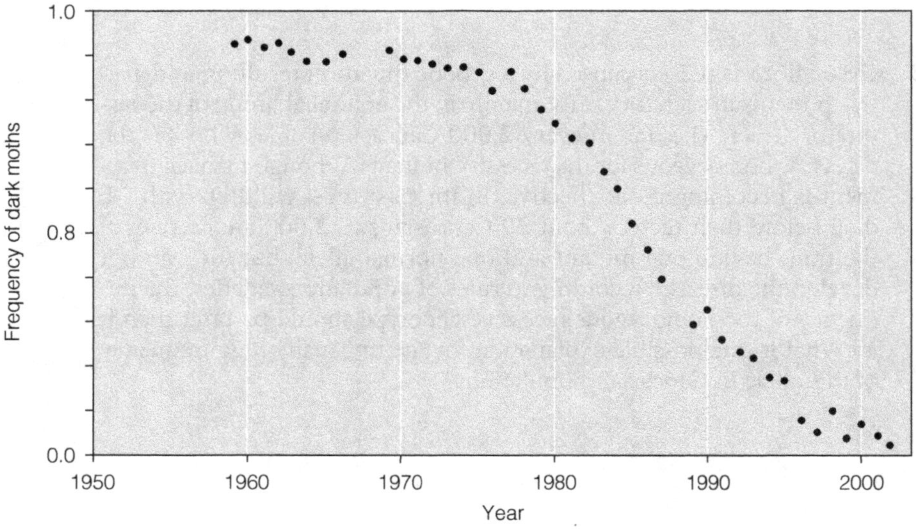

Frequency of peppered moth, dark form, in northwestern England (After Cook, 2003).

Using these results for the peppered moth, describe the roles of genetic variation and natural selection in evolutionary change.

References

Some parts of this lab topic were modified from J. C. Glase, 1993, "A Laboratory on Population Genetics and Evolution: A Physical Model and Computer Simulation," pages 29–41, in *Tested Studies for Laboratory Teaching,* Volume 7/8 (C. A. Goldman and P. L. Hauta, Editors). Proceedings of the 7th and 8th Workshop/Conference of the Association for Biology Laboratory Education (ABLE), 187 pages. Used by permission.

Ayala, F. J. *Population and Evolutionary Genetics: A Primer.* Menlo Park, CA: Benjamin Cummings, 1982.

Cook, L. M. "The Rise and Fall of the *Carbonaria* Form of the Peppered Moth," *The Quarterly Review of Biology,* 2003, 78(4), pp. 399–417.

Freeman, S., and J. C. Herron. *Evolutionary Analysis,* 2nd ed. Upper Saddle River, NJ: Prentice Hall, 2001.

Hardy, G. H. "Mendelian Proportions in a Mixed Population," *Science* (July 10, 1908) pp. 49–50. In this interesting early application of the "Hardy-Weinberg Theorem," this letter written by Hardy to the editor of *Science* refutes a report that dominant characters increase in frequency over time.

Website

Detailed information about sickle-cell anemia:
http://www.emory.edu/PEDS/SICKLE/

Population Genetics II: Determining Genetic Variation

Laboratory Objectives

After completing this lab topic, you should be able to:

1. Use gels to determine the extent of variation in the gene pool of a natural population.
2. Calculate genotypic and allelic frequencies and expected and observed heterozygosity.
3. Use the statistical tool chi-square to analyze results.
4. Describe how enzymes in a tissue extract can be separated by gel electrophoresis.
5. Discuss the relationship between genetic variation and evolution.

Introduction

Rosemary and Peter Grant's thirty-year study of ground finches on the island of Daphne in the Galápagos Islands has shown that a variation in bill sizes of ground finches exists and that there is a correlation between feeding behavior and bill size. Birds with larger bills preferentially feed on larger, harder seeds; birds with smaller bills feed on smaller seeds. In dry years when only large seeds are available, natural selection favors ground finches with large bills. What would happen to the ground finch population in a prolonged drought if there were no genetic variation in bill size and all finches had small bills? Without the presence of genetic variation, natural selection might eliminate all birds with small bills, and the population of ground finches could become extinct. Heritable variation is a requirement for evolutionary change in a population in response to changes in the environment.

Variation in populations is easily observed in almost any species; just look around your laboratory and campus. The variation in human populations seems almost limitless. Some variation in populations is the result of environmental differences, while other variation is genetically determined. Although height in humans has a genetic component, evidence suggests that the increase in the average height in humans over the past 50–100 years is primarily due to improvements in diet. Evolutionary biologists are interested in documenting the amount of genetic variation in populations, but separating environmental effects from genetic effects poses a difficult problem. Our earliest estimates of genetic variation came from artificial selection in plant and animal breeding. However, it is not feasible to conduct genetic crosses and analyses for every species of interest. The problem also is compounded by our inability to determine the genotype of individuals with a dominant phenotype; they could be heterozygous or homozygous.

In the 1960s, molecular biologists developed the technique of gel electrophoresis, which allowed scientists to detect differences in proteins based on their size and charge. These protein differences were the result of changes in the amino acid sequences of the proteins, which in turn were the result of **mutations,** or changes in the DNA sequence. Determining variation in proteins is simply one step from detecting changes in the genes themselves, and gel electrophoresis is much simpler and cheaper than DNA sequencing (determining the nucleotide sequences). In addition, proteins are basically inherited as codominant traits, allowing scientists to distinguish the heterozygous phenotype from the homozygous phenotype on gels. Using gel electrophoresis, population geneticists and evolutionary biologists have been able to survey populations of plants and animals, including humans, to determine the genetic variation present at a large number of genes.

The extent of genetic variation in populations is much greater than expected. One way to estimate genetic variation is to determine the proportion of the population that is heterozygous (having different alleles at a gene locus). On average, invertebrates are heterozygous at 11% of their genes; estimates for vertebrates are 4%, and plants, 16% (Hamrick, Linhart, and Mitton, 1979). Humans are heterozygous at approximately 7% of their genes. Assuming that humans have 100,000 genes in their chromosomes, you would have, on average, two different alleles at 7,000 of your genes. In contrast, the cheetah is heterozygous at only a small percentage (0.07%) of its genes. Understanding genetic variation and the factors that affect variation is essential to the management of this endangered species, which has little potential for evolutionary change because of its enormously reduced genetic variation.

As you begin your study of genetic variation, review the concepts and terminology for population genetics. You will be expected to use and understand the Hardy-Weinberg theorem as you investigate genetic variation in a natural population. Before continuing in this lab topic, complete Table 1, providing definitions and examples.

EXERCISE 1

Interpreting Banding Patterns in a Gel

In this exercise, you will investigate polymorphism in a population of rock pink plants (*Talinum mengesii*), a succulent commonly found growing in shallow soils on rock outcrops in the southeast. You will determine the frequency of (1) different genotypes (genotypic frequency), (2) different alleles (allelic frequency), and (3) heterozygotes (heterozygosity) in the population. These frequencies will allow you to estimate the extent of genetic variation in the rock pink population.

To perform this investigation, you will study diagrammatic reproductions of starch gels that have been stained for selected enzymes found in these plants.

Table 1
Population Genetics Terminology

Gene locus
Allele
Allelic frequency
Genotypic frequency
Heterozygote
Hardy-Weinberg theorem
Natural selection
Genetic drift
Migration
Mutation
Random mating

(Although starch gels were used for this exercise, acrylamide, cellulose acetate, and agarose gels can also be used.) Starch gels are made by boiling purified potato starch in a buffer solution with known pH and ionic strength and then allowing it to solidify in a tray. Paper wicks are soaked in a crude extract made by homogenizing individual flower buds from the various rock pink plants, each wick being soaked in a different plant bud homogenate. The wicks are then inserted in a slot cut along the width of the gel; this slot is referred to as the **origin** (Figure 1a). The gel is linked to two buffer tanks by contact wicks and connected to an electric current, creating a charged field through which the proteins migrate based on their charge and size (Figure 1b and c). Once the enzymes are sufficiently separated to allow the investigator to detect differences in the distances migrated by the enzymes, the gels are removed from the electric field and sliced into three or more thin slabs. Each gel contains all the enzymes present in the original tissue spread throughout the gel, but the investigator stains for only one enzyme in each gel or slice of gel. Since enzymes have specific substrates, each gel can be treated with the substrate for the enzyme of interest plus a salt that reacts with the product of the enzyme reaction to produce a colored band. The result will be one or more colored bands for each individual surveyed in a

Figure 1.
Preparation of starch gels and techniques of gel electrophoresis.
(a) Wicks containing the enzymes are placed in a slot cut in the starch gel. This slot is called the *origin.* (b) The gel is linked to two buffer tanks by contact wicks and connected to an electric current. (c) Enzymes migrate to characteristic positions in the gel.

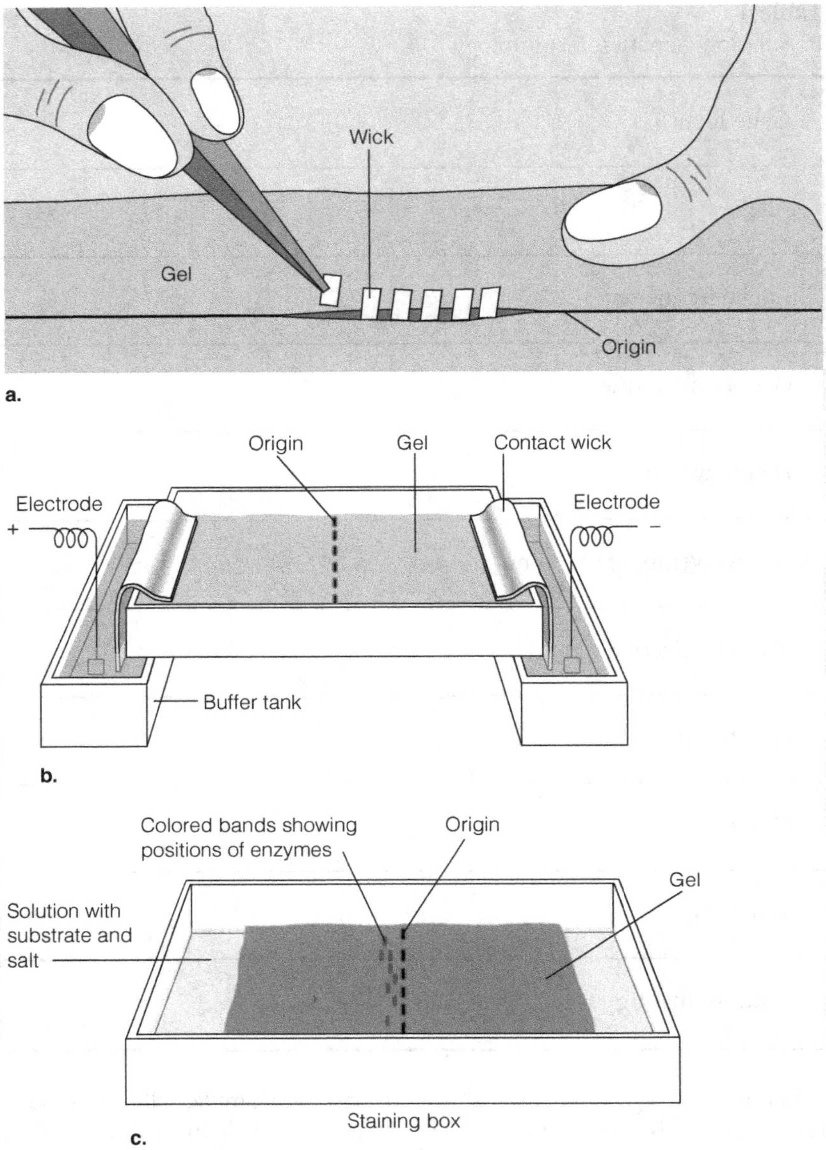

population. The number of bands and the distance migrated can be used to determine the genotype of individual organisms.

Remember that each protein in the gel migrates in a direction and at a rate that depend on two factors: net electrical charge and molecular size. For example, an enzyme with a greater negative charge will move more quickly toward the anode (the positive pole) than an enzyme with a lesser negative charge. Similarly, a smaller molecule will move more rapidly than a larger molecule. The number and type of amino acids that make up an enzyme determine its size and charge, and the differences in number and type of amino acids depend on mutations in genes, producing alternate forms, or alleles. The enzymes you will study in the rock pink population all migrate toward the anode.

The exercise will be carried out using reproductions of photographs of three slabs sliced from a gel. One slab was stained for alcohol dehydrogenase (ADH), another for phosphoglucoisomerase (PGI), and another for phosphoglucomutase (PGM) (Figure 2). This gel contained enzymes from 25 individual plants.

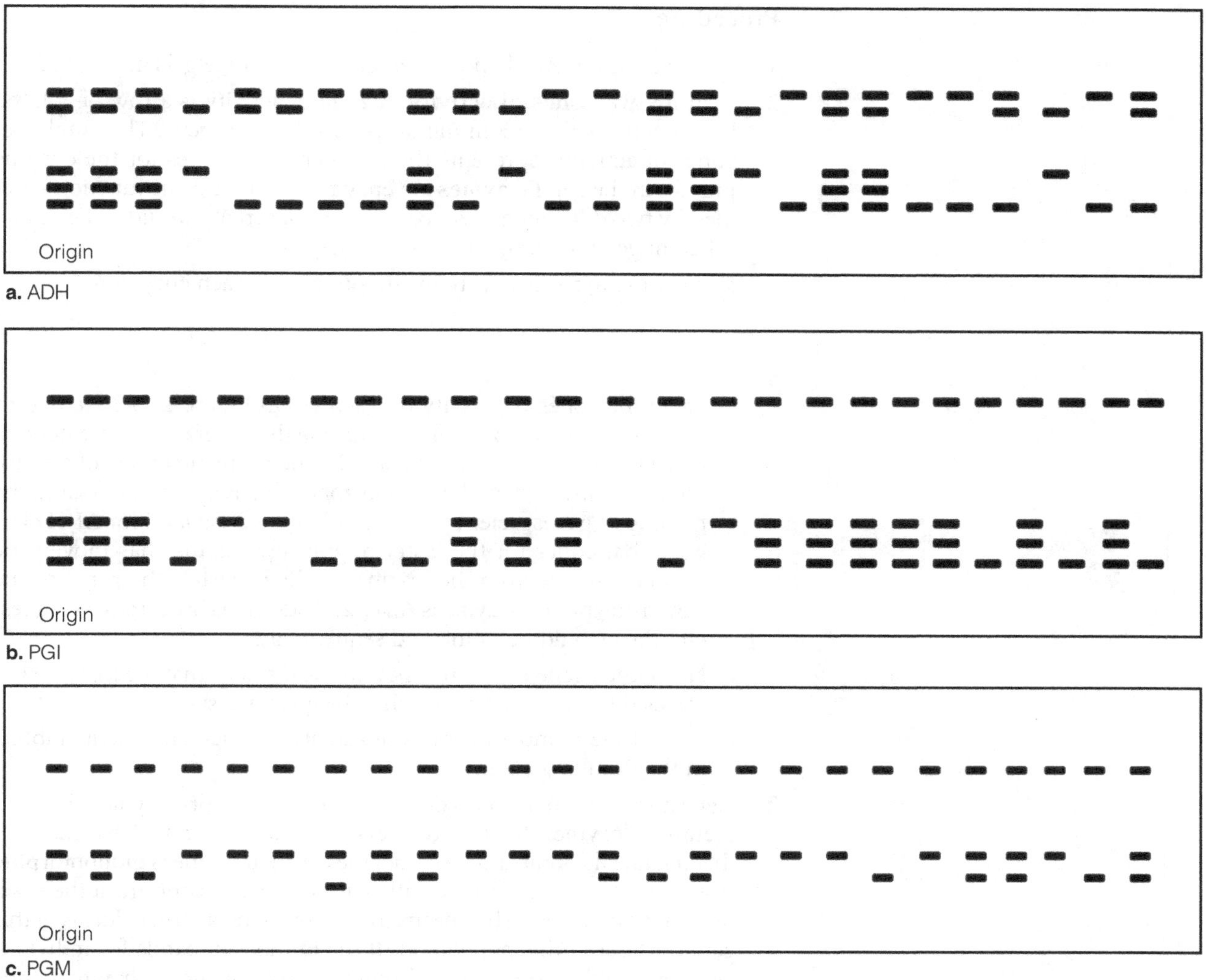

Figure 2.
The gels to be interpreted in Exercise 1. Each gel has been stained to reveal a different enzyme: (a) alcohol dehydrogenase (ADH), (b) phosphoglucoisomerase (PGI), and (c) phosphoglucomutase (PGM).

Lab Study A. Terminology Associated with Enzymes and Gel Electrophoresis

In this lab study, you will become familiar with the terminology used to describe enzymes and the bands that are visible after separating and staining the enzymes.

Materials

No materials are needed for this lab study.

Procedure

1. Observe the enzyme banding patterns in the three gels in Figure 2.
2. Identify two **zones of activity.** A zone of activity is a row of colored bands in the gel, representing the products of one gene. The number of zones of activity represents the number of isozymes for the enzyme present in the gel. **Isozymes** are enzymes with the same function specified by two different genes, so two zones of activity would indicate two different genes coding for the same enzyme.
   a. How many zones of activity are present for each enzyme?

   b. Label the zones of activity on each gel in Figure 2. Where two or more isozymes are present, the enzyme that migrates the greater distance from the origin is considered to be in the first zone of activity, the lesser distance, in the second zone of activity. To understand the naming of genes, refer to the top of Figure 2, stained for ADH. The gene that codes for the faster-migrating isozyme (has moved the greater distance from the origin) is called ADH-1; the gene for the slower-migrating isozyme is ADH-2. If additional isozymes were present, they would be numbered sequentially.
   c. Name each gene by its enzyme and the distance that the isozyme has traveled (isozyme 1 has traveled the greater distance).
   d. Record the number of zones of activity for each enzyme in Table 2 in the Results section.
3. Determine whether each gene is monomorphic or polymorphic and identify allozymes. If all individuals in one activity zone have enzymes that migrate the same distance from the origin, the gene is **monomorphic** (for example, PGI-1). All the bands in this activity zone are at the exact same level in the gel. This means that there are no alternate forms of this gene, at least in this population. If the number of bands for individuals of a population varies and there are two or more enzyme bands within an activity zone, the gene is **polymorphic** (for example, PGI-2), and the variant enzymes are called **allozymes** because they are enzymes coded by alleles of a single gene locus.
   a. Designate which genes are monomorphic and which are polymorphic in Table 2.
   b. Label allozymes on at least one gel in Figure 2.
4. Determine for your study gels (Figure 2) whether each enzyme is monomeric, dimeric, or trimeric. Record your answers in Table 2 in the Results section. Use Figure 3 and the following discussion to help you make your determinations.

When proteins are synthesized from DNA, one polypeptide is made at a time. For some enzymes, this polypeptide is all that is necessary to have a functioning enzyme, and the enzyme is described as being **monomeric.**

Other enzymes may need two or more polypeptides to bind together before the enzyme is active. An enzyme that needs two polypeptides in order to become active is called a **dimeric enzyme,** or **dimer.** If an enzyme requires three polypeptides in order to function, it is called a **trimeric enzyme,** or **trimer;** four polypeptides, a **tetrameric enzyme,** or **tetramer;** and so on.

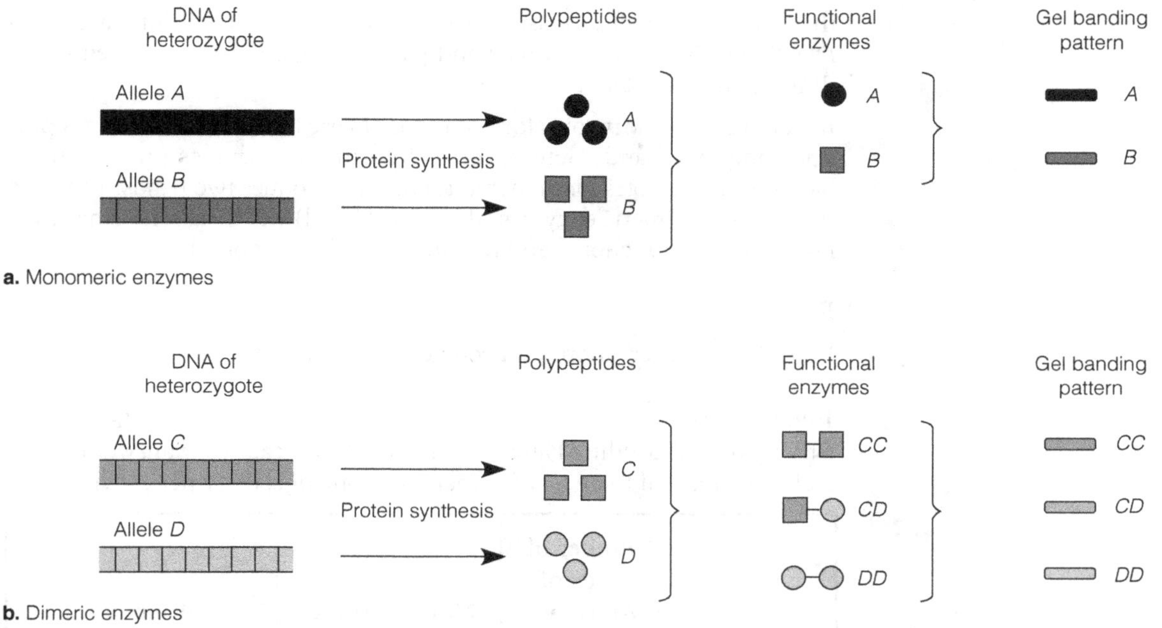

Figure 3.
The interpretation of banding patterns for a heterozygote when the enzyme is monomeric or dimeric.
(a) For monomeric enzymes, two different polypeptides are produced in a heterozygote, but either is a functioning enzyme. Therefore, only two bands will form in the heterozygote: *A* and *B*. (b) For dimeric enzymes, the enzyme can function only if two polypeptides are linked. In a heterozygous individual, the alleles produce two different polypeptides that may link in three configurations. Two like polypeptides can link (*C* to *C* or *D* to *D*), or the two unlike polypeptides can link (*C* to *D*). Each of these three linkages will migrate at different rates on a gel.

Since our staining procedure requires that the enzymes be functioning in order to be seen, we see only enzymes in their active form (whether that form is monomer, dimer, or some other form). Therefore, if some of the individuals on the gel have two different alleles coding for the polypeptides (that is, if the individuals are heterozygous), you can determine if the enzyme is dimeric, trimeric, or tetrameric.

Distinguishing Monomeric and Dimeric Enzymes

If an enzyme is monomeric, in the homozygous individual only one band will appear on the gel, but in the heterozygote two bands will appear on the gel, indicating functional polypeptides, one for each of the codominant alleles (Figure 3a).

If the enzyme is dimeric, it requires two polypeptides bound together to function. An individual that is homozygous for the gene will produce only one kind of polypeptide, which can only bind to the same kind of polypeptide to give one kind of dimer. This will produce only one band on the gel. Heterozygous individuals, however, produce two polypeptides that can bind together in three different ways. Consider a dimeric enzyme with two different polypeptides, one coded for by allele *C*, the other by allele *D*. If *C* polypeptides run faster than *D* polypeptides on the gel (because of charge), then *CC* dimers will run faster than *CD* dimers, which will run faster than *DD* dimers. This gives a three-band pattern (Figure 3b) and is seen in the dimeric enzyme ADH-2.

In summary, homozygotes for both monomeric and dimeric enzymes produce only one band. Heterozygotes for dimeric enzymes produce three bands. Heterozygotes for monomeric enzymes produce two bands. The third band seen in dimeric enzymes (the hybrid band) will be absent, since each polypeptide is functional and hybrid molecules do not form.

Results

Record your observations and conclusions in Table 2.

Table 2
Observation of Banding Patterns in Figure 2. Indicate your answer for each gene locus if there is more than one zone of activity per enzyme.

Enzyme	Number of Zones of Activity (Genes)	Monomorphic or Polymorphic	Monomeric or Dimeric
ADH (Fig 2a)			
PGI (Fig 2b)			
PGM (Fig 2c)			

Discussion

1. What evidence do you have that the zones of activity for PGI represent isozymes rather than allozymes? (Note that the only way to be certain that bands are allozymes of the same gene is to perform genetic crosses and analyses.)

2. Do any of the genes have a rare allele, that is, an allele that appears only occasionally?

3. You see three bands in an individual in the ADH-2 zone of activity. Explain why you conclude that these three bands indicate that this

enzyme is dimeric, that the individual is heterozygous, and that these bands do *not* represent fast, slow, and very slow alleles.

Lab Study B. Scoring the Gel

Materials

calculator

Introduction

Scoring a gel involves examining the banding pattern for each individual represented in the gel and determining the genotype and phenotype of that individual. In this lab study, you will summarize these data for all polymorphic genes represented by the enzymes in the gels (see Figure 2).

Procedure

1. Within each zone of activity, identify allozymes according to their rate of migration from the origin (*f* = fast, or the enzyme band farthest from the origin; *s* = slow; *vs* = very slow). Label Figure 2 with your results.
2. Determine the genotype and phenotype of each polymorphic individual in the population. Note that at the protein level of expression, alleles are codominant and therefore genotype and phenotype correspond. A heterozygote is immediately known because both alleles are expressed in the form of two bands if the enzyme is monomeric or in the form of three bands if dimeric.

Results

Summarize and record your results in Table 3.

Table 3
Number of Individuals of Each Genotype for Each Polymorphic Gene
(*f* = fast allele, *s* = slow allele, *vs* = very slow allele)

Polymorphic Gene Locus	**Phenotype:**	*f*	s	*f*/s	vs	*f*/vs	s/vs	**Total Number of Individuals**
	Genotype:	*f*/*f*	s/s	*f*/s	vs/vs	*f*/vs	s/vs	
ADH-1								
ADH-2								
PGI-2								
PGM-2								

Discussion

How many bands would be present in a heterozygote if the enzyme is a tetramer? Draw the heterozygote for a tetramer.

Lab Study C. Determining Genotypic and Allelic Frequencies

In this lab study, you will use the data from Table 3 to determine the frequencies of genotypes (genotypic frequencies) and frequencies of alleles (allelic frequencies) in the rock pink population.

Materials

calculator

Procedure

1. Determine genotypic frequencies for ADH-1, ADH-2, PGI-2, and PGM-2. To do this, divide the number of individuals of each genotype by the total number of individuals.
2. Determine allelic frequencies for the same enzymes. Count the number of times the allele appears in the population and divide by the total number of alleles in the population. Record your results in Table 4.

   An individual with only a single slow band has two "slow" alleles while a heterozygous fast/slow individual has one "fast" allele and one "slow" allele. The total number of alleles in the sample is twice the number of individuals because each individual carries two alleles.

Results

Record your conclusions in Table 4.

Discussion

Explain how this population of the diploid rock pink can have three alleles present.

Table 4
Genotypic and Allelic Frequencies for ADH-1, ADH-2, PGI-2, and PGM-2

Polymorphic Gene Locus	Genotypic Frequency						Allelic Frequency		
	f/f	*s/s*	*f/s*	*vs/vs*	*f/vs*	*s/vs*	*f*	*s*	*vs*
ADH-1									
ADH-2									
PGI-2									
PGM-2									

Lab Study D. Determining Heterozygosity

Materials

calculator

Introduction

One way to measure the extent of genetic variation in a population is to determine the percentage of genes that are polymorphic—that is, having more than one allele at a gene locus. This estimate of genetic variation can be problematic because a gene with two alleles is counted in the same way as a gene with five alleles. Also, a rare allele (appearing only occasionally in the population) will be included in the same way as an allele that occurs in 50% of the population. Another measure, heterozygosity, appears to provide a better estimate of genetic variation. **Heterozygosity** (*H*) is the average frequency of heterozygous individuals per gene locus.

To calculate *observed* heterozygosity, first determine the frequency of heterozygotes at each gene locus (divide the number of heterozygotes by the total number of individuals in the population). Then total the frequency of heterozygous individuals for all gene loci and divide by the total number of loci. (This final average is calculated by including both monomorphic and polymorphic loci in your total number.)

Table 5
Sample Calculation of Heterozygosity in a Mouse Population

Gene Locus	Number of Heterozygotes	Frequency of Observed Heterozygotes
A-1	9	0.45 (9/20)
A-2	2	0.10
B-1	8	0.40
C-1	0	0
C-2	4	0.20
		Σ 1.15

For example, in a population sample of 20 mice, you might study five gene loci and get the results shown in Table 5. Then the average heterozygosity for this population would be

$$H = \frac{1.15}{5} = 0.23$$

The *observed heterozygosity* in this population of mice is 0.23.

Procedure

1. Using data from Table 3, record the number of heterozygotes for ADH-1, ADH-2, PGI-2, and PGM-2 in Table 6.
2. Divide the number of heterozygotes for each gene locus by the number of individuals in the population. This is the frequency of heterozygotes for that gene locus. Record this information in Table 6.
3. Determine the population average heterozygosity. Divide the sum of heterozygosity for all loci by the total number of loci (including both polymorphic and monomorphic gene loci).

Results

Record all results in Table 6.

Table 6
Heterozygosity for Each Locus and Average Heterozygosity for Population

Polymorphic Gene Locus	Number of Individuals		
	Heterozygotes	Total	Frequency of Observed Heterozygotes
ADH-1			
ADH-2			
PGI-2			
PGM-2			
Population average heterozygosity:			

Discussion

List all the heterozygous genotypes for the PGM-2 locus. Did you record the correct number in Table 6?

Lab Study E. Comparing Observed and Expected Heterozygosity

In natural populations, the amount of genetic variation might be affected by the reproductive behavior of the organisms. For example, populations that are highly inbred, from either mating between close relatives in animals or self-pollination in plants, might have a lower heterozygosity than expected for a population with the same allelic frequencies with random mating.

You can determine the *expected* heterozygosity (expected in a large, randomly mating population) from the allelic frequencies.

To calculate expected heterozygosity for a gene locus with three alleles, the frequency of the alleles would be $f1$, $f2$, and $f3$. The frequency of the homozygotes (from Hardy-Weinberg) would be $(f1)^2$, $(f2)^2$, and $(f3)^2$. Therefore, the expected frequency of heterozygotes would be

$$H_{exp} = 1 - [(f1)^2 + (f2)^2 + (f3)^2 + \cdots]$$

For the mouse example, if two alleles, *a* and *b,* exist for the A-1 gene locus, and the frequency for each of these alleles is known, then the expected heterozygosity for the A-1 gene locus can be calculated. Suppose that the frequency of *a* is 0.6 and the frequency of *b* is 0.4. Then the expected heterozygosity would be

$$H_{exp} = 1 - [(0.6)^2 + (0.4)^2] = 0.48$$

To calculate the expected *number of heterozygotes,* simply multiply the total number of individuals in the population by the expected heterozygosity. For gene locus A-1 in the mouse example, the expected number of heterozygotes in the sample of 20 individuals would be $(20 \times 0.48) = 10$ (rounded off). Using chi-square analysis, you can then determine whether the observed numbers of heterozygotes are significantly different from those expected in a large, randomly mating population.

In this lab study, you will calculate the expected number of heterozygotes for the enzymes in the gels in Figure 2 and then use chi-square analysis to determine whether observed and expected numbers of heterozygotes are significantly different in the rock pink population.

Materials

calculator

Procedure

1. Calculate the expected heterozygosity for ADH-1, ADH-2, PGI-2, and PGM-2. Record your results below. (Refer to Table 4 for allelic frequencies.)

	Expected Heterozygosity
ADH-1	
ADH-2	
PGI-2	
PGM-2	

2. Calculate the expected number of heterozygotes for ADH-1, ADH-2, PGI-2, and PGM-2, rounding to the nearest whole number. Record these data in Table 7.
3. Using data from Table 6, record the observed number of heterozygotes for these gene loci in Table 7.
4. Record the number of homozygous individuals observed for these genes in Table 7.
5. Calculate the expected number of homozygous individuals. To do this, subtract the number of expected heterozygotes from the total number of individuals in the population.
6. On a separate paper, use the chi-square test to determine whether the observed and expected numbers are significantly different. Record your conclusions in Table 7.

Results

Record data and significance of the chi-square test results in Table 7.

Table 7
Observed Heterozygotes and Homozygotes for ADH-1, ADH-2, PGI-2, and PGM-2 and Significance of Chi-Square Test

Polymorphic Gene Locus	Number of Heterozygotes		Number of Homozygotes		Significant Difference	
	Observed	Expected	Observed	Expected	Yes	No
ADH-1						
ADH-2						
PGI-2						
PGM-2						

Discussion

1. What factors, other than nonrandom mating, could account for a significant difference between observed and expected numbers of heterozygotes in living populations?

2. Why do electrophoretic estimates of heterozygosity underestimate genetic variation at the protein level?

EXERCISE 2

Interpreting Results of Gels of a Hypothetical Population

In this exercise, you will apply your knowledge and understanding of genetic variation and gel electrophoresis to a hypothetical problem.

Problem

Another species of *Talinum*, called *rock red,* has been found on sandstone outcrops in south Georgia. This rare plant is a succulent that inhabits the shallow soils found on rock outcrops. These rock outcroppings are isolated islands of rock found within a sea of forests, fields, and suburban developments. Although the rock red is insect-pollinated, the position of the reproductive structures in the flowers of some populations promotes self-pollination when the flower closes.

In this exercise, you will evaluate gels for the enzymes aconitase (ACN), glyceraldehyde phosphate dehydrogenase (GDH), and PGI. You will pose hypotheses and make predictions, interpret the gels, score the isozymes and allozymes, determine the genotypic and allelic frequencies, and calculate heterozygosity.

Hypothesis

For this newly discovered species, state a hypothesis concerning the amount of genetic variation present in the population based on the species characteristics (as previously stated) and the factors that affect genetic variation.

Prediction

Predict whether the observed heterozygosity will differ significantly from the expected heterozygosity.

Procedure

1. Interpret the bands and score the gel in Figure 4. Determine isozymes, allozymes, and monomorphic and polymorphic loci, and whether the enzymes are monomeric, dimeric, and so on. (If you need assistance, refer to Exercise 1.)

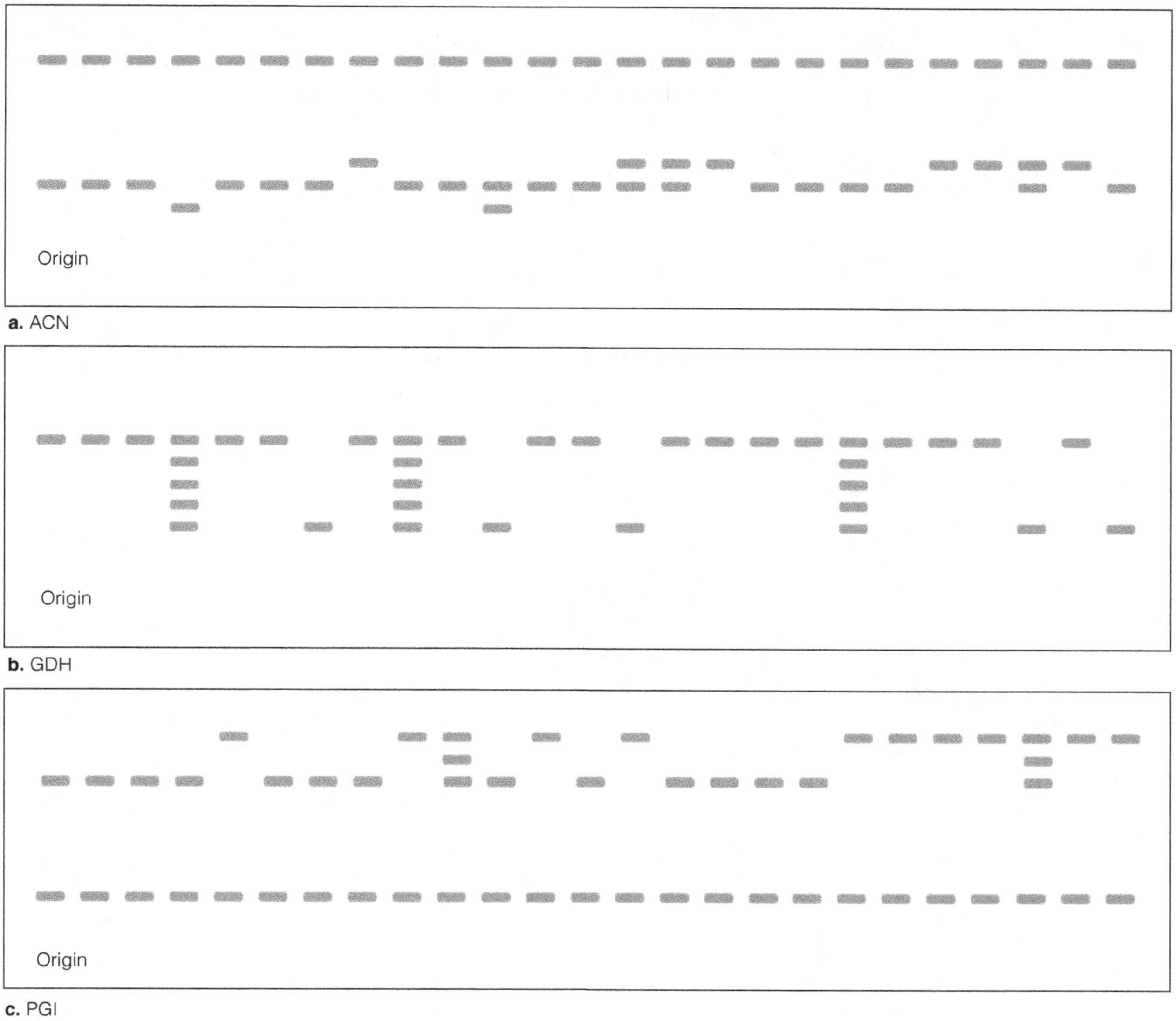

Figure 4.
Gels representing the hypothetical population. (a) Gel stained for aconitase (ACN). (b) Gel stained for glyceraldehyde phosphate dehydrogenase (GDH). (c) Gel stained for phosphoglucoisomerase (PGI).

2. In the Results section, design appropriate tables to record your data. (Use Tables 3 and 4 as examples.) You should have one row for each gene locus (include monomorphic and polymorphic genes) and one column for each genotype.
3. Count and record the number of individuals of each genotype for the gene products stained in the gels.
4. Be prepared to present your results in a class discussion.

Results

1. Determine genotypic and allelic frequencies for the genes, recording your data in tables that you have designed.

2. Calculate the frequency of heterozygotes for each locus and the average heterozygosity for the population. Record your data in an appropriate table.

3. Calculate the expected heterozygosity for each gene locus. Record your data in the margin of your lab manual. Use the formula

$$H_{exp} = 1 - [(f1)^2 + (f2)^2 + \cdots]$$

4. Calculate the expected number of heterozygotes for each gene locus. Multiply heterozygosity by the number of individuals in the population. Record your data in an appropriate table.

5. On separate paper, use the chi-square test to determine if observed and expected numbers are significantly different.

Discussion

1. What was the observed average heterozygosity for this population?

2. Discuss the significance of the chi-square test results.

3. Was your hypothesis supported? Describe the factors that may affect the genetic variation in this population.

4. What is the average heterozygosity for this population?

5. Based on your results, what is the evolutionary potential for this species?

Questions for Review

1. Define the following terms, giving examples when appropriate: *heterozygosity, isozymes, allozymes, monomorphic, polymorphic, monomeric, dimeric, trimeric.*
2. Using a separate paper, practice calculating genotypic frequencies, allelic frequencies, and heterozygosity by solving the following problems (from Ayala, 1982).
   a. Three genotypes were observed at the PGM-1 locus in a human population. In a sample of 1,110 individuals, the three genotypes occurred in the following numbers (1 and 2 represent two different alleles):

Genotypes:	1/1	1/2	2/2
Numbers:	634	391	85

   Calculate the genotypic and allelic frequencies.

b. Two human serum haptoglobins are determined by two alleles at a single locus. In a sample of 219 Egyptians, the three genotypes occurred in the following numbers (1 and 3 represent the two alleles):

Genotypes:	1/1	1/3	3/3
Numbers:	9	135	75

What are the frequencies of the two alleles?

c. Calculate the expected frequency of heterozygotes, assuming random mating, from the data given in problems 2a and 2b. Use the chi-square test to determine whether the observed and expected numbers of heterozygous individuals are significantly different.

3. Observe the two gels below (from Hebert and Beaton, 1989). Gel A is stained for the enzyme leucine aminopeptidase (LAP); gel B, for the enzyme phosphoglucose isomerase (PGI). For each gel:
   a. Identify and label zones of activity.
   b. Indicate isozymes and allozymes.
   c. Tell if the gene is monomorphic or polymorphic.
   d. Determine if the enzyme is monomeric, dimeric, or trimeric.
   e. Calculate allelic and genotypic frequencies for all genes.

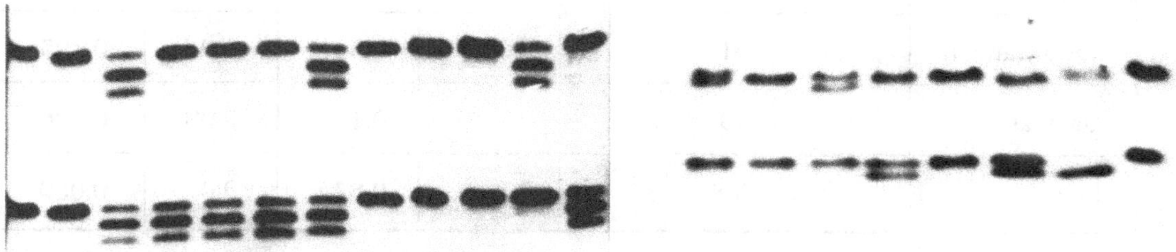

a. Leucine aminopeptidase (LAP) **b.** Phosphoglucoisomerase (PGI)

(After Hebert and Beaton, 1989)

Applying Your Knowledge

1. Table 8 (from Ayala, 1982) gives the number of individuals in each of the MN blood groups in samples from various human populations. Using a separate paper, calculate the genotypic and allelic frequencies,

Table 8
Number of Individuals in Each of the MN Blood Groups

Population	M	MN	N	Total
Belgians	896	1,559	645	3,100
English	121	200	101	422
Egyptians	140	245	117	502
Ainu	90	253	161	504
Fijians	22	89	89	200
Papuans	14	48	138	200

as well as the expected number of heterozygous individuals, for each population. Test whether the observed and expected numbers of heterozygotes agree.

Table 9
Frequencies of the Slow (*s*), Fast (*f*), and Very Fast (*vf*) Alleles of Alcohol Dehydrogenase (ADH) in Populations of Adult *Drosophila mojavensis*

Locality	Number of Individuals	*s*	*f*	*vf*	*H*
Agua Caliente	124	0.448	0.552	0.0	0.363
Grand Canyon	41	0.659	0.341	0.0	0.195
Guaymas	49	0.755	0.163	0.082	0.326
Mulege	50	0.130	0.870	0.0	0.060

H = heterozygosity determined by direct count

2. Table 9 (from Cleland et al., 1996) gives the results of starch gel electrophoresis of fruit fly enzymes from four localities in Arizona.

Complete the following table describing populations of *D. mojavensis* studied:

a. Using the heterozygosity data, determine the number of heterozygotes and homozygotes in the population.

b. Calculate the number of homozygous *ss* or *ff* individuals in the population. Remember that each individual in the population has two alleles and that heterozygotes will have one *f* and one *s*. (*Hint:* This population is *not* in Hardy-Weinberg equilibrium.)

Locality	Number of Individuals				Number of *vf* Alleles in Population
	Heterozygotes	Homozygotes	*ss*	*ff*	
Agua Caliente					
Grand Canyon					
Guaymas					
Mulege					

How would you describe the *vf* allele?

Can you determine if *vf* alleles are in heterozygous or homozygous individuals?

References

Ayala, F. J. *Population and Evolutionary Genetics: A Primer.* Menlo Park, CA: Benjamin Cummings, 1982.

Cleland, S., G. D. Hocutt, C. M. Breitmeyer, T. A. Markow, and E. Pfeiler. "Alcohol Dehydrogenase Polymorphism in Barrel Cactus Populations of *Drosophila mojavensis*." *Genetica* 1996, vol. 98, pp. 115–117.

Grant, Peter. "Natural selection and Darwin's finches." *Scientific American,* October, 1991, pp. 82–87.

Hamrick, J. L., Y. B. Linhart, and J. B. Mitton. "Relationships between Life History Characteristics and Electrophoretically Detectable Genetic Variation in Plants." *Annual Review of Ecology and Systematics* 1979, pp. 173–200.

Hebert, D. N., and M. J. Beaton. *Methodologies for Allozyme Analysis Using Cellulose Acetate Electrophoresis.* Helena Laboratories, 1989.

May, B. "Starch Gel Electrophoresis of Allozymes." in *Molecular Genetic Analysis of Populations—A Practical Approach,* A. R. Hoelzel, editor. 1992, pp. 1–27.

Soltis, D. E., and P. S. Soltis, eds. *Isozymes in Plant Biology. Advances in Plant Sciences Series,* vol. 4. Portland, OR: Dioscorides Press, 1989.

Protists and Fungi

This lab topic gives you another opportunity to practice scientific processes. Be prepared to use this information to design an experiment with protists or fungi.

Laboratory Objectives

After completing this lab topic, you should be able to:

1. Discuss the diversity of protists and fungi, and the current interest in their phylogenetic relationships.
2. Describe the diversity of protists, explaining the means of obtaining nutrition and method of locomotion for each group.
3. Identify representative organisms in several major protistan clades.
4. Discuss the ecological role and economic importance of protists.
5. Describe the characteristics and representative organisms of the green algae and their relationship to land plants.
6. Describe the phyla of the kingdom Fungi, recognizing and identifying representative organisms in each.
7. Describe differences in reproduction in fungal phyla.
8. Discuss the ecological role and economic importance of fungi.
9. Design and perform an independent investigation of a protist or an organism in the kingdom Fungi.

Introduction

Unicellular eukaryotic organisms originated over 2 billion years ago, and today they are found in every habitable region of Earth. The enormous diversity of organisms, their numerous adaptations, and their cellular complexity reflect the long evolutionary history of eukaryotes. For almost 30 years, scientists placed these diverse groups of unicellular organisms into

---

From *Investigating Biology Laboratory Manual*, Fifth Edition, Judith G. Morgan and M. Eloise Brown Carter.

the kingdom Protista. The Protista usually included all organisms not placed in the other eukaryotic kingdoms of Plants, Animals, and Fungi. This catchall kingdom included not only the unicellular eukaryotes, but also their multicellular relatives, like the giant kelps and seaweeds. However, most scientists now agree that the kingdom Protista should be divided into several kingdoms within the domain Eukarya. Some propose six eukaryotic kingdoms, others propose more. In this lab topic we will refer to this diverse group as protists meaning a general term, not a taxonomic category.

The most familiar protists, commonly called algae and protozoans, have been well studied since the earliest development of the microscope. Therefore, one might assume that the taxonomic relationships among these groups are well understood. However, their phylogeny (evolutionary history) has been difficult to determine from comparisons of cell structure and function, nutrition, and reproduction. Recent molecular and biochemical research, particularly the ability to sequence ribosomal and transfer RNA genes, has provided strong new evidence for reconstructing the relationships of the protists. As scientists have discovered more of the molecular biology of these and other organisms, the work has challenged not only the five-kingdom classification scheme, but also our definition of a kingdom.

Most recently scientists have suggested that studies of protists using **clades** can be meaningful for indicating evolutionary relationships. A clade is a group of species, all of which are descended from one ancestral species, representing one phylogenetic group. Many characteristics, including molecular and biochemical evidence, are used when organizing clades. As more information from a variety of sources becomes available, major groupings or clades will surely be modified. These investigations into the nature of eukaryotic diversity demonstrate the process of scientific inquiry. New technologies, new ideas, and novel experiments are used to test hypotheses, and the resulting evidence must be consistent with the existing body of knowledge and classification scheme. The results lead to modification of our hypotheses and further research. No matter how many groups or clades are proposed, remember that this is a reflection of the evolution of eukaryotes over the rich history of the earth. It is not surprising that the diversity of life does not easily fit into our constructed categories.

In this lab topic, we will study diverse examples of protists. These protists represent some of the most common clades. In addition to evolutionary relationships, you will give particular attention to nutrition, locomotion, and cellular complexity of each example.

Fungi, one of the kingdoms of the five-kingdom scheme, are studied in this lab topic, and you will investigate plant evolution and animal evolution in subsequent lab topics.

At the end of this lab topic, you will be asked to design a simple experiment to further your investigation of the behavior, ecology, or physiology of one of the organisms studied. As you proceed through the exercises, ask questions about your observations and consider an experiment that you might design to answer one of your questions.

EXERCISE 1

The Protists

In this exercise you will study examples of seven major groups (clades) of protists. (See Figure 28.5 in Campbell and Reese, 2005 and Table 1 below.)

Table 1
Groups of Protists Investigated in this Exercise

Group	Lab Study	Examples
Euglenozoans	A	*Trypanosoma levisi*
Alveolates	B	Paramecia Dinoflagellates
Stramenopiles	C	Diatoms Brown algae
Cercozoans and Radiolarians	D	Foraminiferans Radiolarians
Amoebozoans	E	*Amoeba* *Physarum*
Rhodophyta	F	Red algae
Chlorophyta	G	Green algae: *Spirogyra, Ulva, Chara*

Protists may be **autotrophic** (photosynthetic) or **heterotrophic** (depending on other organisms for food). Autotrophic organisms are able to convert the sun's energy to organic compounds. The amount of energy stored by autotrophs is called **primary production**. Traditionally, autotrophic protists are called **algae** and heterotrophic protists are called **protozoa**—protists that ingest their food by **phagocytosis** (the uptake of large particles or whole organisms by the pinching inward of the plasma membrane). Some protozoa, euglenoids for example, are **mixotrophic**, capable of photosynthesis and ingestion. As you investigate the diversity of protists and their evolutionary relationships in this exercise, ask questions about the nutritive mode of each. Note morphological characteristics of examples studied. Ask which characteristics are found in organisms in the same clade and those shared with organisms in other clades or groups. Many of these characteristics are examples of evolutionary convergence. Ask questions about the ecology of the organisms. What means of locomotion do they possess, if any? What role do they play in an ecosystem? Do they have any economic value? Where do they live? (Protists live in a diversity of habitats, but most are aquatic. A great variety of protists may be found in **plankton**, the community of organisms found floating in the ocean or in bodies of freshwater.)

Lab Study A. Euglenozoans—Example: *Trypanosoma levisi*

Materials

compound microscope
prepared slides of *Trypanosoma levisi*

Introduction

Organisms in the clade Euglenozoa are grouped together based on the ultrastructure (structure that can be seen only with an electron microscope) of their **flagella** and their mitochondria. Included in this group are some heterotrophs, some autotrophs, and some parasitic species. The many diverse single-celled and colonial flagellates have been a particular challenge to taxonomists. Under the old two-kingdom system of classification, the heterotrophic flagellates were classified as animals, and the autotrophic flagellates (with chloroplasts) were classified as plants. However, euglenozoans include members of each type. The common flagellated, mixotrophic *Euglena* belongs in this clade.

The organism that you will investigate in this exercise, *Trypanosoma levisi,* moves using flagella supported by microtubules. Organisms in the genus *Trypanosoma* are parasites that alternate between a vertebrate and an invertebrate host. *Trypanosoma levisi* lives in the blood of rats and is transmitted by fleas. Its flagellum originates near the posterior end but passes to the front end as a marginal thread of a long undulating membrane. Another organism in this same genus, *T. gambiense,* causes African sleeping sickness in humans. Its invertebrate host is the tsetse fly.

If you did not observe several other examples of flagellates when you studied the organisms living in a termite's gut, turn to that section of the laboratory manual and, following the procedure, observe these organisms. You may see *Trichonympha* and other flagellates, including *Pyrsonympha* with four to eight flagella, *Trichomonas,* and *Calonympha* with numerous flagella originating from the anterior end of the cell.

Procedure

1. Obtain a prepared slide of *Trypanosoma levisi* (Figure 1) and observe it using low, intermediate, and high powers in the compound microscope.
2. Locate the organisms among the blood cells of the parasite's host.
3. Identify the **flagellum**, the **undulating membrane**, and the **nucleus** in several organisms.

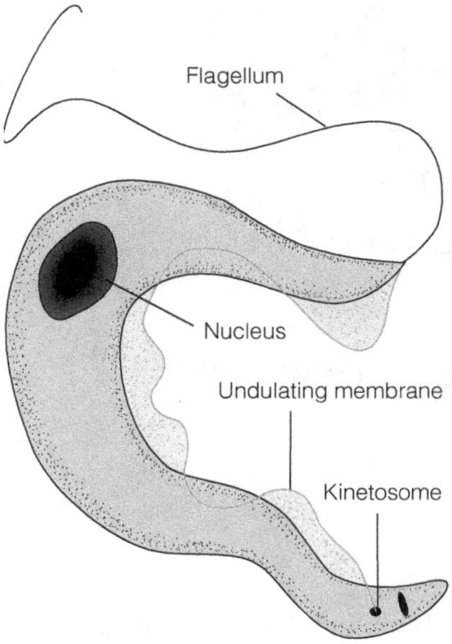

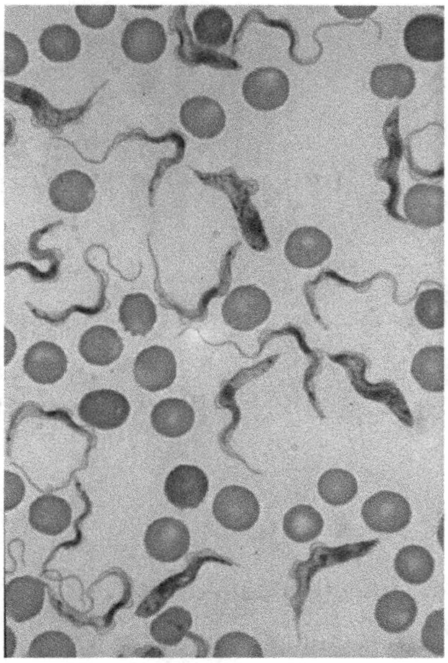

Figure 1.
***Trypanosoma*, a euglenozoan,** is a flagellated parasite that lives in the blood of its mammalian host. The flagellum originates near the posterior end, but passes along an undulating membrane to the anterior end.

Results

1. In the margin of your lab manual, draw several representative examples of *T. levisi* and several blood cells to show relative cell sizes.
2. Turn to Table 5 and list the characteristics, ecological roles, and economic importance of *T. levisi*.

Lab Study B. Alveolates—Examples: Paramecia and Dinoflagellates

Materials

compound microscope
slides and coverslips
cultures of living *Paramecium caudata*
Protoslo or other quieting agent
solution of yeast stained with Congo red
cultures of *Paramecium caudata* that have been fed yeast stained with Congo red (optional)
dropper bottle of 1% acetic acid
transfer pipettes
living cultures or prepared slides of dinoflagellates

Introduction

Alveolates are single-celled organisms; some are heterotrophic, others autotrophic. The common characteristic of all alveolates is the presence of membrane-bound sac-like structures (**alveoli**) just under the cell membrane. New groupings of protistans into clades place ciliates and dinoflagellates in the Alveolates.

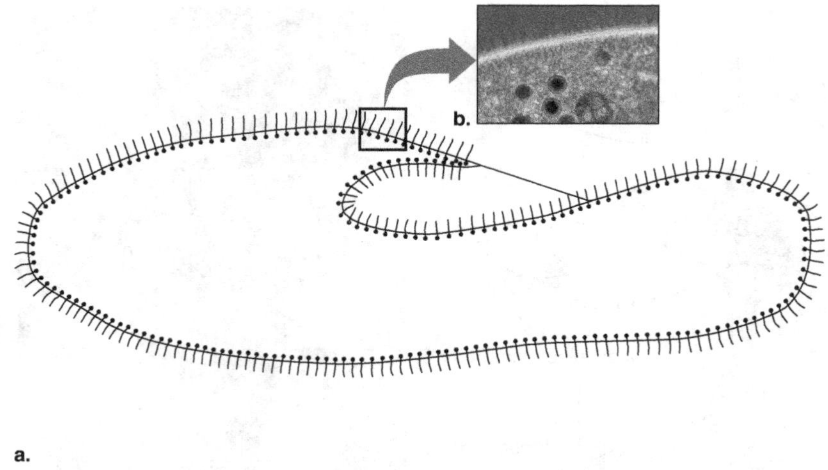

Figure 2.
(a) Complete the drawing of a *Paramecium,* labeling organelles and structures. (b) An enlarged view of cilia and the region of alveoli just under the cell membrane.

Paramecium caudatum

The first example you will investigate in this lab study is *Paramecium caudatum,* a heterotrophic organism that moves about using cilia (short projections from the cell surface). Cilia are generally shorter and more numerous than flagella. Internally both structures are similar in their microtubular arrangement.

Procedure

1. Using the compound microscope, examine a living *Paramecium* (Figure 2). Place a drop of water from the bottom of the culture on a clean microscope slide. Add a *small* drop of Protoslo or some other quieting solution to the water drop, then add the coverslip.
2. Observe paramecia on the compound microscope using low, then intermediate powers.
3. Describe the movement of a single paramecium. Does movement appear to be directional or is it random? Does the organism reverse direction only when it encounters an object, or does it appear to reverse direction even with no obstruction?
4. Locate a large, slowly moving organism, switch to high power and identify the following organelles:

   Oral groove: depression in the side of the cell that runs obliquely back to the mouth that opens into a **gullet.**

   Food vacuole: forms at the end of the gullet. Food vacuoles may appear as dark vesicles throughout the cell.

   Macronucleus: large, grayish body in the center of the cell. The macronucleus has many copies of the genome and controls most cellular activities, including asexual reproduction.

   Micronucleus: often difficult to see in living organisms, this small round body may be lying close to the macronucleus. Micronuclei are involved in sexual reproduction. Many species of paramecia have more than one micronucleus.

   Contractile vacuole: used for water balance, two of these form, one at each end of the cell. Each contractile vacuole is made up of a ring of radiating tubules and a central spherical vacuole. Your organism may be under osmotic stress because of the Protoslo, and the contractile vacuoles may be filling and collapsing as they expel water from the cell.

5. Observe feeding in a paramecium. Add a drop of yeast stained with Congo red to the edge of the coverslip and watch as it diffuses around the paramecium. Study the movement of food particles from the oral groove to the gullet to the formation of a food vacuole that will subsequently move through the cell as the food is digested in the vacuole. You may be able to observe the discharge of undigested food from the food vacuole at a specific site on the cell surface.
6. Observe the discharge of **trichocysts,** structures that lie just under the outer surface of the paramecium. When irritated by a chemical or attacked by a predator, the paramecium discharges these long thin threads that may serve as a defense mechanism, as an anchoring device, or to capture prey. Make a new slide of paramecia. Add a drop of 1% acetic acid to the edge of the coverslip and carefully watch a paramecium. Describe the appearance of trichocysts in this species.

Results

1. Complete the drawing of a paramecium (Figure 2), labeling all the organelles and structures shown in bold in the text.
2. Turn to Table 5 and list the characteristics, ecological roles, and economic importance of paramecia.

Dinoflagellates

Swirl your hand through tropical ocean waters at night and you may notice a burst of tiny lights. Visit a warm, stagnant inlet and you might notice that the water appears reddish and dead fish are floating on the surface. Both of these phenomena may be due to activities of dinoflagellates—single-celled organisms that are generally photosynthetic. Some dinoflagellates are able to bioluminesce, or produce light. They sometimes can *bloom* (reproduce very rapidly) and cause the water to appear red from pigments in their bodies. If the organisms in this "red tide" are a species of dinoflagellate that releases toxins, fish and other marine animals can be poisoned. Red tides in the Chesapeake Bay are thought to be caused by *Pfiesteria,* a dinoflagellate that produces deadly toxins resulting in invertebrate and fish kills, and that also may be implicated in human illness and death. Dinoflagellates have a cellulose cell wall often in the form of an armor of numerous plates with two perpendicular grooves, each containing a flagellum. Most of these organisms are autotrophic and play an important role in **primary production** in oceans—photosynthesis that ultimately provides food for all marine organisms.

Dinoflagellates have traditionally been considered algae, but they are now thought to share a common ancestor with ciliates, as evidenced by the presence of alveoli.

Procedure

1. Obtain a prepared slide or make a wet mount of dinoflagellates (Figure 3).
2. Focus the slide on low power and attempt to locate the cells. You may have to switch to intermediate power to see them.
3. Switch to high power.
4. Identify the perpendicular **grooves** and the **cellulose plates** making up the cell wall. Are the plates in your species elongated into spines? **Flagella** may be visible in living specimens.

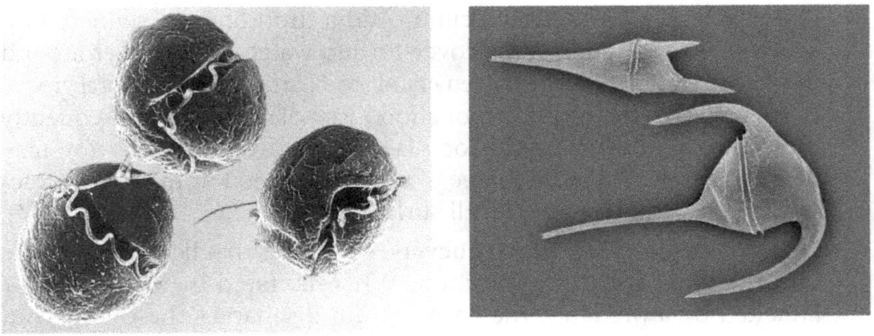

Figure 3.
Dinoflagellates. The cell wall is made of cellulose plates with two perpendicular grooves, each containing a flagellum.

Results

1. Draw several examples of cell shapes in the margin of your lab manual. Note differences between the species on your slide and those in Figure 3.
2. Turn to Table 5 and list the characteristics, ecological roles, and economic importance of dinoflagellates.

Lab Study C. Stramenopiles—Examples: Diatoms and Brown Algae

Materials

compound microscope
slides and coverslips
living cultures of diatoms
transfer pipettes
prepared slides of diatomaceous earth (demonstration only)
demonstration materials of brown algae

Introduction

The clade Stramenopila includes water molds (phylum Oomycetes), diatoms (phylum Bacillariophyta), golden algae (phylum Chrysophyta), and brown algae (phylum Phaeophyta). These organisms are grouped in this clade based on the structure of their flagella (when present). The flagellum has many hair-like lateral projections.

In this lab study you will investigate two examples: diatoms and brown algae. Both are autotrophic organisms that play an important role in primary production in oceans.

Diatoms (Bacillariophyta)

Diatoms are important autotrophic organisms in plankton. In fact, they are the most important photosynthesizers in cold marine waters. They can be unicellular, or they can aggregate into chains or star-like groups. Protoplasts of these organisms are enclosed by a cell wall made of silica that persists after the death of the cell. These cell wall deposits are mined as **diatomaceous earth** and have numerous economic uses (for example, in swimming pool filters and as an abrasive in toothpaste and silver polish). Perhaps the

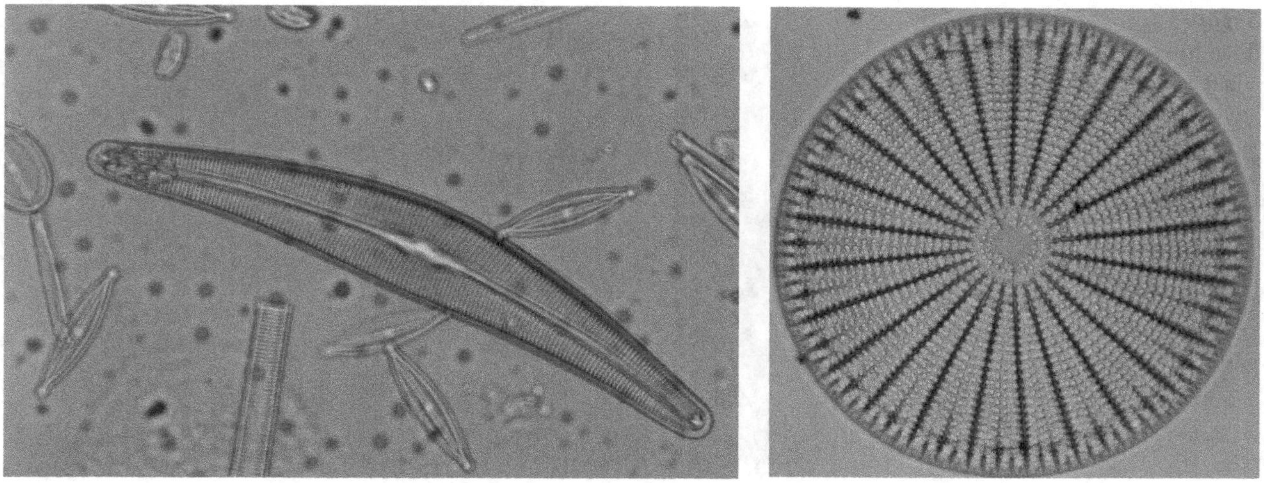

Figure 4.
Diatoms are important autotrophs found in plankton. Many different species and forms exist. All have cell walls made of silica.

greatest value of diatoms, however, is the carbohydrate and oxygen they produce that can be utilized by other organisms. Ecologists are concerned about the effects of acid rain and changing climatic conditions on populations of diatoms and their rate of primary productivity.

Diatom cells are either elongated, boat-shaped, bilaterally symmetrical **pennate** forms or radially symmetrical **centric** forms. The cell wall consists of two valves, one fitting inside the other, in the manner of the lid and bottom of a petri dish.

Procedure

1. Prepare a wet mount of diatoms (Figure 4) from marine plankton samples or other living cultures.
2. Observe the organisms on low, intermediate, and high powers.
3. Describe the form of the diatoms in your sample. Are they centric, pennate, or both?
4. If you are studying living cells, you may be able to detect locomotion. The method of movement is uncertain, but it is thought that contractile fibers just inside the cell membrane produce waves of motion on the cytoplasmic surface that extends through a groove in the cell wall. What is the body form of motile diatoms?

5. Observe a single centric form on high power and note the intricate geometric pattern of the cell wall. Can you detect the two valves?
6. Look for chloroplasts in living forms.
7. Observe diatomaceous earth on demonstration and identify pennate and centric forms.

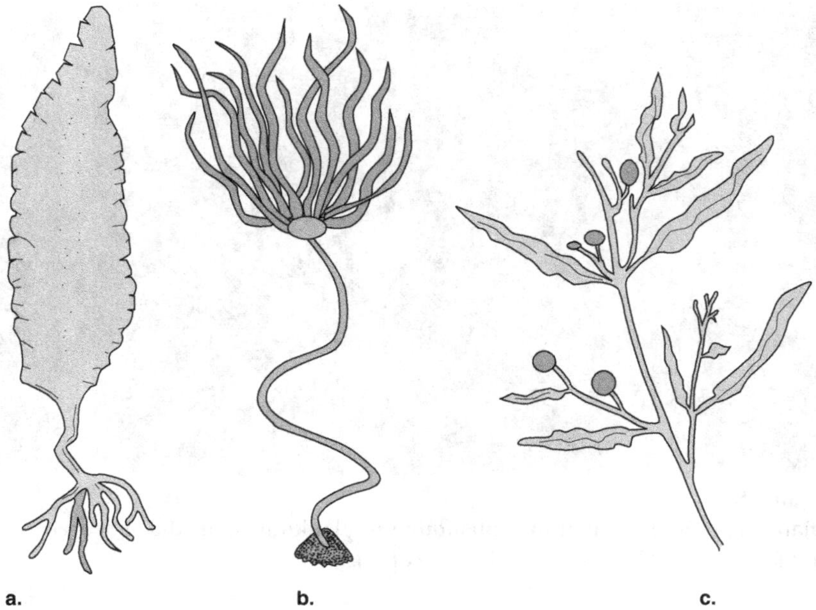

Figure 5.
Examples of multicellular brown algae (phylum Phaeophyta). The body of a brown alga consists of a broad blade, a stemlike stipe, and a holdfast for attachment. These body parts are found in the kelps (a) Laminaria and (b) Nereocystis. Rounded air bladders for flotation are seen in (c) Sargassum and other species of brown algae.

Results

1. Sketch several different shapes of diatoms in the margin of your lab manual.
2. Turn to Table 5 and list the characteristics, ecological roles, and economic importance of diatoms.

Brown Algae (Phaeophyta)

Some of the largest algae, the **kelps,** are brown algae. The Sargasso Sea is named after the large, free-floating brown algae *Sargassum*. These algae appear brown because of the presence of the brown pigment **fucoxanthin** in addition to chlorophyll *a*. Brown algae are perhaps best known for their commercial value. Have you ever wondered why commercial ice cream is smoother in texture than homemade ice cream? Extracts of **algin,** a polysaccharide in the cell wall of some brown algae, are used commercially as thickening or emulsifying agents in paint, toothpaste, ice cream, pudding, and in many other commercial food products. *Laminaria,* known as *kombu* in Japan, is added to soups, used to brew a beverage, and covered with icing as a dessert.

Procedure

Observe examples of brown algae on demonstration (Figure 5).

Results

1. In Table 2, list the names and distinguishing characteristics of each brown algal species on demonstration. Compare the examples with those illustrated in Figure 5.
2. Turn to Table 5 and list the key characteristics, ecological roles, and economic importance of brown algae.

Table 2
Representative Brown Algae

Name	Body Form (single-celled, filamentous, colonial, leaf-like; broad or linear blades)	Characteristics (pigments, reproductive structures, structures for attachment and flotation)

Lab Study D. Cercozoans and Radiolarians—Examples: Foraminiferans and Radiolarians

Materials

compound microscope
prepared slides of foraminiferans
prepared slides of radiolarian skeletons (demonstration only)

Introduction

Cercozoans and radiolarians are closely related groups composed of ameboid, heterotrophic organisms with **thread-like pseudopodia** or cellular extensions used in feeding and, in some species, locomotion. You will study two examples, foraminiferans and radiolarians.

Foraminiferans

Foraminiferans, commonly called **forams,** are another example of organisms that move and feed using pseudopodia. Forams are marine planktonic (freely floating) or benthic (bottom dwelling) organisms that secrete a calcium carbonate shell-like *test* (a hard outer covering) made up of chambers. In many species, the test consists of chambers secreted in a spiral pattern, and the organism resembles a microscopic snail. Although most forams are microscopic, some species, called *living sands,* may grow to the size of several centimeters, an astounding size for a single-celled protist. Thread-like pseudopodia extend through special pores in the calcium carbonate test. The test can persist after the organism dies, becoming part of marine sand. Remains of tests can form vast limestone deposits.

Procedure

1. Obtain a prepared slide of representative forams (Figure 6).
2. Observe the organisms first on the lowest power of the compound microscope and then on intermediate and high powers.

Figure 6.
Forams are heterotrophic organisms that move using thread-like pseudopodia. Their shell-like tests are made of calcium carbonate.

3. Note the arrangement and attempt to count the number of chambers in the test. In most species, the number of chambers indicates the relative age of the organisms, with older organisms having more chambers. Which are more abundant on your slide, older or younger organisms?

   Chambers can be arranged in a single row, in multiple rows, or wound into a spiral. Protozoologists determine the foram species based on the appearance of the test. Are different species present?

Results

1. Sketch several different forams in the margin of your lab manual. Note differences in the organisms on your slide and those depicted in Figure 6.
2. Turn to Table 5 and list the characteristics, ecological roles, and economic importance of brown algae.

Radiolarians

The **radiolarians** studied here are common in marine plankton. They secrete skeletons of silicon dioxide that can, as with the forams, collect in vast deposits on the ocean floor. Their thread-like pseudopodia, called **axopodia**, extend outward through pores in the skeleton in all directions from the central spherical cell body.

Procedure

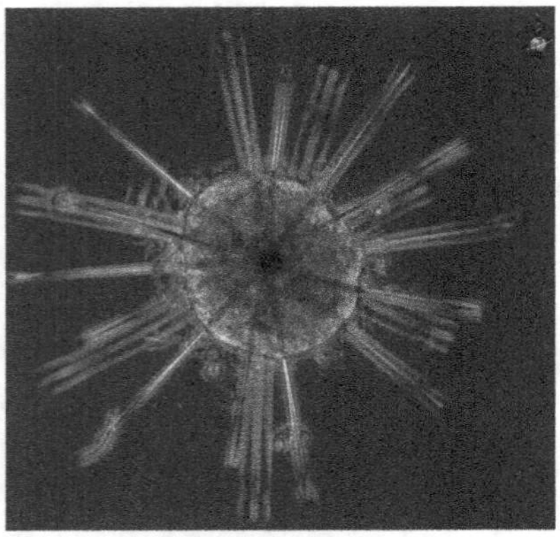

Figure 7.
Radiolarians are supported by a skeleton of silicon dioxide. They use thread-like pseudopodia to obtain food.

1. Observe slides of radiolarians on demonstration (Figure 7).
2. Observe the size and shape of the skeletons and compare your observations with Figure 7.

Results

1. Sketch several different radiolarians skeletons in the margin of your lab manual, noting any differences between the organisms on demonstration and those in the figure.
2. Turn to Table 5 and list the characteristics, ecological roles, and economic importance of radiolarians.

Lab Study E. Amoebozoans—Examples: *Amoeba,* Slime Molds

Materials

cultures of *Amoeba proteus*
slides and coverslips (for amoeba)
stereoscopic microscopes
Physarum growing on agar plates

Introduction

Amebozoans have pseudopodia as seen in cercozoans and radiolarians, but the structure is different. Rather than thread-like pseudopodia as seen in forams and radiolarians, amebozoans' pseudopodia are *lobe-shaped*. Based on their ameboid characteristics, their phagocytic mode of obtaining nutrition, and molecular systematics, both amoeba and slime molds are included in the clade **Amoebozoa.**

Amoeba

You have studied ***Amoeba proteus,*** a protozoan species of organisms that move using lobed-shaped pseudopodia. Amoeba have no fixed body shape and they are naked; that is, they do not have a shell. Different species may be found in a variety of habitats, including freshwater and marine habitats. Recall that pseudopodia are cellular extensions. As the pseudopod extends, endoplasm flows into the extension. By extending several pseudopodia in sequence and flowing into first one and then the next, the amoeba proceeds along in an irregular, slow fashion. Pseudopodia are also used to capture and ingest food. When a suitable food particle such as a bacterium, another protist, or a piece of detritus (fragmented remains of dead organisms) contacts an amoeba, a pseudopod will flow completely around the particle and take it into the cell by phagocytosis.

Slime Molds (Mycetozoa)

William Crowder, in a classic *National Geographic* article (April, 1926) describes his search for strange creatures in a swamp on the north shore of Long Island. This is his description of his findings: "Behold! Seldom ever before had such a gorgeous sight startled my unexpectant gaze. Spreading out over the bark [of a dead tree] was a rich red coverlet . . . consisting of thousands of small, closely crowded, funguslike growths. . . . A colony of these tiny organisms extended in an irregular patch . . . covering an area nearly a yard in length and slightly less in breadth. . . . Each unit, although actually less than a quarter of an inch in height, resembled . . . a small mushroom, though more marvelous than any I have ever seen."

The creatures described by Crowder are heterotrophic organisms called **slime molds.** They have been called plants, fungi, animals, fungus animals, protozoa, Protoctista, Protista, Mycetozoa, and probably many more names. Classifying slime molds as fungi (as in previous classification schemes) causes difficulties because whereas slime molds are phagocytic like protozoa, fungi are never phagocytic but obtain their nutrition by absorption. Characteristics other than feeding mode, including cellular ultrastructure, cell wall chemistry, and other molecular studies, indicate that slime molds fit better with the ameboid protists than with the fungi. These studies suggest that slime molds descended from unicellular amoeba-like organisms.

There are two types of slime molds, plasmodial slime molds and cellular slime molds. In this lab study, you will observe the plasmodial slime mold *Physarum.* The vegetative stage is called a **plasmodium,** and it consists of a multinucleate mass of protoplasm totally devoid of cell walls. This mass feeds on bacteria as it creeps along the surface of moist logs or dead leaves. When conditions are right, it is converted into one or more reproductive structures, called **fruiting bodies,** that produce spores. You may choose to investigate slime molds further in Exercise 3.

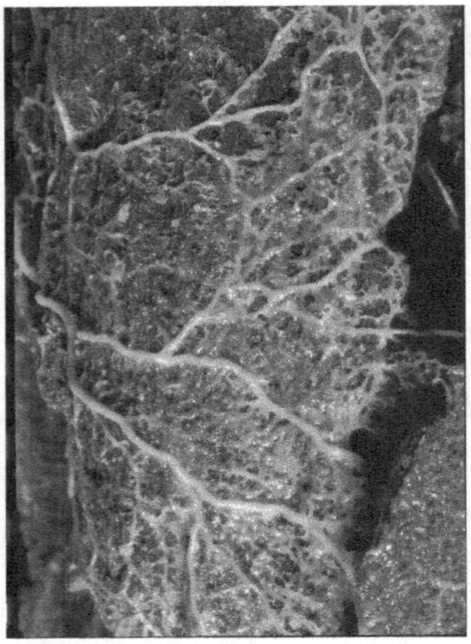

Figure 8.
Slime mold. Slime molds are protists that share some characteristics with both protozoa and fungi. The vegetative stage of a plasmodial slime mold includes an amoeboid phase consisting of a multinucleate mass known as a plasmodium.

Procedure

1. Obtain a petri dish containing *Physarum* and return to your lab bench to study the organism. Keep the dish closed.
2. With the aid of your stereoscopic microscope, examine the plasmodium (Figure 8). Describe characteristics such as color, size, and shape. Look for a system of branching veins. Do you see any movement? Speculate about the source of the movement. Is the movement unidirectional or bidirectional–that is, flows first in one direction and then in the other? Your instructor may have placed oat flakes or another food source on the agar. How does the appearance of the plasmodium change as it contacts a food source?
3. Examine the entire culture for evidence of forming or mature fruiting bodies. Are the fruiting bodies stalked or are they sessile, that is, without a stalk? If a stalk is present, describe it.

Results

1. Sketch the plasmodium and fruiting bodies in the margin of your lab manual. Label structures where appropriate.
2. Turn to Table 5 and list the characteristics, ecological roles, and economic importance of slime molds.

Lab Study F: Red Algae (Rhodophyta)

Materials

examples of red algae on demonstration

Introduction

The simplest red algae are single celled, but most species have a macroscopic, multicellular body form. The red algae, unlike all the other algae, do not have flagella at any stage in their life cycle. Some scientists suggest that the red algae represent a monophyletic (having a single origin) group and should be placed in their own kingdom. Red algae are autotrophic, containing chlorophyll *a* and the accessory pigments **phycocyanin** and **phycoerythrin** that often mask the chlorophyll, making the algae appear red. These pigments absorb green and blue wavelengths of light that penetrate deep into ocean waters. Many red algae also appear green or black or even blue, depending on the depth at which they are growing. Because of this, color is not always a good characteristic to use when determining the classification of algae. Recall that you grow bacteria and fungi on plates of agar. This substance, **agar,** is a polysaccharide extracted from the cell wall of red algae. Another extract of red algae cell walls, **carrageenan,** is used to give the texture of thickness and richness to foods such as dairy drinks and soups. In Asia and elsewhere, the red algae *Porphyra* (known as *nori*) are used as seaweed wrappers for sushi. The cultivation and production of *Porphyra* constitute a billion-dollar industry.

Procedure

Observe the examples of red algae that are on demonstration (Figure 9).

Results

1. In Table 3, list the names and distinguishing characteristics of the red algae on demonstration. Compare the demonstration examples with those illustrated in Figure 9.
2. Turn to Table 5 and list the key characteristics, ecological roles, and economic importance of red algae.

a. b. c.

Figure 9.
Examples of multicellular red algae (phylum Rhodophyta). (a) Some red algae have deposits of carbonates of calcium and magnesium in their cell walls and are important components of coral reefs. (b) Most red algae have delicate, finely dissected blades. (c) *Porphyra* (or *nori*) is used to make sushi.

Table 3
Representative Red Algae

Name	Body Form (single-celled, filamentous, colonial, leaf-like)	Characteristics (reproductive structures, structures for attachment or flotation, pigments)

Lab Study G. Green Algae (Chlorophyta)—The Protist-Plant Connection

Materials

cultures or prepared slides of *Spirogyra* sp.
preserved *Ulva lactuca*
preserved *Chara* sp.

Introduction

The green algae include unicellular motile and nonmotile, colonial, filamentous, and multicellular species that inhabit primarily freshwater environments. Because green algae share many characteristics with land plants, including storage of amylose (starch) and the presence of chlorophylls *a* and *b*, photosynthetic pathways, and organic compounds called flavonoids, most botanists support the hypothesis that plants evolved from green algae. Results of recent work in sequencing ribosomal and transfer RNA genes confirm the close relationship between green algae and land plants, and have led some scientists to propose that green algae, or at least those known as charophytes, be included in the Plant Kingdom. In this exercise you will view several body forms of green algae on demonstration: single-celled, filamentous, colonial, and multicellular. Finally, you will observe the multicellular, branched green algae *Chara* (the stonewort), believed to be most similar to the green algae that gave rise to land plants over 475 million years ago.

You may remember observing aggregates of single-celled algae, *Protococcus*, and the colonial green algae *Volvox*. In this lab study you will observe the filamentous alga *Spirogyra* and the multicellular algae *Ulva* and *Chara*.

Procedure

1. Using your compound microscope, observe living materials or prepared slides of the filamentous alga *Spirogyra* (Figure 10a). This organism is common in small, freshwater ponds. The most obvious structure in the cells of the filament is a long chloroplast. Can you determine how the alga got its name? Describe the appearance of the chloroplast.

   Can you see a nucleus in each cell of the filament?
2. Observe the preserved specimen of *Ulva* sp., commonly called sea lettuce (Figure 10b). This multicellular alga is commonly found on rocks or docks in marine and brackish water.
   a. Describe the appearance and body form of *Ulva*.

   b. Are structures present that would serve to attach *Ulva* to its substrate (dock or rock)? If so, describe them.

   c. Compare your specimen of *Ulva* with that shown in the figure and color plate.
3. Examine the preserved specimen of the multicellular green alga *Chara* (Figure 10c). This alga grows in muddy or sandy bottoms of clear lakes or ponds. Its body form is so complex that it is often mistaken for a plant, but careful study of its structure and reproduction confirms its classification as a green alga.

   Note the cylindrical branches attached to nodes. Compare your specimen to Figure 10c. Sketch the appearance of your specimen in the margin of your lab manual.

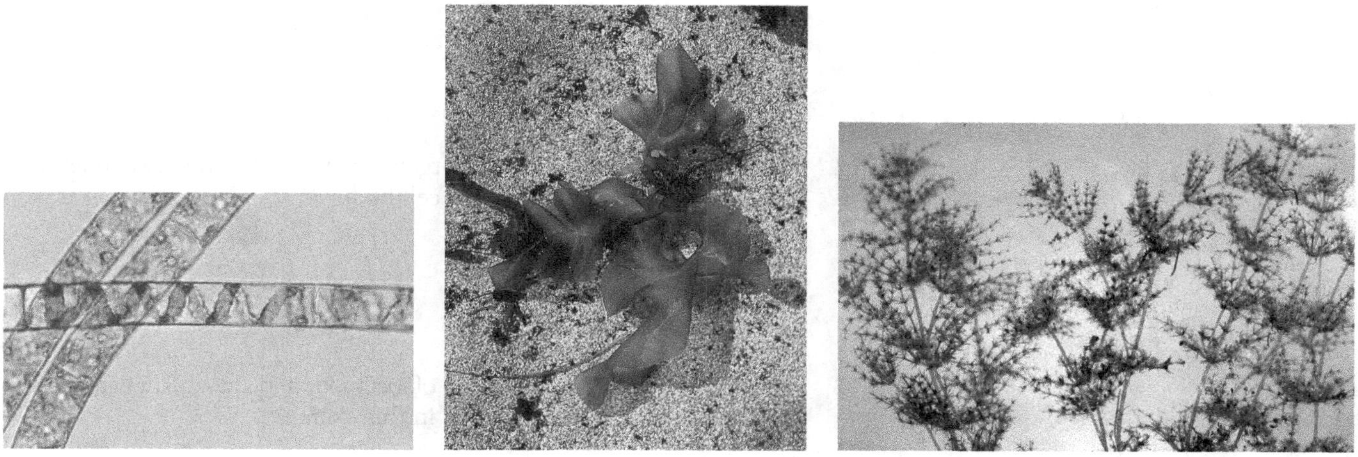

a. b. c.

Figure 10.
Examples of multicellular green algae (phylum Chlorophyta). (a) A filamentous green alga, *Spirogyra.* (b) Some green algae are multicellular as in *Ulva,* sea lettuce. (c) A multicellular, branched green alga, *Chara.*

Table 4
Representative Green Algae

Name	**Body Form** (single-celled, filamentous, colonial, leaf-like)	**Characteristics** (pigments, specialized structures, flagella, structures for attachment)
Spirogyra		
Ulva		
Chara		

Results

1. In Table 4, list the names and distinguishing characteristics of each green algal species studied. Compare these examples with those illustrated in Figure 10.
2. Turn to Table 5 and list the key characteristics, ecological roles, and economic importance of green algae.

Discussion

1. Describe the mechanism for feeding in amoeboid, flagellated, and ciliated protozoans.

2. How do you think amoeboid organisms with skeletons, such as the radiolarians, move food to their cell bodies?

3. Compare the appearance and rate of locomotion in amoeboid, flagellated, and ciliated organisms observed in this exercise.

4. Describe mechanisms for defense in the organisms studied.

5. Compare dinoflagellates and diatoms. What important ecological role is shared by these two groups?

6. What is one characteristic that you could observe under the microscope to distinguish diatoms and dinoflagellates?

7. Slime molds were once placed in the kingdom Fungi. What characteristics suggest that these organisms are protistan?

8. What important ecological role is shared by the macroscopic algae (green, red, and brown)?

9. Based on your observations in the laboratory, what two characteristics might you use to distinguish brown and red algae?

EXERCISE 2

The Kingdom Fungi

Introduction

The kingdom Fungi includes a diverse group of organisms that play important economic and ecological roles. These organisms are unicellular (yeasts) or multicellular, heterotrophic organisms that obtain their nutrients by absorption, digesting their food outside their bodies and absorbing the digestion products into their cells. They often have complex life cycles with alternating sexual and asexual (vegetative) reproduction. They may produce spores either asexually by mitosis or sexually by meiosis.

Fungi are beneficial to humans in many ways. We have long used fungi to make wine and bake leavened bread. Yeast, a single-celled fungus, is used in the production of wine, beer, and bread. Fungi are also a source of food in many cultures, with truffles being the most expensive. Truffles are dark, edible subterranean fungi that sell for $200 per pound, with an annual harvest of 30 tons. Truffles cannot be grown in a lab or greenhouse, and are located by specially trained truffle-sniffing pigs or dogs. *Penicillium* is a fungus that is used to produce antibiotics.

In ecosystems, fungi share with bacteria the essential role of decomposition, returning to the ecosystem the matter trapped in dead organisms. One extremely important ecological role played by fungi is their mutualistic association with roots of most plants, forming "mycorrhizae." Mycorrhizal fungi increase the plant's ability to capture water and provide the plant with minerals and essential elements. This association greatly enhances plant growth, and may have played a role in plant colonization of land.

Although many fungi are beneficial, others play destructive roles in nature. Some species parasitize animals and plants. Athlete's foot and ringworm are diseases commonly known to humans. Wheat rust, potato late blight, and sudden oak death (a potentially devastating disease discovered in the United States in 1995) are plant diseases caused by fungi. The ergot fungus that parasitizes rye causes convulsive ergotism in humans who eat bread made with infested grains. The bizarre behavior of young women who were later convicted of witchcraft in Salem Village, Massachusetts, in 1692 has been attributed to convulsive ergotism.

In this exercise, you will learn about the structure of typical fungi and the characteristics of four important phyla of fungi: Zygomycota, Ascomycota, Basidiomycota, and Deuteromycota. You will see examples of lichens that are associations between fungi and algae. As you observe these examples, consider interesting questions that might be asked about fungi diversity or ecology. You can choose one of these questions to design a simple experiment in Exercise 3.

Lab Study A. Zygote Fungi—Zygomycota

Materials

- compound microscope
- stereoscopic microscope
- cultures of *Rhizopus stolonifer* with sporangia
- cultures of *Pilobolus crystallinus* on demonstration
- forceps, ethyl alcohol, alcohol lamp
- slides and coverslips
- dropper bottles of water

Introduction

One common organism in the phylum Zygomycota is probably growing in your refrigerator right now. The common bread mold, *Rhizopus stolonifer,* grows on many foods as well as bread. In this lab study, you will observe the structure of this species to see many general fungi characteristics. Fungi are made up of thread-like individual filaments, called **hyphae,** which are organized into the body of the fungus, called the **mycelium.** This filamentous mass secretes enzymes into the substrate and digests food that will then be absorbed into its cells. Cells of fungi have cell walls made of **chitin** combined with other complex carbohydrates, including cellulose. You may recall that chitin is the main component of insect exoskeletons.

Rhizopus stolonifer

Rhizopus reproduces both sexually and asexually. In the zygomycetes (fungi in the phylum Zygomycota), cells of the hyphae are haploid. Hyphae grow over a substrate, for example, a slice of bread, giving the bread a fuzzy appearance. In asexual reproduction, certain hyphae grow upright and develop **sporangia,** round structures, on their tips. Haploid spores develop in the sporangia following mitosis, and when they are mature, they are dispersed through the air. If they fall on a suitable medium, they will absorb water and germinate, growing a new mycelium.

Rhizopus also reproduces sexually when compatible mating types designated as (+) and (–) grow side by side. In this case, (+) and (–) hyphae produce extensions called **gametangia** that fuse forming **zygosporangia.** Within the zygosporangia, haploid nuclei fuse (*karyogamy*) producing diploid nuclei. The diploid nuclei then undergo meiosis. Following meiosis, haploid spores are produced in sporangia borne on filaments that emerge from the zygosporangia (Figure 11).

Pilobolus crystallinus

Pilobolus crystallinus (also called the *fungus gun,* or *shotgun fungus*) is another member of the phylum Zygomycota. This fungus is called a **coprophilous** fungus because it grows on dung. It displays many unusual behaviors, one of which is that it is positively phototropic. Perhaps you can investigate this behavior in Exercise 3. Bold et al. (1980) describe asexual reproduction in *Pilobolus*. This species has sporangia as does *Rhizopus,* but rather than similarly dispersing single spores, in *Pilobolus* the sporangium is forcibly discharged as a unit; the dispersion is tied to moisture and diurnal cycles. In nature, in the early evening the sporangia form; shortly after midnight, a swelling appears below the sporangium. Late the following morning, turgor pressure causes the swelling to explode, propelling the sporangium as far as 2 meters. The sticky sporangium will adhere to grass leaves and subsequently may be eaten by an animal—horse, cow, or rabbit. The intact sporangia pass through the animal's digestive tract and are excreted, and the spores germinate in the fresh dung.

In this lab study you will investigate *Rhizopus* and observe *Pilobolus* on demonstration.

Procedure

1. Obtain a culture of *Rhizopus* and carry it to your lab station.
2. Examine it using the stereoscopic microscope.
3. Identify the **mycelia, hyphae,** and **sporangia.**
4. Review the life cycle of *Rhizopus* (Figure 11). Locate the structures in this figure that are visible in your culture. Circle the structures involved in asexual reproduction.
5. Using forceps and aseptic technique, remove a small portion of the mycelium with several sporangia and make a wet mount.
6. Examine the hyphae and sporangia using the compound microscope. Are spores visible? How have the spores been produced?

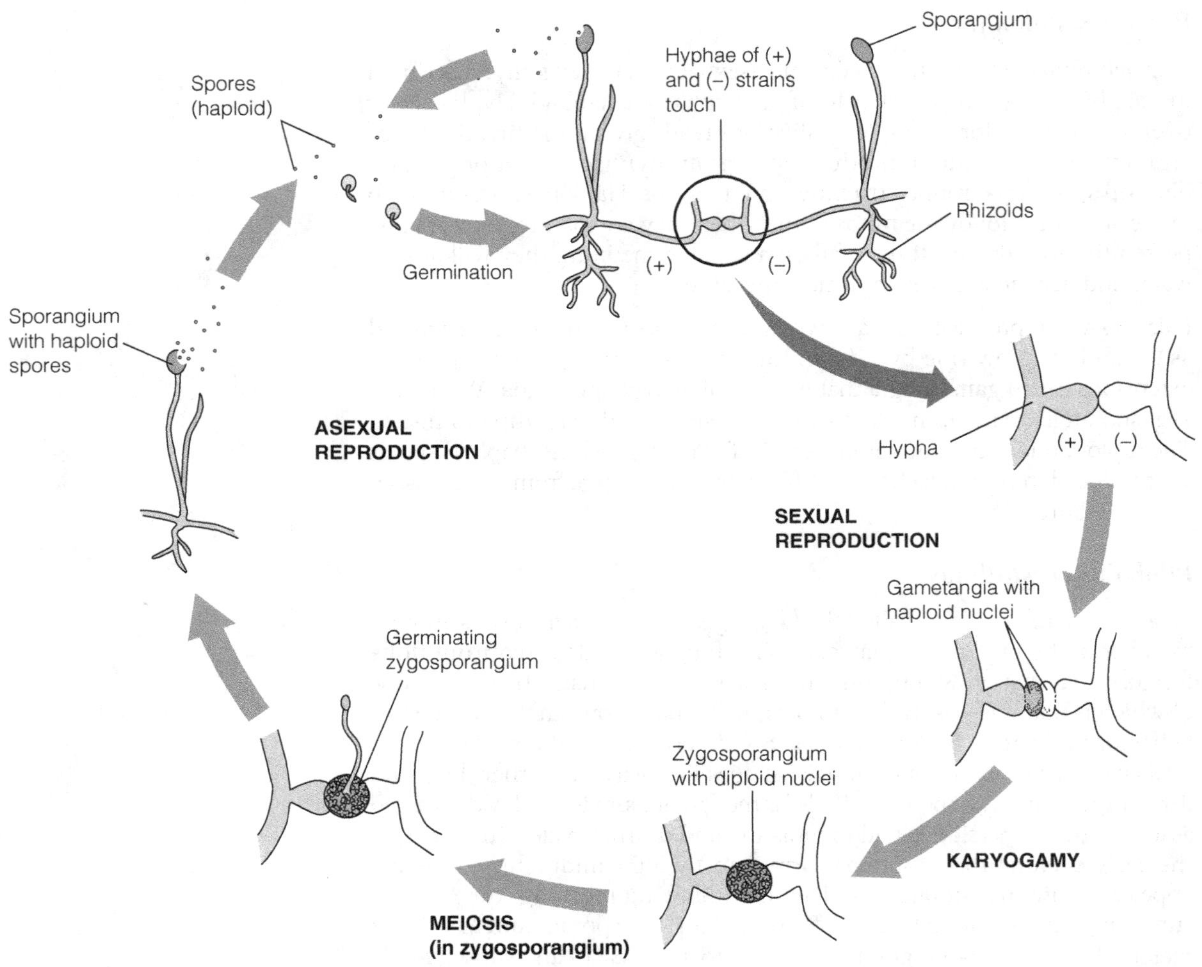

Figure 11.
Rhizopus stolonifer. *Rhizopus* reproduces both sexually by zygosporangia and asexually by sporangia producing asexual spores. In sexual reproduction, (+) and (−) mating types fuse and a zygosporangium with diploid nuclei ultimately results.

How do the spores compare with the hyphal cells genetically?

How would spores produced by sexual reproduction differ from spores produced asexually?

7. Observe the cultures of *Pilobolus* (Figure 12) growing on rabbit dung agar that are on demonstration.
8. Identify the **sporangia, mycelia,** and **hyphae.** What color are the sporangia and spores?

Results

1. Review the life cycle of *Rhizopus* and the structures observed in the living culture and compare with Figure 11.
2. Review the structures observed in *Pilobolus* and compare with Figure 12.

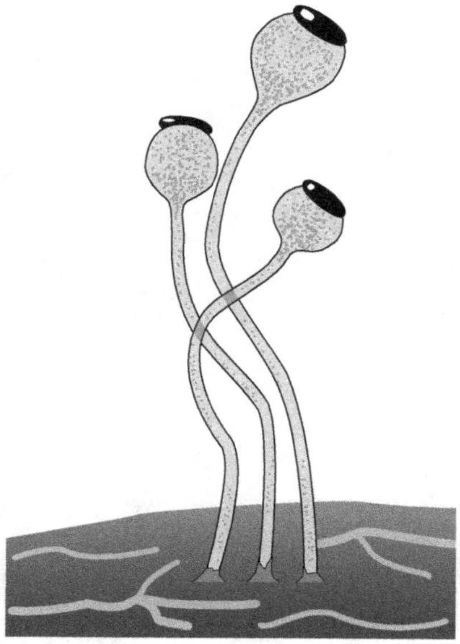

Figure 12.
Pilobolus crystallinus.

Discussion

1. The body form of most fungi, including *Rhizopus,* is a mycelium composed of filamentous hyphae. Using your observations as a basis for your thinking, state why this body form is well adapted to the fungus mode of nutrition.

2. Refer back to the description of *Pilobolus*. Speculate about the adaptive advantage of having a system to propel sporangia, as seen in *Pilobolus*.

Lab Study B. Sac Fungi—Ascomycota

Materials

compound microscope
stereoscopic microscope
dried or preserved *Peziza* specimen
prepared slide of *Peziza* ascocarp
preserved or fresh morels
plastic mounts of ergot in rye or wheat

Introduction

Fungi in the phylum Ascomycota are called *sac fungi,* or ascopore-producing fungi. This division includes edible fungi, morels, and truffles, but it also includes several deadly plant and animal parasites. For example, chestnut blight and the Dutch elm disease have devastated native populations of chestnut and American elm trees. The fungi causing these diseases were introduced into the United States from Asia and Europe. You have already examined one example of the phylum Ascomycota when you studied meiosis and crossing over in *Sordaria fimicola.*

Sexual reproduction in the ascomycota fungi produces either four or eight haploid **ascospores** after meiosis in an **ascus.** Recall that spores in *Sordaria* form after meiosis within asci. Asci form within a structure called an **ascocarp.** In *Sordaria* the ascocarp, called a *perithecium,* is a closed, spherical structure that develops a pore at the top for spore dispersal. In some species of sac fungi, the asci are borne on open cup-shaped ascocarps called *apothecia* (sing., *apothecium*). In asexual reproduction, spores are produced, but rather than being enclosed within a sporangium as in zygote fungi, the spores, called **conidia,** are produced on the surface of special reproductive hyphae.

Other features of sac fungi also vary. For example, yeasts are ascomycetes, yet they are single-celled organisms. Yeasts most frequently reproduce asexually by **budding,** a process in which small cells form by pinching off the parent cell. When they reproduce sexually, however, they produce asci, each of which produces four or eight spores.

In this lab study, you will examine a slide of the sac fungi *Peziza* and will observe demonstrations of additional examples of Ascomycota.

Procedure

1. Obtain a dried or preserved specimen of *Peziza* (Figure 13a). Notice the open, cup-shaped apothecium, the **ascocarp,** that bears asci within the cup (not visible with the naked eye). Fungi with ascocarps shaped in this fashion are called **cup fungi.** The cup may be supported by a stalk.
2. Examine a prepared slide of *Peziza* using low and intermediate magnifications on the compound microscope. This slide is a section through the ascocarp. Identify **asci.** How many spores are present per ascus? Are they diploid or haploid?
3. Complete the sketch of the ascocarp section below, labeling **asci, spores, hyphae,** and **mycelium.**

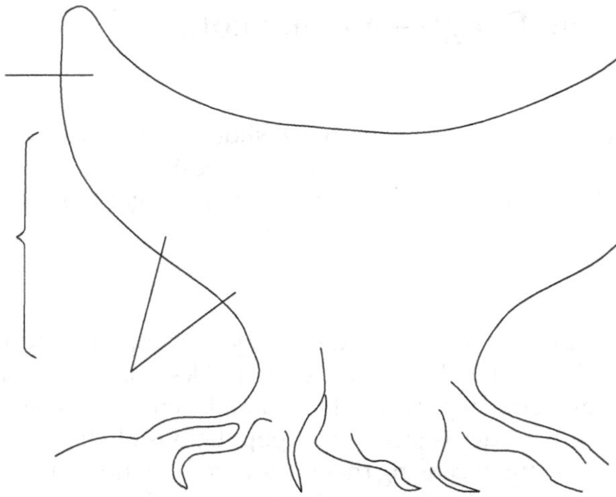

4. Observe the preserved **morels** that are on demonstration (Figure 13b). These fungi resemble mushrooms, but the "cap" is convoluted. Asci are located inside the ridges.
5. Observe demonstrations of the mature inflorescence of wheat or rye grass infected with the ascomycete *Claviceps purpurea,* the **ergot** fungus. The large black structures seen among the grains are the ergot.

Results

Review the structures observed in *Peziza,* morels, and ergot. Modify Figures 13a and 13b to reflect features of your examples not included in these figures. Sketch ergot examples in the margin of your lab manual.

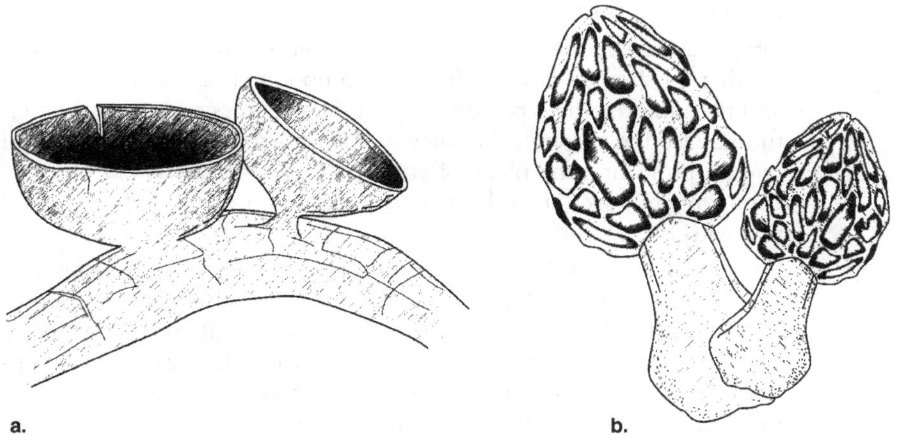

Figure 13.
Examples of sac fungi, phylum Ascomycota. (a) *Peziza* has a cup-shaped ascocarp with asci within the cup. (b) Morels are cup fungi that resemble mushrooms.

Discussion

What characteristics are common to all sac fungi?

Lab Study C. Club Fungi—Basidiomycota

Materials

compound microscope
stereoscopic microscope
fresh, ripe mushroom basidiocarps
prepared slides of *Coprinus* pileus sections

Introduction

The Basidiomycota phylum (club fungi, or basidiospore-producing fungi) includes the fungi that cause the plant diseases wheat rust and corn smut as well as the more familiar puffballs, shelf fungi, and edible and nonedible mushrooms (the latter often called *toadstools*). A mushroom is actually a reproductive structure called a basidiocarp that produces spores by meiosis. Basidiocarps grow upward from an underground mycelial mass. When basidiocarps form around the rim of the mass, a "fairy ring" of mushrooms appears. In asexual reproduction, conidia form by mitosis. In this lab study, you will study mushrooms and learn some features of their life cycle.

Procedure

1. Obtain a fresh mushroom, a **basidiocarp,** and identify its parts: The stalk is the **stipe;** the cap is the **pileus.** Look under the cap and identify **gills.** Spores form on the surface of the gills. Examine the gills with the stereoscopic microscope. Do you see spores? Children often make spore prints in scouts or in elementary school by placing a ripe mushroom pileus with the gill side down on a piece of white paper for several hours, allowing the spores to drop to the paper. Scientists use similar spore prints to accurately identify mushrooms.

2. Label the parts of the mushrooms in Figure 14a.
3. Obtain a prepared slide of a section through the pileus of *Coprinus* or another mushroom. Observe it on the compound microscope using low and then intermediate powers. Is your slide a cross section or a longitudinal section through the pileus? Make a sketch in the lab manual margin indicating the plane of your section through the basidiocarp. Compare your section with the fresh mushroom you have just studied and with Figure 14b.
4. Using the prepared slide, observe the surface of several gills using high power. Spores are produced at the tips of small club-shaped structures called **basidia.** Locate a basidium and focus carefully on its end. Here you may see four knoblike protuberances. Each protuberance has a haploid nucleus that formed following meiosis, and each becomes a **basidiospore.** When the spores are mature, they are discharged from the basidium and are dispersed by the wind.

Results

Review the structures observed and label Figure 14a. Modify the figure to include features observed in your materials that differ from the figure.

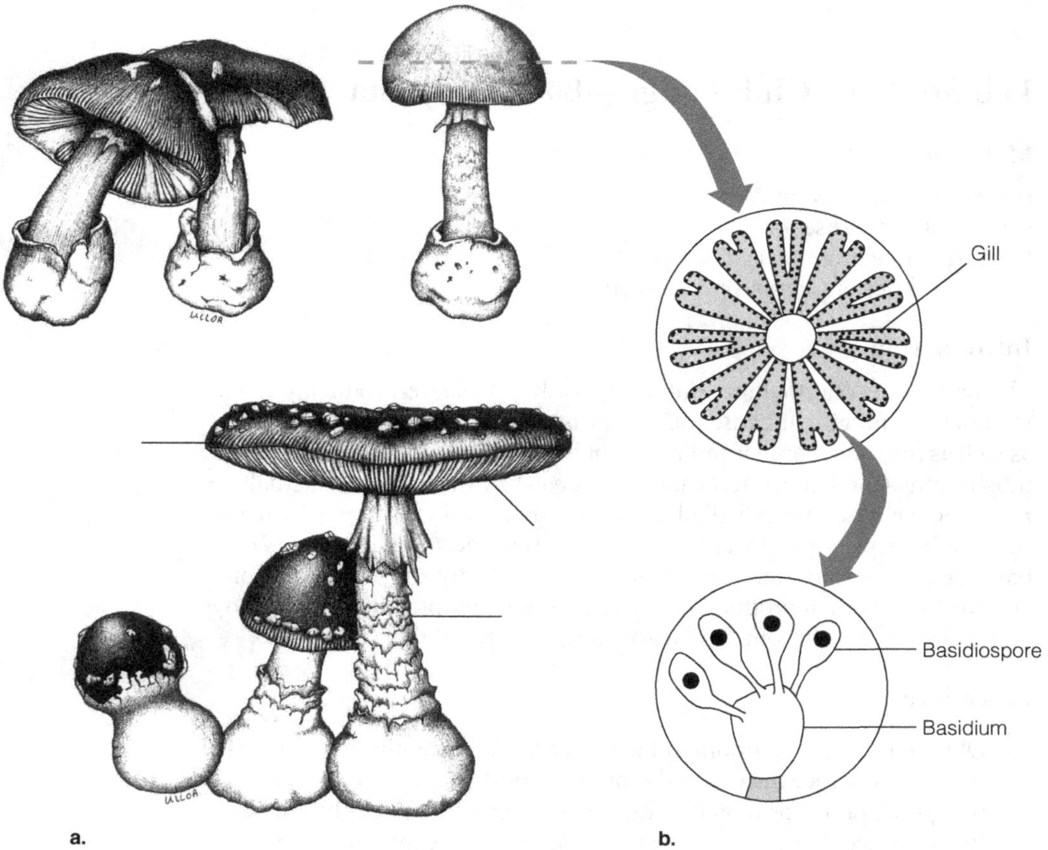

Figure 14.
Club fungi, phylum Basidiomycota. (a) Mushrooms, or basidiocarps, each consisting of a cap, the pileus; and a stalk, the stipe. (b) A section through the gills on a whole basidiocarp reveals basidia and basidiospores.

Discussion

State the characteristics shared by all Basidiomycota.

Lab Study D. Imperfect Fungi—Deuteromycota

Materials

cultures of *Penicillium* on demonstration
Roquefort cheese on demonstration

Introduction

Most fungi are classified based on their sexual reproductive structures; however, many fungi (as far as is known) reproduce only vegetatively. Because the sexual reproductive stages of these fungi do not exist or have not been found, they are called **asexual,** or **imperfect fungi** (following the botanical use of "imperfect" to indicate a flower lacking one reproductive part). This group is of interest because several human diseases—athlete's foot, ringworm, and candida "yeast" infections—are caused by species of imperfect fungi. Also in this group are several beneficial species—for example, one species of *Penicillium* that produces the antibiotic penicillin and another that is used to make Roquefort and blue cheeses.

Procedure

1. Observe the *Penicillium* on demonstration. You may have observed something similar growing on oranges or other foods in your refrigerator.
2. Describe the texture and the color of the mycelium.

Results

Sketch your observations of *Penicillium* in the margin of your lab manual. Note any features that may be important in distinguishing this organism.

Discussion

Compare the appearance of *Penicillium* with that of *Rhizopus*.

Lab Study E. Lichens

Materials

examples of foliose, crustose, and fruticose lichens on demonstration

Introduction

Lichens are symbiotic associations between fungi and usually algae or cyanobacteria forming a body that can be consistently recognized. The fungal component is usually a sac fungus or a club fungus. The lichen body, called a **thallus,** varies in shape and colors, depending on the species of the components. Reproductive structures can be bright red or pink or green. Photosynthesis in the algae provides nutrients for the fungus, and the fungus provides a moist environment for the algae or cyanobacterium. Because lichens can survive extremely harsh environments, they are often the first organisms to colonize a newly exposed environment such as volcanic flow or rock outcrops, and they play a role in soil formation.

Procedure

Observe the demonstrations of different lichen types: those with a leafy thallus (**foliose**), a crustlike thallus (**crustose**), or a branching, cylindrical thallus (**fruticose**) (Figure 15). Look for cup-shaped or club-like reproductive structures.

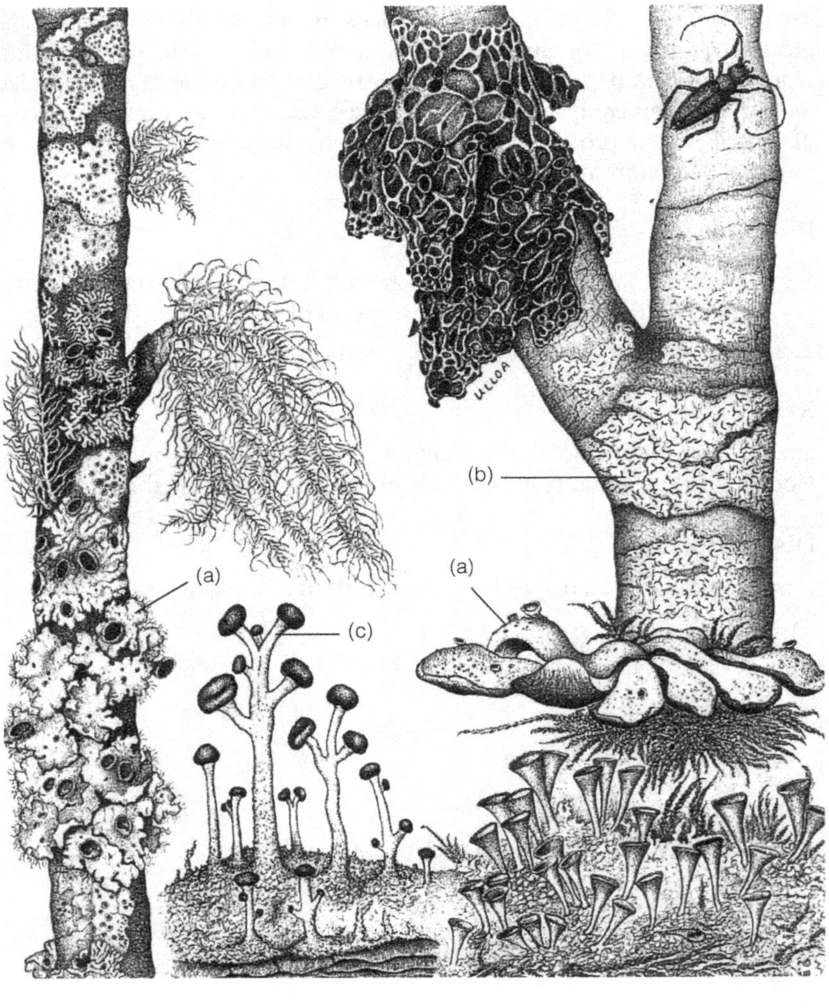

Figure 15.
Lichen types. Lichens may have (a) a leafy thallus (foliose), (b) a crustlike thallus (crustose), or (c) a cylindrical thallus (fruticose).

Results

1. Sketch the lichens on demonstration in the margins of your lab manual.
2. Identify and label each according to lichen type.

Discussion

Imagine that you are the first scientist to observe a lichen microscopically. What observations would lead you to conclude that the lichen is composed of a fungus and an alga?

EXERCISE 3
Designing Your Independent Investigation

Introduction

In this exercise, you will choose one of the organisms observed in this lab topic and design a simple experiment answering a question about its behavior, growth patterns, or interactions with other species.

Be ready to assign tasks to members of your lab team. Be sure that everyone understands the techniques that will be used. Your experiment will be successful only if you plan carefully, cooperate with your team members, perform lab techniques accurately and systematically, and record and report data accurately.

Materials

protozoa and algae cultures
cultures of slime molds *Physarum, Didymium, Dictyostelium*
cultures of *Pilobolus crystallinus, Rhizopus, Penicillium*
sterile agar plates to grow each species
sterile agar with oat flakes
sterile agar with sugar
sterile agar with albumin
sterile agar with pH 6, 7, or 8
aluminum foil
various breads from the health food store—wheat, rye, corn, potato, rice
bread with preservatives
sterilized dung from various animals
mycorrhizae inoculate

Procedure

1. Choose a question from this list to investigate or choose a question from your own observations. *Write your question in the margin of your lab manual.*
   a. Will varying the molarity of the culture medium change the rate of contractile vacuole formation in paramecia?
   b. Do plasmodia of the same species of slime mold unite when growing on the same agar plate? How about different species of slime mold?

c. Do slime mold plasmodia demonstrate chemotaxis (response to chemical stimuli such as food molecules) or phototaxis (response to light)?

d. What happens to slime molds if grown in different temperatures?

e. Do the same fungi grow on different varieties of bread?

f. How effective are preservatives in preventing fungal growth on foods?

g. Is *Pilobolus* phototaxic? What about other fungi?

h. Does succession take place in dung cultures of fungi? Refer to the milk bacteria succession study and design a similar experiment to investigate this phenomenon in fungi growing on dung.

i. Is there a difference in the growth of plants growing with and without mycorrhizae?

j. Can the growth of fungi be altered by supplying different nutrients (e.g., sugar or albumin) in agar culture?

2. Formulate a testable hypothesis.

   Hypothesis:

3. Summarize the experiment. (Use separate paper.)

4. Predict the results of your experiment based on your hypothesis.

   Prediction: (If/then)

5. Outline the procedures used in the experiment.

   a. On a separate sheet of paper, list in numerical order each exact step of your procedure.

   b. Remember to include the number of replicates (usually a minimum of five), levels of treatment, appropriate time intervals, and controls for each procedure.

   c. If you have an idea for an experiment that requires materials other than those provided, ask your laboratory instructor about availability. If possible, additional supplies will be provided.

   d. When carrying out an experiment, remember to quantify your measurements when possible.

6. Perform the experiment, making observations and collecting data for analysis.

7. **Record observations and data** on a separate sheet of paper. Design tables and graphs, at least one of each. Be thorough when collecting data. Do not just write down numbers, but record what they mean as well. Do not rely on your memory for information that you will need when reporting your results.

8. **Prepare your discussion.** Discuss your results in light of your hypothesis.
   a. Review your hypothesis. Review your results (tables and graphs). Do your results support or falsify your hypothesis? Explain your answer, using data for support.
   b. Review your prediction. Did your results correspond to the prediction you made? If not, explain how your results are different from your predictions, and why this might have occurred.
   c. If you had problems with the procedure or questionable results, explain how they might have influenced your conclusion.
   d. If you had an opportunity to repeat and expand this experiment to make your results more convincing, what would you do?
   e. Summarize the conclusion you have drawn from your results.
9. **Be prepared to report your results to the class.** Prepare to persuade your fellow scientists that your experimental design is sound and that your results support your conclusions.
10. If your instructor requires it, **submit a written laboratory report** in the form of a scientific paper. Keep in mind that although you have performed the experiments as a team, you must turn in a lab report of *your original writing.* Your tables and figures may be similar to those of your team members, but your paper must be the product of your own literature search and creative thinking.

Questions for Review

1. Complete Table 5 comparing characteristics of all protists investigated in Exercise 1.
2. Complete Table 6 comparing characteristics of fungi (Exercise 2).
3. Compare spore formation in sac fungi and club fungi.

4. Using observations of pigments present, body form, and distinguishing characteristics of the three groups of macroscopic green, brown, and red algae, speculate about where they might be most commonly found in ocean waters.

Table 5
Comparison of Protists Studied in Exercise 1

Group (Clade)	Example(s)	Characteristics	Ecological Role	Economic Importance
Euglenozoans	*Trypanosoma levisi*			
Alveolates	Paramecia			
	Dinoflagellates			
Stramenopiles	Diatoms			
	Brown algae			
Cercozoans and Radiolarians	Foraminiferans			
	Radiolarians			
Amoebozoans	Amoeba			
	Physarum			
Rhodophyta	Red algae			
Chlorophyta	Green algae: *Spirogyra, Ulva, Chara*			

Table 6
Comparison of Fungi by Major Features

Phylum	Example(s)	Sexual Reproductive Structures	Asexual Reproductive Structures
Zygomycota (Zygote Fungi)			
Ascomycota (Sac Fungi)			
Basidiomycota (Club Fungi)			
Deuteromycota (Imperfect Fungi)			

Applying Your Knowledge

1. Scientists are concerned that the depletion of the ozone layer will result in a reduction of populations of marine algae such as diatoms and dinoflagellates. Recall the ecological role of these organisms and comment on the validity of this concern.

2. Imagine an ecosystem with no fungi. How would it be modified?

3. In 1950 the living world was classified simply into two kingdoms: plants and animals. More recently, scientists developed the five-kingdom system of classification: plants, animals, monerans, protists, and fungi. In 2000 there was a general consensus among scientists that three domains with more than five kingdoms was a better system for classifying the diversity of life on Earth. However, there is still no consensus on the number of kingdoms or the clustering of organisms that best represents their evolutionary relationships. Using the protists studied in this lab topic, explain why the classification of this diverse group in particular is problematic. How is solving the problem of organizing protistan diversity a model for understanding the process of science?

References

Ahmadjian, V. "Lichens Are More Important Than You Think," *BioScience,* 1995, vol. 45, p. 124.

Alexopoulos, C., C. Mims, and M. Blackwell. *Introductory Mycology,* 4th ed. New York, NY: John Wiley and Sons, Inc., 1996.

Anderson, R. "What to Do with Protists?" *Australian Systematic Botany,* 1998, vol. 11, p. 185.

Bold, H., C. J. Alexopoulos, and T. Delevoryas. *Morphology of Plants and Fungi.* New York: Harper & Row, 1980, p. 654.

Campbell, N., and J. Reece. *Biology,* 7th ed. Menlo Park, CA: Benjamin Cummings, 2005.

Crowder, W. "Marvels of Mycetozoa." *National Geographic Magazine,* 1926, vol. 49, pp. 421–443.

Doolittle, W. F. "Uprooting the Tree of Life," *Scientific American,* 2000, vol. 282, pp. 90–95.

Litten, W. "The Most Poisonous Mushrooms," *Scientific American,* 1975, vol. 232.

Protists and Fungi

Excellent site discussing Protistan systematics:
http://www.ucmp.berkeley.edu/alllife/eukaryotasy.html

Protist Image Data. Excellent page links:
http://megasun.bch.umontreal.ca/protists/protists.html

Links to pictures of red, brown, and green algae:
http://www.sonoma.edu/biology/algae/algae.html

Seaweeds:
http://www.botany.uwc.ac.za/Envfacts/seaweeds/

Mycological Resources on the Internet:
http://mycology.cornell.edu

See an amoeba video and find interesting information on amoebas:
http://www.microscopy.fsu.edu/moviegallery/pondscum/protozoa/amoeba/

Lichens:
www.lichen.com

Plant Anatomy

Laboratory Objectives

After completing this lab topic, you should be able to:

1. Identify and describe the structure and function of each cell type and tissue type.
2. Describe the organization of tissues and cells in each plant organ.
3. Relate the function of an organ to its structure.
4. Describe primary and secondary growth and identify the location of each in the plant.
5. Relate primary and secondary growth to the growth habit (woody or herbaceous).
6. Discuss adaptation of land plants to the terrestrial environment as illustrated by the structure and function of plant anatomy.
7. Apply your knowledge of plants to the kinds of produce you find in the grocery store.

Introduction

Vascular plants have been successful on land for over 400 million years, and their success is related to their adaptations to the land environment. An aquatic alga lives most often in a continuously homogeneous environment: The requirements for life are everywhere around it, so relatively minor structural adaptations have evolved for functions such as reproduction and attachment. In contrast, the terrestrial habitat, with its extreme environmental conditions, presents numerous challenges for the survival of plants. Consequently, land plants have evolved structural adaptations for functions such as the absorption of underground water and nutrients, the anchoring of the plant in the substrate, the support of aerial parts of the plant, and the transportation of materials throughout the relatively large plant body. In angiosperms, the structural adaptations required for these and other functions are divided among three vegetative plant organs: stems, roots, and leaves. Unlike animal organs, which are often composed of unique cell types (for example, cardiac muscle fibers are found only in the heart, osteocytes only in bone), plant organs have many tissues and cell types in common, but they are organized in different ways. The structural organization of basic tissues and cell types in different plant organs is

---

directly related to their different functions. For example, leaves function as the primary photosynthetic organ and generally have thin, flat blades that maximize light absorption and gas exchange. Specialized cells of the root epidermis are long extensions that promote one of the root functions, absorption. The interrelationship of structure and function is a major theme in biology, and you will continue to explore it in this lab topic.

Use the figures in this lab topic for orientation and as a study aid. Be certain that you can identify all items by examining the living specimens and microscope slides. These, and not the diagrams, will be used in the laboratory evaluations.

Summary of Basic Plant Tissue Systems and Cell Types

The plant body is constructed into **tissue systems** based on their shared structural and functional features. There are three tissue systems—**dermal, ground,** and **vascular**—that are continuous throughout the organs of roots, stems, and leaves. The plant tissues that actively divide by mitosis are called **meristematic tissues.** These are located in specific regions—for example the root tip. Following is a review of plant tissue systems and the most common types of cells seen in plant organs, as well as their functions. Other specialized cells will be described as they are discussed in lab. Refer back to this summary as you work through the exercises.

Dermal Tissue System: Epidermis

The **epidermis** forms the outermost layer of cells, usually one cell thick, covering the entire plant body. The epidermal cells are often flattened and rectangular in shape (Figure 1a and b). Specialized epidermal cells include the **guard cells** of the stomata, hairs called **trichomes,** and unicellular **root hairs.** Most epidermal cells on aboveground structures are covered by a waxy **cuticle,** which prevents water loss. The epidermis provides protection and regulates movement of materials.

Ground Tissue System: Parenchyma, Collenchyma, and Sclerenchyma

The ground tissue system is distributed throughout the plant beneath the epidermis and surrounding vascular tissues. Parenchyma, collenchyma, and/or sclerenchyma cells are typically found in ground tissue as seen in the cross-section of a pumpkin stem (Figure 1c).

Parenchyma cells are the most common cell in plants and are characteristically thin-walled with large vacuoles. These cells may function in photosynthesis, support, storage of materials, and lateral transport.

Collenchyma cells are usually found near the surface of the stem, leaf petioles, and veins. These living cells are similar to parenchyma cells but are characterized by an uneven thickening of cell walls. They provide flexible support to young plant organs.

Sclerenchyma cells have thickened cell walls that may contain lignin. They provide strength and support to mature plant structures and may be dead at functional maturity. The most common type of sclerenchyma cells are long, thin **fibers.**

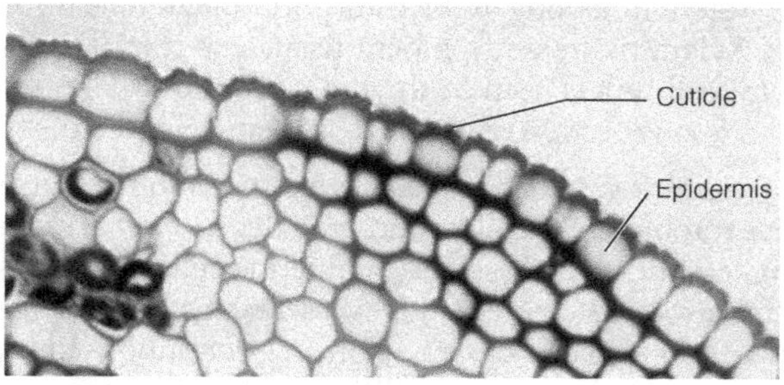

a.

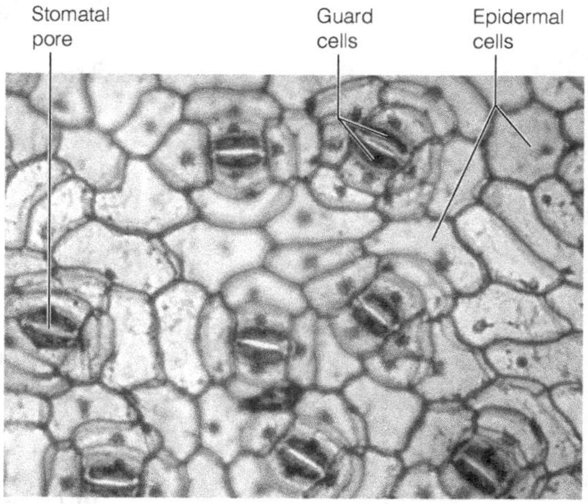

b.

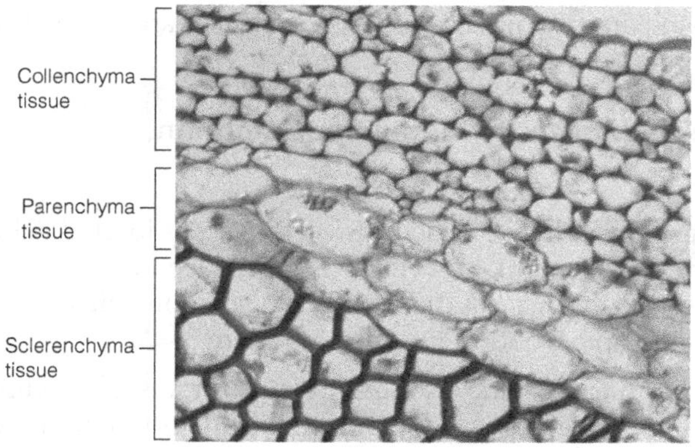

c.

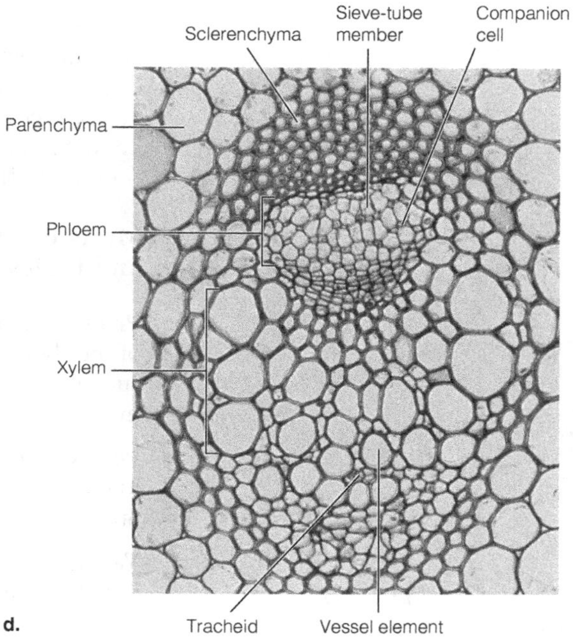

d.

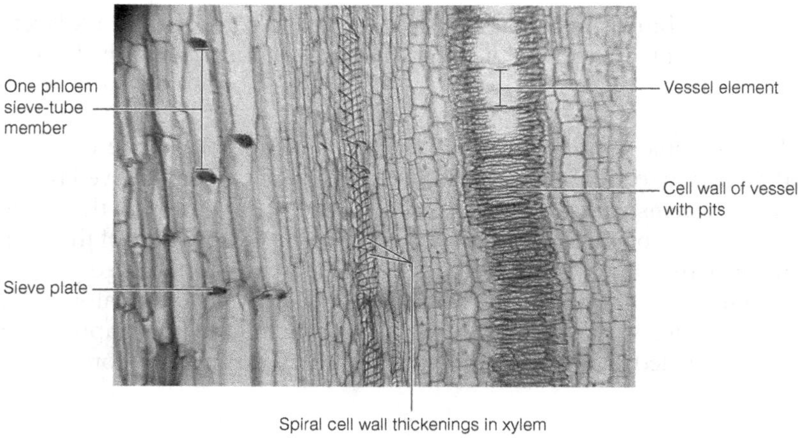

e.

Figure 1.
Plant tissue systems and cell types.
(a) Dermal tissue—a single layer of epidermis covered by waxy cuticle; (b) Leaf surface showing epidermis with stomata and guard cells; (c) Ground tissue—cross section of pumpkin stem; (d) Vascular tissue—cross section of a vascular bundle in a buttercup stem; (e) Long section through xylem and phloem of pumpkin stem.

Vascular Tissue System: Xylem and Phloem

The vascular tissue system functions in the transport of materials throughout the plant body. Xylem tissue and phloem tissue are complex tissues (composed of several cell types) seen in the cross section of a buttercup stem (Figure 1d) and a long section of a pumpkin stem (Figure 1e).

Xylem cells form a complex vascular tissue that functions in the transport of water and minerals throughout the plant and provides support. **Tracheids** and **vessel elements** are the primary water-conducting cells. Tracheids are long, thin cells with perforated tapered ends. Vessel elements are larger in diameter, open-ended, and joined end to end, forming continuous transport systems referred to as **vessels.** Parenchyma cells are present in the xylem and function in storage and lateral transport. Fibers in the xylem provide additional support.

Phloem tissue transports the products of photosynthesis throughout the plant as part of the vascular tissue system. This complex tissue is composed of living, conducting cells called **sieve-tube members,** which lack a nucleus and have **sieve plates** for end walls. The cells are joined end to end throughout the plant. Each sieve-tube member is associated with one or more adjacent **companion cells,** which are thought to regulate sieve-tube member function. Phloem parenchyma cells function in storage and lateral transport, and phloem fibers provide additional support.

Meristematic Tissue: Primary Meristem, Cambium, and Pericycle

Primary meristems consist of small, actively dividing cells located in buds of the shoot and in root tips of plants. These cells produce the primary tissues along the plant axis throughout the life of the plant. You will study primary meristems in the apical bud in Exercise 2 (Figure 3).

Pericycle is a layer of meristematic cells just outside the vascular cylinder in the root. These cells divide to produce lateral branch roots (Exercise 3 Lab Study B, Figure 6).

Vascular cambium is a lateral meristem also composed of small, actively dividing cells that are located between the xylem and phloem vascular tissue. These cells divide to produce secondary growth, which results in an increase in girth (Exercise 4, Figure 10).

Cork cambium is a lateral meristem located just inside the cork layer of a woody plant. These cells divide to produce secondary growth (Exercise 4, Figure 10).

This lab topic begins with a study of the shape and form of the whole plant, then moves to an investigation of the primary plant body derived from apical meristems. You will look at a slide of the apical bud from the tip of the stem. Next you will look at the structure of the three organs of the primary plant body: stems, roots, and leaves. Some plants continue to grow from lateral meristems producing secondary tissues, which you will investigate in stems of a woody plant. The lab topic concludes with an application of your knowledge to plants commonly found in the grocery store.

EXERCISE 1
Plant Morphology

Materials

living bean or geranium plant
squirt bottle of water
paper towel

Introduction

As you begin your investigation of the structure and function of plants, you need an understanding of the general shape and form of the whole plant. In this exercise, you will study a bean or geranium plant, identifying basic features of the three vegetative organs: roots, stems, and leaves. In the following exercises, you will investigate the cellular structure of these organs as viewed in cross sections. Refer to the living plant for orientation before you view your slides.

Procedure

1. Working with another student, examine a living **herbaceous** (nonwoody) plant and identify the following structures in the shoot (stems and leaves):
   a. **Nodes** are regions of the stem from which leaves, buds, and branches arise and which contain meristematic tissue (areas of cell division).
   b. **Internodes** are the regions of the stem located between the nodes.
   c. **Terminal buds** are located at the tips of stems and branches. They enclose the shoot apical meristem, which gives rise to leaves, buds, and all primary tissue of the stem. Only stems produce buds.
   d. **Axillary,** or **lateral, buds** are located in the leaf axes at nodes; they may give rise to lateral branches.
   e. Leaves consist of flattened **blades** attached at the node of a stem by a stalk, or **petiole.**
2. Observe the root structures by gently removing the plant from the pot and loosening the soil from the root structure. You may need to rinse a few roots with water to observe the tiny, active roots. Identify the following structures:
   a. **Primary** and **secondary roots.** The primary root is the first root produced by a plant embryo and may become a long taproot. Secondary roots arise from meristematic tissue deep within the primary root.
   b. Root tips consist of a **root apical meristem** that gives rise to a **root cap** (protective layer of cells covering the root tip) and to all the primary tissues of the root. A short distance from the root tip is a zone of **root hairs** (specialized epidermal cells), the principal site of water and mineral absorption.

Results

1. Label Figure 2.
2. Sketch in the margin of your lab manual any features not included in this diagram that might be needed for future reference.

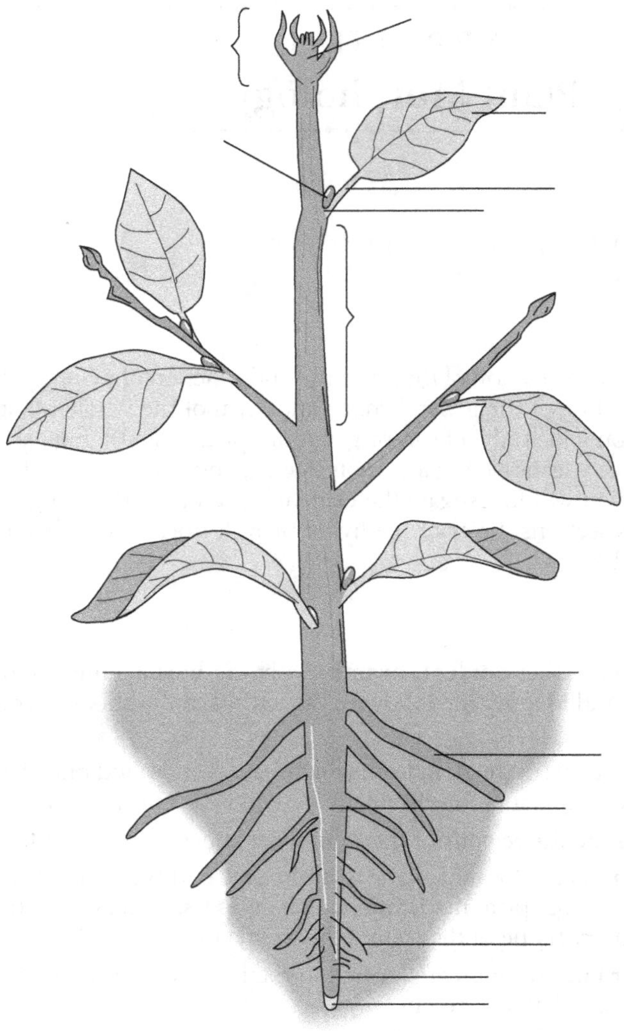

Figure 2.
A herbaceous plant. The vegetative plant body consists of roots, stems, and leaves. The buds are located in the axils of the leaves and at the shoot tip. The roots also grow from meristem tissues in the root tip. Label the diagram based on your observations of a living plant and the structures named in Exercise 1.

Discussion

1. Look at your plant and discuss with your partner the possible functions of each plant organ. Your discussion might include evidence observed in the lab today or prior knowledge. Describe proposed functions (more than one) for each organ.

   Stems:

   Roots:

   Leaves:

2. Imagine that you have cut each organ—roots, stems, and leaves—in cross section. Sketch the overall shape of that cross section in the margin of your lab manual. Remember, you are not predicting the internal structure, just the overall shape.

EXERCISE 2
Plant Primary Growth and Development

Materials

prepared slides of *Coleus* stem (long section)
compound microscope

Introduction

Plants produce new cells throughout their lifetime as a result of cell divisions in meristems. Tissues produced from apical meristems are called **primary tissues,** and this growth is called **primary growth.** Primary growth occurs along the plant axis at the shoot and the root tip. Certain meristem cells divide in such a way that one cell product becomes a new body cell and the other remains in the meristem. Beyond the zone of active cell division, new cells become enlarged and specialized for specific functions (resulting, for example, in vessels, parenchyma, and epidermis). The investigation of the genetic and biochemical basis of this cell differentiation continues to be an area of exciting biological research.

In this exercise, you will examine a longitudinal section through the tip of the stem, observing the youngest tissues and meristems at the apex, then moving down the stem, where you will observe more mature cells and tissues.

Procedure

1. Examine a prepared slide of a longitudinal section through a terminal bud of *Coleus*. Use low power to get an overview of the slide; then increase magnification. Locate the **apical meristem,** a dome of tissue nestled between the **leaf primordia,** young developing leaves. Locate the axillary **bud primordia** between the leaf and the stem.
2. Move the specimen under the microscope so that cells may be viewed at varying distances from the apex. The youngest cells are at the apex of the bud, and cells of increasing maturity and differentiation can be seen as you move away from the apex. Follow the early development of vascular tissue, which differentiates in relation to the development of primordial leaves.
   a. Locate the narrow, dark tracks of **undifferentiated vascular tissue** in the leaf primordia.
   b. Observe changes in cell size and structure of the vascular system as you move away from the apex and end with a distinguishable vessel element of the **xylem,** with its spiral cell wall thickening in the older leaf primordia and stem. You may need to use the highest power on the microscope to locate these spiral cell walls.

Results

1. Label Figure 3, indicating the structures visible in the young stem tip.
2. Modify the figure or sketch details in the margin of the lab manual for future reference.

Discussion

1. Describe the changes in cell size and structure in the stem tip. Begin at the youngest cells at the apex and continue to the xylem cells.

2. The meristems of plants continue to grow throughout their lifetime, an example of **indeterminate growth.** Imagine a 200-year-old oak tree, with active meristem producing new buds, leaves, and stems each year. Contrast this with the growth pattern in humans.

EXERCISE 3

Cell Structure of Primary Tissues

All **herbaceous** (nonwoody) flowering plants produce a complete plant body composed of primary tissue, derived from apical primary meristem. This plant body consists of *organs*—roots, stems, leaves, flowers, fruits, and seeds—and *tissue systems*—**dermal, ground,** and **vascular.** In this exercise, you will investigate the cellular structure and organization of plant organs and tissues by examining microscopic slides. You will make your own thin cross sections of stems, and view prepared slides of stems, roots, and leaves. Woody stems will be examined in Exercise 4.

Lab Study A. Stems

Materials

prepared slide of herbaceous dicot stem
dropper bottle of distilled water
small petri dish with 50% ethanol
dropper bottle of 50% glycerine
dropper bottle of 0.2% toluidine blue stain
nut-and-bolt microtome
warm paraffin
living plant for sections
new single-edged razor blade
forceps
microscope slides
coverslips
compound microscope
dissecting needles

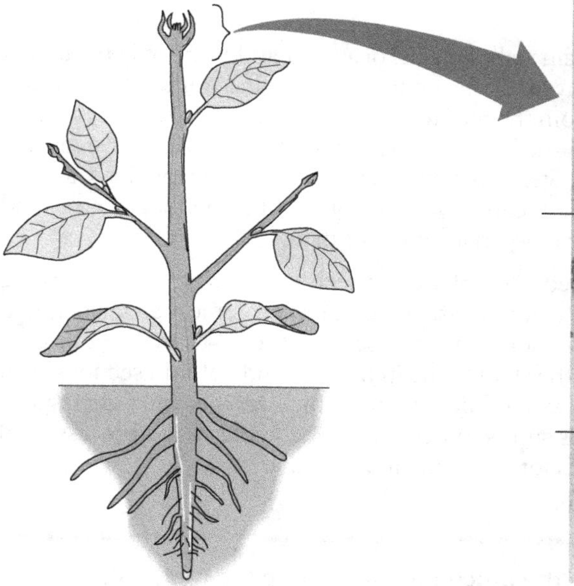
a.

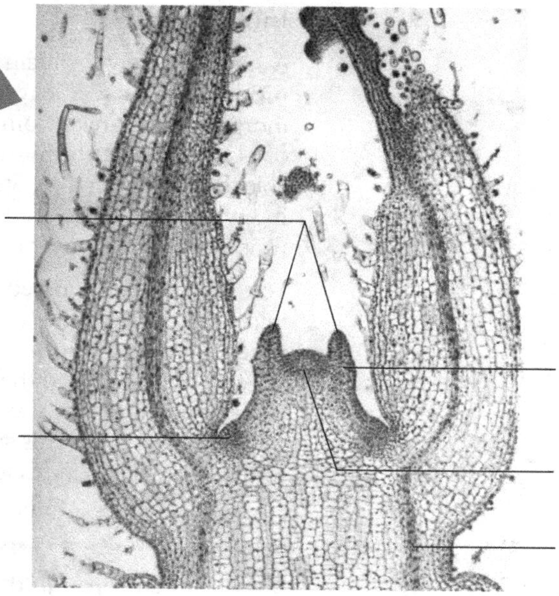
b.

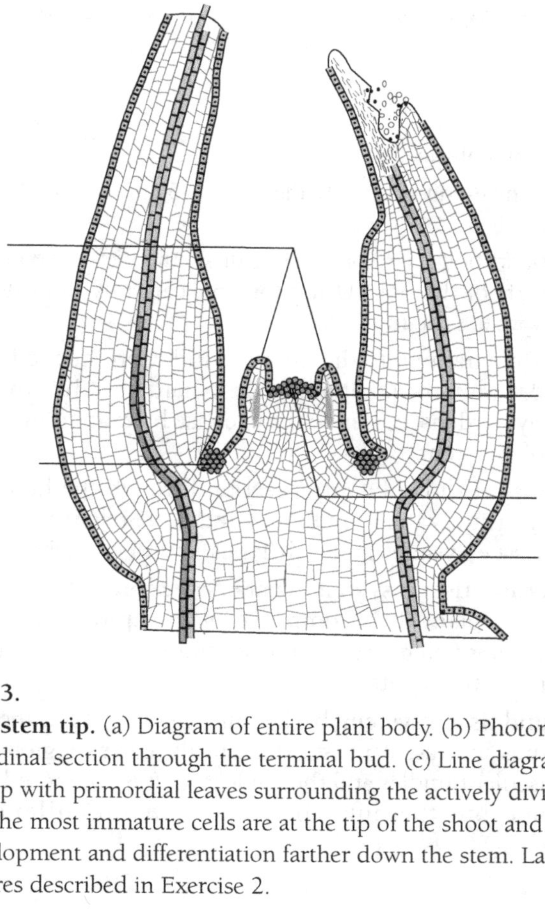
c.

Figure 3.

***Coleus* stem tip.** (a) Diagram of entire plant body. (b) Photomicrograph of a longitudinal section through the terminal bud. (c) Line diagram of the growing shoot tip with primordial leaves surrounding the actively dividing apical meristem. The most immature cells are at the tip of the shoot and increase in stages of development and differentiation farther down the stem. Label the cells and structures described in Exercise 2.

Introduction

A stem is usually the main stalk, or axis, of a plant and is the only organ that produces buds and leaves. Stems support leaves and conduct water and inorganic substances from the root to the leaves and carbohydrate products of photosynthesis from the leaves to the roots. Most herbaceous stems are able to photosynthesize. Stems exhibit several interesting adaptations, including water storage in cacti, carbohydrate storage in some food plants, and thorns that reduce herbivory in a variety of plants.

You will view a prepared slide of a cross section of a stem, and, working with another student, you will use a simple microtome—an instrument used for cutting thin sections for microscopic study—to make your own slides. You will embed the stem tissue in paraffin and cut thin sections. You will stain your sections with toluidine blue, which will help you distinguish different cell types. This simple procedure is analogous to the process used to make prepared slides for subsequent lab studies.

Read through the procedure and set up the materials before beginning.

Procedure

1. Embed the sections of the stem.
   a. Using a new single-edged razor blade, cut a 0.5 cm section of a young bean stem.
   b. Obtain a nut-and-bolt microtome. The nut should be screwed just into the first threads of the bolt. Using forceps, carefully hold the bean stem upright inside the nut.
   c. Pour the warm paraffin into the nut until full. Continue to hold the top of the stem until the paraffin begins to harden. While the paraffin completely hardens, continue the exercise by examining the prepared slide of the stem.
2. Examine a prepared slide of a cross section through the herbaceous dicot stem. As you study the stem tissues and cells, refer to "Summary of Basic Plant Tissue Systems and Cell Types," and Figure 1.
3. Identify the **dermal tissue system,** characterized by a protective cell layer covering the plant. It is composed of the **epidermis** and the **cuticle.** Occasionally, you may also observe multicellular **trichomes** on the outer surface of the plants.
4. Locate the **ground tissue system,** background tissue that fills the spaces between epidermis and vascular tissue. Identify the **cortex region** located between the vascular bundles and the epidermis. It is composed mostly of **parenchyma,** but the outer part may contain **collenchyma** as well.

5. Next find the **pith region,** which occupies the center of the stem, inside the ring of vascular bundles; it is composed of parenchyma. In herbaceous stems, these cells provide support through turgor pressure. This region is also important in storage.
6. Now identify the **vascular system,** a continuous system of xylem and phloem providing transport and support. In your stems and in many stems, the **vascular bundles** (clusters of xylem and phloem) occur in rings that surround the pith; however, in some groups of flowering plants, the vascular tissue is arranged in a complex network.
7. Observe that each bundle consists of phloem tissue toward the outside and xylem tissue toward the inside. A narrow layer of vascular cambium, which may become active in herbaceous stems, is situated between the xylem and the phloem. Take note of the following information as you make your observations.

   Phloem tissue is composed of three cell types:

   a. Dead, fibrous, thick-walled **sclerenchyma cells** that provide support for the phloem tissue and appear in a cluster as a **bundle cap.**
   b. **Sieve-tube members,** which are large, living, elongated cells that lack a nucleus at maturity. They become vertically aligned to form sieve tubes, and their cytoplasm is interconnected through sieve plates located at the ends of the cells. Sieve plates are not usually seen in cross sections.
   c. **Companion cells,** which are small, nucleated parenchyma cells connected to sieve-tube cells by means of cytoplasmic strands.

   Xylem tissue is made up of two cell types:

   a. **Tracheids,** which are elongated, thick-walled cells with closed, tapered ends. They are dead at functional maturity, and their lumens are interconnected through pits in the cell walls.
   b. **Vessel elements,** which are cylindrical cells that are large in diameter and dead at functional maturity. They become joined end to end, lose their end walls, and form long, vertical vessels.

   Vascular cambium is a type of tissue that is located between the xylem and the phloem and which actively divides to give rise to secondary tissues.
8. Complete the Results section below for this slide, then return to step 9 to prepare and observe your own handmade sections of stem preparations.
9. Cut the stem sections in the hardened paraffin.

   a. Support the nut-and-bolt microtome with the bolt head down and, using the razor blade, carefully slice off any excess paraffin extending above the nut. Be careful to slice in a direction away from your body and to keep your fingers away from the edge of the razor blade (Figure 4).

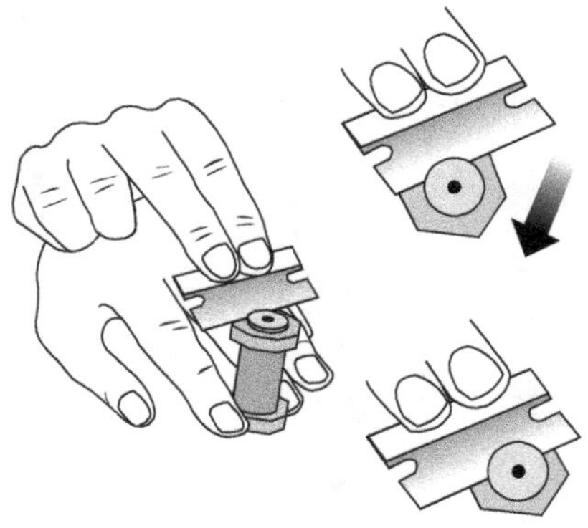

Figure 4.
Using the nut-and-bolt microtome. A piece of stem is embedded in paraffin in the bolt. As you twist the bolt up, slice thin sections to be stained and viewed. Slide the entire blade through the paraffin to smoothly slice thin sections. Follow the directions in Exercise 3, Lab Study A carefully.

Be careful to keep fingers and knuckles away from the razor blade. Follow directions carefully.

   b. Turn the bolt *just a little,* to extend the stem/paraffin above the edge of the nut.

c. Produce a thin section by slicing off the extension using the full length of the razor blade, beginning at one end of the blade and slicing to the other end of the blade (see Figure 4).

d. Transfer each section to a small petri dish containing 50% ethanol.

e. Continue to produce thin sections of stem in this manner. The thinnest slices may curl, but this is all right if the stem section remains in the paraffin as you make the transfer. Cell types are easier to identify in very thin sections or in the thin edges of thicker sections.

10. Stain the sections.

a. Leave the sections in 50% ethanol in the petri dish for 5 minutes. The alcohol *fixes,* or preserves, the tissue. Using dissecting needles and forceps, carefully separate the tissue from the surrounding paraffin.

b. Using forceps, move the stem sections, free of the paraffin, to a clean slide.

c. Add several drops of toluidine blue to cover the sections. Allow the sections to stain for 10 to 15 seconds.

d. Carefully draw off the stain by placing a piece of paper towel at the edge of the stain.

e. Rinse the sections by adding several drops of distilled water to cover the sections. Draw off the excess water with a paper towel. Repeat this step until the rinse water no longer looks blue.

f. Add a drop of 50% glycerine to the sections and cover them with a coverslip, being careful not to trap bubbles in the preparation.

g. Observe your sections using a compound microscope. Survey the sections at low or intermediate power, selecting the specimens with the clearest cell structure. You may have to study more than one specimen to see all structures.

11. Follow steps 3–7 above and identify all structures and cells. Incorporate your observations into the Results section (4, following).

Results

1. Label the stem section in Figure 5b and c.
2. Were any epidermal trichomes present in your stem?
3. Note any features not described in the procedure. Sketch these in the margin of your lab manual for future reference. Return to Procedure step 9 in this lab study and complete the preparation of hand sections of the bean stem.
4. Compare your hand sections with the prepared slide. Modify Figure 5 or sketch your hand section in the margin. Is there any evidence of vascular cambium and secondary growth (Exercise 4)? Compare your results with those of other students.

The functions of cells were described in the Summary of Basic Plant Tissue Systems and Cell Types, which appeared near the beginning of this lab topic (Figure 1).

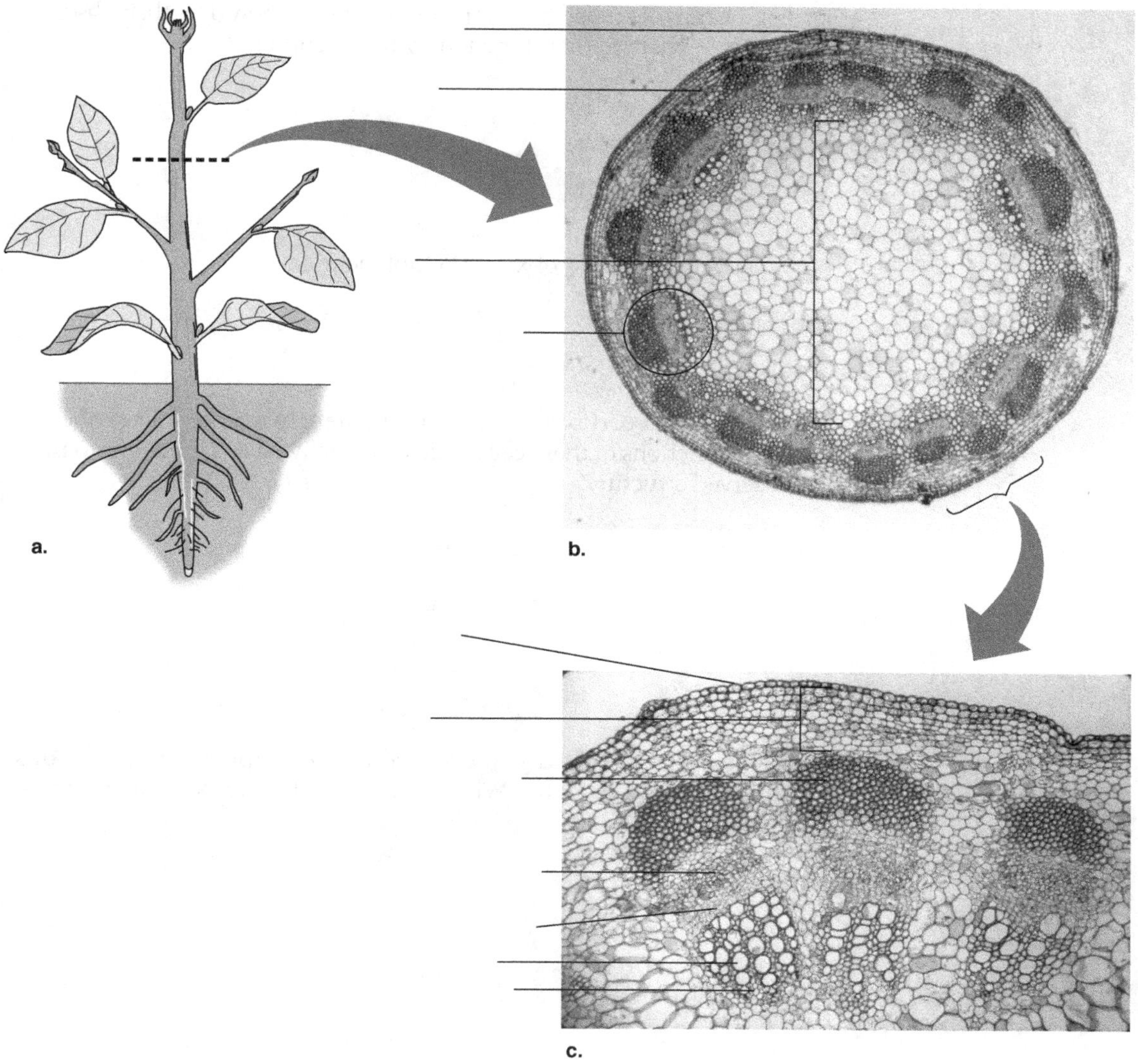

Figure 5.
Stem anatomy. (a) Diagram of whole plant. (b) Photomicrograph of cross section through the stem portion of the plant. (c) Enlargement of one vascular bundle as seen in cross section of the stem.

Discussion

1. Which are larger and more distinct, xylem cells or phloem cells?

2. What types of cells provide support of the stem? Where are these cells located in the stem?

3. For the cells described in your preceding answer, how does their observed structure relate to their function, which is support?

4. What is the function of xylem? Of phloem?

5. The pith and cortex are made up of parenchyma cells. Describe the many functions of these cells. Relate parenchyma cell functions to their observed structure.

6. What differences did you observe in the prepared stem sections and your hand sections? What factors might be responsible for these differences?

Lab Study B. Roots

Materials

prepared slide of buttercup (*Ranunculus*) root (cross section)
demonstration of fibrous roots and taproots
colored pencils
compound microscope

Introduction

Roots and stems often appear to be similar, except that roots grow in the soil and stems above the ground. However, some stems (rhizomes) grow underground, and some roots (adventitious roots) grow aboveground. Roots and stems may superficially appear similar, but they differ significantly in their functions.

What are the primary functions of stems?

Roots have four primary functions:

1. anchorage of the plant in the soil
2. absorption of water and minerals from the soil
3. conduction of water and minerals from the region of absorption to the base of the stem
4. starch storage to varying degrees, depending on the plant

Hypothesis

Our working hypothesis for this investigation is that the *structure* of the plant body is related to particular *functions.*

Prediction

Based on our hypothesis, make a prediction about the similarity of root and stem structures that you expect to observe (if/then).

You will now test your hypothesis and predictions by observing the external structure of roots and their internal cellular structure and organization in a prepared cross section. This activity is an example of collecting evidence from observations rather than conducting a controlled experiment.

Procedure

1. Examine the external root structure. When a seed germinates, it sends down a **primary root,** or **radicle,** into the soil. This root sends out side branches called lateral roots, and these in turn branch out until a root system is formed.

   If the primary root continues to be the largest and most important part of the root system, the plant is said to have a **taproot** system. If many main roots are formed, the plant has a **fibrous root** system. Most grasses have a fibrous root system, as do trees with roots occurring within 1 m of the soil surface. Carrots, dandelions, and pine trees are examples of plants having taproots.

   a. Observe examples of fibrous roots and taproots on demonstration in the laboratory.

   b. Sketch the two types of roots in the margin of your lab manual.

2. Examine the internal root structure.

   a. Study a slide of a cross section through a buttercup (*Ranunculus*) root. Note that the root lacks a central pith. The vascular tissue is located in the center of the root and is called the **vascular cylinder** (Figure 6b).

   b. Look for a cortex. The **cortex** is primarily composed of large parenchyma cells filled with numerous purple-stained organelles. Which of the four

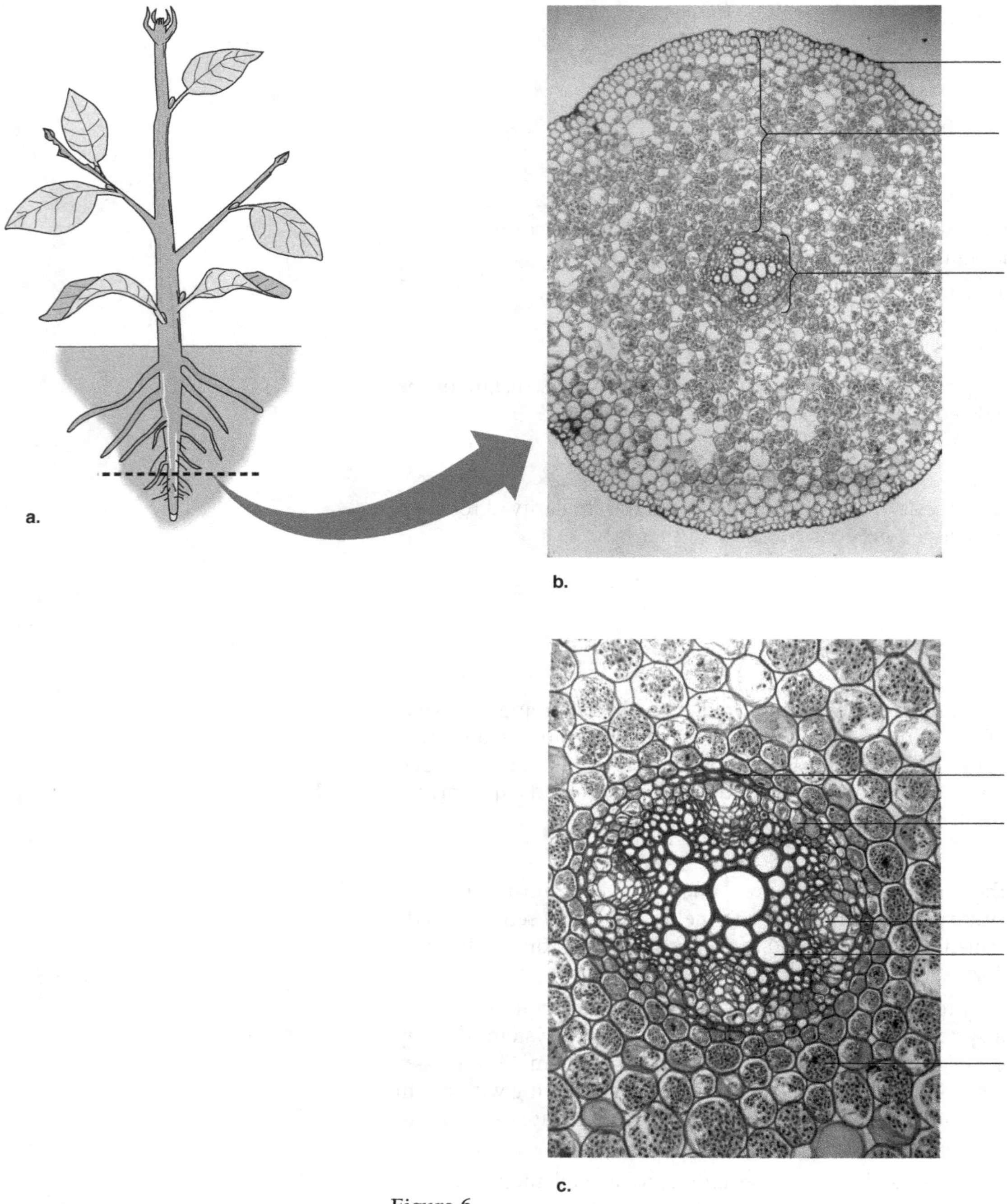

Figure 6.
Cross section of the buttercup root. (a) Whole plant. (b) Photomicrograph of a cross section of a root. (c) Enlargement of the vascular cylinder. Label the root based on your observations of a prepared microscope slide.

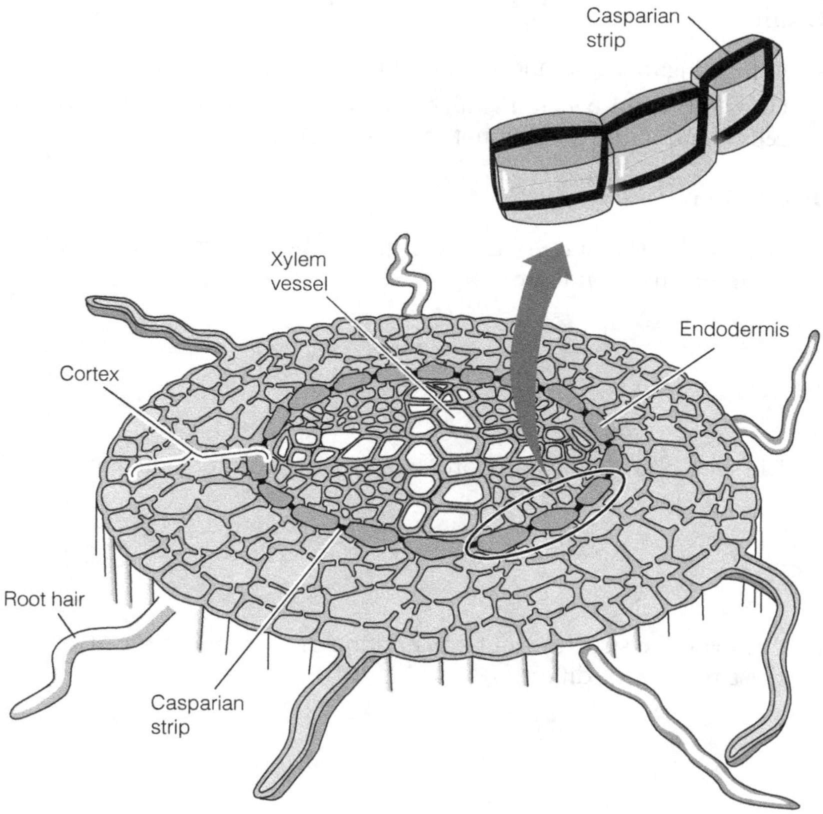

Figure 7.
Root endodermis. The endodermis is composed of cells surrounded by a band containing *suberin,* called the *Casparian strip* (seen in enlargement), that prevents the movement of materials along the cells' walls and intercellular spaces into the vascular cylinder. Materials must cross the cell membrane before entering the vascular tissue.

functions of roots listed in the introduction to this lab study do you think is related to these cortical cells and their organelles?

c. Identify the following tissues and regions and label Figure 6b and c accordingly: **epidermis**, parenchyma of **cortex, vascular cylinder, xylem, phloem, endodermis**, and **pericycle.** The endodermis and the pericycle are unique to roots. The endodermis is the innermost cell layer of the cortex. The walls of endodermal cells have a band called the **Casparian strip**—made of **suberin,** a waxy material—that extends completely around each cell, as shown in Figure 7. This strip forms a barrier to the passage of anything moving between adjacent cells of the endodermis. All water and dissolved materials absorbed by the epidermal root hairs and transported inward through the cortex must first pass through the living cytoplasm of endodermal cells before entering the vascular tissues. The pericycle is a layer of dividing cells immediately inside the endodermis; it gives rise to lateral roots. Refer to "Summary of Basic Plant Tissue Systems and Cell Types" and Figure 1.

Results

1. Review Figure 6 and note comparable structures in Figure 7.
2. Using a colored pencil, highlight the representations of structures or cells found in the root but not seen in the stem.

Discussion

1. Suggest the advantage of taproots and of fibrous roots under different environmental conditions.

2. Did your observations support your hypothesis and predictions?

3. Compare the structure and organization of roots and stems. How do these two organs differ?

4. Explain the relationship of structure and function for two structures or cells found only in roots.

5. Note that the epidermis of the root lacks a cuticle. Can you explain why this might be advantageous?

6. What is the function of the endodermis? Why is the endodermis important to the success of plants in the land environment?

Lab Study C. Leaves

Materials

prepared slide of lilac (*Syringia*) leaf
slides
compound microscope
coverslips
dropper bottles of water
leaves of purple heart (*Setcreasia*) kept in saline and DI water

Introduction

Leaves are organs especially adapted for photosynthesis. The thin blade portion provides a very large surface area for the absorption of light and the uptake of carbon dioxide through stomata. The leaf is basically a layer of parenchyma cells (the **mesophyll**) between two layers of epidermis. The loose arrangement of parenchyma cells within the leaf allows for an extensive surface area for the rapid exchange of gases. Specialized epidermal cells called guard cells allow the exchange of gases and evaporation of water at the leaf surface. Guard cells are photosynthetic (unlike other epidermal cells), and are capable of changing shape in response to complex environmental and physiological factors. Current research indicates that the opening of the stomata is the result of the active uptake of K^+ and subsequent changes in turgor pressure in the guard cells.

In this lab study, you will examine the structure of a leaf in cross section. You will observe stomata on the leaf epidermis and will study the activity of guard cells under different conditions.

Procedure

1. Before beginning your observations of the leaf cross section, compare the shape of the leaf on your slide with Figure 8a and b on the next page.
2. Observe the internal leaf structure.
   a. Examine a cross section through a lilac leaf and identify the following cells or structures: **cuticle** (a waxy layer secreted by the epidermis), **epidermis** (upper and lower), parenchyma with chloroplasts (**mesophyll**), **vascular bundle** with **phloem** and **xylem**, and **stomata** with **guard cells** and **substomatal chamber.** Refer to "Summary of Basic Plant Tissue Systems and Cell Types" and Figure 1.
   b. The vascular bundles of the leaf are often called **veins** and can be seen in both cross section and longitudinal sections of the leaf. Observe the structure of cells in the central midvein. Is xylem or phloem on top in the leaf?
   c. Observe the distribution of stomata in the upper and lower epidermis. Where are they more abundant?
   d. Label the cross section of the leaf in Figure 8.
3. Observe the leaf epidermis and stomata.
   a. Obtain two *Setcreasia* leaves, one placed in saline for an hour and the other placed in distilled water for an hour.

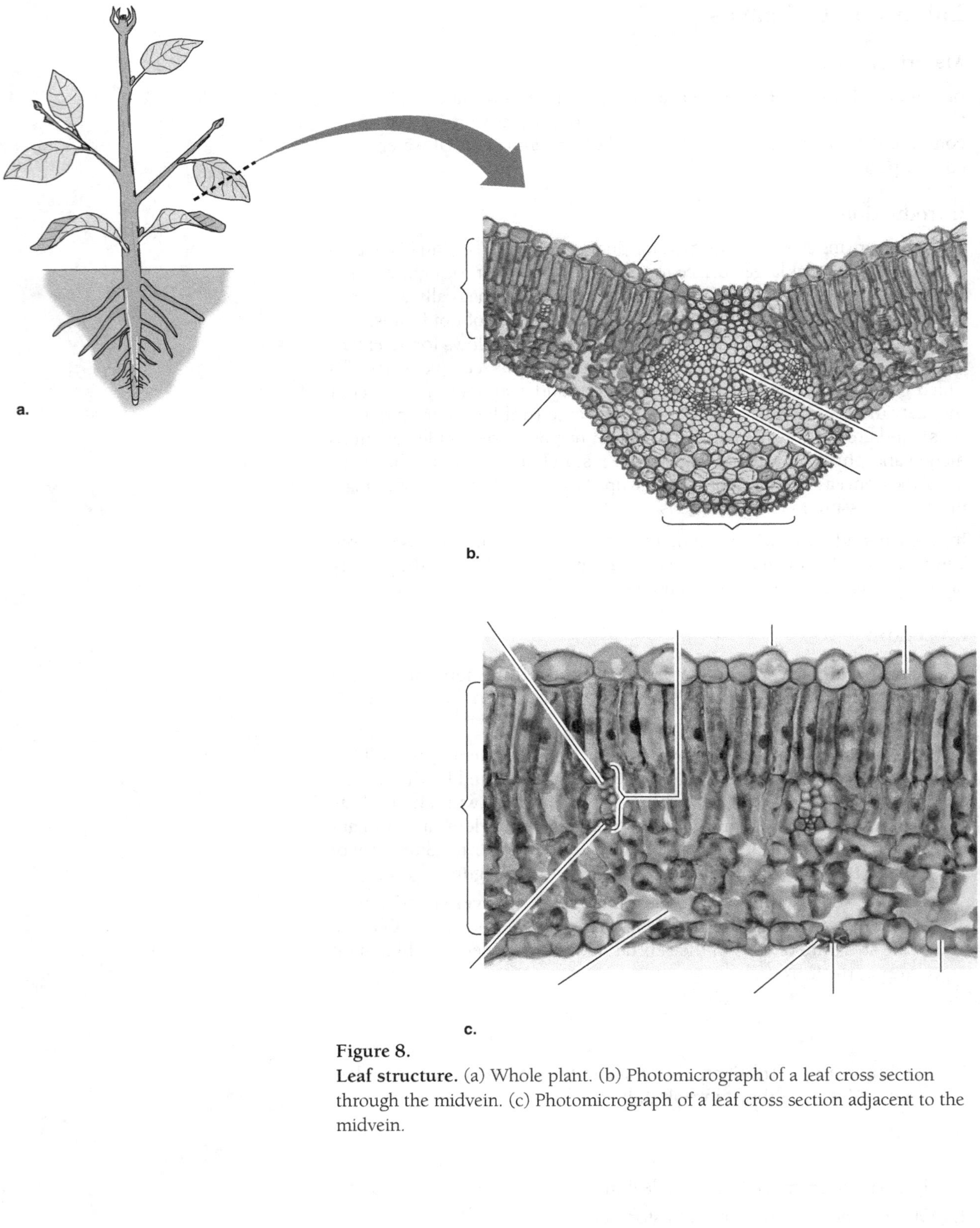

Figure 8.
Leaf structure. (a) Whole plant. (b) Photomicrograph of a leaf cross section through the midvein. (c) Photomicrograph of a leaf cross section adjacent to the midvein.

b. Label two microscope slides, one "saline" and the other "H_2O."

c. To remove a small piece of the lower epidermis, fold the leaf in half, with the lower epidermis to the inside. Tear the leaf, pulling one end toward the other, stripping off the lower epidermis (Figure 9). If you do this correctly, you will see a thin purple layer of lower epidermis at the torn edge of the leaf.

d. Remove a small section of the epidermis from the leaf in *DI water* and mount it in water on the appropriate slide, being sure that the outside surface of the leaf is facing up. View the slide at low and high power on your microscope, and observe the structure of the stomata. Sketch your observations in the margin of your lab manual.

e. Remove a section of the epidermis from the leaf in *saline* and mount it on the appropriate slide in a drop of the *saline*. Make sure that the outside surface of the leaf is facing up. View the slide with low power on your microscope, and observe the structure of the stomata. Sketch your observations in the margin of your lab manual.

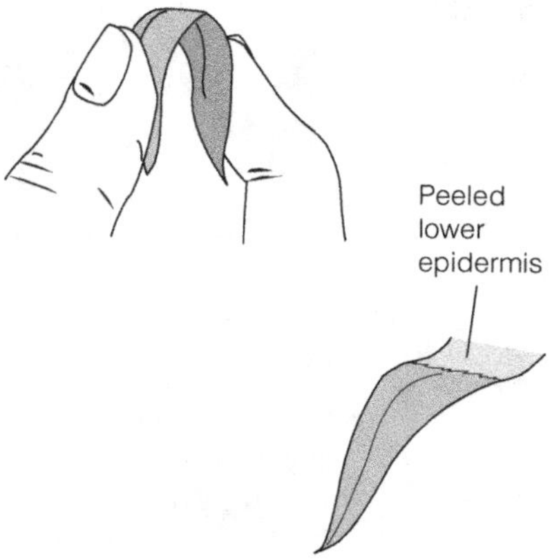

Figure 9.
Preparation of leaf epidermis peel. Bend the leaf in half and peel away the lower epidermis. Remove a small section of lower epidermis and make a wet mount.

Results

1. Review the leaf cross section in Figure 8.
2. Describe the structure of the stomata on leaves kept in DI water.

3. Describe the structure of the stomata on leaves kept in saline.

Discussion

1. Describe the functions of leaves.

2. Provide evidence from your observations of leaf structure to support the hypothesis that structure and function are related. Be specific in your examples.

3. Explain the observation that more stomata are found on the lower surface of the leaf than on the upper.

4. Explain the differences observed, if any, between the stomata from leaves kept in DI water and those kept in saline. Utilize your knowledge of osmosis to explain the changes in the guard cells. (In this activity, you stimulated stomatal closure by changes in turgor pressure due to saline rather than K^+ transport.)

EXERCISE 4

Cell Structure of Tissues Produced by Secondary Growth

Materials

prepared slides of basswood (*Tilia*) stem
compound microscope

Introduction

Secondary growth arises from meristematic tissue called cambium. Vascular cambium and cork cambium are two types of cambium. The vascular cambium is a single layer of meristematic cells located between the secondary phloem and secondary xylem. Dividing cambium cells produce a new cell at one time toward the xylem, at another time toward the phloem. Thus, each cambial cell produces files of cells, one toward the inside of the stem, another toward the outside, resulting in an increase in stem girth (diameter). The secondary phloem cells become differentiated into sclerenchyma fiber cells, sieve-tube members, and companion cells. Secondary xylem cells become differentiated into tracheids and vessel elements. Certain cambial cells produce parenchyma ray cells that can extend radially through the xylem and phloem of the stem.

The cork cambium is a type of meristematic tissue that divides, producing cork tissue to the outside of the stem and other cells to the inside. The cork cambium and the secondary tissues derived from it are called periderm. The periderm layer replaces the epidermis and cortex in stems and roots with secondary growth. These layers are continually broken and sloughed off as the woody plant grows and expands in diameter.

Procedure

1. Examine a cross section of a woody stem.
   a. Observe the cork cambium and periderm in the outer layers of the stem. The outer **cork** cells of the periderm have thick walls impregnated with a waxy material called **suberin.** These cells are dead at matu-

rity. The thin layer of nucleated cells that may be visible next to the cork cells is the **cork cambium.** The **periderm** includes the layers of cork and associated cork cambium. The term **bark** is used to describe the periderm and phloem on the outside of woody plants.

b. Observe the cellular nature of the listed tissues or structures, beginning at the periderm and moving inward to the central pith region. **Sclerenchyma fibers** have thick, dark-stained cell walls and are located in bands in the phloem. **Secondary phloem** cells with thin cell walls alternate with the rows of fibers. The **vascular cambium** appears as a thin line of small, actively dividing cells lying between the outer phloem tissue and the extensive secondary xylem. **Secondary xylem** consists of distinctive open cells that extend in layers to the central **pith** region. Lines of parenchyma cells one or two cells thick form **lateral rays** that radiate from the pith through the xylem and expand to a wedge shape in the phloem, forming a **phloem ray.**

2. Note the **annual rings** of xylem, which make up the **wood** of the stem surrounding the pith. Each annual ring of xylem has several rows of **early wood,** thin-walled, large-diameter cells that grew in the spring and, outside of these, a few rows of **late wood,** thick-walled, smaller-diameter cells that grew in the summer, when water is less available.
3. By counting the annual rings of xylem, determine the age of your stem. Note that the phloem region is not involved with determining the age of the tree.

Results

1. Review Figure 10 on the next page.
2. Sketch in the margin of your lab manual any details not represented in the figure that you might need for future reference.
3. Indicate on your diagram the region where primary tissues can still be found.

Discussion

1. What has happened to the several years of phloem tissue production?

2. Based on your observations of the woody stem, does xylem or phloem provide structural support for trees?

3. What function might the ray parenchyma cells serve?

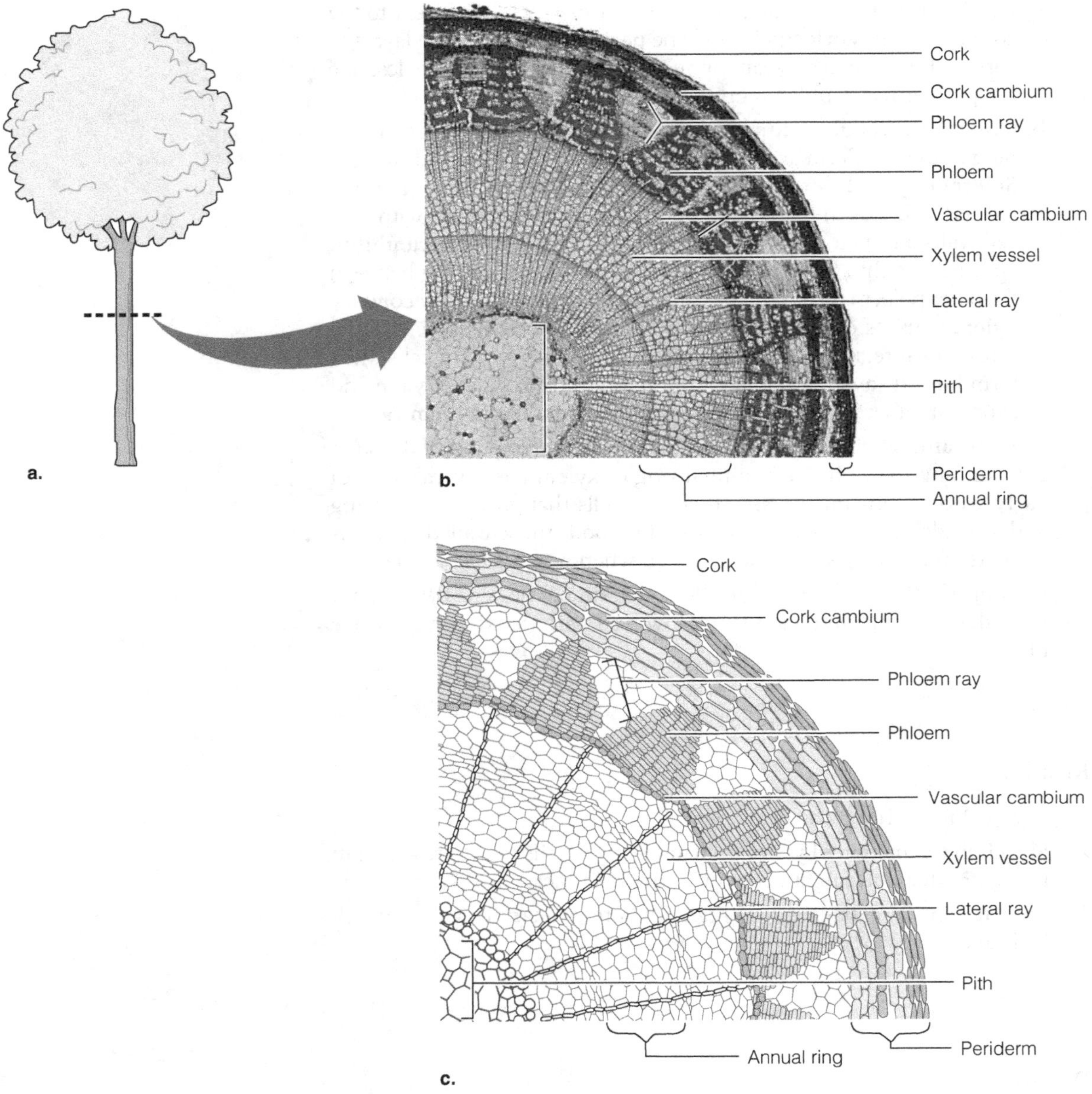

Figure 10.
Secondary growth. (a) Whole woody plant. (b) Photomicrograph of a cross section of a woody stem. (c) Compare the corresponding diagram with your observations of a prepared slide. If necessary, modify the diagram to correspond to your specimen.

4. How might the structure of early wood and late wood be related to seasonal conditions and the function of the cells? Think about environmental conditions during the growing season.

EXERCISE 5

Grocery Store Botany: Modifications of Plant Organs

Materials

variety of produce: squash, lettuce, celery, carrot, white potato, sweet potato, asparagus, onion, broccoli, and any other produce you wish to examine

Introduction

Every day you come into contact with the plant world, particularly in the selection, preparation, and enjoyment of food. Most agricultural food plants have undergone extreme selection for specific features. For example, broccoli, cauliflower, cabbage, and brussels sprouts are all members of the same species that have undergone selection for different features. In this exercise, you will apply your botanical knowledge to the laboratory of the grocery store.

Procedure

1. Working with another student, examine the numerous examples of root, stem, and leaf modifications on demonstration. (There may be some reproductive structures as well.
2. For each grocery item, determine the type of plant organ, its modification, and its primary function. How will you decide what is a root, stem, or leaf? Review the characteristics of these plant organs and examine your produce carefully.

Results

Complete Table 1 on the next page.

Discussion

1. What feature of the white potato provided key evidence in deciding the correct plant organ?

2. Based on your knowledge of the root, why do you think roots have been selected so often as food sources?

Table 1
Grocery Store Botany

Name of Item	Plant Organ (Root, Stem, Leaf, Flower, Fruit)	Function/Features (Storage, Support, Reproduction, Photosynthesis)

Questions for Review

1. Use Table 2 to describe the structure and function of the cell types seen in lab today. Indicate the location of these in the various plant organs examined. Refer to "Summary of Tissue Systems and Cell Types," Figure 1.
2. Some tissues are composed of only one type of cell; others are more complex. List the cell types observed in xylem and in phloem.

   Xylem:

   Phloem:

Table 2
Structure and Function of Plant Cells

Cell Type	Structure	Function	Plant Organ
Epidermis			
Guard cells			
Parenchyma			
Collenchyma			
Sclerenchyma			
Tracheids			
Vessels			
Sieve tubes			
Endodermis			
Primary meristems			
Vascular cambium			
Pericycle			
Periderm			
Ray parenchyma			

3. What characteristic of sieve-tube structure provides a clue to the role of companion cells?

4. Compare primary and secondary growth. What cells divide to form primary tissue? To form secondary tissue? Can a plant have both primary growth and secondary growth? Explain, providing evidence to support your answer.

Applying Your Knowledge

1. Cells of the epidermis frequently retain a capability for cell division. Why is this important? (*Hint:* What is their function?)

2. Why is the endodermis essential in the root but not in the stem?

3. When lateral roots grow outward from the pericycle, what effect does this have on the cortex and the epidermis? (*Hint:* Review the structure of the root and the location of these tissues.)

4. In the summer of 1998, after extremely hot, dry weather, the Georgia corn harvest was expected to be reduced by at least 25%. Using your knowledge of the dual functions of guard cells relative to water retention and gas exchange, explain the reduction in photosynthetic productivity.

5. The belt buckle of a standing 20-year-old man may be a foot higher than it was when he was 10, but a nail driven into a 10-year-old tree will be at the same height 10 years later. Explain.

6. Explain, from a cellular point of view, how it is possible to determine the age of a tree.

7. The oldest living organisms on Earth are plants. Some bristlecone pines ar[illegible]ut 4,600 years old, and a desert creosote bush is known to be [illegible]ears old. What special feature of plants provides for this incred-[illegible]vity? How do plants differ from animals in their pattern of [illegible]d development?

[illegible]e cell walls and animal cells do not. How does this difference [illegible]rences in plant and animal function?

[illegible] structural features studied in this laboratory evolved in [illegible]the environmental challenges of the terrestrial habitat. [illegible]ble 3 naming the cells, tissues, and organs that have allowed [illegible]ts to adapt to each environmental factor.

Table 3
Adaptations of Plant Cells and Structures to the Land Environment

Environmental Factor	Adaptations to Land Environment
Desiccation	
Transport of materials between plant and environment	
Gas exchange	
Anchorage in substrate	
Transport of materials within plant body	
Structural support in response to gravity	
Sexual reproduction without water	
Dispersal of offspring from immobile parent	

Investigative Extensions

1. The nut-and-bolt microtome can be used to separate a section of almost any part of a plant. You might grow your own plants from seeds and then embed small sections of each plant organ in paraffin and prepare slides for observation. Visualize the orientation of your material and sections before embedding.
2. Using the technique described in 1 or prepared slides, you can investigate plants that follow a different organization of tissues, including a group of angiosperms known as monocots. Stem sections and leaf sections should be different from those studied in lab.
3. C3 and C4 plants use different photosynthetic pathways with corresponding differences in leaf anatomy. Investigate proposed C3 and C4 plants by comparing leaf anatomy.

References

Figure 3 and the idea for the nut-and-bolt microtome are from Dickey, J. *Laboratory Investigations for General Biology.* Redwood City, CA: Benjamin Cummings, 1994. Used by permission.

Mauseth, J. D. *Botany: An Introduction to Plant Biology,* 3rd ed. Sudbury, MA: Jones and Bartlett Publishers, 2003.

Raven, P. H., R. F. Evert, and S. E. Eichorn. *Biology of Plants,* 6th ed. New York: W. H. Freeman Publishers, 1999.

Websites

Click on General Botany and browse this site for images of plant cells and tissues and plant organ anatomy.

http://botit.botany.wisc.edu

Photomicrographs of plant organs can be viewed at this site.

http://www.emc.maricopea.edu/faculty/farabee/BIOBK/BioBook PLANT ANATII.html

Plant Diversity I: Nonvascular Plants (Bryophytes) and Seedless Vascular Plants

Laboratory Objectives

After completing this lab topic, you should be able to:

1. Describe the distinguishing characteristics of nonvascular plants and seedless vascular plants.
2. Discuss the primitive and advanced features of nonvascular plants and seedless vascular plants relative to their adaptations to the land environment.
3. Recognize and identify representative members of each phylum of nonvascular plants and seedless vascular plants.
4. Describe the general life cycle and alternation of generations in the nonvascular plants and the seedless vascular plants, and discuss the differences between the life cycles of the two groups of plants using examples.
5. Identify fossil members and their extant counterparts in the seedless vascular plants.
6. Describe homospory and heterospory, including the differences in spores and gametophytes.
7. Discuss the ecological role and economic importance of these groups of plants.

Introduction

In the history of life on Earth, one of the most revolutionary events was the colonization of land, first by plants, then by animals. Evidence from comparisons of extant land plants and phyla of algae suggests that the first land plants were related to the green algae. These first colonists are thought to be most similar to the living, branched, multicellular green alga *Chara*. Once these primitive plants arrived on land over 475 million years ago, they faced new and extreme challenges in their physical environment. Only individuals that were able to survive the variations in temperature, moisture, gravitational forces, and substrate would thrive. Out of this enormous selective regime would come new and different adaptations and new and different life forms: the land plants.

Land plants generally have complex, multicellular plant bodies that are specialized for a variety of functions. Specialized structures have evolved for protection of the vulnerable stages of sexual reproduction. The plant body

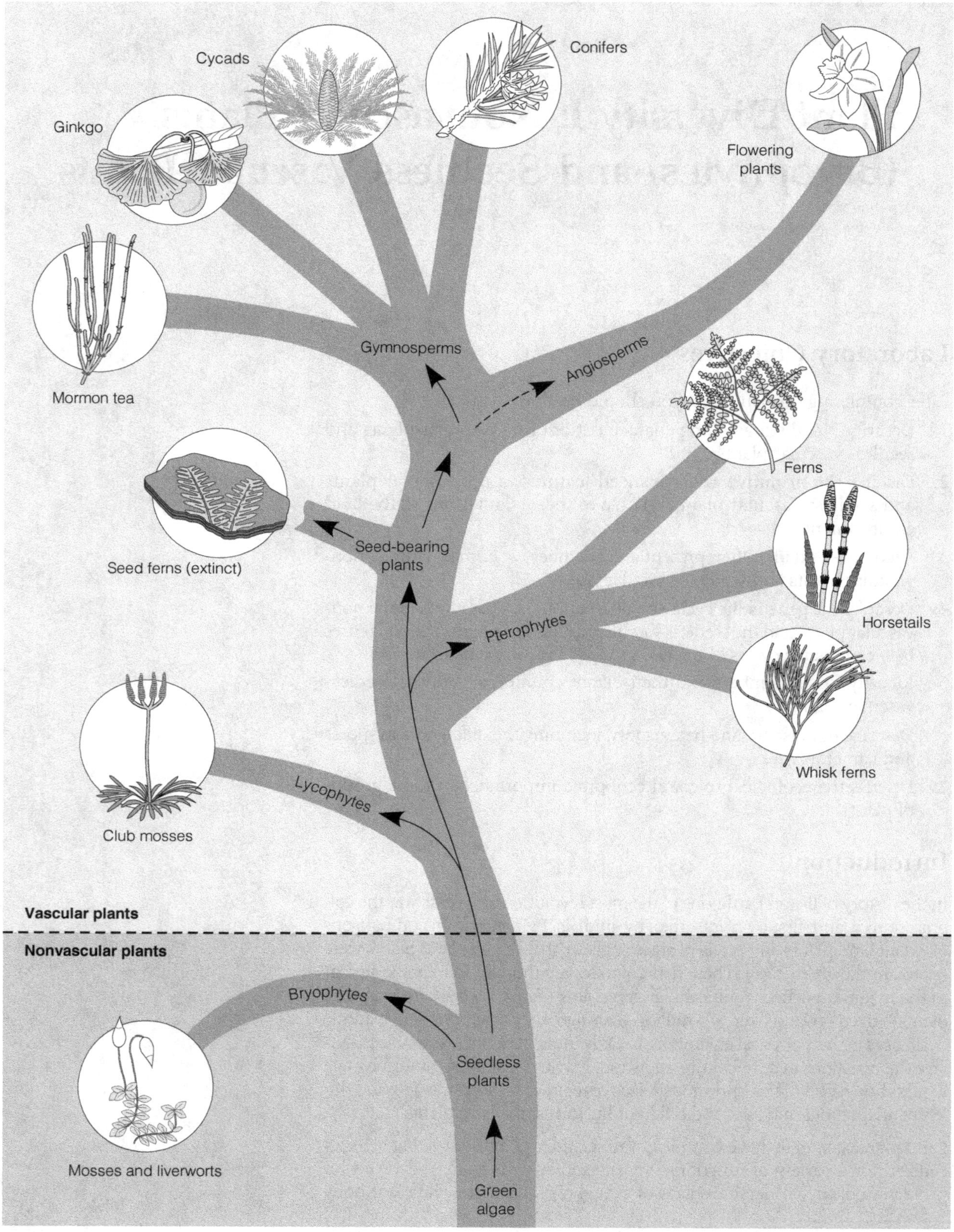
Cycads
Conifers
Ginkgo
Flowering plants
Mormon tea
Gymnosperms
Angiosperms
Ferns
Seed ferns (extinct)
Seed-bearing plants
Horsetails
Pterophytes
Whisk ferns
Lycophytes
Club mosses
Vascular plants
Nonvascular plants
Bryophytes
Seedless plants
Mosses and liverworts
Green algae

Table 1
Classification of Land Plants

Classification	Common Name	Illustration
Nonvascular Plants (Bryophytes)		
Bryophyta	Mosses	
Hepatophyta	Liverworts	
Anthocerophyta	Hornworts	
Vascular Plants		
Seedless Plants		
Lycophyta	Club mosses	
Pterophyta	Ferns, horsetails, whisk ferns	
Seed Plants		
Gymnosperms		
Coniferophyta	Conifers	
Cycadophyta	Cycads	
Ginkgophyta	Ginkgo	
Gnetophyta	Gnetae	
Angiosperms		
Anthophyta	Flowering plants	

is often covered with a waxy cuticle that prevents desiccation. However, the waxy covering also prevents gas exchange, a problem solved by the presence of openings called **stomata** (sing., **stoma**). Some land plants have developed vascular tissue for efficient movement of materials throughout these complex bodies, which are no longer bathed in water. As described in the following section, the reproductive cycles and reproductive structures of these plants are also adapted to the land environment.

In the two plant diversity labs, you will be investigating the diversity of land plants (Table 1 and Figure 1), some of which will be familiar to you (flowering plants, pine trees, and ferns) and some of which you may never have seen before (whisk ferns, horsetails, and liverworts). Remember as you view the classification that the designations *phylum* and *division* are equivalent taxonomic groupings. You will study the nonvascular plants and seedless vascular plants in this lab topic, Plant Diversity I, and seed plants later.

Figure 1.
Evolution of land plants. The nonvascular plants and vascular plants probably evolved from green algae over 475 million years ago. Seedless vascular plants dominated Earth 300 million years ago, and representatives of two phyla have survived until the present. Seed plants replaced the seedless plants, and today flowering plants are the most diverse and successful group in an amazing variety of habitats. The representatives studied in Plant Diversity I and II are indicated.

1. What are the special adaptations of these plants to the land environment?
2. How are specialized plant structures related to functions in the land environment?
3. What are the major trends in the plant kingdom as plant life evolved over the past 500 million years?
4. In particular, how has the fundamental reproductive cycle of alternation of generations been modified in successive groups of plants?

Plant Life Cycles

All land plants have a common sexual reproductive life cycle called **alternation of generations,** in which plants alternate between a haploid **gametophyte** generation and a diploid **sporophyte** generation (Figure 2). In living land plants, these two generations differ in their morphology. In all land plants except the bryophytes (mosses and liverworts), the diploid sporophyte generation is the dominant (more conspicuous) generation. The sporophyte generation undergoes meiosis to produce haploid **spores** in a protective, nonreproductive jacket of cells called the **sporangium.** The spores germinate to produce the haploid gametophyte, which produces **gametes** inside a jacket of cells forming **gametangia** (sing., **gametangium**). **Eggs** are produced in **archegonia** (sing., **archegonium**), and **sperm** are produced in **antheridia** (sing., **antheridium**). These haploid gametes are formed by mitosis. The gametes fuse, usually by the entrance of the sperm into the archegonium, forming a diploid **zygote,** the first stage of the diploid sporophyte generation.

Note that both gametes and spores are haploid in this life cycle. Unlike the animal life cycle, however, *the plant life cycle produces gametes by mitosis; spores are produced by meiosis.* The difference between these two cells is that

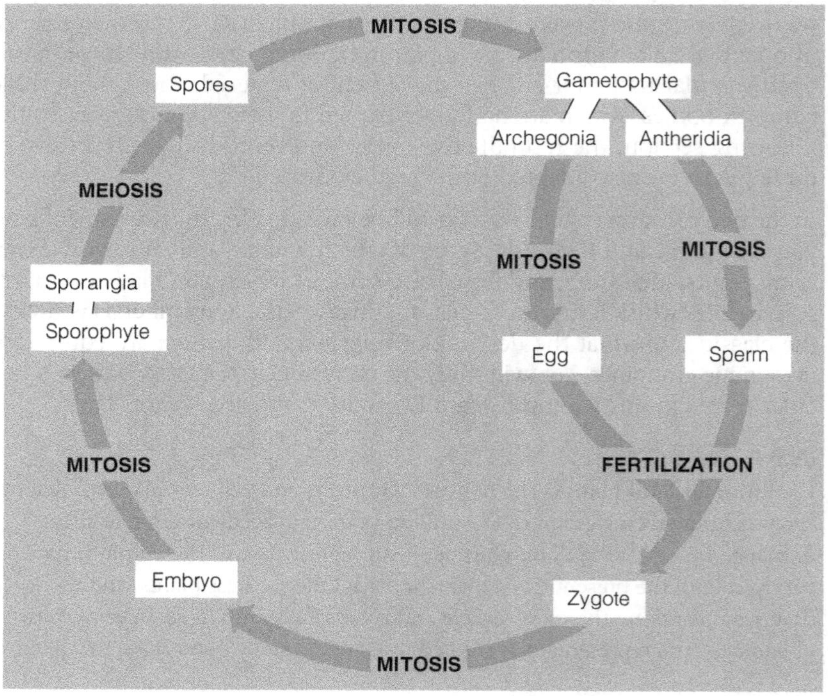

Figure 2.
Alternation of generations. In this life cycle, a diploid sporophyte plant alternates with a haploid gametophyte plant. Note that haploid spores are produced on the sporophyte by meiosis, and haploid gametes are produced in the gametophyte by mitosis. *Using a colored pencil, indicate the structures that are haploid, and with another color, note the structures that are diploid.*

gametes fuse with other gametes to form the zygote and restore the diploid number, while spores germinate to form a new haploid gametophyte plant.

Review the generalized diagram of this life cycle in Figure 2. *Using colored pencils, note the structures that are diploid and those that are haploid.* As you become familiar with variations of this life cycle through specific examples, you will want to continue referring to this general model for review.

Major trends in the evolution of this life cycle include the increased importance of the sporophyte as the photosynthetic and persistent plant that dominates the life cycle; the reduction and protection of the gametophyte within the body of the sporophyte; and the evolution of seeds and then flowers.

Nonvascular Plants (Bryophytes) and Seedless Vascular Plants

In this lab topic, terrestrial plants will be used to illustrate how life has undergone dramatic changes during the past 500 million years. Not long after the transition to land, plants diverged into at least two separate lineages. One gave rise to the bryophytes, a group of nonvascular plants, including the mosses, and the other to the vascular plants (see Figure 1). Nonvascular bryophytes first appear in the fossil record dating over 400 million years ago and remain unchanged, whereas the vascular plants have undergone enormous diversification. As you review the evolution of land plants, refer to the geological time chart for an overview of the history of life on Earth (Figure 3, on the next page).

EXERCISE 1
Nonvascular Plants (Bryophytes)

The nonvascular plants are composed of three phyla of related plants that share some key characteristics and include mosses (Bryophyta) and liverworts (Hepatophyta). The third phylum, hornworts (Anthocerophyta), will not be seen in lab. (See again Figure 1 and Table 1.) The term *bryophytes* does not refer to a taxonomic category; rather, bryophytes are an ancient group of nonvascular plants that appear to have evolved into several different groups independently and did not give rise to any other living groups of plants. They are small plants generally lacking vascular tissue (specialized cells for the transport of material), although water-conducting tubes appear to be present in some mosses. (However, these tubes may be unrelated to the vascular tissue in vascular plants.) The life cycle for the bryophytes differs from all other land plants because the gametophyte is the dominant and conspicuous plant. Because bryophytes are nonvascular, they are restricted to moist habitats for their reproductive cycle and have never attained the size and importance of other groups of plants. The gametophyte plants remain close to the ground, enabling the motile sperm to swim from the antheridium to the archegonium and fertilize the egg. They have a cuticle but lack stomata on the surface of the gametophyte **thallus** (plant body), which is not organized into roots, stems, and leaves. Stomata are present on the sporophyte in some mosses.

Years Ago (millions)	**Era** / **Period** / **Epoch**	**Life on Earth**	
	CENOZOIC Quaternary: Recent, Pleistocene	• Origin of agriculture and artificial selection; *H. sapiens*	
1.8	Tertiary: Pliocene	• Large carnivores; hominoid apes	
5	Miocene	• Forests dwindle; grassland spreads	
23	Oligocene	• Anthropoid apes	
35	Eocene	• Diversification of mammals and flowering plants	
57	Paleocene	• Specialized flowers; sophisticated pollinators and seed distributors	
65	**MESOZOIC** Cretaceous	• Flowering plants established and diversified; many modern families present; extinction of many dinosaurs	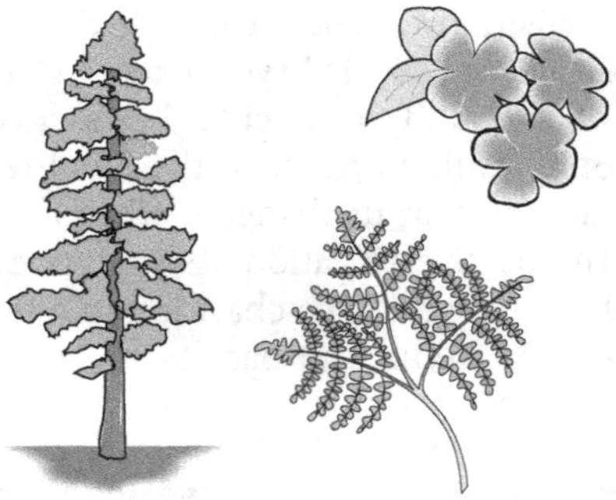
145	Jurassic	• Origin of birds; reptiles dominant; cycads and ferns abundant; first modern conifers and immediate ancestors of flowering plants	
208	Triassic	• First dinosaurs and mammals; forests of gymnosperms and ferns; cycads	
245	**PALEOZOIC** Permian	• Diversification of gymnosperms; origin of reptiles; amphibians dominant	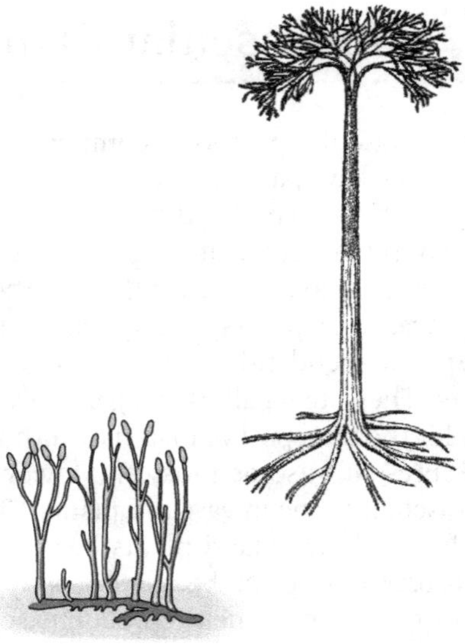
290	Carboniferous	• First treelike plants; giant woody lycopods and sphenopsids form extensive forests in swampy areas; evolution of early seeds (seed ferns) and first stages of leaves	
363	Devonian	• Diversification of vascular plants; sharks and fishes dominant in the oceans	
409	Silurian	• First vascular plants	
439	Ordovician	• Diversification of algae and plants invade land	
510	Cambrian	• Diversification of major animal phyla	
570	**PRECAMBRIAN** Precambrian	• Origin of bacteria, archaea, and eukaryotes	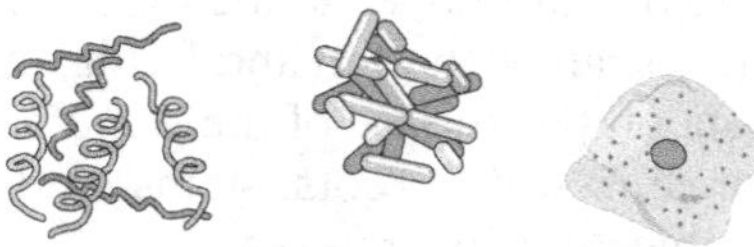
Earth is about 4.6 billion years old			

Bryophytes are not important economically, with the exception of sphagnum moss, which in its harvested and dried form is known as *peat moss*. Peat moss is absorbent, has an antibacterial agent, and was reportedly once used as bandages and diapers. Today peat moss is used in the horticultural industry, and dried peat is burned as fuel in some parts of the world. Peat lands cover more than one percent of the Earth's surface and store 400 billion metric tons of organic carbon. Harvesting and burning peat releases CO_2 to the atmosphere, thus contributing to changes in the global carbon cycle.

Lab Study A. Bryophyta: Mosses

Materials

living examples of mosses
prepared slides of *Mnium* archegonia and antheridia
colored pencils

Introduction

The mosses are the most common group of nonvascular plants, occurring primarily in moist environments but also found in dry habitats that are periodically wetj10

. Refer to Figure 4 on the next page as you investigate the moss life cycle, which is representative of the bryophytes.

Procedure

1. Examine living colonies of mosses on demonstration. Usually you will find the two generations, gametophyte and sporophyte, growing together.
2. Identify the leafy **gametophytes** and the dependent **sporophytes,** which appear as elongated structures growing above them. Tug gently at the sporophyte and notice that it is attached to the gametophyte. Recall that the sporophyte develops and matures while attached to the gametophyte and receives its moisture and nutrients from the gametophyte.
3. The gametes are produced by the gametophyte in **gametangia,** which protect the gametes but are not readily visible without a microscope. Observe under the microscope's low-power lens prepared slides containing long sections of heads of the unisex moss *Mnium,* which contain the gametangia. One slide has been selected to show the **antheridia** (male); the other is a rosette of **archegonia** (female). Sperm-forming tissue will be visible inside the antheridia. On the archegonial slide, look for an archegonium. The moss archegonium has a very long neck and rounded base. It will be difficult to find an entire archegonium in any one section. Search for a single-celled **egg** in the base of the archegonium.

(☞) **Figure 3.**
Geological time chart. The history of life can be organized into time periods that reflect changes in the physical and biological environment. Refer to this table as you review the evolution of land plants in Plant Diversity I and II.

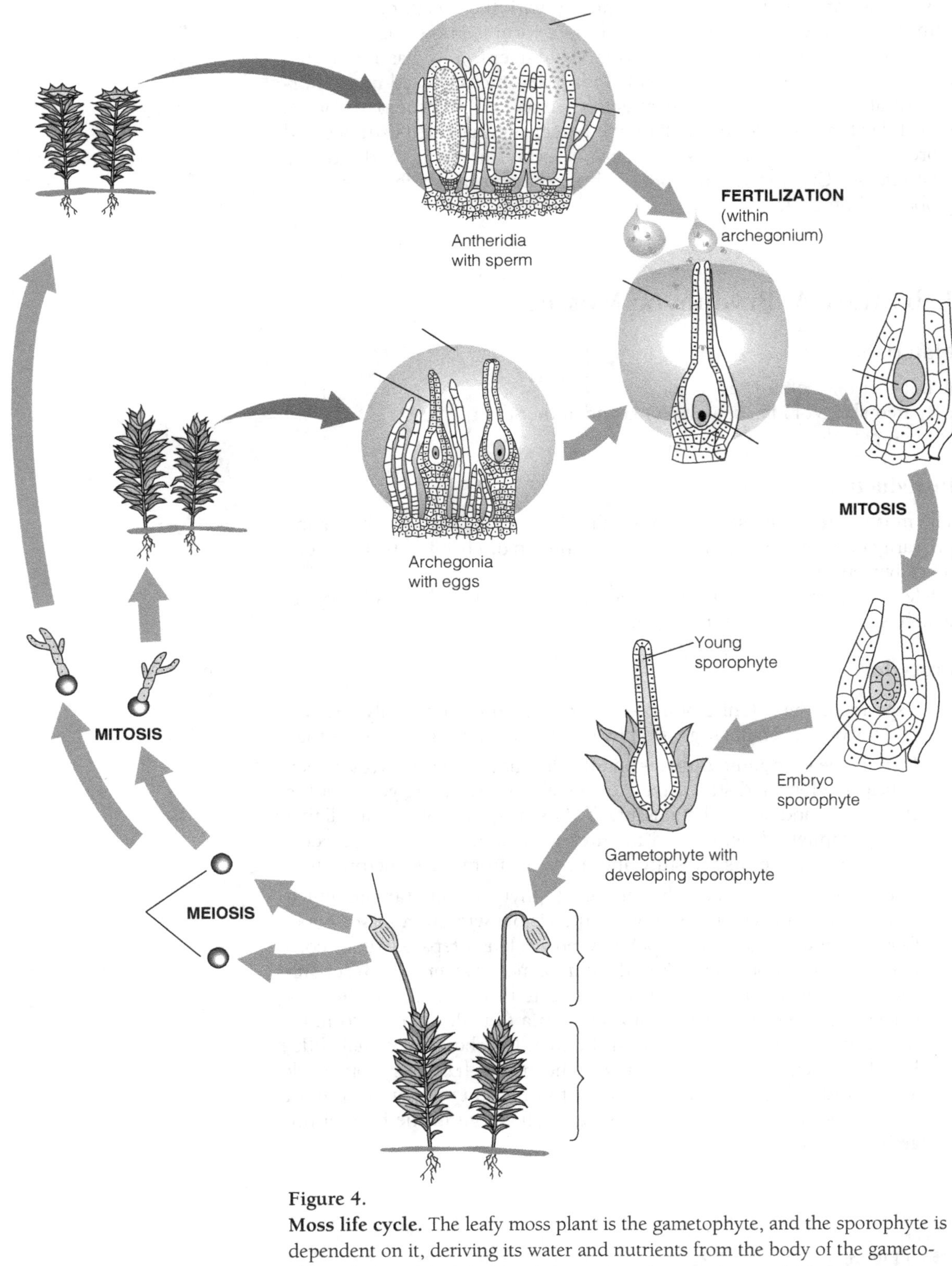

Figure 4.
Moss life cycle. The leafy moss plant is the gametophyte, and the sporophyte is dependent on it, deriving its water and nutrients from the body of the gametophyte. Review this variation of alternation of generations and label the structures described in Lab Study A. *Using colored pencils, highlight the haploid and diploid structures in different colors. Circle the processes of mitosis and meiosis.*

4. Refer to Figure 4 as you follow the steps of fertilization through formation of the gametophyte in the next generation. The sperm swim through a film of water to the archegonium and swim down the neck to the egg, where fertilization takes place. The diploid zygote divides by mitosis and develops into an embryonic sporophyte within the archegonium. As the sporophyte matures, it grows out of the gametophyte but remains attached, deriving water and nutrients from the gametophyte body. **Spores** develop in the **sporangium** at the end of the sporophyte. The spores are discharged from the sporangium and in a favorable environment develop into new gametophytes.

Results

1. Review the structures and processes observed and then label the moss life cycle diagram in Figure 4.
2. Using colored pencils, indicate if structures are haploid or diploid and circle the processes of mitosis and meiosis.

Discussion

Refer to Figure 2, the generalized diagram of the plant life cycle.

1. Are the spores produced by the moss sporophyte formed by meiosis or mitosis? Are they haploid or diploid?

2. Do the spores belong to the gametophyte or sporophyte generation?

3. Are the gametes haploid or diploid? Are they produced by meiosis or mitosis?

4. Is the dominant generation for the mosses the gametophyte or the sporophyte?

5. Can you suggest any ecological role for mosses?

6. What feature of the life cycle differs for bryophytes compared with all other land plants?

Lab Study B. Hepatophyta: Liverworts

Materials

living liverworts

Introduction

Liverworts are so named because their bodies are flattened and lobed. Early herbalists believed that these plants were beneficial in the treatment of liver disorders. Although less common than mosses, liverworts can be found along streams on moist rocks, but because of their small size, you must look closely to locate them.

Procedure

Examine examples of liverworts on demonstration. Liverworts have a flat **thallus** (plant body). Note the **rhizoids,** rootlike extensions on the lower surface, that primarily anchor plants. Observe the **pores** on the surface of the leaflike thallus. These openings function in gas exchange; however, they are always open since they lack guard cells. On the upper surface of the thallus you should see circular cups called **gemmae cups,** which contain flat disks of green tissue called **gemmae.** The gemmae are washed out of the cups when it rains, and they grow into new, genetically identical liverworts.

Results

Sketch the overall structure of the liverwort in the margin of your laboratory manual. Label structures where appropriate.

Discussion

1. Is the plant you observed the gametophyte or sporophyte?

2. Are the gemmae responsible for asexual or sexual reproduction? Explain.

3. Why are these plants, like most bryophytes, restricted to moist habitats, and why are they always small?

4. In this lab topic, you are asked to complete tables that summarize features advantageous to the adaptation of plant groups to the land environment. You may be asked to compare these derived (advanced) features with others that have changed little (primitive) in the evolution of land plants. For example, for nonvascular plants, motile sperm might be considered a primitive feature, while the cuticle would be considered advanced.

   Complete Table 2, relating the features of nonvascular plants to their success in the land environment. Refer to the lab topic introduction for assistance.

Table 2
Primitive and Advanced Features of Nonvascular Plants as They Relate to Adaptation to Land

Primitive Features	Advanced Features

EXERCISE 2

Seedless Vascular Plants

Seedless, terrestrial plants are analogous to the first terrestrial vertebrate animals, the amphibians, in their dependence on water for external fertilization and development of the unprotected, free-living embryo. Both groups were important in the Paleozoic era but have undergone a steady decline in importance since that time. Seedless plants were well suited for life in the vast swampy areas that covered large areas of the Earth in the Carboniferous period but were not suited for the drier areas of the Earth at that time or for later climatic changes that caused the vast swamps to decline and disappear. The fossilized remains of the swamp forests are the coal deposits of today (Figure 3 and Figure 7).

Although living representatives of the seedless vascular plants have survived for millions of years, their limited adaptations to the land environment have restricted their range. All seedless vascular plants have vascular tissue, which is specialized for conducting water, nutrients, and photosynthetic products. Their life cycle is a variation of alternation of generations, in which the sporophyte is the dominant plant; the gametophyte is usually independent of the sporophyte. These plants have stomata and structural support tissue. However, since they still retain the primitive feature of motile sperm that require water for fertilization, the gametophyte is small and restricted to moist habitats.

Economically, the only important members of this group are the ferns, a significant horticultural resource.

The phyla included in the seedless vascular plants are Lycophyta and Pterophyta (see again Table 1 and Figure 1).

Lab Study A. Lycophyta: Club Mosses

Materials

living *Selaginella* and *Lycopodium*
preserved *Selaginella* with microsporangia and megasporangia
prepared slide of *Selaginella* strobilus, l.s.

Introduction

Living members of Lycophyta are usually found in moist habitats, including bogs and streamsides. However, one species of *Selaginella,* the resurrection plant, inhabits deserts. It remains dormant throughout periods of low rainfall, but then comes to life—resurrects—when it rains. During the Carboniferous period, lycophytes were not inconspicuous parts of the flora but rather formed the forest canopy; they were the ecological equivalent of today's oaks, hickories, and pines (Figure 7).

Nonvascular plants and most seedless vascular plants produce one type of spore (**homospory**), which gives rise to the gametophyte by mitosis. One advanced feature occasionally seen in seedless vascular plants is the production of two kinds of spores (**heterospory**). Large spores called **megaspores** divide by mitosis to produce the female gametophyte. The numerous small spores, **microspores,** produce the male gametophytes by mitosis. Heterospory and separate male and female gametophytes, as seen in *Selaginella,* are unusual in seedless vascular plants, but characteristic of seed-producing vascular plants.

Procedure

1. Examine living club mosses, *Selaginella* and *Lycopodium.* Are they dichotomously branched? (The branches would split in two, appearing to form a Y.) Locate sporangia, which may be present either clustered at the end of the leafy stem tips, forming **strobili,** or **cones,** or dispersed along the leafy stems. Note that these plants have small leaves, or bracts, along the stem.
2. Examine preserved strobili of *Selaginella.* Observe the round sporangia clustered in sporophylls (leaflike structures) at the tip of the stem (Figure 5a). These sporangia contain either four megaspores or numerous microspores. Can you observe any differences in the sporangia or spores?
3. Observe the prepared slide of a long section through the strobilus of *Selaginella.* Begin your observations at low power. Are both microspores and megaspores visible on this slide?

   How can you distinguish these spores?
4. Identify the **strobilus, microsporangium, microspores, megasporangium,** and **megaspores** and label Figure 5.

Figure 5.
Selaginella. (a) The leafy plant is the sporophyte. The sporangia are clustered at the tips in strobili. (b) Photomicrograph of a longitudinal section through the strobilus of *Selaginella.*

Results

1. Sketch the overall structure of the club mosses in the margin of your lab manual. Label structures where appropriate.
2. Review Figure 5 of *Selaginella.* Using a colored pencil, highlight the structures that are haploid and part of the gametophyte generation.

Discussion

1. Are these leafy plants part of the sporophyte or the gametophyte generation? Do you have any evidence to support your answer?

2. What features would you look for to determine if this were a seedless vascular plant?

3. Are microspores and megaspores produced by mitosis or meiosis? (Review the life cycle in Figure 2.)

4. Will megaspores divide to form the female gametophyte or the sporophyte?

Having trouble with life cycles? Return to the introduction and review the generalized life cycle in Figure 2. Reread the introduction to the study of seedless vascular plants. The key to success is to determine where meiosis occurs and to remember the ploidal level for the gametophyte and the sporophyte.

Lab Study B. Pterophyta: Ferns, Horsetails, and Whisk Ferns

Materials

living and/or preserved horsetails (*Equisetum*)
living and/or preserved whisk ferns (*Psilotum*)
living ferns

Introduction

If a time machine could take us back 400 million years to the Silurian period, we would find that vertebrate animals were confined to the seas, and early vascular plants had begun to diversify on land (Table 3). By the Carboniferous period, ferns, horsetails, and whisk ferns grew alongside the lycophytes. Until recently, these three groups of seedless vascular plants were placed in separate phyla: Pterophyta (ferns), Sphenophyta (horsetails), and Psilophyta (whisk ferns). Strong evidence from molecular biology now reveals a close relationship among these three groups, supporting a common ancestor for the group and their placement in one phylum, Pterophyta.

Psilophytes (**whisk ferns**) are diminutive, dichotomously branched (repeated Y branches), photosynthetic stems that reproduce sexually by aerial spores. Today, whisk ferns can be found in some areas of Florida and in the tropics. Sphenophytes (**horsetails**) have green jointed stems with occasional clusters of leaves or branches. Their cell walls contain silica that give the stem a rough texture. These plants were used by pioneers to scrub dishes—thus their name, scouring rushes. In cooler regions of North America, horsetails grow as weeds along roadsides. **Ferns** are the most successful group of seedless vascular plants, occupying habitats from the desert to tropical rain forests. Most ferns are small plants that lack woody tissue. An exception is the tree ferns found in tropical regions. Many cultivated ferns are available for home gardeners.

In this lab study you will investigate the diversity of pterophytes, including whisk ferns, horsetails, and a variety of ferns. The plants on demonstration are sporophytes, the dominant generation in seedless vascular plants. You will investigate the life cycle of a fern in Lab Study C, Fern Life Cycle.

Procedure

1. Examine a living **whisk fern** (*Psilotum nudum*) on demonstration. This is one of only two extant genera of psilophytes.
2. Observe the spherical structures on the stem. If possible, cut one open and determine the function of these structures. Note the dichotomous branching, typical of the earliest land plants.

's (*Equisetum* sp.) on demonstration. Note the ribs . Also examine the nodes or joints along the stem leaves may occur in some species. Locate the **stro-** r preserved specimens on demonstration. These are **ngia**, which produce **spores.**

iving **ferns** on demonstration. Note the deeply dissected ch arise from an underground stem called a **rhizome,** which s like a root to anchor the plant. Roots arise from the rhizome. Observe the dark spots, or **sori** (sing. **sorus**), which are clusters of sporangia, on the underside of some leaves, called **sporophylls**.

Results

1. Sketch the overall structure of the whisk fern, horsetail, and fern in the margin of your lab manual. Label structures where appropriate.
2. Are there any leaves on the whisk fern? On the horsetails?
3. Are sporangia present on the whisk fern? On the horsetails? On the ferns?

Discussion

1. Are the spores in the sporangia produced by mitosis or meiosis?

2. Are the sporangia haploid or diploid? Think about which generation produces them.

3. Once dispersed, will these spores produce the gametophyte or sporophyte generation?

Lab Study C. Fern Life Cycle

Materials

living ferns
living fern gametophytes with archegonia and antheridia
living fern gametophytes with young sporophytes attached
stereoscopic microscope
compound microscope
prepared slide of fern gametophytes with archegonia, c.s.
colored pencils
Protoslo®
glycerol in dropping bottle

Introduction

In the previous Lab Study you examined the features of the fern sporophyte. In this lab study you will examine the fern life cycle in more detail, beginning with the sporophyte.

Procedure

1. Examine the sporophyte leaf with sori (sporophyll) at your lab bench. Make a wet mount of a sorus, using a drop of glycerol, and do not add a cover slip. Examine the sporangia using a dissecting microscope. You will find the stalked **sporangia** in various stages of development. Find a sporangium still filled with **spores** and another that has discharged its spores. The sporangia contain cells in different stages of meiosis, leading to spores that are seen in different stages of maturation. These stages will not be distinguishable to you under the microscope.
2. Refer to Figure 6 as you observe the events and important structures in the life cycle of the fern. The haploid spores of ferns fall to the ground and grow into heart-shaped, **gametophyte** plants. All seedless terrestrial plants depend on an external source of water for a sperm to swim to an egg to effect fertilization and for growth of the resulting sporophyte plant. The sexual organs, which bear male and female gametes, are borne on the underside of the gametophyte. Egg cells are borne in urn-like structures called **archegonia,** and sperm cells are produced in globular structures called **antheridia.** Archegonia are usually found around the notch of the heart-shaped gametophyte, while antheridia occur over most of the undersurface.
3. To study whole gametophytes, make a slide of living gametophytes. View them using the stereoscopic microscope or the scanning lens on the compound microscope. Note their shape and color and the presence of **rhizoids,** rootlike multicellular structures. Locate archegonia and antheridia. Which surface will you need to examine? Sketch in the margin of your lab manual any details not included in Figure 6.
4. If you have seen antheridia on a gametophyte, remove the slide from the microscope. Gently but firmly press on the coverslip with a pencil eraser. View using the compound microscope first on intermediate and then on high power. Look for motile **sperm** swimming with a spiral motion. Each sperm has two flagella. Add a drop of Protoslo to slow down movement of sperm.
5. Observe the cross section of a fern gametophyte with archegonia. Each archegonium encloses an **egg,** which may be visible on your slide.
6. Make a wet mount of a fern gametophyte with a **young sporophyte** attached. Look for a young **leaf** and **root** on each sporophyte.

   Share slides of living gametophytes with archegonia, antheridia and sperm, and sporophytes until everyone has observed each structure.

Results

1. Review the structures and processes observed, and then label the stages of fern sexual reproduction outlined in Figure 6.
2. Using colored pencils, circle those parts of the life cycle that are sporophytic (diploid). Use another color to encircle the gametophytic (haploid) stages of the life cycle. Highlight the processes of meiosis and mitosis.

Discussion

Refer to Figure 2, the generalized diagram of the plant life cycle, and Figure 6, a representation of the fern life cycle.

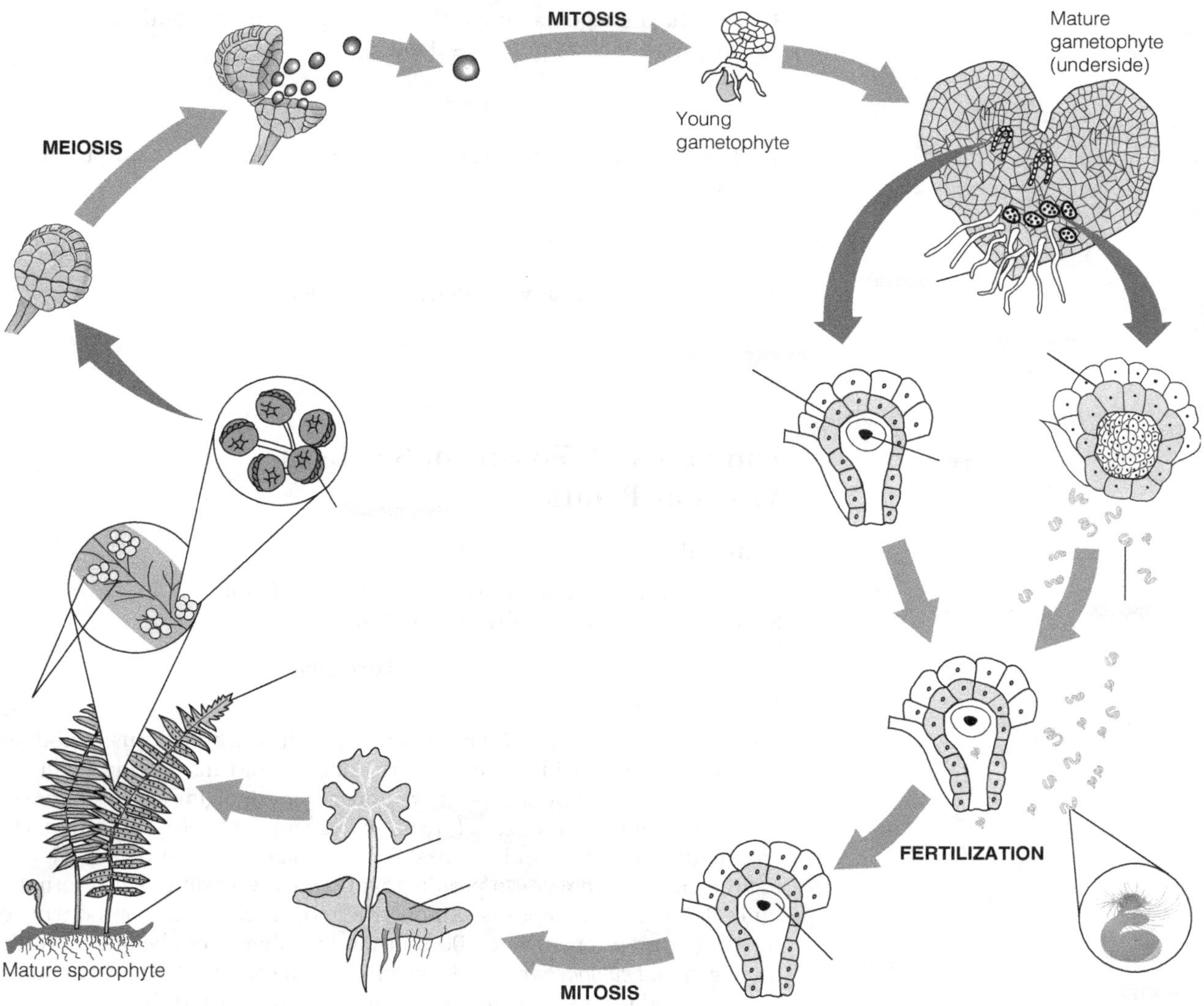

Figure 6.
Fern life cycle. The familiar leafy fern plant is the sporophyte, which alternates with a small, heart-shaped gametophyte. Review this life cycle, a variation of alternation of generations, and label the structures and processes described in Lab Study C. *Using colored pencils, highlight the haploid and diploid structures in different colors.*

1. Are the spores produced by the fern sporophyte formed by meiosis or mitosis?

2. Do the spores belong to the gametophyte or the sporophyte generation?

3. Are the gametes produced by mitosis or meiosis?

4. Are the archegonia and antheridia haploid or diploid? Think about which generation produces them.

5. Is the dominant generation for the fern the gametophyte or the sporophyte?

6. Can you suggest any ecological role for ferns?

Lab Study D. Fossils of Seedless Vascular Plants

Materials

fossils of extinct lycophytes (*Lepidodendron, Sigillaria*)
fossils of extinct sphenophytes (*Calamites*)
fossils of extinct ferns

Introduction

If we went back in time 300 million years to the Carboniferous period, we would encounter a wide variety of vertebrate amphibians moving about vast swamps dominated by spore-bearing forest trees. Imagine a forest of horsetails and lycophytes the size of trees, amphibians as large as alligators, and enormous dragonflies and roaches! Seedless plants were at their peak during this period and were so prolific that their carbonized remains form the bulk of Earth's coal deposits. Among the most spectacular components of the coal-swamp forest were 100-foot-tall lycophyte trees belonging to the fossil genera *Lepidodendron* and *Sigillaria,* tree ferns, and 60-foot-tall horsetails assigned to the fossil genus *Calamites* (Figures 3 and 7).

Procedure

Examine flattened fossil stems of *Lepidodendron, Sigillaria, Calamites,* and fossil fern foliage, all of which were recovered from coal mine tailings. Compare these with their living relatives, the lycophytes (club mosses), sphenophytes (horsetails), and ferns, which today are diminutive plants found in restricted habitats.

Results

1. For each phylum of seedless vascular plants, describe those characteristics that are similar for both living specimens and fossils. For example, do you observe dichotomous branching and similar shape and form of leaves, stems, or sporangia? Refer to the living specimens or your sketches.

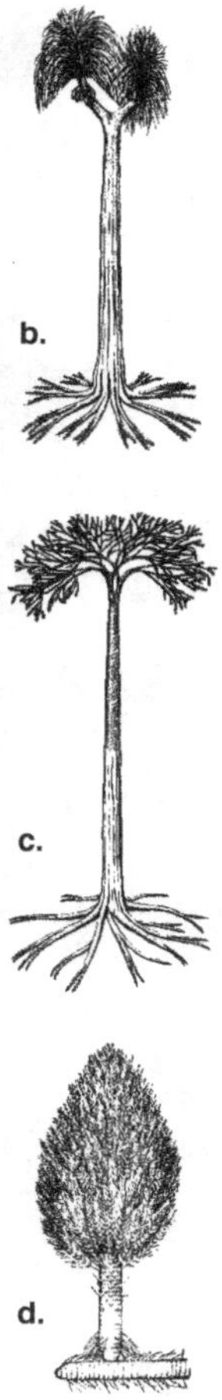

Figure 7.
Seedless vascular plants of the Carboniferous period. (a) Reconstruction of a swamp forest dominated by lycophytes (b) *Lepidodendron* and (c) *Sigillaria.* (d) *Calamites* was a relative of horsetails. *(No. Geo. 7500c, Field Museum of Natural History, Chicago)*

Lycophytes:

Sphenophytes:

Ferns:

2. Sketch in the margin of your lab manual the overall structure of the fossils. How would you recognize these fossils at a later date? Label structures where appropriate.

Discussion

The lycophytes, sphenophytes, and ferns were once the giants of the plant kingdom and dominated the landscape. Explain why they are presently restricted to certain habitats and are relatively small in stature.

Questions for Review

1. Complete Table 3, indicating the primitive and advanced features of seedless vascular plants relative to success in land environments. Recall that in this context the term *primitive* means an ancestral trait, while the term *advanced* indicates a derived trait, or adaptation, to land. For example, traits shared with the nonvascular plants (such as sperm requiring water for fertilization) are primitive, while the presence of vascular tissue is advanced.

Table 3
Primitive and Advanced Features of Seedless Vascular Plants as They Relate to Adaptation to Land

Primitive Features	Advanced Features

2. For each of the listed features, describe its contribution, if any, to the success of land plants.

   gametangium

   cuticle

   rhizoid

motile sperm

vascular tissue

gemma

3. Complete Table 4. Identify the function of the structures listed. Indicate whether they are part of the gametophyte or sporophyte generation, and provide an example of a plant that has this structure.
4. What is the major difference between the alternation of generations in the life cycles of nonvascular plants and seedless vascular plants?

Table 4
Structures and Functions of the Nonvascular Plants and Seedless Vascular Plants

Structure	Function	Sporophyte/ Gametophyte	Example
Antheridium			
Archegonium			
Spore			
Gamete			
Rhizome			
Gemma			
Sporangium			
Strobilus			
Sorus			

Applying Your Knowledge

1. The fossil record provides little information about ancient mosses. Do you think that nonvascular plants could ever have been large tree-sized plants? Provide evidence from your investigations to support your answer.

2. On a walk through a botanical garden, you notice a small leafy plant that is growing along the edge of a small stream in a shady nook. You hypothesize that this plant is a lycophyte. What information can you gather to test your hypothesis?

3. Fern antheridia release sperm that then swim toward archegonia in a watery film. The archegonia release a fluid containing chemicals that attract the sperm. This is an example of chemotaxis, the movement of cells or organisms in response to a chemical. What is the significance of chemotaxis to fern (and moss) reproduction?

4. German scientists studied air pollution from heavy metals (cadmium, copper, lead, nickel, and zinc) by analyzing the concentration of these metals in moss samples. They compared mosses collected between 1845 and 1974, which were preserved as herbarium specimens, with mosses collected in 1991. In general, the 1991 mosses had lower heavy metal concentrations. These results were attributed to increased air pollution controls. Based on your knowledge of the structure of the moss gametophyte, can you suggest one or more reasons why mosses are particularly useful indicators of air pollution?

5. Heterospory occasionally occurs in lycophytes and ferns, and in all seed plants. Botanists are convinced that heterospory must have originated more than once in the evolution of plants. Can you suggest one or more advantages that heterospory might provide to plants?

Investigative Extensions

Students may investigate chemotaxis in *C-Fern* sperm. This investigation uses 12–18 day old gametophytes of *C-Fern, Ceratopteris.* Using a simple system, students determine the sperm activity after exposure to organic acids which may be present in the fluid released by the archegonia. The materials are available from Carolina Biological Supply: *C-Fern* Chemotaxis Kit and *C-Fern* Culture Kit. Laboratory procedures and preparation instructions are available at http://cfern.biology.utk.edu. To use this investigation as part of this lab topic, omit observation of the gametophyte in Lab Study C. Use only three of the test solutions and the control. Students should work in pairs.

References

Herpin, U., B. Markert, V. Wechert, J. Berklekamp, K. Friese, U. Siewers, and H. Lieth. "Retrospective Analysis of Heavy Metal Concentrations at Selected Locations in the Federal Republic of Germany Using Moss Materials from a Herbarium," *Science of the Total Environment,* 1997, vol. 205, pp. 1–12.

Hickock, L. G. and T. R. Warne. *C-Fern Manual.* Burlington, NC: Carolina Biological Supply, 2000.

Mauseth, J. D. *Botany: An Introduction to Plant Biology,* 3rd ed. Sudbury, MA: Jones and Bartlett Publishers, 2003.

Nabors, M. W. *Introduction to Botany.* San Francisco, CA: Benjamin Cummings, 2004.

Raven, P. H., R. F. Evert, and S. E. Eichhorn. *Biology of Plants,* 6th ed. New York: W. H. Freeman Publishers, 1999.

Websites

Links to images of horsetails:

http://www.wisc.edu/botit/systematics/Phyla/Sphenophyta/Sphenophyta.html

Links to images of whisk ferns:

http://www.wisc.edu/botit/systematics/Phyla/Psilophyta/Psilophyta.html

Links to images of lycophytes:

http://www.wisc.edu/botit/systematics/Phyla/Lycophyta/Lycophyta.html

Plant Diversity II: Seed Plants

Before lab, read the following material on gymnosperms and angiosperms and complete Table 1 by listing (and comparing) the traits of each.

Laboratory Objectives

After completing this lab topic, you should be able to:

1. Identify examples of the phyla of seed plants.
2. Describe the life cycle of a gymnosperm (pine tree) and an angiosperm.
3. Describe features of flowers that ensure pollination by insects, birds, bats, and wind.
4. Describe factors influencing pollen germination.
5. Identify types of fruits, recognize examples, and describe dispersal mechanisms.
6. Relate the structures of seed plants to their functions in the land environment.
7. Compare the significant features of life cycles for various land plants and state their evolutionary importance.
8. Summarize major trends in the evolution of land plants and provide evidence from your laboratory investigations.

Gymnosperms

For over 500 million years, plants have been adapting to the rigors of the land environment. The nonvascular bryophytes with their small and simple bodies survived in moist habitats, habitats moist at least for part of their life cycle. During the cool Carboniferous period, vascular seedless plants dominated the landscape of the swamp forests that covered much of the earth. Although these plants were more complex and better adapted to the challenges of the land environment, they still were dependent on water for sperm to swim to the egg. During the Mesozoic era, 150 million years ago,

Earth became warmer and drier and the swamp forests declined, presenting another challenge to terrestrial plants and animals. Earth at that time was a world dominated by reptilian vertebrates, including the flying, running, and climbing dinosaurs. The landscape was dominated by a great variety of seed-bearing plants called **gymnosperms** (literally, "naked seeds"), which in the Carboniferous period had been restricted to dry sites. During the Mesozoic, a number of distinct gymnosperm groups diversified, and a few of the spore-bearing plants survived. As you review the evolution of land plants, refer to the geological time chart for an overview of the history of life on Earth.

Vertebrate animals became fully terrestrial during the Mesozoic with the emergence of reptiles, which were free from a dependence on water for sexual reproduction and development. The development of the amniotic egg along with an internal method of fertilization made this major transition possible. The amniotic egg carries its own water supply and nutrients, permitting early embryonic development to occur on dry land, a great distance from external water. In an analogous manner, the gymnosperms became free from dependence on water through the development of a process of internal fertilization via the pollen grain and development of a seed, which contains a dormant embryo with a protective cover and special nutrient tissue.

Several features of the gymnosperms have been responsible for their success. They have reduced (smaller-sized) gametophytes; the male gametophyte is a multinucleated pollen grain, and the female gametophyte is small and retained within the sporangium in the ovule of the sporophyte generation. The pollen grain is desiccation resistant and adapted for wind pollination, removing the necessity for fertilization in a watery medium. The pollen tube conveys the sperm nucleus to an egg cell, and the embryonic sporophyte develops within the gametophyte tissues, which are protected by the previous sporophyte generation. The resulting seed is not only protected from environmental extremes, but also is packed with nutritive materials and can be dispersed away from the parent plant. In addition, gymnosperms have advanced vascular tissues: xylem for transporting water and nutrients and phloem for transporting photosynthetic products. The xylem cells are called *tracheids* and are more efficient for transport than those of the seedless vascular plants.

Angiosperms

A visit to Earth 60 million years ago, during the late Cretaceous period, would reveal a great diversity of mammals and birds and a landscape dominated by **flowering plants,** or **angiosperms** (phylum **Anthophyta**). Ultimately, these plants would diversify and become the most numerous, widespread, and important plants on Earth. Angiosperms now occupy well over 90% of the vegetated surface of Earth and contribute virtually 100% of our agricultural food plants.

The evolution of the flower resulted in enormous advances in the efficient transfer and reception of pollen. Whereas gymnosperms are all wind-pollinated, producing enormous amounts of pollen that reach the appropriate species by chance, the process of flower pollination is mediated by specific agents—insects, birds, and bats—in addition to water and wind. Pollination agents such as the insect are attracted to the flower with its rewards of nectar and pollen. Animal movements provide precise placement of pollen on the receptive portion of the female structures, increasing the probability of fertilization. The process also enhances the opportunity for cross-fertilization among distant plants and therefore the possibility of increased genetic variation.

Angiosperm reproduction follows the trend for reduction in the size of the gametophyte. The pollen grain is the male gametophyte, and the eight-nucleated **embryo sac** is all that remains of the female gametophyte. This generation continues to be protected and dependent on the adult sporophyte plant. The female gametophyte provides nutrients for the developing sporophyte embryo through a unique triploid **endosperm** tissue. Another unique feature of angiosperms is the **fruit.** The seeds of the angiosperm develop within the flower ovary, which matures into the fruit. This structure provides protection and enhances dispersal of the young sporophyte into new habitats.

In addition to advances in reproductive biology, the angiosperms evolved other advantageous traits. All gymnosperms are trees or shrubs, with a large investment in woody, persistent tissue; and their life cycles are long (5 or more years before they begin to reproduce and 2 to 3 years to produce a seed). Flowering plants, on the other hand, can be woody, but many are herbaceous, with soft tissues that survive from one to a few years. It is possible for angiosperms to go from seed to seed in less than one year. As you perform the exercises in this lab, think about the significance of this fact in terms of the evolution of this group. How might generation length affect the rate of evolution? Angiosperms also have superior conducting tissues. Xylem tissue is composed of *tracheids* (as in gymnosperms), but also contains large-diameter, open-ended *vessels.* The phloem cells, called *sieve-tube members,* provide more efficient transport of the products of photosynthesis.

Review the characteristics of gymnosperms and angiosperms described in this introduction, and summarize in Table 1 the advantages of these groups relative to their success on land. You should be able to list several characteristics for each. At the end of the lab, you will be asked to modify and complete the table, based on your investigations.

You will want to return to this table after the laboratory to be sure that the table is complete and that you are familiar with all these important features.

EXERCISE 1
Gymnosperms

The term *gymnosperms* refers to a diverse group of seed plants that do not produce flowers. Although they share many characteristics, including the production of pollen, they represent four distinct groups, or phyla. In this exercise, you will observe members of these phyla and investigate the life cycle of a pine, one of the most common gymnosperms.

Table 1
Traits for Gymnosperms and Angiosperms
Relative to Their Success on Land

	Adaptation to the Land Environment
Gymnosperms 	
Angiosperms 	

Lab Study A. Phyla of Gymnosperms

Materials

living or pressed examples of conifers, ginkgos, cycads, and Mormon tea

Introduction

Gymnosperms are composed of several phyla. The largest and best known is Coniferophyta, which includes pines and other cone-bearing trees and shrubs. Cycads (Cycadophyta), which have a palmlike appearance, are found primarily in tropical regions scattered around the world. Ginkgos (Ginkgophyta), with their flat fan-shaped leaves, are native to Asia and are prized as urban trees. An extract of Ginkgo is used as an herbal medicine purported to improve memory. Gnetophyta is composed of three distinct and unusual groups of plants: gnetums, which are primarily vines of Asia, Africa, and South America; *Welwitschia,* a rare desert plant with two leathery leaves; and Mormon tea (*Ephedra*), desert shrubs of North and Central America. Compounds from *Ephedra,* ephedrines, used in diet aids and decongestants, have raised serious concerns due to side effects including cardiac arrest.

Procedure

1. Observe demonstration examples of all phyla of gymnosperms and be able to recognize their representatives. Note any significant ecological and economic role for these plants.
2. Record your observations in Table 2.

Table 2
Phyla of Gymnosperms

Phyla	Examples	Characteristics/Comments
Coniferophyta 		
Ginkgophyta 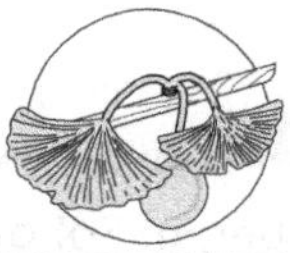		
Cycadophyta 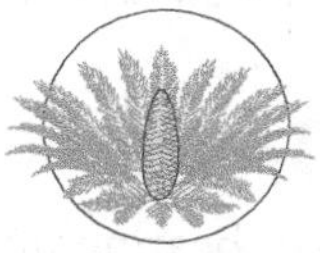		
Gnetophyta 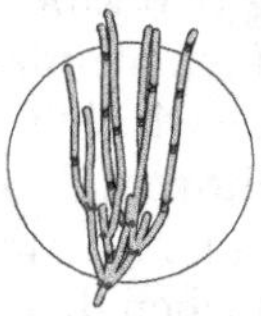		

Results

1. In the margin of your manual, sketch the overall structure of the plants. Label structures where appropriate.
2. Are there any reproductive structures present for these plants? If so, make notes in the margin of your lab manual.

Discussion

1. What are the key characteristics shared by all gymnosperms?

2. What is the ecological role of conifers in forest systems?

3. What economically important products are provided by conifers?

Lab Study B. Pine Life Cycle

Materials

living or preserved pine branch, male and female cones (1, 2, and 3 years old)
fresh or dried pine pollen or prepared slide of pine pollen
coverslips
prepared slides of male and female pine cones
colored pencils
slides

Review the pine life cycle (Figure 1) before you begin. Follow along as you complete the exercise.

Introduction

All gymnosperms are **wind-pollinated** trees or shrubs, most bearing unisexual, male, and female reproductive structures on different parts of the same plant. Gymnosperms are **heterosporous**, producing two kinds of spores: male **microspores**, which develop into **pollen**, and female **megaspores.** The megaspore develops into the female gametophyte, which is not free-living as with ferns but retained within the **megasporangium** and nourished by the sporophyte parent plant. Numerous pollen grains (the male gametophytes) are produced in each **microsporangium**, and when they are mature they are released into the air and conveyed by wind currents to the female cone. **Pollen tubes** grow through the tissue of the megasporangium, and the **sperm nucleus** is released to fertilize the egg. After fertilization, development results in the formation of an **embryo.** A **seed** is a dormant embryo embedded in nutrient tissue of the female gametophyte and surrounded by the hardened sporangium wall, or **seed coat.**

Having trouble with life cycles? The key to success is to determine where meiosis occurs and to remember the ploidal level for the gametophyte and sporophyte.

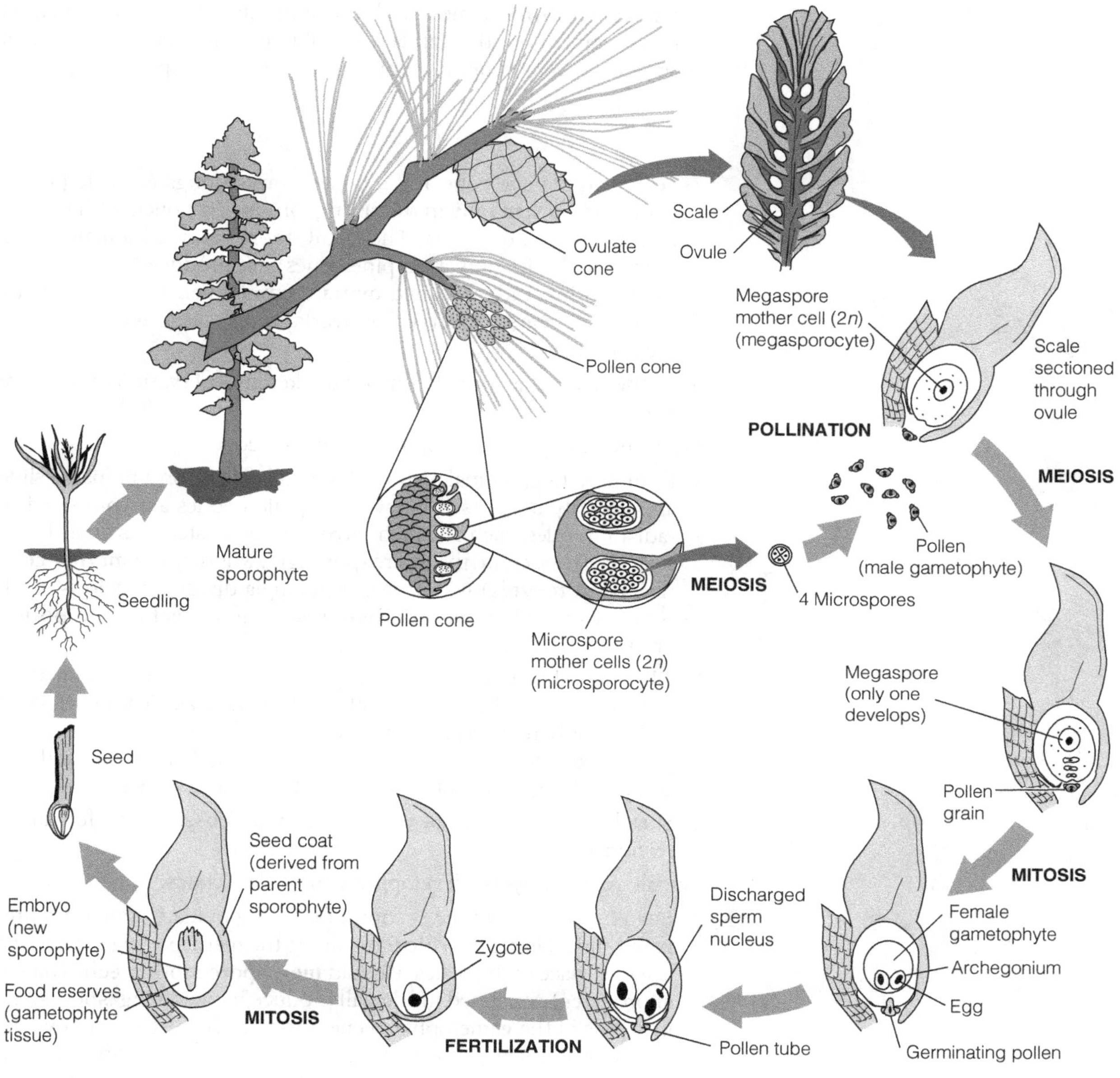

Figure 1.
Pine life cycle. Observe the structures and processes as described in Exercise 1. *Using colored pencils, indicate the structures that are haploid or diploid. Circle the terms* mitosis, meiosis, *and* fertilization.

Procedure

1. Pine sporophyte.
   a. Examine the pine branch and notice the arrangement of leaves in a bundle. A new twig at the end of the branch is in the process of producing new clusters of leaves. Is this plant haploid or diploid?

b. Examine the small **cones** produced at the end of the pine branch on this specimen or others in lab. Recall that cones contain clusters of sporangia. What important process occurs in the sporangia?

c. Locate an ovulate cone and a pollen cone. Elongated male **pollen cones** are present only in the spring, producing pollen within overlapping bracts, or scales. The small, more rounded female cones (which look like miniature pine cones) are produced on stem tips in the spring and are called **ovulate cones.** Female cones persist for several years. Observe the overlapping scales, which contain the sporangia.

d. In the margin of your lab manual, sketch observations for future reference.

2. Male gametophyte—development in pollen cones.

a. Examine a longitudinal section of the pollen cone on a prepared slide and identify its parts. Observe that pollen cones are composed of radiating scales, each of which carries two elongated sacs on its lower surface. The sacs are the **microsporangia. Microspore mother cells (microsporocytes)** within microsporangia divide by meiosis. Each produces four haploid **microspores,** which develop into **pollen grains.**

b. Observe a slide of pine pollen. If pollen is available, you can make a wet mount. Note the wings on either side of the grain. The pollen grain is the greatly reduced male gametophyte. The outer covering of the pollen is desiccation resistant. Once mature, pollen will be wind dispersed, sifting down into the scales of the female cones.

c. Sketch, in the margin of your lab manual, observations for future reference.

3. Female gametophyte—development in ovulate cones.

a. Examine a longitudinal section of a young ovulate cone on a prepared slide. Note the **ovule** (containing the megasporangium) on the upper surface of the scales. Diploid **megaspore mother cells (megasporocytes)** contained inside will produce haploid **megaspores,** the first cells of the gametophyte generation. In the first year of ovulate cone development, pollen sifts into the soft bracts (pollination) and the pollen tube begins to grow, digesting the tissues of the ovule.

b. Observe a second-year cone at your lab bench. During the second year, the ovule develops a multicellular female gametophyte with two archegonia in which an egg will form. Fertilization will not occur until the second year, when the pollen tube releases a sperm nucleus into the archegonium, where it unites with the egg to form the **zygote.** In each ovule only one of the archegonia and its zygote develops into a seed.

c. Observe a mature cone at your lab bench. The development of the embryo sporophyte usually takes another year. The female gametophyte will provide nutritive materials stored in the seed for the early stages of growth. The outer tissues of the ovule will harden to form the **seed coat.**

d. In the margin of your lab manual, sketch observations for future reference.

Results

1. Review the structures and processes observed.
2. Using colored pencils, indicate the structures of the pine life cycle in Figure 1 that are haploid or diploid, and circle the processes of mitosis, meiosis, and fertilization.

Discussion

1. What is the function of the wings on the pollen grain?

2. Why is wind-dispersed pollen an important phenomenon in the evolution of plants?

3. Are microspores and megaspores produced by mitosis or meiosis?

4. Can you think of at least two ways in which pine seeds are dispersed?

5. One of the major trends in plant evolution is the reduction in size of the gametophytes. Describe the male and female gametophyte in terms of size and location.

EXERCISE 2
Angiosperms

All flowering plants (angiosperms) are classified in the phylum **Anthophyta** (Gk. *anthos,* "flower"). A unique characteristic of angiosperms is the **carpel,** a vessel in which ovules are enclosed. After fertilization, the ovule develops into a seed (as in the gymnosperms), while the carpel matures into a fruit (unique to angiosperms). Other important aspects of angiosperm reproduction include additional reduction of the gametophyte, double fertilization, and an increase in the rapidity of the reproduction process.

The **flowers** of angiosperms are composed of male and female reproductive structures, which are frequently surrounded by attractive or protective leaflike structures collectively known as the **perianth**. The flower functions both to protect the developing gametes and to ensure pollination and fertilization. Although many angiosperm plants are self-fertile, cross-fertilization is important in maintaining genetic diversity. Plants, rooted and stationary, often require transfer agents to complete fertilization. A variety of insects, birds, and mammals transfer pollen from flower to flower. The pollen then germinates into a pollen tube and grows through the female carpel to deliver the sperm to the egg.

Plants must attract pollinators to the flower. What are some features of flowers that attract pollinators? Color and scent are important, as is the shape of the flower. Nectar and pollen provide nutritive rewards for the pollinators as well. The shape and form of some of the flowers are structured to accommodate pollinators of specific size and structure, providing landing platforms, guidelines, and even special mechanisms for the placement of pollen on body parts. While the flower is encouraging the visitation by one type of pollinator, it also may be excluding visitation by others. The more specific the relationship between flower and pollinator, the more probable that the pollen of that species will be successfully transferred. But many successful flowers have no specific adaptations for particular pollinators and are visited by a wide variety of pollinators.

Some plants do not have colorful, showy flowers and are rather inconspicuous, often dull in color, and lacking a perianth. These plants are usually wind-pollinated, producing enormous quantities of pollen and adapted to catch pollen in the wind.

The origin and diversification of angiosperms cannot be understood apart from the coevolutionary role of animals in the reproductive process. Colorful petals, strong scents, nectars, food bodies, and unusual perianth shapes all relate to pollinator visitation. Major trends in the evolution of angiosperms involve the development of mechanisms to exploit a wide variety of pollinators.

In Lab Study A, you will investigate a variety of flowers, observing their shape, structure, and traits that might attract pollinators of various kinds. Following this, in Lab Study B, you will use a key to identify the probable pollinators for some of these flowers. You will follow the life cycle of the lily in Lab Study C and complete the lab by using another key to identify types of fruits and their dispersal mechanisms.

Lab Study A. Flower Morphology

Materials

living flowers provided by the instructor and/or students
stereoscopic microscope

Introduction

Working in teams of two students, you will investigate the structure of the flower (Figure 2). The instructor will provide a variety of flowers, and you may have brought some with you to lab. You will need to take apart each flower carefully to determine its structure, since it is unlikely that all your flowers will follow the simple diagram used to illustrate the structures. Your observations will be the basis for predicting probable pollinators in Lab Study B.

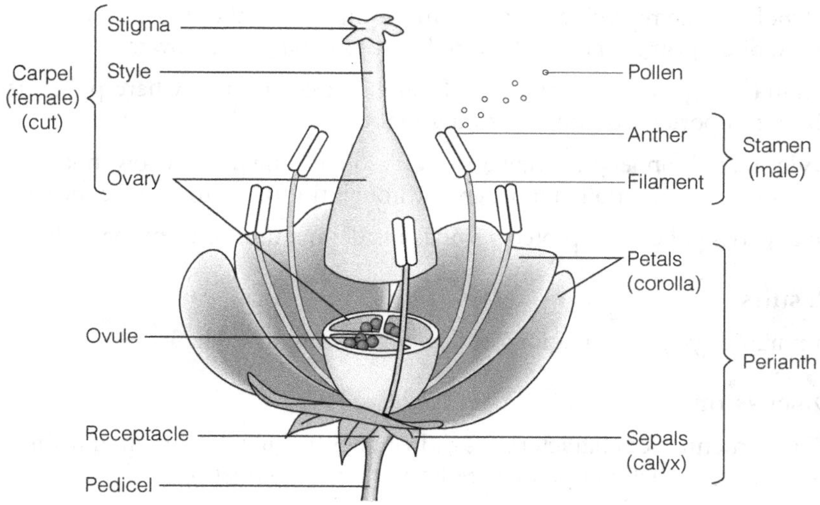

Figure 2.
Flower structures. Determine the structures of flowers in the laboratory by reviewing this general diagram.

Procedure

1. Examine fresh flowers of four different species, preferably with different floral characteristics.
2. Identify the parts of each flower using Figure 2 and the list provided following the heading Floral Parts. You may be able to determine the floral traits for large, open flowers by simply observing. However, most flowers will require that you remove the floral structures from the outside toward the center of the flower. Some flowers or structures may require the use of the stereoscopic microscope. For example, the ovary is positively identified by the presence of tiny crystal-like ovules, and these are best seen with the stereoscopic scope.
3. In the margin of your lab manual, sketch any flower shapes or structures that you might need to refer to in the future.
4. Record the results of your observations in Table 3. You will determine pollinators in Lab Study B.

Floral Parts

Pedicel: stalk that supports the flower.

Receptacle: tip of the pedicel where the flower parts attach.

Sepal: outer whorl of bracts, which may be green, brown, or colored like the petals; may appear as small scales or be petal-like.

Calyx: all the sepals, collectively.

Petal: colored, white, or even greenish whorl of bracts located just inside the sepals.

Corolla: all the petals, collectively.

Stamen: pollen-bearing structure, composed of filament and anther.

Filament: thin stalk that supports the anther.

Anther: pollen-producing structure.

Carpel: female reproductive structure, composed of the stigma, style, and ovary, often pear-shaped and located in the center of the flower.

Stigma: receptive tip of the carpel, often sticky or hairy, where pollen is placed; important to pollen germination.

Style: tissue connecting stigma to ovary, often long and narrow, but may be short or absent; pollen must grow through this tissue to fertilize the egg.

Ovary: base of carpel; protects ovules inside, matures to form the fruit.

Results

Summarize your observations of flower structure in Table 3.

Discussion

What structures or characteristics did you observe in your (or other teams') investigations that you predict are important to pollination?

Lab Study B. Pollinators

Materials

living flowers provided by the instructor and/or students
stereoscopic microscope

Introduction

Flowers with inconspicuous sepals and petals are usually pollinated by wind. Most showy flowers are pollinated by animals. Some pollinators tend to be attracted to particular floral traits, and, in turn, some groups of plants have coevolved with a particular pollination agent that ensures successful reproduction. Other flowers are generalists, pollinated by a variety of organisms, and still others may be visited by only one specific pollinator. Based on the floral traits that attract common pollinators (bees, flies, butterflies, and hummingbirds), you will predict the probable pollinator for some of your flowers using a dichotomous key. (Remember, *dichotomous* refers to the branching pattern and means "divided into two parts.")

In biology, we use a key to systematically separate groups of organisms based on sets of characteristics. Most keys are based on couplets, or pairs of characteristics, from which you must choose one or the other, thus, the term *dichotomous*. For example, the first choice of characteristics in a couplet might be *plants with showy flowers and a scent,* and the other choice in the pair might be *plants with tiny, inconspicuous flowers with no scent.* You must choose one or the other statement. In the next step, you would choose from a second pair of statements listed directly below your first choice. With each choice, you would narrow the group more and more until, as in this case, the pollinator is identified. *Each couplet or pair of statements from which you must choose will be identified by the same letter or number.*

Table 3
Flower Morphology and Pollinators

Features	Plant Names			
	1	2	3	4
Number of petals				
Number of sepals				
Parts absent (petals, stamens, etc.)				
Color				
Scent (+/–)				
Nectar (+/–)				
Shape (including corolla shape: tubular, star, etc.)				
Special features (landing platform, guidelines, nectar spur, etc.)				
Predicted pollinator (see Lab Study B)				

Key to Pollination

I. Sepals and petals reduced or inconspicuous; feathery or relatively large stigma; flower with no odor **wind**

I. Sepals and/or petals large, easily identified; stigma not feathery; flower with or without odor

- A. Sepals and petals white or subdued (greenish or burgundy); distinct odor
  - 1. Odor strong, heavy, sweet **moth**
  - 1. Odor strong, fermenting or fruitlike; flower parts and pedicel strong **bat**
  - 1. Odor of sweat, feces, or decaying meat **fly**
- A. Sepals and/or petals colored; odor may or may not be present
  - 1. Flower shape regular or irregular,* but not tubular
    - a. Flower shape irregular; sepals or petals blue, yellow, or orange; petal adapted to serve as a "landing platform"; may have dark lines on petals; sweet, fragrant odor **bee**
    - a. Flower shape regular; odor often fruity, spicy, sweet, or carrionlike **beetle**
  - 1. Flower shape tubular
    - a. Strong, sweet odor **butterfly**
    - a. Little or no odor; flower usually red **hummingbird**

*A regular flower shape is one that has radial symmetry (like a daisy or carnation), with similar parts (such as petals) having similar size and shape. Irregular flowers have bilateral symmetry.

Procedure

Using the key above, classify the flowers used in Lab Study A based on their floral traits and method of pollination.

Results

1. Record your results in Table 3.
2. If you made sketches of any of your flowers, you may want to indicate the pollinator associated with that flower.

Discussion

1. Review the Key to Pollination and describe the characteristics of flowers that are adapted for pollination by each of the following agents:

   a. wind

   b. hummingbird

   c. bat

2. Discuss with your lab partner other ways in which keys are used in biology. Record your answers in the space provided.

Lab Study C. Angiosperm Life Cycle

Materials

pollen tube growth medium in dropper bottles
dropper bottle of water
petri dish with filter paper to fit inside
prepared slides of lily anthers and ovary
dissecting probe
brush bristles
compound microscope
flowers for pollen

Introduction

In this lab study, you will study the life cycle of flowering plants, including the formation of pollen, pollination, fertilization of the egg, and formation of the seed and fruit. You will also investigate the germination of the pollen grain as it grows toward the egg cell.

Refer to Figures 2 (flower structures) and 3 (angiosperm life cycle) as you complete the exercise.

Procedure

1. Pollen grain—the male gametophyte.
   a. Examine a prepared slide of a cross section through the **stamens** of *Lilium.* The slide shows six anthers and may include a centrally located ovary that contains ovules.
   b. Observe a single **anther,** which is composed of four **anther sacs** (microsporangia). Note the formation of **microspores** (with a single nucleus) from diploid **microspore mother cells** (microsporocytes). You may also see mature **pollen grains** with two nuclei.
2. Development of the female gametophyte.
   a. Examine a prepared slide of the *Lilium* ovary and locate the developing ovules. Each **ovule,** composed of the megasporangium and other tissues, contains a diploid **megaspore mother cell** (megasporocyte), which produces **megaspores** (haploid), only one of which survives. The megaspore will divide three times by mitosis to produce the eight nuclei in the **embryo sac,** which is the greatly reduced female gametophyte. Note that angiosperms do not even produce an archegonium.

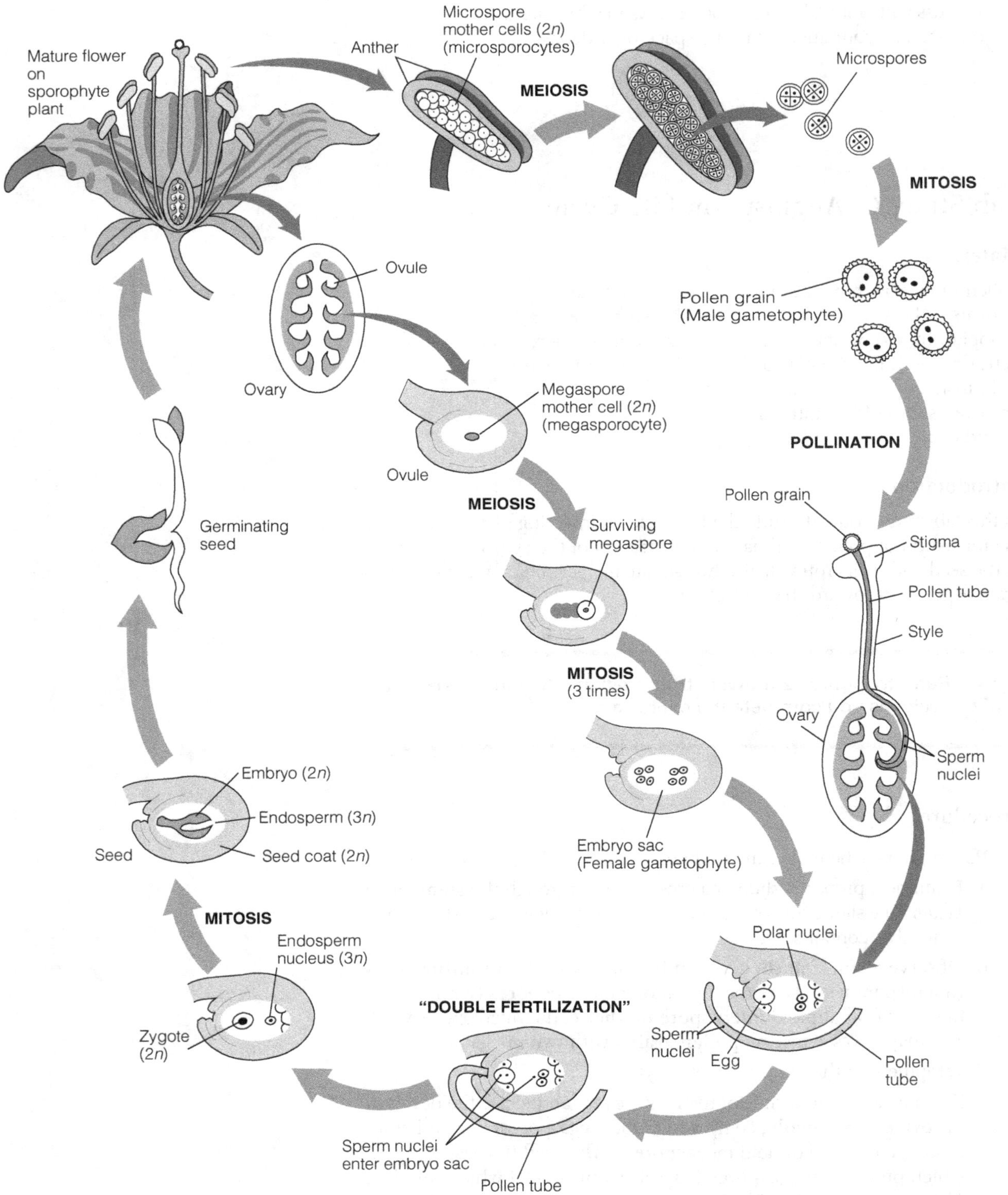

Figure 3.
Angiosperm life cycle. Observe the structures and processes as described in Exercise 2. *Using colored pencils, indicate the structures that are haploid or diploid. Circle the terms* mitosis, meiosis, *and* double fertilization.

b. Your slide will not contain all stages of development, and it is almost impossible to find a section that includes all eight nuclei. Locate the three nuclei near the opening to the ovule. One of these is called the **egg cell.** The two nuclei in the center are the **polar nuclei.**

3. Pollination and fertilization.

When pollen grains are mature, the anthers split and the pollen is released. When pollen reaches the stigma, it germinates to produce a **pollen tube,** which grows down the style and eventually comes into contact with the opening to the ovule. During this growth, one pollen nucleus divides into two **sperm nuclei.** One sperm nucleus fuses with the egg to form the **zygote,** and the second fuses with the two polar nuclei to form the triploid **endosperm,** which will develop into a rich nutritive material for the support and development of the embryo. The fusion of the two sperm nuclei with nuclei of the embryo sac is referred to as **double fertilization.** Formation of triploid endosperm and double fertilization are unique to angiosperms.

Once the pollen grain is deposited on the stigma of the flower, it must grow through the stylar tissue to reach the ovule. You will examine pollen tube growth by placing pollen in pollen growth medium to stimulate germination. Pollen from some plants germinates easily; for others a very specific chemical environment is required. Work with a partner, following the next steps.

a. Using a dissecting probe, transfer some pollen from the anthers of one of the plants available in the lab to a slide on which there are 2 to 3 drops of pollen tube growth medium and a few brush bristles or grains of sand (to avoid crushing the pollen). Add a coverslip. Alternatively, touch an anther to the drop of medium, then add brush bristles and a coverslip.

b. Examine the pollen under the compound microscope. Observe the shape and surface features of the pollen.

c. Prepare a humidity chamber by placing moistened filter paper in a petri dish. Place the slide in the petri dish, and place it in a warm environment.

d. Examine the pollen after 30 minutes and again after 60 minutes to observe pollen tube growth. The pollen tubes should appear as long, thin tubes extending from the surface or pores in the pollen grain.

e. Record your results in Table 4 in the Results section. Indicate the plant name and the times when pollen tube germination was observed.

4. Seed and fruit development.

The zygote formed at fertilization undergoes rapid mitotic phyla, forming the embryo. The endosperm also divides; the mature ovule forms a seed. At the same time, the surrounding ovary and other floral tissues are forming the fruit. In Lab Study D, you will investigate the types of fruits and their function in dispersal.

Results

1. Review the structures and processes observed in the angiosperm life cycle, Figure 3. Indicate the haploid and diploid structures in the life cycle, using two different colored pencils.

Having trouble with life cycles? Review the generalized life cycle. The key to success is to determine where meiosis occurs and to remember the ploidal level for the gametophyte and sporophyte.

2. Sketch observations of slides in the margin of your lab manual for later reference.
3. Record the results of pollen germination studies in Table 4. Compare your results with those of other teams who used different plants. This is particularly important if your pollen did not germinate.

Table 4
Results of Pollen Germination Studies

Plant Name	30 min (+/–)	60 min (+/–)

Discussion

1. What part of the life cycle is represented by the mature pollen grain?
2. How does the female gametophyte in angiosperms differ from the female gametophyte in gymnosperms?
3. Do you think that all pollen germinates indiscriminately on all stigmas? How might pollen germination and growth be controlled?

Lab Study D. Fruits and Dispersal

Materials

variety of fruits provided by the instructor and/or students

Introduction

The seed develops from the ovule, and inside is the embryo and its nutritive tissues. The fruit develops from the ovary or from other tissues in the flower. It provides protection for the seeds, and both the seed and the fruit may be involved in dispersal of the sporophyte embryo.

Procedure

1. Examine the fruits and seeds on demonstration.
2. Use the Key to Fruits on the next page to help you complete Table 5. Remember to include the dispersal mechanisms for fruits and their seeds in the table.

Results

1. Record in Table 5 the fruit type for each of the fruits keyed. Share results with other teams so that you have information for all fruits in the lab.

Table 5
Fruit Types and Dispersal Mechanisms

Plant Name	Fruit Type	Dispersal Method

2. For each fruit, indicate the probable method of dispersal—for example, wind, water, gravity, ingestion by birds, mammals, or insects, or adhesion to fur and socks.
3. For some fruits, the seeds rather than the fruit are adapted for dispersal. In the milkweed, for example, the winged seeds are contained in a dry ovary. Indicate in Table 5 if the seeds have structures to enhance dispersal. Recall that seeds are inside fruits. The dandelion "seed" is really a fruit with a fused ovary and seed coat.

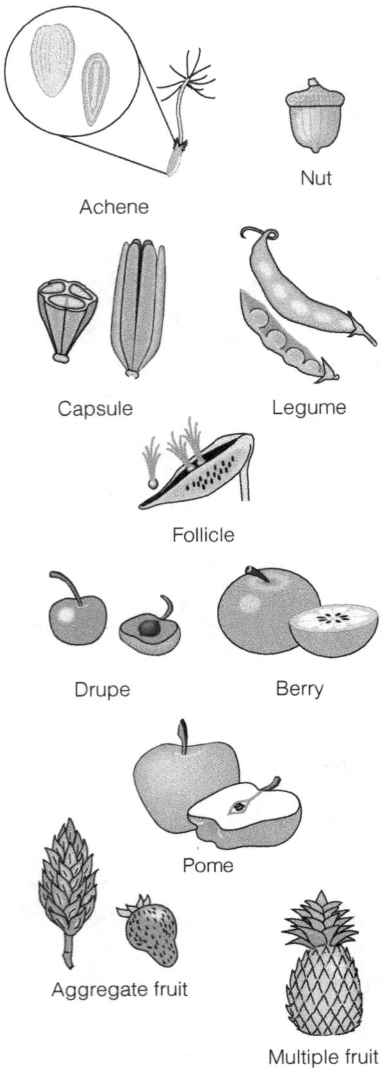

Key to Fruits

I. Simple fruits (one ovary)
  A. Dry fruits (at maturity)
    1. Fruits with one seed
      a. Ovary wall and seed coat are fused **achene***
      a. Ovary wall hard or woody but can be separated from the seed **nut**
    1. Fruits with two to many seeds
      a. Ovary with several cavities (seen when cut in cross section) and several to many seeds **capsule**
      a. Ovary with one cavity
        b. Mature ovary opens along both sides **legume**
        b. Mature ovary opens along one side **follicle**
  A. Fleshy fruits
    1. Ovary with one seed, which is surrounded by a very hard stone (outer covering of the seed is formed from the inner ovary wall) **drupe**
    1. Ovary with many seeds; does not have a "stone"
      a. All of mature ovary tissue is soft and fleshy; surrounding flower tissue does not develop into fruit **berry†**
      a. Fleshy fruit develops in part from surrounding tissue of the flower (base of sepals and petals); therefore, ovary wall seen as "core" around seeds **pome**
I. Compound fruits (more than one ovary)
  A. Fruit formed from ovaries of many flowers **multiple fruit**
  A. Fruit formed from several ovaries in one flower **aggregate fruit**

*In the grass family, an achene is called a **grain.**

†Berries of some families have special names: citrus family = **hesperidium**; squash family = **pepo.**

Discussion

1. How might dry fruits be dispersed? Fleshy fruits?

2. Describe the characteristics of an achene, drupe, and berry.

Questions for Review

1. Complete Table 6. Compare mosses, ferns, conifers, and flowering plants relative to sexual life cycles and adaptations to the land environment. Return to Table 1 and modify your entries.
2. Identify the function of each of the following structures found in seed plants. Consider their function in the land environment.

   pollen grain:

   microsporangium:

   flower:

   carpel:

Table 6
Comparison of Important Characteristics of Land Plants

Features	 Moss	 Fern	 Conifer	 Flowering Plant
Gametophyte or sporophyte dominant				
Vascular tissue (+/–)				
Seed (+/–)				
Fruit (+/–)				
Water required for fertilization				
Pollen grain (+/–)				
Homosporous or heterosporous				
Examples				

seed:

fruit:

endosperm:

3. Plants have evolved a number of characteristics that attract animals and ensure pollination, but what are the benefits to animals in this relationship?

4. Why is internal fertilization essential for true terrestrial living?

Applying Your Knowledge

1. Explain how the rise in prominence of one major group (angiosperms, for example) does not necessarily result in the total replacement of a previously dominant group (gymnosperms, for example).

2. How have gymnosperm ovules evolved to withstand desiccation and herbivorous animals?

3. Your neighbor's vegetable garden is being attacked by Japanese beetles, so she dusts her garden with an insecticide. Now, to her dismay, she realizes that the beans and squash are no longer producing. Explain to your neighbor the relationship among flowers, fruits (vegetables, in the gardening language), and insects.

4. Seed plants provide food, medicine, fibers, beverages, building materials, dyes, and psychoactive drugs. Using web resources, your textbook, and library references, describe examples of human uses of plants in Table 7. Indicate whether your example is a gymnosperm or angiosperm. Based on your research, what is the relative economic importance of angiosperms and gymnosperms?

Table 7
Uses of Seed Plants: Angiosperms and Gymnosperms

Uses of Plants	Example	Angiosperm/ Gymnosperm
Food		
Beverage		
Medicine		
Fibers		
Materials		
Dyes		
Drugs		

5. Describe the major trends in the evolution of land plants.

Investigative Extensions

Pollen germinates easily in the lab for some species and not at all for others. In some species, a biochemical signal is required from the stigma to initiate germination. If the pollen has not germinated after 30 minutes, you can design an experiment to test the hypothesis that a substance in the stigma is necessary for pollen germination. Mince a small part of the stigma in sucrose and then add it to the slide preparation. The percent sucrose in the growth medium can also be varied. Try 10%, then doubling and halving the sucrose concentration in the growth medium. Some cultivated plants are simply sterile, so do not expect positive results for all species.

References

Levetin, E. and K. McMahon. *Plants and Society,* 2nd ed. New York: McGraw Hill Co., 1999.

Mauseth, J. D. *Botany: An Introduction to Plant Biology,* 3rd ed. Sudbury, MA: Jones and Bartlett Publishers, 2003.

Nabors, M. W. *Introduction to Botany.* San Francisco, CA: Benjamin Cummings, 2004.

Raven, P. H., R. F. Evert, and S. E. Eichhorn. *Biology of Plants,* 6th ed. New York: W. H. Freeman Publishers, 1999.

Websites

Interesting and informative sites describing human uses of plants. *Wayne's Word: A Newsletter of Natural History Trivia.*

http://daphne.palomar.edu/wayne/wayne.htm

Ethnobotanical Leaflets

http://www.siu.edu/~ebl/

Animal Diversity I

Laboratory Objectives

After completing this lab topic, you should be able to:

1. Compare the anatomy of the representative animals, describing similarities and differences in organs and body form that allow the animal to carry out body functions.
2. Discuss the impact of molecular studies on traditional phylogenetic trees.
3. Discuss the relationship between body form and the lifestyle or niche of the organism.

Introduction

Animals are classified in the domain **Eukarya,** kingdom **Animalia.** They are multicellular organisms and are **heterotrophic,** meaning that they obtain food by ingesting other organisms or their by-products. Careful study of comparative anatomy, embryology, and most recently, genetic and molecular data, reveals many similarities in structure and development. Collectively, this evidence implies an ancestral evolutionary relationship among all animals. Animals are thought to have arisen about 565 million years ago, with most body forms appearing by the end of the Cambrian period. Scientists recognize over 35 major groups of present-day animals based on differences in body architecture. In this and the following lab topic, you will investigate body form and function in examples of nine major groups of animals. You will use these investigations to ask and answer questions comparing general features of morphology and relating these features to the lifestyle of each animal.

Since the beginning of the scientific study of animals, scientists have attempted to sort and group closely related organisms. Taxonomists have divided the animal kingdom into two major groups: **Parazoa,** which includes the sponges, and **Eumetazoa,** which includes all other animals. This division is made because the body form of sponges is so different from that of other animals that most biologists think that sponges are not closely related to any other animal groups.

Animals in Eumetazoa (multicular animals) differ in physical characteristics, such as symmetry which may be **radial** (parts arranged around a central axis), or **bilateral** (right and left halves are mirror images). Other differences include the type of body cavity (coelom) and such basic embryological differences as the number of germ layers present in the embryo and the embryonic development of the digestive tract. Some animals have a saclike body form with only one opening into a digestive cavity. Others have two outer openings, a mouth and an anus, and the digestive tract forms essentially a "tube within a tube." Those animals that are bilaterally symmetrical are divided into two major groups, depending on differences in early development and the origin of the mouth and the anus. An embryonic structure, the blastopore, develops into a mouth in the **protostomes** and into an anus in the **deuterostomes.**

In the study of the protists, you learned that "traditional" phylogenetic trees have been challenged by the results of molecular studies, particularly evidence from ribosomal RNA (rRNA). This is true not only for protists, but also for animals. Particularly in the protostomes, molecular studies have led to a regrouping of many traditionally established phylogenetic relationships. For example, for over 200 years zoology publications have assumed that annelids (segmented worms in the phylum Annelida) and arthropods (e.g., insects) are closely related based on their segmented bodies. Zoologists also noted, however, that annelids have developmental patterns similar to several groups that are not segmented. For example, annelids are like molluscs (e.g., clams) in having a developmental stage called the "trochophore larva." Recent rRNA evidence helps to clarify this puzzle as it supports the hypothesis that annelids and molluscs are closely related, and separate from arthropods.

Molecular studies have led taxonomists to create two large groups within the protostomes, **Lophotrochozoa** and **Ecdysozoa.** Annelids, molluscs, and several more phyla not studied here are placed in the group or clade Lophotrochozoa. The name reflects the trochophore larvae found in annelids and molluscs. Also included in this clade are flatworms (phylum Platyhelminthes). Although flatworms lack such characteristics as a body cavity, the "tube-within-a-tube" body plan with mouth and anus, and elaborate internal organs, their rRNA indicates that they should be grouped with annelids and molluscs in the Lophotrochozoa clade. Ecdysozoa includes the roundworms or nematodes (phylum Nematoda), arthropods (phylum Arthropoda), and several other phyla. Animals in Ecdysozoa undergo molting (ecdysis) or the shedding of an outer body cover. In nematodes this covering is called the **cuticle.** In arthropods the covering is the **exoskeleton.**

Another surprising result of rRNA evidence is that the nature of the body cavity may not be a characteristic that indicates major phylogenetic branching. In traditional phylogenetic groupings, flatworms and nematodes were considered primitive, neither group having a true coelom. Ribosomal evidence has now moved nematodes to a different position with arthropods in the metazoan tree.

Figure 1a is a diagram showing organisms classified in the *traditional* organization of animal phylogeny. This phylogeny is based on *morphology* and *development.* Figure 1b is a diagram showing the *new molecular-based* phylogeny. The order of animals is based on Figure 1b, the molecular-based phylogeny. However, as you study the animals, note those morphological characteristics that were the basis of the traditional system of classification. These characteristics may give evidence of the influence of ecological events in the development of different morphologies. Be ready to discuss how these similarities or differences may have arisen secondarily or through secondary simplifications.

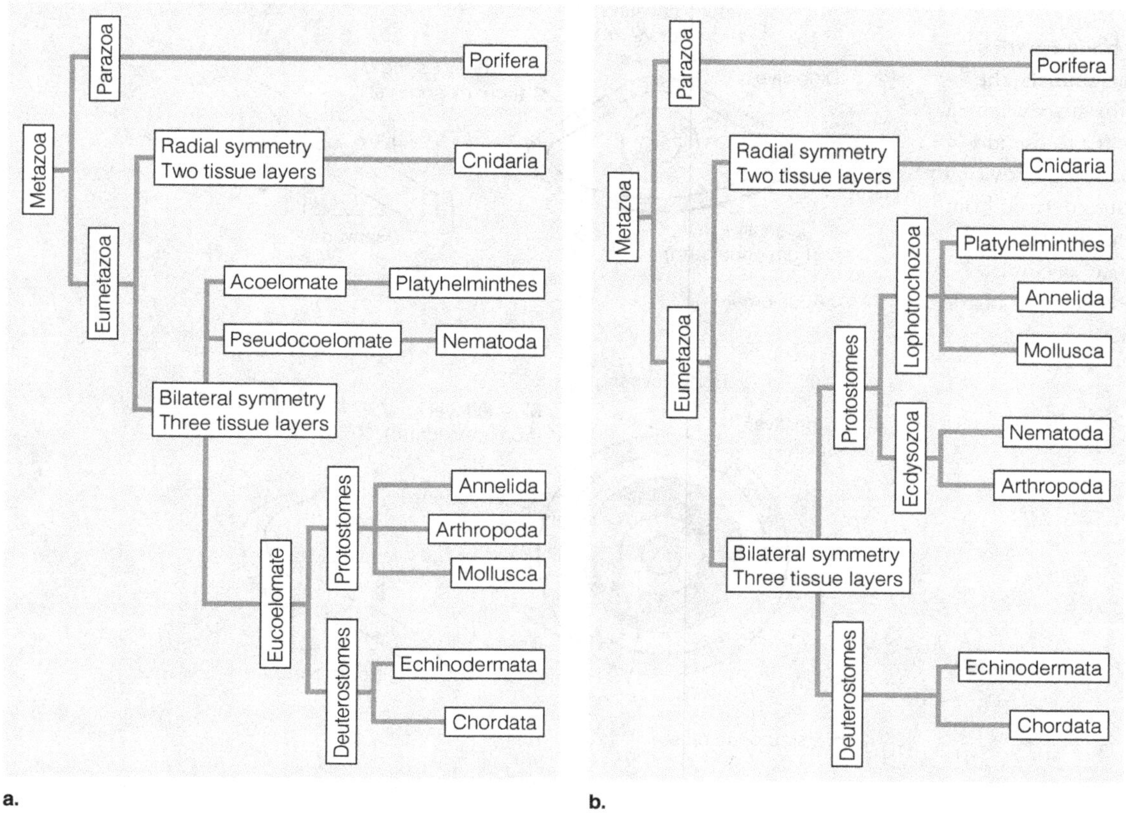

Figure 1.
Organization of animal phylogeny. (a) A traditional phylogeny based on morphology and embryology. (b) Proposed phylogeny based on new molecular evidence. Protostomes are grouped in Lophotrochozoa or Ecdysozoa.

Much work remains to resolve the branching order within the lophotrochozoan and ecdysozoan clades. Evidence is being collected from other studies such as gene sequencing (e.g., HOX genes—see your text). Thus far, these data are supporting the proposed groupings based on rRNA.

The animals you will study in this lab topic are the sponge, hydra, planarian, clamworm, earthworm, and clam (mussel). You will study the roundworm, crayfish, grasshopper, sea star, amphioxus (lancelet), and pig later. As you study each animal, relate your observations to the unifying themes of this lab: *phylogenetic relationships* and criteria that are the basis for animal classification, the *relationship between form and function,* and the *relationship of the environment and lifestyle to form and function.* The questions at the end of the lab topics will help you do this.

In your comparative study of these organisms, you will investigate 13 characteristics. Before you begin the dissections, become familiar with the following characteristics and their descriptions:

1. *Symmetry.* Is the animal (a) radially symmetrical (parts arranged around a central axis), (b) bilaterally symmetrical (right and left halves are mirror images), or (c) asymmetrical (no apparent symmetry)?
2. *Tissue organization.* Are cells organized into well-defined tissue layers (structural and functional units)? How many distinctive layers are present?

Figure 2.
Three types of body cavities.
(a) In acoelomate animals, the mesoderm fills the space where a cavity might be. (b) In pseudocoelomate animals, the body cavity lies between tissues derived from endoderm and mesoderm.
(c) In eucoelomate (coelomate) animals, the body cavity is lined with mesoderm.

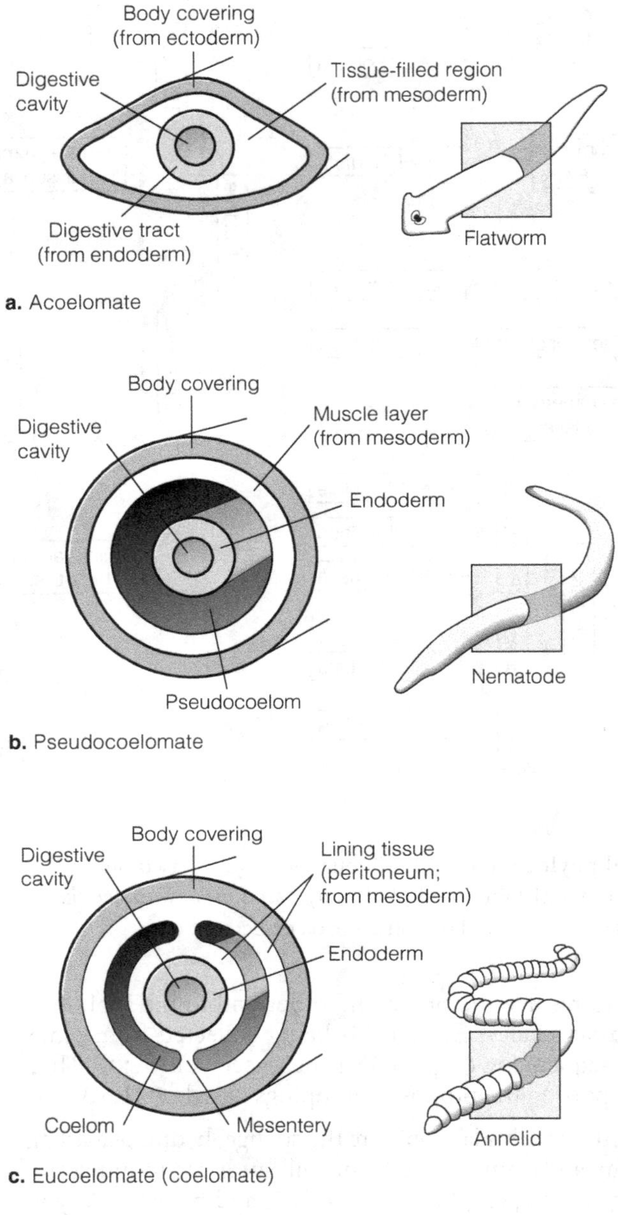

3. *Body cavity.* Is a body cavity present? A body cavity—the space between the gut and body wall—is present only in three-layered organisms, that is, in organisms with the embryonic germ layers ectoderm, mesoderm, and endoderm. There are three types of body forms related to the presence of a body cavity and its type (Figure 2).
   a. Acoelomate, three-layered bodies without a body cavity. Tissue from the mesoderm fills the space where a cavity might be; therefore, the tissue layers closely pack on one another.
   b. Pseudocoelomate, three-layered bodies with a cavity between the endoderm (gut) and mesoderm (muscle).
   c. Eucoelomate (coelomate), three-layered bodies with the coelom, or cavity, *within* the mesoderm (completely surrounded by mesoderm).

In coelomate organisms, mesodermal membranes suspend the gut within the body cavity.

4. *Openings into the digestive tract.* Can you detect where food enters the body and digestive waste exits the body? Some animals have only one opening, which serves as both a mouth and an anus. Others have a body called a "tube within a tube," with an anterior mouth and a posterior anus.
5. *Circulatory system.* Does this animal have open circulation (the blood flows through coelomic spaces in the tissue as well as in blood vessels), or does it have closed circulation (the blood flows entirely through vessels)?
6. *Habitat.* Is the animal terrestrial (lives on land) or aquatic (lives in water)? Aquatic animals may live in marine (sea) or fresh water.
7. *Organs for respiration (gas exchange).* Can you detect the surface where oxygen enters the body and carbon dioxide leaves the body? Many animals use their skin for respiration. Others have special organs, including gills in aquatic organisms and lungs in terrestrial organisms. Insects have a unique system for respiration, using structures called *spiracles* and *tracheae.*
8. *Organs for excretion.* How does the animal rid its body of nitrogenous waste? In many animals, these wastes pass out of the body through the skin by diffusion. In others, there are specialized structures, such as Malpighian tubules, lateral excretory canals, lateral canals with flame cells, structures called *nephridia,* and kidneys.
9. *Type of locomotion.* Does the organism swim, crawl on its belly, walk on legs, burrow in the substrate, or fly? Does it use cellular structures, such as cilia, to glide its body over the substrate?
10. *Support systems.* Is there a skeleton present? Is it an endoskeleton (inside the epidermis or skin of the animal), or is it an exoskeleton (outside the body wall)? Animals with no true skeleton can be supported by water: Fluid within and between cells and in body chambers such as a gastrovascular cavity or coelom provides a "hydrostatic skeleton."
11. *Segmentation.* Can you observe linear repetition of similar body parts? The repetition of similar units, or segments, is called *segmentation.* Segments can be more similar (as in the earthworm) or less similar (as in a lobster). Can you observe any degree of segmentation? Have various segments become modified for different functions?
12. *Appendages.* Are there appendages (organs or parts attached to a trunk or outer body wall)? Are these appendages all along the length of the body, or are they restricted to one area? Are they all similar, or are they modified for different functions?
13. *Type of nervous system.* Do you see a brain and nerve cord? Is there more than one nerve cord? What is the location of the nerve cord(s)? Are sensory organs or structures present? Where and how many? What purpose do such structures serve (for example, eyes for light detection)?

As you carefully study or dissect each organism, refer to these thirteen characteristics, observe the animal, and record your observations in the summary table. You may find it helpful to make sketches of difficult structures or dissections in the margin of your lab manual for future reference.

Before you begin this study, become thoroughly familiar with dissection techniques, orientation terms, and planes and sections of the body.

Wear gloves while dissecting preserved animals.

EXERCISE 1

Phylum Porifera—Sponges (*Scypha*)

Materials

dissecting needle
compound microscope
stereoscopic microscope
preserved and dry bath sponges
prepared slide of *Scypha* in longitudinal section
preserved *Scypha* in watch glass

Introduction

Sponges are classified in a separate group, Parazoa, because of their unique body form. You will observe the unique sponge structure by observing first a preserved specimen and then a prepared slide of a section taken through the longitudinal axis of the marine sponge *Scypha*. You will observe other more complex and diverse sponges on demonstration.

Procedure

1. Obtain the preserved sponge *Scypha* and observe its external characteristics using the stereoscopic microscope, comparing your observations with Figure 3a.
   a. Note the vaselike shape of the sponge and the **osculum,** a large opening to the body at one end. The end opposite the osculum attaches the animal to the substrate.
   b. Note the invaginations in the body wall, which form numerous folds and channels. You may be able to observe needlelike **spicules** around the osculum and protruding from the surface of the body. These spicules are made of calcium carbonate: They give support and protection to the sponge body and prevent small animals from entering the sponge's internal cavity.
2. Using the compound microscope, examine a prepared slide of a sponge body in longitudinal section and compare it with Figure 3b.
   a. Again, locate the osculum. This structure is not a mouth, as its name implies, but an opening used as an outlet for the current of water passing through the body wall and the **central cavity,** or **spongocoel.** The water enters the central cavity from channels and pores in the body. The central cavity is not a digestive tube or body cavity, but is only a channel for water.

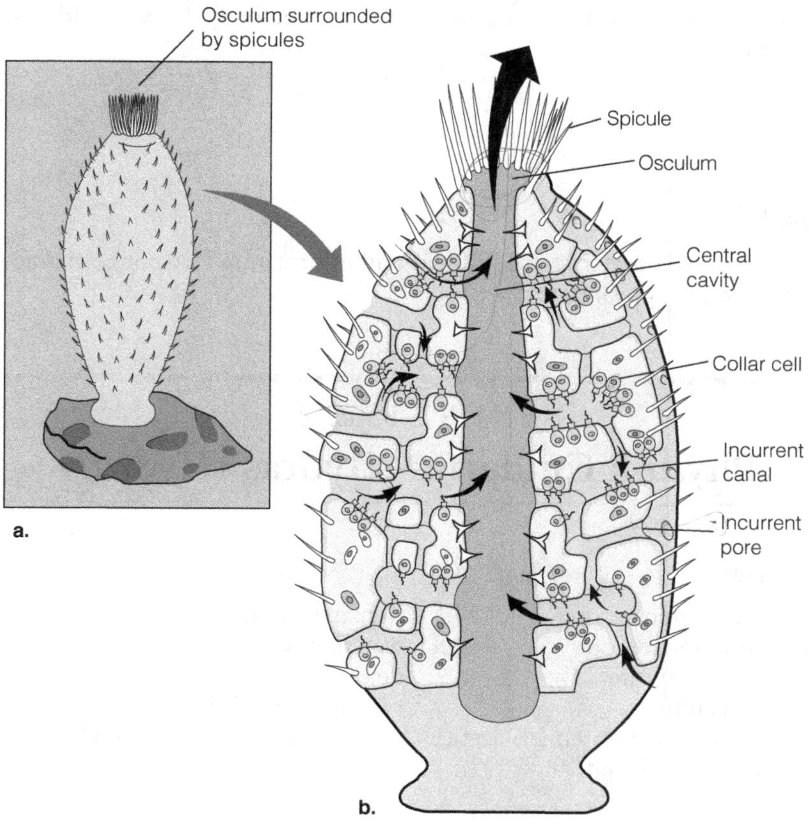

Figure 3.
The sponge *Scypha*. (a) The entire sponge; (b) a longitudinal section through the sponge.

b. Note the structure of the body wall. Are cells organized into definite tissue layers, or are they best described as a loose organization of various cell types? Various cells in the body wall carry out the functions of digestion, contractility, secretion of the spicules, and reproduction (some cells develop into sperm and eggs). One cell type unique to sponges is the **choanocyte,** or **collar cell.** These cells line the central cavity and the channels leading into it. Each collar cell has a flagellum extending from its surface. The collective beating of all flagella moves water through the sponge body. Small food particles taken up and digested by collar cells are one major source of nutrition for the sponge. How would you hypothesize about the movement of oxygen and waste throughout the sponge body and into and out of cells?

3. Observe examples of more complex sponges on demonstration. The body of these sponges, sometimes called "bath sponges," contains a complex series of large and small canals and chambers. The same cells that were described in *Scypha* are present in bath sponges, but, in addition to spicules, there is supportive material that consists of a soft proteinaceous substance called **spongin.** These sponges often grow to fit the shape of the space where they live, and observing them gives you a

good clue about the symmetry of the sponge body. How would you describe it?

Results

Complete the summary table, filling in all information for sponge characteristics in the appropriate row.

EXERCISE 2
Phylum Cnidaria—Hydras (*Hydra*)

Materials

stereoscopic microscope
compound microscope
living *Hydra* culture
water flea culture
dropper bottles of water, 1% acetic acid, and methylene blue
prepared slide of *Hydra* sections
watch glass
depression slide
pipettes and bulbs
microscope slide and coverslip

Introduction

Cnidarians are a diverse group of organisms, all of which have a **tissue grade** of organization, meaning that tissues, but no complex organs, are present. Included in this group are corals, jellies, sea anemones, and Portuguese men-of-war. Most species are marine; however, there are a few freshwater species. Two body forms are present in the life cycle of many of these animals—an umbrella-like, free-swimming stage, and a cylindrical, attached or stationary form. The stationary forms often grow into colonies of individuals. In this exercise you will observe some of the unique features of this group by observing the solitary, freshwater organism *Hydra*.

Procedure

1. Place several drops of freshwater pond or culture water in a watch glass or depression slide. Use a dropper to obtain a living hydra from the class culture, and place the hydra in the drop of water. Using a stereoscopic microscope, observe the hydra structure and compare it with Figure 4a. Note any movement, the symmetry, and any body structures present. Note the **tentacles** that surround the "mouth," the only opening into the central cavity. Tentacles are used in capturing food and in performing a certain type of locomotion, much like a "handspring." To accomplish this motion, the hydra attaches its tentacles to the substrate and flips the basal portion of its body completely over, reattaching the base to a new position. If water fleas (*Daphnia*) are available, place one or two near the tentacles of the hydra and note the hydra's behavior. Set aside the hydra in the depression slide and return to it in a few moments.

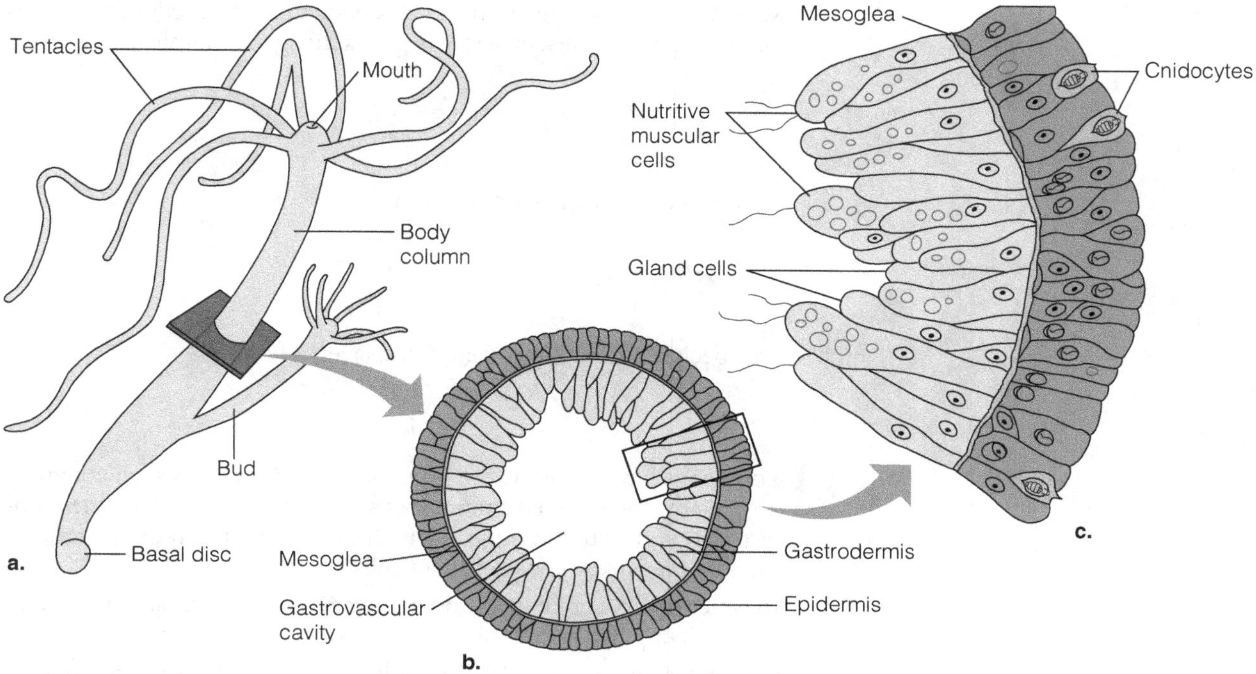

Figure 4.
Hydra. (a) A whole mount of *Hydra;* (b) enlargement showing a cross section through the body wall, revealing two tissue layers; and (c) further enlargement showing details of specialized cells in the body wall, including cnidocytes.

2. Study a prepared slide of *Hydra* sections using the compound microscope and compare your observations with Figure 4b and c.

   Are definite tissue layers present? If so, how many?

   Given what you know of embryology, what embryonic layers would you guess give rise to the tissue layers of this animal's body?

3. Not visible with the microscope is a network of nerve cells in the body wall, which serves as the nervous system. There is no concentration of nerve cells into any kind of brain or nerve cord.
4. Observe the central cavity, called a **gastrovascular cavity.** Digestion begins in this water-filled cavity (**extracellular digestion**), but many food particles are drawn into cells in the **gastrodermis** lining the cavity, where **intracellular digestion** occurs.
5. Do you see signs of a skeleton or supportive system? How do you think the body is supported? Are appendages present?

6. Recalling the whole organism and observing this cross section, are organs for gas exchange present? How is gas exchange accomplished?

7. Do you see any organs for excretion?

8. Are specialized cell types seen in the layers of tissues?

Cnidarians have a unique cell type called **cnidocytes,** which contain a stinging organelle called a **nematocyst.** When stimulated, the nematocyst will evert from the cnidocyte with explosive force, trapping food or stinging predators. Look for these cells.

9. To better observe cnidocytes and nematocysts, turn your attention again to your living hydra and follow this procedure:
   a. Using a pipette, transfer the hydra to a drop of water on a microscope slide and carefully add a coverslip.
   b. Use your microscope to examine the hydra, first on low, then intermediate, and finally on high powers, focusing primarily on the tentacles. The cnidocytes will appear as swellings. If your microscope is equipped with phase contrast, switch to phase. Alternatively, add a drop of methylene blue to the edge of the coverslip. Locate several cnidocytes with nematocysts coiled inside.
   c. Add a drop of 1% acetic acid to the edge of the coverslip and, watching carefully using intermediate power, observe the rapid discharge of the nematocyst from the cnidocyte.
   d. Using high power, study the discharged nematocysts that will appear as long threads, often with large spines, or barbs, at the base of the thread.

Results

Complete the summary table, recording all information for *Hydra* characteristics in the appropriate row.

Discussion

What major differences have you detected between *Scypha* and *Hydra* body forms? List and describe them.

EXERCISE 3
Phylum Platyhelminthes—Planarians (*Dugesia*)

Materials

stereoscopic microscope
compound microscope
living planarian
watch glass
prepared slide of whole mount of planarian
prepared slide of planarian cross sections

Introduction

The phylum Platyhelminthes (clade Lophotrochozoa) includes planarians, free-living flatworms; that is, they are not parasitic and their body is dorsoventrally flattened. They are found under rocks, leaves, and debris in freshwater ponds and creeks. They move over these surfaces using a combination of muscles in their body wall and cilia on their ventral sides.

Procedure

1. Add a dropperful of pond or culture water to a watch glass. Use a dropper to obtain a living planarian from the class culture. Using your stereoscopic microscope, observe the planarian. Describe its locomotion. Is it directional? What is the position of its head? Does its body appear to contract?

   As you observe the living planarian, you will see two striking new features with regard to symmetry that you did not see in the two phyla previously studied. What are they?

2. Add a *small* piece of fresh liver to the water near the planarian. The planarian may approach the liver and begin to feed by extending a long tubular **pharynx** out of the **mouth,** a circular opening on the ventral side of the body. If the planarian feeds, it will curve its body over the liver and extend the pharynx, which may be visible in the stereoscopic microscope.

   After observing the planarian's feeding behavior, return it to the culture dish, if possible, without the liver.

3. Using the lowest power on the compound microscope, observe the prepared slide of a whole planarian and compare it with Figure 5.

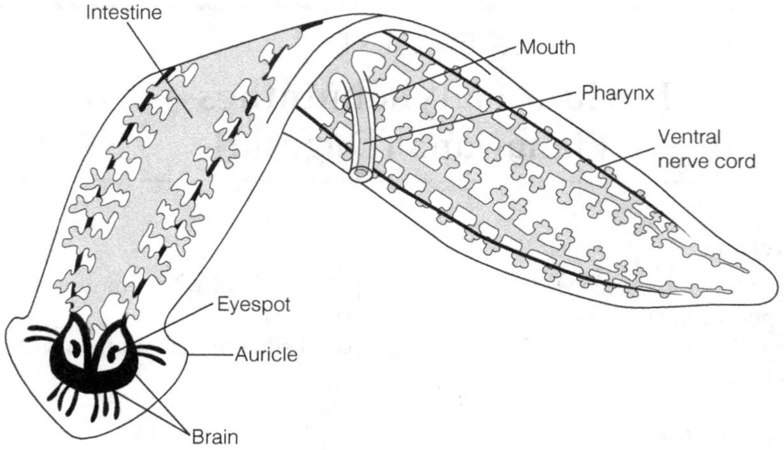

Figure 5.
A planarian. The digestive system consists of a mouth, a pharynx, and a branched intestine. A brain and two ventral nerve cords (plus transverse nerves connecting them, not shown) make up the nervous system.

> **Do not observe these slides using high power! The high power objective may crack the coverslip, resulting in damage to the lens.**

Examine the body for possible digestive tract openings. How many openings to the digestive tract are present?

Observe again the pharynx and the mouth. The pharynx lies in a **pharyngeal chamber** inside the mouth. The proximal end of the pharynx opens into a dark-colored, branched intestine. If the intestine has been stained on your slide, you will see the branching more easily.

4. Continue your study of the whole planarian. The anterior blunt end of the animal is the head end. At each side of the head is a projecting **auricle.** It contains a variety of sensory cells, chiefly of touch and chemical sense. Between the two auricles on the dorsal surface are two pigmented **eyespots.** These are pigment cups into which retinal cells extend from the brain, with the photosensitive end of the cells inside the cup. Eyespots are sensitive to light intensities and the direction of a light source but can form no images. Beneath the eyespots are two cerebral ganglia that serve as the **brain.** Two ventral nerve cords extend posteriorly from the brain. These are connected by transverse nerves to form a ladderlike **nervous system.**
5. Study the prepared slide of cross sections of a planarian. You will have several sections on one slide. One section should have been taken at the level of the pharynx and pharyngeal chamber. Do you see a body cavity in any of the sections? (The pharyngeal chamber and spaces in the gut are not a body cavity.) What word describes this body cavity condition (see Figure 2a)?

a. How many tissue layers can be detected? Speculate about their embryonic origin.

Flatworms are the first group of animals to have three well-defined embryonic tissue layers, enabling them to have a variety of tissues and organs. Reproductive organs and excretory organs consisting of two lateral excretory canals and "flame cells" that move fluid through the canals are derived from the embryonic mesoderm. Respiratory, circulatory, and skeletal systems are lacking.

b. How do you think the body is supported?

c. How does gas exchange take place?

Results

1. Diagram the flatworm as seen in a cross section at the level of the pharynx. Label the **epidermis, muscle** derived from **mesoderm,** the lining of the digestive tract derived from **endoderm**, the **pharynx,** and the **pharyngeal chamber.**
2. Complete the summary table, recording all information for planarian characteristics in the appropriate row.

Discussion

One of the major differences between Cnidaria and Platyhelminthes is radial versus bilateral symmetry. Discuss the advantage of radial symmetry for sessile (attached) animals and bilateral symmetry for motile animals.

EXERCISE 4

Phylum Annelida—Clamworms (*Nereis*) and Earthworms (*Lumbricus terrestris*)

The phylum Annelida (clade Lophotrochozoa) includes a diverse group of organisms inhabiting a variety of environments. Examples range in size from microscopic to several meters in length. Most species are marine, living free in the open ocean or burrowing in ocean bottoms. Others live in fresh water or in soils. One group of annelids, the leeches, are parasitic and live on the blood or tissues of their hosts. In this exercise, you will study the clamworm, a marine annelid, and the earthworm, a terrestrial species. Keep in mind features that are adaptations to marine and terrestrial habitats as you study these organisms.

Lab Study A. Clamworms (*Nereis*)

Materials

dissecting tools
dissecting pan
preserved clamworm
disposable gloves
dissecting pins

Introduction

Species of *Nereis* (clamworms) are commonly found in mud flats and on the ocean floor. These animals burrow in sediments during the day and emerge to feed at night. As you observe the clamworm, note features that are characteristic of all annelids, as well as features that are special adaptations to the marine environment.

Procedure

1. Observe the preserved, undissected clamworm and compare it with Figure 6. How would you describe the symmetry of this organism?

2. Determine the anterior and posterior ends. At the anterior end, the well-differentiated head bears **sensory appendages.** Locate the mouth, which leads into the digestive tract.

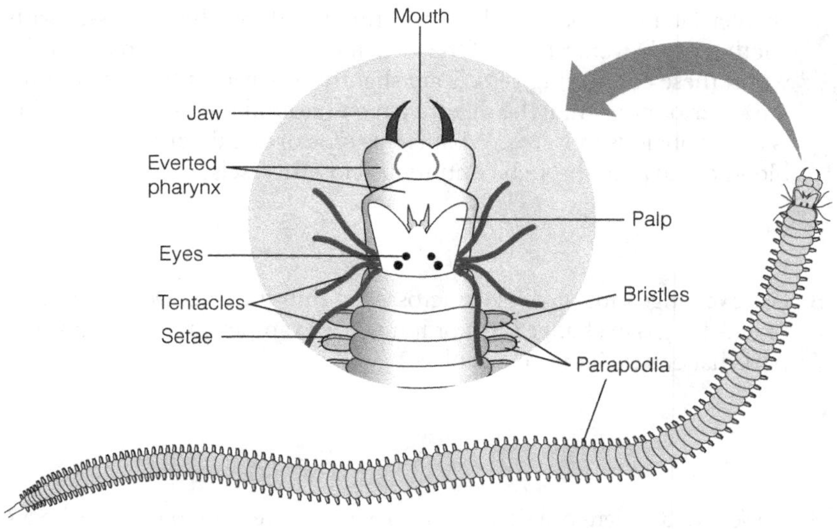

Figure 6.
The clamworm, *Nereis*. The head has sensory appendages, and each segment of the body bears two parapodia with setae.

3. A conspicuous new feature of these organisms is the presence of **segmentation,** the division of the body along its length into segments. Posterior to the head region, the segments bear fleshy outgrowths called **parapodia.** Each parapodium contains several terminal bristles called **setae.** In Lab Study B, you will see that the earthworm has setae but does not have parapodia. Suggest functions for parapodia and setae in the marine clamworm.

4. Holding the animal in your hand and using sharp-pointed scissors, make a middorsal incision the full length of the body. Carefully insert the tip of the scissors and lift up with the tips as you cut. Pin the opened body in the dissecting pan but do not put pins through the head region.
5. Locate the **intestine.** Do you see the "tube-within-a-tube" body plan?

6. Two **muscle layers,** one inside the skin and a second lying on the surface of the intestine, may be visible with the stereoscopic microscope. With muscle in these two positions, what kind of coelom does this animal have (see Figure 2c)?

7. Continuing your observations with the unaided eye and the stereoscopic microscope, look for **blood vessels,** particularly a large vessel lying on the dorsal wall of the digestive tract. This vessel is contractile and propels the blood throughout the body. You should be able to observe

smaller lateral blood vessels connecting the dorsal blood vessel with another on the ventral side of the intestine. As you will see, in the earthworm these connecting vessels are slightly enlarged as "hearts" around the anterior portion of the digestive tract (around the esophagus). This is not as obvious in *Nereis*. What is this type of circulatory system, with blood circulating through continuous closed vessels?

8. Gas exchange must take place across wet, thin surfaces. Do you see any organs for gas exchange (gills or lungs, for example)? How do you suspect that gas exchange takes place?

9. Do you see any signs of a skeleton? What would serve as support for the body?

10. Clamworms and earthworms have a small bilobed brain (a pair of ganglia) lying on the surface of the digestive tract at the anterior end of the worm. You can see this more easily in an earthworm.

Lab Study B. Earthworms (*Lumbricus terrestris*)

Materials

dissecting instruments
compound microscope
stereoscopic microscope
preserved earthworm
prepared slide of cross section of earthworm

Introduction

Lumbricus species, commonly called *earthworms*, burrow through soils rich in organic matter. As you observe these animals, note features that are adaptations to the burrowing, terrestrial lifestyle.

Procedure

1. Obtain a preserved earthworm and identify its anterior end by locating the mouth, which is overhung by a fleshy dorsal protuberance called the **prostomium.** The anus at the posterior end has no such protuberance. Also, a swollen glandular band, the **clitellum** (a structure that secretes a cocoon that holds eggs), is located closer to the mouth than to the anus (Figure 7).
    a. Using scissors, make a middorsal incision along the anterior third of the animal, as you did for *Nereis*. You can identify the dorsal surface in a couple of ways. The prostomium is dorsal, and the ventral surface of the worm is usually flattened, especially in the region of the clitellum. Cut to the prostomium. Pin the body open in a dissecting pan near the edge. You may need to cut through the septa that divide the body cavity into segments.

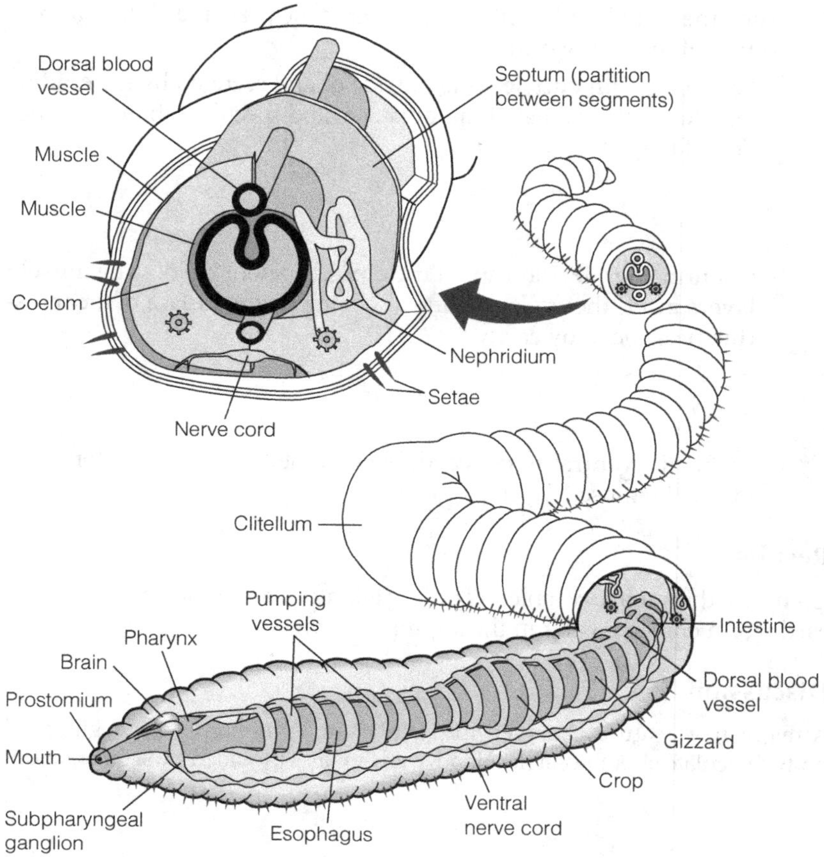

Figure 7.
The earthworm. The small brain leads to a ventral nerve cord. A pair of nephridia lie in each segment.

b. Using a stereoscopic microscope or hand lens, look for the small **brain** just behind the prostomium on the surface of the digestive tract. Note the two nerves that pass from the brain around the pharynx and meet ventrally. These nerve tracts continue posteriorly as a **ventral nerve cord** lying in the floor of the coelom.

c. Look for the large **blood vessel** on the dorsal wall of the digestive tract. You may be able to see the enlarged lateral blood vessels (**hearts**) around the anterior portion of the digestive tract.

d. Identify (from anterior to posterior) the **pharynx, esophagus, crop** (a soft, swollen region of the digestive tract), **gizzard** (smaller and more rigid than the crop), and **intestine.**

e. Excretion in the clamworm and earthworm is carried out by organs called **nephridia.** A pair of these minute, white, coiled tubes is located in each segment of the worm body. Nephridia are more easily observed in the earthworm than in *Nereis* and should be studied here. To view these organs, cut out an approximately 2-cm-long piece of the worm posterior to the clitellum and cut it open along its dorsal surface. Cut through the septa and pin the piece to the dissecting pan near the edge to facilitate observation with the stereoscopic microscope. The coiled tubules of the nephridia are located in the coelomic cavity, where waste is collected and discharged to the outside through a small pore.

2. Using the compound microscope, observe the prepared slide of a cross section of the earthworm.
   a. Locate the **thin cuticle** lying outside of and secreted by the **epidermis.** Recall the habitat of this organism and speculate about the function of the cuticle.

   b. Confirm your decision about the type of coelom by locating **muscle layers** inside the epidermis and also lying on the surface of the **intestine** near the body cavity.

   c. Locate the **ventral nerve cord,** lying in the floor of the coelom, just inside the muscle layer.

Results

Complete the summary table, recording all information for clamworm and earthworm characteristics in the appropriate row.

Discussion

A major new feature observed in the phylum Annelida is the segmented body. Speculate about possible adaptive advantages provided by segmentation.

EXERCISE 5
Phylum Mollusca—Clams

Materials

dissecting instruments
dissecting pan
preserved clam or mussel
disposable gloves

Introduction

Second only to the phylum Arthropoda in numbers of species, the phylum Mollusca (clade Lophotrochozoa) includes thousands of species living in many diverse habitats. Most species are marine. Others live in fresh water or on land. Many mollusks are of economic importance, being favorite human foods. Most mollusks share four characteristic features: (1) a hard external **shell** for protection; (2) a thin structure called the **mantle,** which secretes the shell; (3) a **visceral mass** in which most organs are located; and (4) a muscular **foot** used for locomotion.

In this exercise, you will dissect a clam, a molluscan species with a shell made of two parts called **valves.** Most clams are marine, although many genera live in freshwater lakes and ponds.

Wear gloves while dissecting preserved animals.

Procedure

1. Observe the external anatomy of the preserved clam. Certain characteristics will become obvious immediately. Can you determine symmetry, support systems, and the presence or absence of appendages? Are there external signs of segmentation?
2. Before you continue making observations, determine the dorsal, ventral, anterior, posterior, right, and left regions of the animal. Identify the two valves. The valves are held together by a **hinge** near the **umbo,** a hump on the valves. The hinge and the umbo are located **dorsally,** and the valves open **ventrally.** The umbo is displaced **anteriorly.** Hold the clam vertically with the umbo away from your body, and cup one of your hands over each valve. The valve in your right hand is the right valve; the valve in your left hand is the left valve. The two valves are held together by two strong **adductor** muscles inside the shell. Compare your observations with Figure 8.

Be cautious as you open the clam! Hold the clam in the dissecting pan in such a way that the scalpel will be directed toward the bottom of the pan.

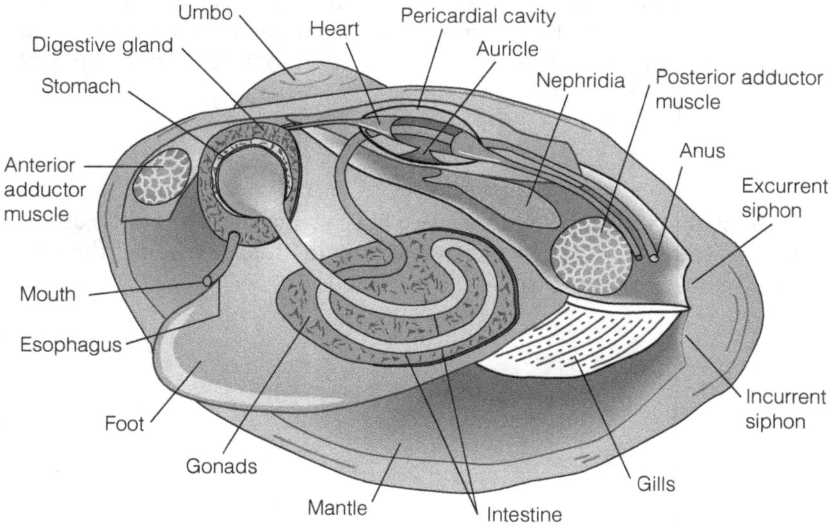

Figure 8.
Anatomy of a clam. The soft body parts are protected by the shell valves. Two adductor muscles hold the valves closed. Most major organs are located in the visceral mass. In this diagram, the left mantle, left pair of gills, and half of the visceral mass have been removed.

3. To study the internal anatomy of the clam, you must open it by prying open the valves. (A wooden peg may have been inserted between the two valves.) Insert the handle of your forceps or scalpel between the valves and twist it to pry the valves farther open. Carefully insert a scalpel blade, directed toward the dorsal side of the animal, into the space between the left valve and a flap of tissue lining the valve. The blade edge should be just ventral to (that is, below) the anterior adductor muscle (see Figure 8). The flap of tissue is the left **mantle.** Keeping the scalpel blade pressed flat against the left valve, carefully loosen the mantle from the valve and press the blade dorsally. You will feel the tough **anterior adductor muscle.** Cut through this muscle near the valve.
4. Repeat the procedure at the posterior end and cut the posterior adductor muscle. Lay the clam on its right valve and carefully lift the left valve. As you do this, use your scalpel to loosen the mantle from the valve. If you have been successful, you should have the body of the clam lying in the right valve. It should be covered by the mantle. Look for pearls between the mantle and the shell. How do you think pearls are formed?

5. Look at the posterior end of the animal where the left and right mantle come together. Hold the two mantle flaps together and note the two gaps formed. These gaps are called **incurrent** (ventral) and **excurrent** (dorsal) **siphons.** Speculate about the function of these siphons.

6. Lift the mantle and identify the **visceral mass** and the **muscular foot.**
7. Locate the **gills,** which have a pleated appearance. One function of these structures is obvious, but they have a second function as well. As water comes into the body (how would it get in?), it passes through the gills, and food particles are trapped on the gill surface. The food is then moved anteriorly (toward the mouth) by coordinated ciliary movements.
8. Locate the **mouth** between two flaps of tissue just ventral to the anterior adductor muscle. Look just above the posterior adductor muscle and locate the **anus.** How is it oriented in relation to the excurrent siphon?

9. Imagine that this is the first time you have seen a clam. From the observations you have made, what evidence would indicate whether this animal is aquatic or terrestrial?

10. The **heart** of the clam is located in a sinus, or cavity, just inside the hinge, dorsal to the visceral mass (see Figure 8). This cavity, called the *pericardial cavity,* is a reduced **true coelom.** The single ventricle of the heart actually surrounds the **intestine** passing through this cavity. Thin auricles, usually torn away during the dissection, empty into the heart via openings called **ostia.** Blood passes from **sinuses** in the body into the auricles. What type of circulatory system is this?

11. Ventral to the heart and embedded in mantle tissue are a pair of greenish brown tissue masses, the **nephridia,** or kidneys. The kidneys remove waste from the pericardial cavity.
12. Open the visceral mass by making an incision with the scalpel, dividing the mass into right and left halves. Begin this incision just above the foot and cut dorsally. You should be able to open the flap produced by this cut and see organs such as the **gonads, digestive gland, intestine,** and **stomach.** Clam chowder is made by chopping up the visceral mass.
13. It is difficult to observe the nervous system in the clam. It consists of three ganglia, one near the mouth, one in the foot, and one below the posterior adductor muscle. These ganglia are connected by nerves.

Now that you have dissected the clam, you should have concluded that there is no sign of true segmentation. Also, appendages (attached to a trunk or body wall) are absent.

Results

Complete the summary table, recording all information for clam characteristics in the appropriate row.

Discussion

List several features of clam anatomy that enable it to survive in a marine environment.

Applying your Knowledge

A hydra (*Chlorophyra viridissima*) is bright green, and yet it does not synthesize chlorophyll. Think about the structure of the hydra and its feeding and digestive habits. What do you think is the origin of the green pigment in this species?

References

Adoutte, A., G. Balavoine, N. Lartillot, O. Lespinet, B. Prud'homme, and R. de Rosa. "The New Animal Phylogeny: Reliability and Implications," *Proc. Natl. Acad. Sci.* USA, 2000, vol. 97, no. 9, pp. 4453–4456.

Balavoine, G. "Are Platyhelminthes Coelomates Without a Coelom? An Argument Based on the Evolution of Hox Genes," *American Zoologist,* 1989, vol. 38, pp. 843–858.

Erwin, D., J. Valentine, and D. Jablonski. "The Origin of Animal Body Plans," *American Scientist,* 1997, vol. 85, pp. 126–137.

Mallatt, J. and C. Winchell. "Testing the New Animal Phylogeny: First Use of Combined Large-Subunit and Small-Subunit rRNA Sequences to Classify Protostomes," *Molecular Biology and Evolution,* 2002, vol. 19, pp. 289–301.

Website

Includes descriptions of many invertebrates and vertebrates, links to insect keys, references:

http://animaldiversity.ummz.umich.edu/site/index.html

Animal Diversity II

This lab is a continuation of observations of organisms in the animal kingdom. Review the descriptions of the 13 characteristics you are investigating in the study and dissection of these animals.

In this lab topic you will study examples of two protostome phyla included in the group or clade **Ecdysozoa,** Nematoda (Exercise 1) and Arthropoda (Exercise 2). Recall that these organisms have coverings on their body surfaces. In Exercises 4 and 5, you will study two deuterostome phyla, Echinodermata and Chordata.

As you continue your study of representative organisms, continue to record your observations in Table 1 at the end of this lab topic. Keep in mind the big themes you are investigating.

1. What clues do similarities and differences among organisms provide about phylogenetic relationships?
2. How is body form related to function?
3. How is body form related to environment and lifestyle?
4. What characteristics can be the criteria for major branching points in producing a phylogenetic tree (representing animal classification)?

EXERCISE 1

Phylum Nematoda—Roundworms (*Ascaris*)

Materials

dissecting instruments
dissecting pan
dissecting pins
compound microscope
disposable gloves
preserved *Ascaris*
prepared slide of cross section of *Ascaris*
hand lens (optional)

Introduction

Ascaris is a **roundworm,** or nematode (clade Ecdysozoa), that lives as a parasite in the intestines of mammals such as horses, pigs, and humans. Its body is covered with a proteinaceous **cuticle** that sheds periodically. Most often these parasites are introduced into the mammalian body when food contaminated with nematode eggs is eaten. Keep in mind the problem of adaptation to a parasitic lifestyle as you study the structure of this animal.

Wear gloves while dissecting preserved animals.

Procedure

1. Wearing disposable gloves, obtain a preserved *Ascaris* and determine its sex. Females are generally larger than males. The posterior end of the male is sharply curved.
2. Use a hand lens or a stereoscopic microscope to look at the ends of the worm. A mouth is present at the anterior end. Three "lips" border this opening. A small slitlike **anus** is located ventrally near the posterior end of the animal.
3. Open the animal by making a middorsal incision along the length of the body with a sharp-pointed probe or sharp scissors. Remember that the anus is slightly to the ventral side (Figure 1). Be careful not to go too deep. Once the animal is open, pin the free edges of the body wall to the dissecting pan, spreading open the body. Pinning the animal near the edge of the pan will allow you to view it using the stereoscopic microscope. As you study the internal organs, you will note that there is a **body cavity.** This is not a true coelom, however, as you will see shortly when you study microscopic sections. From your observations, you should readily identify such characteristics as symmetry, tissue organization, and digestive tract openings.
   a. The most obvious organs you will see in the dissected worm are **reproductive organs,** which appear as masses of coiled tubules of varying diameters.
   b. Identify the flattened **digestive tract,** or intestine, extending from mouth to anus. This tract has been described as a "tube within a tube," the outer tube being the body wall.
   c. Locate two pale lines running laterally along the length of the body in the body wall. The excretory system consists of two longitudinal tubes lying in these two **lateral lines.**
   d. There are no organs for gas exchange or circulation. Most parasitic roundworms are essentially anaerobic (require no oxygen).
   e. How would nourishment be taken into the body and be circulated?

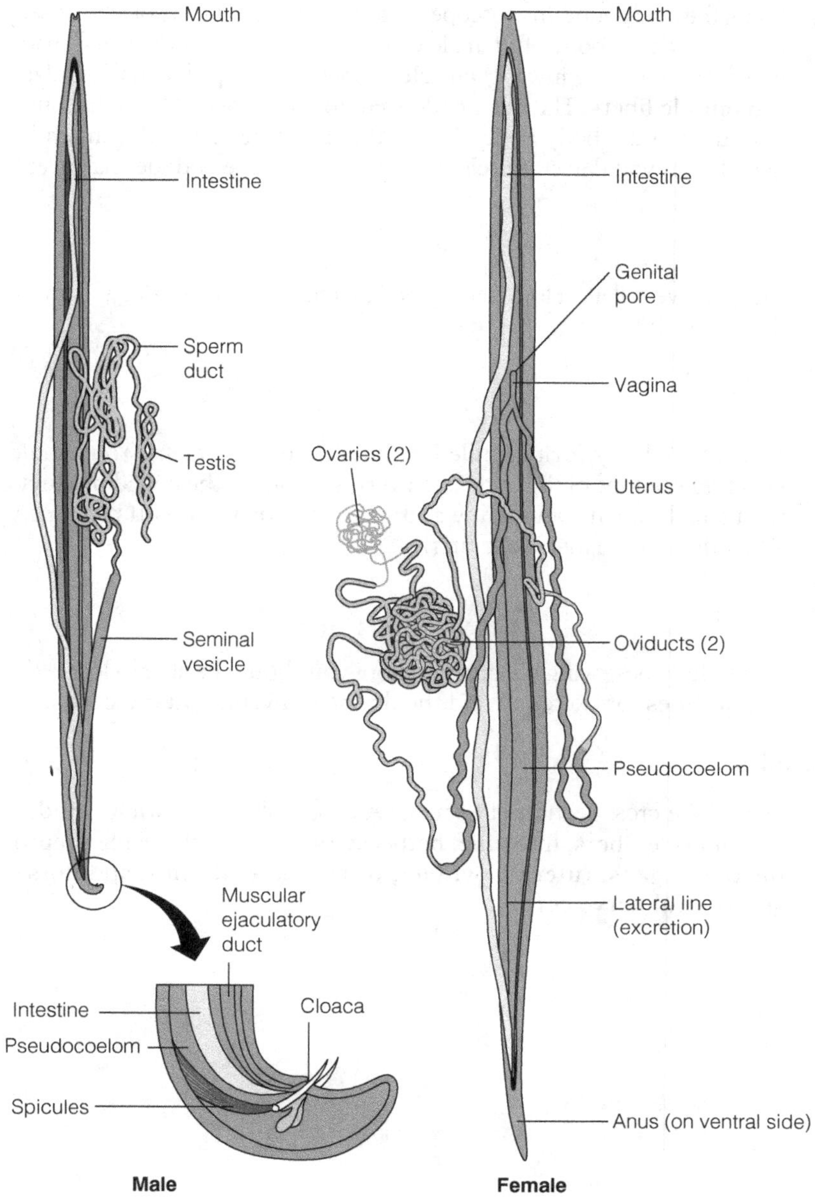

Figure 1.
Male and female *Ascaris*.
The digestive tract originates at the mouth and terminates in the anus. Reproductive structures fill the body cavity.

f. The nervous system consists of a ring of nervous tissue around the anterior end of the worm, with one dorsal and one ventral nerve cord. These structures will be more easily observed in the prepared slide.

g. Do you see signs of segmentation in the body wall or in the digestive, reproductive, or excretory systems?

h. Do you see signs of a support system? What do you think supports the body?

4. Using the compound microscope, observe a prepared slide of a cross section through the body of a female worm. Note that the body wall is made up of (from outside inward) **cuticle** (noncellular), **epidermis** (cellular), and **muscle fibers.** The muscle (derived from mesoderm) lies at the outer boundary of the body cavity. Locate the **intestine** (derived from endoderm). Can you detect muscle tissue adjacent to the endodermal layer?

   What do we call a coelom that is lined by mesoderm (outside) and endoderm (inside)?

5. Most of the body cavity is filled with reproductive organs. You should see cross sections of the two large **uteri**, sections of the coiled **oviducts** with small lumens, and many sections of the **ovaries** with no lumen. What do you see inside the uteri?

6. By carefully observing the cross section, you should be able to locate the **lateral lines** for excretion and the dorsal and ventral **nerve cords.**

Results

1. Sketch the cross section of a female *Ascaris*. Label the **cuticle, epidermis, muscle fibers, intestine, body cavity** (give specific name), **reproductive organs, (uterus, oviduct, ovary), lateral lines,** and **dorsal** and **ventral nerve cords.**

2. List some features of *Ascaris* that are possible adaptations to parasitic life.

3. Complete the summary table, Table 1, recording all information for roundworm characteristics in the appropriate row. You will use this information to answer questions in the Applying Your Knowledge section at the end of this lab topic.

Discussion

1. Discuss the significance of an animal's having two separate openings to the digestive tract, as seen in *Ascaris*.

2. What are the advantages of a body cavity being present in an animal?

EXERCISE 2
Phylum Arthropoda

Organisms in the phylum Arthropoda (clade Ecdysozoa) have been very successful species. Evidence indicates that arthropods may have lived on Earth half a billion years ago. They can be found in almost every imaginable habitat: marine waters, fresh water, and almost every terrestrial niche. Many species are directly beneficial to humans, serving as a source of food. Others make humans miserable by eating their homes, infesting their domestic animals, eating their food, and biting their bodies. These organisms have an exoskeleton that periodically sheds as they grow. In this exercise, you will observe the morphology of two arthropods: the crayfish (an aquatic arthropod) and the grasshopper (a terrestrial arthropod).

Lab Study A. Crayfish (*Cambarus*)

Materials

dissecting instruments
dissecting pan
preserved crayfish
disposable gloves

Introduction

Crayfish live in streams, ponds, and swamps, usually protected under rocks and vegetation. They may walk slowly over the substrate of their habitat, but they can also swim rapidly using their tails. The segmentation seen in annelids is seen also in crayfish and all arthropods; however, you will see that the segments are grouped into functional units.

Procedure

1. Obtain a preserved crayfish, study its external anatomy, and compare your observations with Figure 2. Describe the body symmetry, supportive structures, appendages, and segmentation, and state the adaptive advantages of each characteristic.
   a. body symmetry

   b. supportive structures

   c. appendages

   d. segmentation

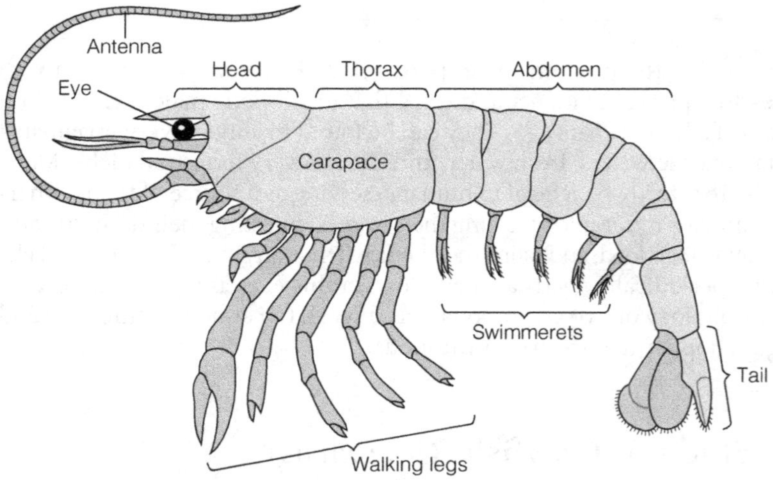

Figure 2.
External anatomy of a crayfish.
The body is divided into head, thorax, and abdominal regions. Appendages grouped in a region perform specific functions.

2. Identify the three regions of the crayfish body: the **head, thorax** (fused with the head), and **abdomen.** Note the appendages associated with each region. Speculate about the functions of each of these groups of appendages.
   a. head appendages

   b. thoracic appendages

   c. abdominal appendages

3. Feathery **gills** lie under the lateral extensions of a large, expanded exoskeletal plate called the **carapace** (see Figure 2). To expose the gills, use scissors to cut away a portion of the plate on the left side of the animal. What is the function of the gills? Speculate about how this function is performed.

4. Remove the dorsal portion of the carapace to observe other organs in the head and thorax. Compare your observations with Figure 3.
   a. Start on each side of the body at the posterior lateral edge of the carapace and make two lateral cuts extending along each side of the thorax and forward over the head, meeting just behind the eyes. This should create a dorsal flap in the carapace.

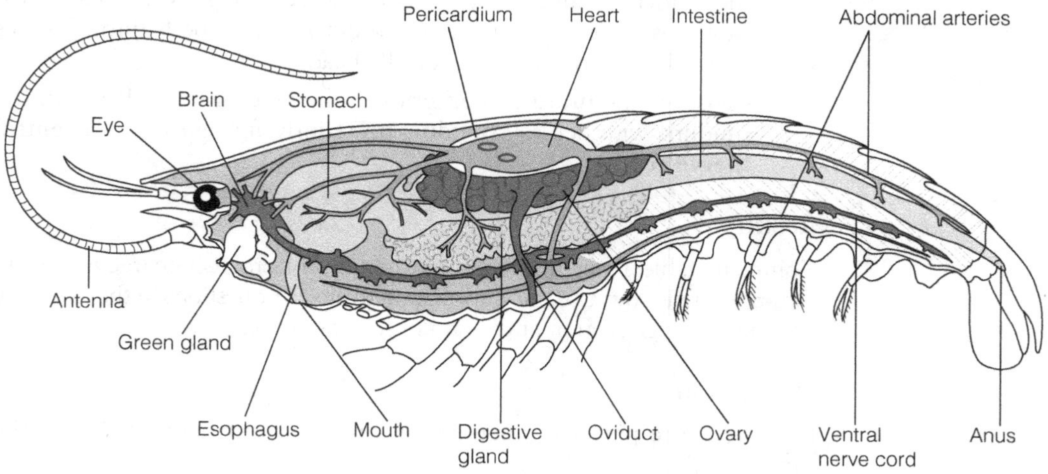

Figure 3.
Internal anatomy of the crayfish. Large digestive glands fill much of the body cavity. The intestine extends from the stomach through the tail to the anus. The green glands lie near the brain in the head.

b. Carefully insert a needle under this flap and separate the underlying tissues as you lift the flap.

c. Observe the **heart,** a small, angular structure located just under the carapace near the posterior portion of the thorax. (If you were not successful in leaving the tissues behind as you removed the carapace, you may have removed the heart with the carapace.) Thin threads leading out from the heart are **arteries.** Look for holes in the heart wall. When blood collects in **sinuses** around the heart, the heart relaxes, and these holes open to allow the heart to fill with blood. The holes then close, and the blood is pumped through the arteries, which distribute it around the body. Blood seeps back to the heart, since no veins are present. What is the name given to this kind of circulation?

d. Locate the **stomach** in the head region. It is a large, saclike structure. It may be obscured by the large, white **digestive glands** that fill the body cavity inside the body wall. Leading posteriorly from the stomach is the **intestine.** Make longitudinal cuts through the exoskeleton on either side of the dorsal midline of the abdomen. Lift the exoskeleton and trace the intestine to the anus. (When shrimp are "deveined" in preparation for eating, the intestine is removed.) Given all of the organs and tissues around the digestive tract and inside the body wall in the body cavity, what kind of coelom do you think this animal has?

e. Turn your attention to the anterior end of the specimen again. Pull the stomach posteriorly (this will tear the esophagus) and look inside the most anterior portion of the head. Two **green glands** (they do not look green), the animal's excretory organs, are located in this region. These are actually long tubular structures that resemble nephridia but are compacted into a glandular mass. Waste and excess water pass from these glands to the outside of the body through pores at the base of the antennae on the head.

f. Observe the **brain** just anterior to the green glands. It lies in the midline with nerves extending posteriorly, fusing to form a **ventral nerve cord.**

Results

Complete Table 1, recording all information for crayfish characteristics in the appropriate row. Use this information to answer questions in the Applying Your Knowledge section at the end of this lab topic.

Discussion

How does the pattern of segmentation differ in the crayfish and the earthworm?

Lab Study B. Grasshoppers *(Romalea)*

Materials

dissecting instruments
dissecting pan
preserved grasshopper
disposable gloves

Introduction

The grasshopper, an insect, is an example of a terrestrial arthropod. Insects are the most successful and abundant of all land animals. They are the principal invertebrates in dry environments, and they can survive extreme temperatures. They are the only invertebrates that can fly. As you study the grasshopper, compare the anatomy of this terrestrial animal with that of the aquatic crayfish, just studied. This comparison should suggest ways that terrestrial animals have solved the problems of life out of water.

Procedure

1. Observe the external anatomy of the grasshopper. Compare your observations with Figure 4.
   a. Note the symmetry, supportive structures, appendages, and segmentation of the grasshopper.
   b. Observe the body parts. The body is divided into three regions: the **head,** the **thorax** (to which the legs and wings are attached), and the **abdomen.** Examine the appendages on the head, speculate about their functions, and locate the mouth opening into the digestive tract.
   c. Turning your attention to the abdomen, locate small dots along each side. These dots are **spiracles,** small openings into elastic air tubes, or **tracheae,** that branch to all parts of the body and constitute the respiratory system of the grasshopper. This system of tubes brings oxygen directly to the cells of the body.

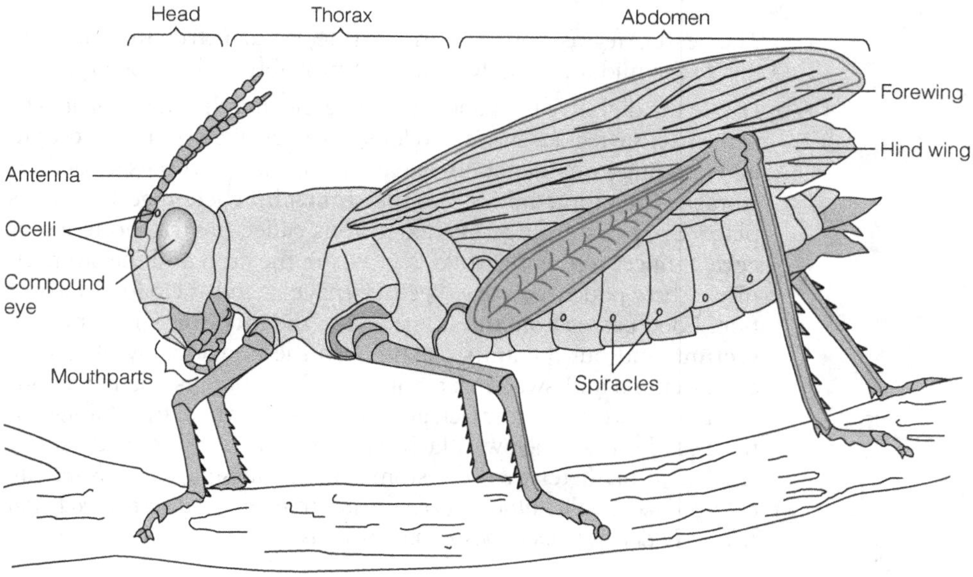

Figure 4.
External anatomy of the grasshopper. The body is divided into head, thorax, and abdominal regions. Wings and large legs are present. Small openings, called *spiracles,* lead to internal tracheae, allowing air to pass into the body.

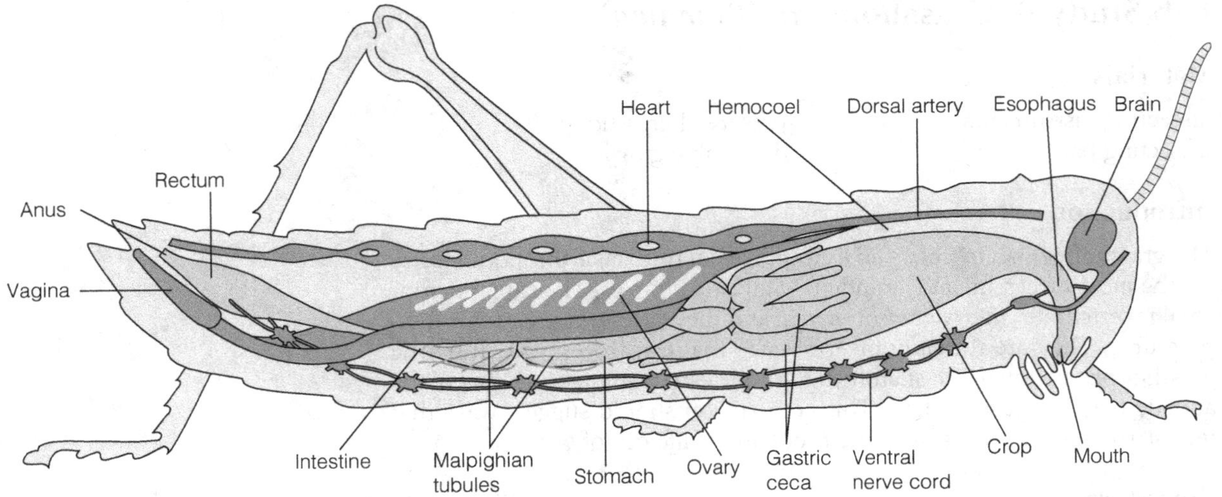

Figure 5.
Internal anatomy of the grasshopper. The digestive tract, extending from mouth to anus, is divided into specialized regions: the esophagus, crop, stomach, intestine, and rectum. Gastric ceca attach at the junction of the crop and the stomach. Malpighian tubules empty excretory waste into the anterior end of the intestine.

2. Remove the exoskeleton. First take off the wings and, starting at the posterior end, use scissors to make two lateral cuts toward the head. Remove the dorsal wall of the exoskeleton and note the segmented pattern in the muscles inside the body wall. Compare your observations with Figure 5 as you work.

   a. A space between the body wall and the digestive tract, the **hemocoel** (a true coelom), in life is filled with colorless blood. What type of circulation does the grasshopper have?

   The heart of a grasshopper is an elongate, tubular structure lying just inside the middorsal body wall. This probably will not be visible.

   b. Locate the digestive tract and again note the mouth. Along the length of the tract are regions specialized for specific functions. A narrow **esophagus** leading from the mouth expands into a large **crop** used for food storage. The crop empties into the **stomach,** where digestion takes place. Six pairs of fingerlike extensions called **gastric pouches** or **ceca** connect to the digestive tract where the crop and the stomach meet. These pouches secrete digestive enzymes and aid in food absorption. Food passes from the stomach into the **intestine,** then into the **rectum,** and out the **anus.** Distinguish these regions by observing constrictions and swellings along the tube. There is usually a constriction between the stomach and the intestine where the Malpighian tubules (discussed below) attach. The intestine is shorter and usually smaller in diameter than the stomach. *The intestine expands into an enlarged rectum that absorbs excess water from any undigested food, and relatively dry excrement passes out the anus.*

c. The excretory system is made up of numerous tiny tubules, the **Malpighian tubules,** which empty their products into the anterior end of the intestine. These tubules remove wastes and salts from the blood. Locate these tubules.

d. Push aside the digestive tract and locate the **ventral nerve cord** lying medially inside the ventral body wall. Ganglia are expanded regions of the ventral nerve cord found in each body segment. Following the nerve cord anteriorly, note that branches from the nerve cord pass around the digestive tract and meet, forming a brain in the head.

Results

Complete Table 1, recording all information for grasshopper characteristics in the appropriate row. Use this information to answer questions in the Applying Your Knowledge section at the end of this lab topic.

Discussion

1. Describe how each of the following external structures helps the grasshopper live successfully in terrestrial environments.
   a. Exoskeleton

   b. Wings

   c. Large, jointed legs

   d. Spiracles

2. Describe how each of the following internal structures helps the grasshopper live successfully in terrestrial environments.
   a. Tracheae

   b. Malpighian tubules

   c. Rectum

EXERCISE 3

Deuterostome—Phylum Echinodermata—Sea Star

Echinodermata is one of three phyla in the group of animals called deuterostomes. You will study another deuterostome phylum in Exercise 4, phylum Chordata. Examples of echinoderms include the sea star, sea urchin, sea cucumber, and sea lily. Some of the most familiar animals in the animal kingdom are in the phylum Chordata—fish, reptiles, amphibians, and mammals. Take a look at a sea star (starfish) in the salt-water aquarium in your lab or in a tidal pool on a rocky shore. What are the most obvious characteristics of this animal? Then imagine a chordate—a fish, dog, or even yourself. You might question why these two phyla are considered closely related phylogenetically. The most obvious difference is a very basic characteristic—the sea star has radial symmetry and most chordates that you imagine have bilateral symmetry. The sea star has no head or other obvious chordate features and it crawls around using hundreds of small suction cups called tube feet. Most chordates show strong cephalization and move using appendages. Your conclusion from the superficial observations might be that these two phyla are not closely related. Your observations are a good example of the difficulty faced by taxonomists when comparing animals based only on the morphology of adults. Taxonomists must collect data from studies of developmental and—as we discovered with the protostomes—molecular similarities before coming to final conclusions.

In this and the following exercise, you will examine an echinoderm, the adult sea star (demonstration only), and two chordates, asking questions about their morphology and adaptation to their habitats. You may not be convinced of their phylogentic relationships, however, until you study early development in sea urchins and sea stars. In that lab topic, you will see that chordates and echinoderms have similar early embryonic developmental patterns, including the formation of the mouth and anus and the type of cleavage.

Materials

whole preserved sea stars on demonstration

several dissected sea stars on demonstration showing the internal contents of the body and the inside surface of oral and aboral halves of the body

Introduction

The sea star is classified in the phylum Echinodermata. They are marine animals with an endoskeleton of small, spiny calcareous plates bound together by connective tissue. Their symmetry is radial pentamerous (five-parted). They have no head or brain and few sensory structures. All animals in this phylum have a unique **water-vascular system** that develops from mesoderm and consists of a series of canals carrying water that enters the body through an outer opening, the **madreporite.** The canals are located inside the body and include a ring around the central disk of the body and tubes or canals that extend out into each arm. The canals then terminate in many small structures called **tube feet** along the groove on the oral side of each arm. Tube

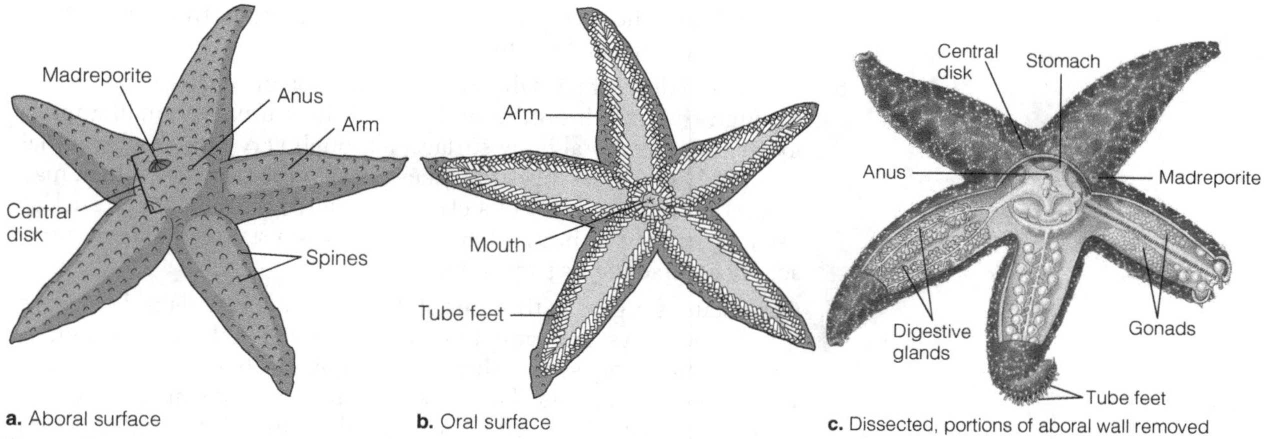

Figure 6.
(a) Aboral surface of a sea star. (b) Oral surface of a sea star. (c) Dissected sea star with portions of the aboral wall removed.

feet extend to the outside of the body and end in a small suction cup in most species. By contracting muscles and forcing fluid into its tube feet, the sea star can extend and attach the feet to hard surfaces such as the surface of a clamshell, or rocks on the ocean shore.

Procedure

1. Observe the preserved sea star on demonstration. Locate the **aboral** surface—the "upper" surface away from the mouth (Figure 6a). The downside is the **oral** surface where the mouth is located (Figure 6b).
2. Count the number of arms that extend out from the **central disk.** Echinoderms are usually pentamerous, meaning that their arms are in multiples of five. Occasionally a sea star with six arms will be found. Arms that are damaged or lost can be regenerated, and an extra arm may regenerate.
3. Observe the animal's aboral surface (Figure 6a). Locate the **madreporite,** a small porous plate displaced to one side of the central disk that serves to take water into the water vascular system.

   Notice that the surface of the animal's body is spiny. The spines project from calcareous plates of the **endoskeleton.** The endoskeleton is derived from the embryonic germ layer mesoderm. In life, the entire surface of the body is covered with an **epidermis** derived from ectoderm that may not be visible with the naked eye.
4. Observe the dissected sea star on demonstration (Figure 6c). In this dissection the entire aboral surface has been lifted off the body and placed to the side, inside up. This exposes the internal organs. The endoskeleton and its calcareous plates are obvious as viewed from the inside of the body.
5. Inside the body the organs are located in a **true body cavity.** Small delicate projections of the body cavity protrude between the plates of the endoskeleton to the outside of the body. These projections, covered with epidermis, are called **skin gills** or dermal branchiae, and function in the exchange of oxygen and carbon dioxide with the water bathing the animal's body. In addition, nitrogenous waste passes through these

skin gills into the surrounding water; these structures thus having both respiratory and excretory functions.

6. The central disk contains the stomach, a portion of which can be everted through the mouth on the oral side of the animal. A small anus is located on the aboral body surface, although very little fecal material is ejected here. Most digestion takes place in the stomach, which may be everted into the body of a clam. The digested broth is then sucked up into the sea star body. After feeding, the sea star draws in its stomach by contracting its stomach muscles.
7. Conspicuous organs in the arms of the animal are gonads and digestive glands. Other systems cannot be easily observed in this preparation. A reduced circulatory system (hemal system) exists, but its function is not well defined. It consists of tissue strands and unlined sinuses. The nervous system includes a nerve ring around the mouth and radial nerves with epidermal nerve networks. There is no central nervous system.

Results

Complete Table 1, recording in the appropriate row as much information as you have been able to observe.

Discussion

1. Imagine that you are a zoologist studying sea stars for the first time. What characteristics would you note from the dissection of an adult animal that might give a clue to its phylogenetic relationships—that it belongs with deuterostomes rather than protostomes?

2. What structures have you observed that appear to be unique to echinoderms?

3. How would you continue your study to obtain more information that might help in classifying these animals?

4. Given the fact that other deuterostomes are bilaterally symmetrical, what is one explanation for the radial symmetry of most adult echinoderms?

EXERCISE 4
Deuterostome—Phylum Chordata

Up to this point, all the animals you have studied are commonly called **invertebrates,** a somewhat artificial designation based on the absence of a backbone. Those animals with a backbone are called **vertebrates.** The phylum Chordata studied in this exercise includes two subphyla of invertebrates and a third subphylum of vertebrates, animals that have a bony or cartilaginous endoskeleton with a vertebral column. Chordates inhabit terrestrial and aquatic (freshwater and marine) environments. One group has developed the ability to fly. The body plan of chordates is unique in that these animals demonstrate a complex of four important characteristics at some stage in their development. In this exercise, you will discover these characteristics.

You will study two chordate species: the lancelet, an invertebrate in the subphylum Cephalochordata, and the pig, a vertebrate in the subphylum Vertebrata. The third subphylum, Urochordata, will not be studied.

Lab Study A. Lancelets (*Branchiostoma,* formerly *Amphioxus*)

Materials

compound microscope
stereoscopic microscope
preserved lancelet in watch glass
prepared slide of whole mount of lancelet
prepared slide of cross section of lancelet

Introduction

Lancelets are marine animals that burrow in sand in tidal flats. They feed with their head end extended from their burrow. They resemble fish superficially, but their head is poorly developed, and they have unique features not found in fish or other vertebrates. They retain the four unique characteristics of chordates throughout their life cycle and are excellent animals to use to demonstrate these features. In this lab study, you will observe preserved lancelets, prepared slides of whole mounts, and cross sections through the body of a lancelet.

Procedure

1. Place a preserved lancelet in water in a watch glass and observe it using the stereoscopic microscope. Handle the specimen with care and *do not dissect it.* Note the fishlike shape of the slender, elongate body. Locate the anterior end by the presence at that end of a noselike **rostrum** extending over the mouth region, surrounded by small tentacles. Notice the lack of a well-defined head. Look for the segmented muscles that surround much of the animal's body. Can you see signs of a tail? If the animal you are studying is mature, you will be able to see two rows of 20 to 25 white gonads on the ventral surface of the body.
2. Return the specimen to the correct container.

Figure 7.
The lancelet, whole mount. The rostrum extends over the mouth region. The pharynx, including the pharyngeal gill slits, leads to the intestine, which exits the body at the anus. Note that a tail extends beyond the anus. Structures positioned from the dorsal surface of the body inward include a dorsal fin, the nerve cord, and the notochord.

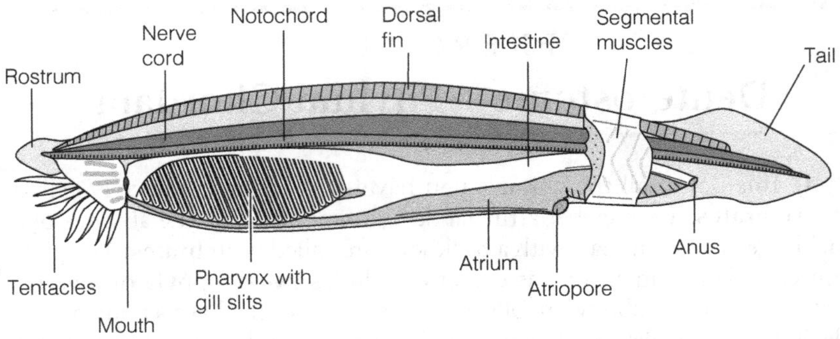

3. Observe the whole mount slide of the lancelet and compare your observations with Figure 7.

Use only the lowest power on the compound microscope to study this slide.

a. Scan the entire length of the body wall. Do you see evidence of segmentation in the muscles?

b. Look at the anterior end of the animal. Do you see evidence of a sensory system? Describe what you see.

c. Locate the mouth of the animal at the anterior end. See if you can follow a tube from just under the rostrum into a large sac with numerous gill slits. This sac is the **pharynx with gill slits,** a uniquely chordate structure. Water and food pass into the pharynx from the mouth. Food passes posteriorly from the pharynx into the intestine, which ends at the anus on the ventral side of the animal, several millimeters before the end. The extension of the body beyond the anus is called a **post-anal tail.** Think of worms. Where was the anus located in these animals? Was a post-anal region present? Explain.

d. Water entering the mouth passes through the gill slits and collects in a chamber, the **atrium,** just inside the body wall. The water ultimately passes out of the body at a ventral pore, the **atripore.** Surprisingly, the gill slits are not the major gas exchange surface in the lancelet body. Because of the great activity of ciliated cells in this region, it is even possible that blood leaving the gill region has less oxygen than that entering the region. The function of gill slits is simply to strain food from the water. The major site for gas exchange is the body surface.

e. Now turn your attention to the dorsal side of the animal. Beginning at the surface of the body and moving inward, identify the listed structures and speculate about the function of each one.

dorsal fin:

nerve cord:

notochord:

The nerve cord is in a dorsal position. Have you seen only a dorsal nerve cord in any of the animals previously studied?

The notochord is a cartilage-like rod that lies ventral to the nerve cord and extends the length of the body. Have you seen a notochord in any of the previous animals?

The lancelet circulatory system is not visible in these preparations, but the animal has **closed circulation** with dorsal and ventral aortae, capillaries, and veins. Excretory organs, or nephridia (not visible here), are located near the true coelom, which surrounds the pharynx.

4. Observe the slide of cross sections taken through the lancelet body. There may be several sections on this slide, taken at several positions along the length of the body. Find the section through the pharynx and compare it with Figure 8.

Study this slide on the lowest power.

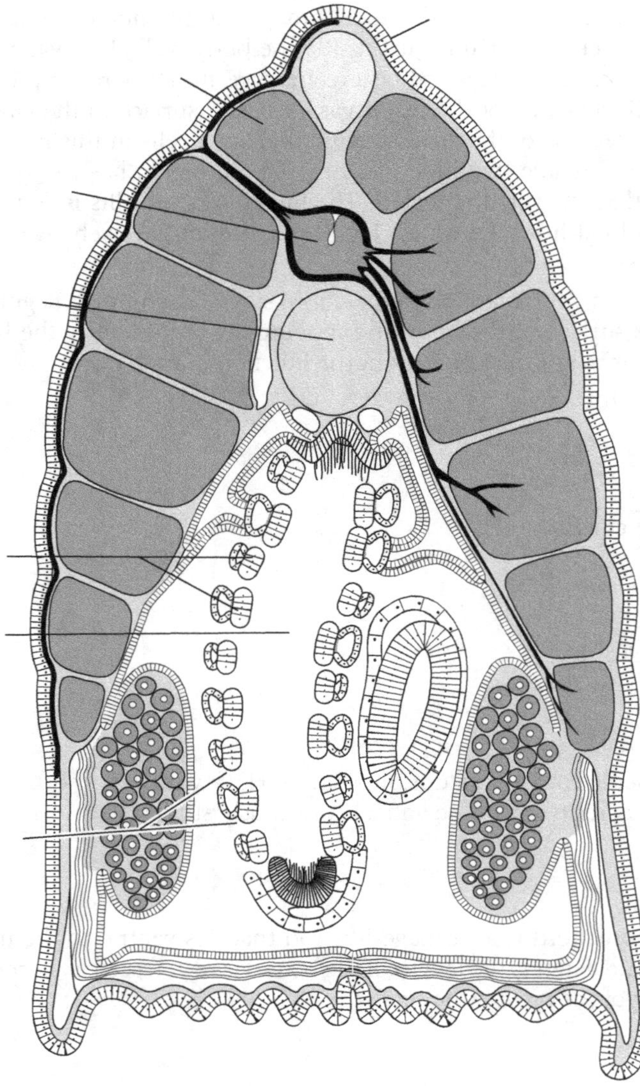

Figure 8.
Cross section through the pharyngeal region of the lancelet.

In cross section, it is much easier to see the structural relationships among the various organs of the lancelet. Identify the following structures and label them on Figure 8.

a. **Segmental muscles.** They are located on each side of the body, under the skin.

b. **Dorsal fin.** This projects upward from the most dorsal surface of the body.

c. **Nerve cord.** You may be able to see that the nerve cord contains a small central canal, thus making it hollow. The nerve cord is located in the dorsal region of the body, ventral to the dorsal fin between the lateral bundles of muscle.

d. **Notochord.** This is a large oval structure located just ventral to the nerve cord.

e. **Pharynx with gill slits.** This structure appears as a series of dark triangles arranged in an oval. The triangles are cross sections of **gill bars.** The spaces between the triangles are **gill slits,** through which water passes into the surrounding chamber.

Results

1. Complete the diagram of the lancelet cross section in Figure 8. Label all the structures listed in step 4 of the Procedure section.
2. Complete Table 1, recording all information for lancelet characteristics in the appropriate row. Use this information to answer questions in the Applying Your Knowledge section at the end of this lab topic.

Discussion

Describe the uniquely chordate features that you have detected in the lancelet that were not present in the animals previously studied.

Lab Study B. Fetal Pigs *(Sus scrofa)*

Materials

preserved fetal pig
dissecting pan
disposable gloves

Introduction

The pig is a terrestrial vertebrate. You will study its anatomy in detail later. In this lab study, working with your lab partner, you will observe external features only, observing those characteristics studied in other animals in previous exercises. Compare the organization of the vertebrate body with the animals previously studied. As you dissect the pig in subsequent labs, come back to these questions and answer the ones that cannot be answered in today's lab study.

Procedure

1. Obtain a preserved fetal pig from the class supply and carry it to your desk in a dissecting pan.

Use disposable gloves to handle preserved animals.

2. With your lab partner, read each of the following questions. Drawing on observations you have made of other animals in the animal diversity lab studies, predict the answer to each question about the fetal pig. Then examine the fetal pig and determine the answer, if possible. Give evidence for your answer based on your observations of the pig, your knowledge of vertebrate anatomy, or your understanding of animal phylogeny.

a. What type of symmetry does the pig body have?
Prediction:

Evidence:

b. How many layers of embryonic tissue are present?
Prediction:

Evidence:

c. Are cells organized into distinct tissues?
Prediction:

Evidence:

d. How many digestive tract openings are present? Would you describe this as a "tube within a tube"?
Prediction:

Evidence:

e. Is the circulatory system open or closed?
Prediction:

Evidence:

f. What is the habitat of the animal?
Prediction:

Evidence:

g. What are the organs for respiration?
Prediction:

Evidence:

h. What are the organs for excretion?
Prediction:

Evidence:

i. What is the method of locomotion?
Prediction:

Evidence:

j. Are support systems internal or external?
Prediction:

Evidence:

k. Is the body segmented?
Prediction:

Evidence:

l. Are appendages present?
Prediction:

Evidence:

m. What is the position and complexity of the nervous system?
Prediction:

Evidence:

Results

Complete Table 1, recording all information for pig characteristics in the appropriate row. Use this information to answer questions in the Applying Your Knowledge section that follows.

Results Summary

Complete the summary table, Table 1, recording in the appropriate row information about characteristics of all animals studied. Use this information to answer questions in the Applying Your Knowledge section that follows.

Applying Your Knowledge

1. Using specific examples from the animals you have studied, describe ways that organisms have adapted to specific environments.
   a. Compare organisms adapted to aquatic environments with those from terrestrial environments.

b. Compare adaptations of parasitic organisms with similar free-living organisms.

2. Using the summary table, Table 2, categorize the animals studied based on the 13 basic characteristics discussed.
3. Upon superficial examination, the body form of certain present-day animals might be described as simple, yet these animals may have developed specialized structures, perhaps unique to their particular phylum. Illustrate this point using examples from some of the simpler organisms you have dissected.

4. One might conclude that certain trends can be detected, trends from "primitive" features (those that arose early in the evolution of animals) to more "advanced" traits (those that arose later). However, animals with these alleged primitive characteristics still successfully exist on Earth today. Why is this so? Why have the more advanced animals not completely replaced the more primitive ones? Use examples from the lab to illustrate your answer.

5. A major theme in biology is the relationship between form and function in organisms. Select one of the major characteristics from Table 1, and illustrate the relationship of form and function for this characteristic using examples from the organisms studied.

Table 1
Summary Table of Animal Characteristics

Animal	Symmetry	Tissue Organization	Type of Body Cavity	Digestive Openings	Circulatory System	Habitat	Respiratory Organs
Sponge 							
Hydra 							
Planarian 							
Clamworm/ earthworm 							
Clam 							
Roundworm 							
Crayfish 							
Grasshopper 							
Sea star 							
Lancelet 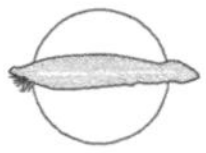							
Pig 							

Table 1
Summary Table of Animal Characteristics *(continued)*

Animal	Excretory System	Locomotion	Support System	Segmentation	Appendages	Nervous System Organization
Sponge 						
Hydra 						
Planarian 						
Clamworm/ earthworm 						
Clam 						
Roundworm 						
Crayfish 						
Grasshopper 						
Sea star 						
Lancelet 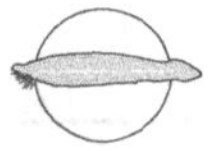						
Pig 						

Table 2
Comparison of Organisms by Major Features

1. **Tissue Organization**
   a. distinct tissues absent:
   b. distinct tissues present:

2. **Symmetry**
   a. radial:
   b. bilateral:

3. **Body Cavity**
   a. acoelomate:
   b. pseudocoelomate:
   c. eucoelomate:

4. **Openings to Digestive Tract**
   a. one:
   b. two:

5. **Circulatory System**
   a. none:
   b. open:
   c. closed:

6. **Habitat**
   a. aquatic:
   b. terrestrial:
   c. parasitic:

7. **Organs for Gas Exchange**
   a. skin:
   b. gills:
   c. lungs:
   d. spiracles/tracheae:

Table 2
Comparison of Organisms by Major Features *(continued)*

8. Organs for Excretion (list organ and animals)	**11. Segmented Body** a. no: b. yes:
	12. Appendages a. yes: b. no:
9. Type of Locomotion (list type and animals)	**13. Nervous System** a. ventral nerve cord: b. dorsal nerve cord: c. other:
10. Support System a. external: b. internal: c. hydrostatic:	

References

Hickman, C. P., L. S. Roberts, A. Larson, and H. I'Anson. *Integrated Principles of Zoology,* 12th ed. Boston: McGraw Hill, 2004.

Website

Includes descriptions of many invertebrates and vertebrates, links to insect keys, references:
http://animaldiversity.ummz.umich.edu/index.html

Vertebrate Anatomy II: The Circulatory and Respiratory Systems

Laboratory Objectives

After completing this lab topic, you should be able to:

1. Identify and describe the function of the main organs and structures in the circulatory system and trace the flow of blood through the pulmonary and systemic circuits.
2. Identify and describe the function of the main organs and structures in the respiratory system and describe the exchange of oxygen and carbon dioxide in the lungs.
3. Describe how the circulatory and respiratory systems work together to bring about the integrated functioning of the body.
4. Apply knowledge and understanding acquired in this lab to problems in human physiology.
5. Apply knowledge and understanding acquired in this lab to explain organismal adaptive strategies.

Introduction

You have learned that nutrients are taken into the digestive tract, where they are processed: chewed, mixed with water and churned to a liquid, mixed with digestive enzymes, and finally digested into the component monomers, or building blocks, from which they were synthesized. For an animal to receive the benefits of these nutrients, these products of digestion must pass across intestinal cells and into the circulatory system to be transported to all the cells of the animal's body. Oxygen is necessary for the release of energy from these digested products. Oxygen from the atmosphere passes into the respiratory system of the animal, where it ultimately crosses cells in the lungs (in a terrestrial vertebrate) or gills (in an aquatic vertebrate) and enters the circulatory system for transport to cells of all organs, to be utilized in nutrient metabolism. Waste products of cellular metabolism—carbon dioxide and urea—are transported from the tissues that produce them via the blood and are eliminated from the body through the lungs of the respiratory system and the kidney of the excretory system, respectively. Thus, the circulatory, respiratory, and excretory systems function collectively, utilizing environmental materials, eliminating wastes, and maintaining a stable internal environment.

In this and the following lab topic, you will investigate the morphology of the circulatory, respiratory, and excretory systems in the fetal pig. As you dissect, relate the structure and specific function of each system to its role in the integrated body.

EXERCISE 1

Glands and Respiratory Structures of the Neck and Thoracic Cavity

Materials

These materials will be used for the entire lab topic.

fetal pig
dissecting pan
dissecting instruments
twine
disposable gloves
plastic bag with twist tie and labels
preservative

Introduction

To study the glands and respiratory structures of the neck, you must first open the thoracic cavity and then remove the skin and muscles in the neck region. This will expose several major glands that lie in the neck region in close proximity to the respiratory structures.

Procedure

Wear disposable gloves when dissecting preserved animals.

1. Begin the dissection by opening the thoracic cavity, which houses the heart and lungs, and making an incision that extends to the jaw.
   a. Use scissors to deepen the superficial incision previously made anterior to the abdominal cavity, and continue deepening this incision to the base of the lower jaw.
   b. Cut through the body wall in the region of the thorax, clipping through the ribs slightly to the right or left of the **sternum** (the flat bone lying midventrally to which ribs attach).
   c. Continue the incision past the rib cage to the base of the lower jaw.
2. Using the blunt probe to separate tissues, carefully remove the skin and muscles in the neck region. You will expose the **thymus gland** on each side of the neck (Figure 1). This gland is large in the fetal pig and in young mammals, but regresses with age. It plays an important role in the development of the body's immune system.
3. Push the two thymus masses to the side to expose the **larynx** and **trachea** lying deep in the masses. Recall your knowledge about the **glottis,** observed in the dissection of the mouth. The glottis leads into the larynx, an expanded structure through which air passes from the mouth to the narrower trachea. The larynx houses vocal cords.

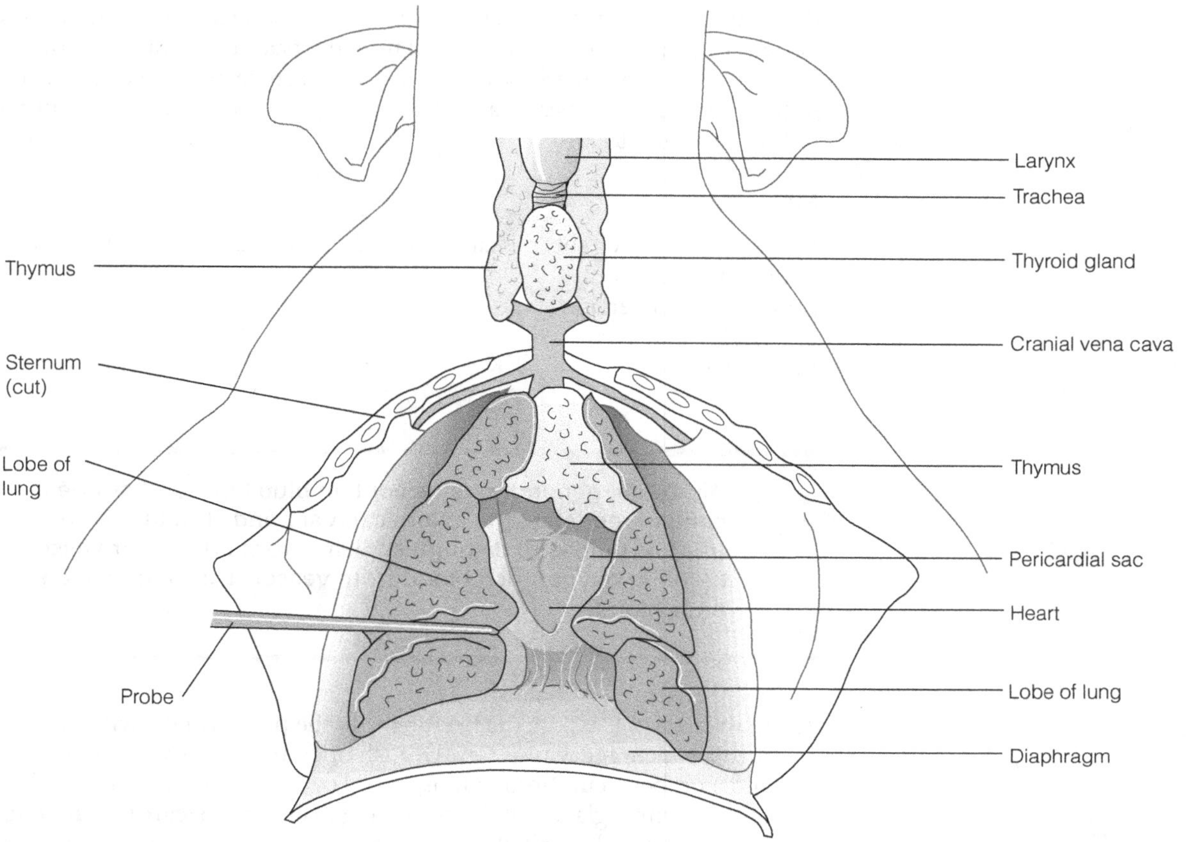

Figure 1.
Ventral view of the anterior region of the pig, showing structures in the neck region and the thoracic cavity. The pericardial sac encloses the heart.

4. A small reddish gland, the **thyroid gland,** covers the trachea. The thyroid gland secretes hormones that influence metabolism. Push this gland aside and observe the rings of cartilage that prevent the collapse of the trachea and allow air to pass to the lungs. Push aside the trachea to observe the dorsally located **esophagus.**
5. Do not continue the dissection of the neck and thoracic regions at this time. To prevent damage to blood vessels, you will complete the dissection of the remainder of the respiratory system (Exercise 5) following the dissection of the circulatory system.

EXERCISE 2
The Heart and the Pulmonary Blood Circuit

The heart and lungs lie in the **pericardial** and **pleural** (Gk. for "rib") cavities, respectively, within the thoracic cavity. In your dissection of the heart and blood vessels, you will distinguish the two circulatory pathways found in mammalian circulation: the **pulmonary circuit,** which carries blood from the heart to the lungs in arteries and back to the heart in veins; and the **systemic circuit,** which carries blood from the heart in arteries to all organs *but the lungs* and back to the heart in veins. This exercise investigates circulation in fetal and adult pig hearts and the pathway of blood to the lungs in the pulmonary circuit.

Materials

isolated adult pig or sheep heart dissected to show chambers and valves, demonstration only
supplies from Exercise 1

Procedure

Although, generally, veins contain blue latex and arteries contain red latex, the colors can vary and should not be used as guides to distinguish veins from arteries or vessels carrying oxygen-rich blood from vessels carrying oxygen-poor blood.

1. In the fetal pig, expose the heart lying in the **pericardial cavity** between the two pleural cavities. Gently push open the rib cage, using scissors and a probe to cut through muscle and connective tissue. Another lobe of the thymus gland will be seen lying over the **pericardial sac** housing the heart. The wall of the pericardial sac is a tough membrane composed of two fused coelomic epithelial linings, the **parietal pericardium** and the **parietal pleura.**
2. Cut into and push aside the pericardial sac. Carefully dissect away membranes adhering to the heart until you can identify the four chambers of the heart (Figure 2). The walls of heart chambers consist of cardiac muscle.

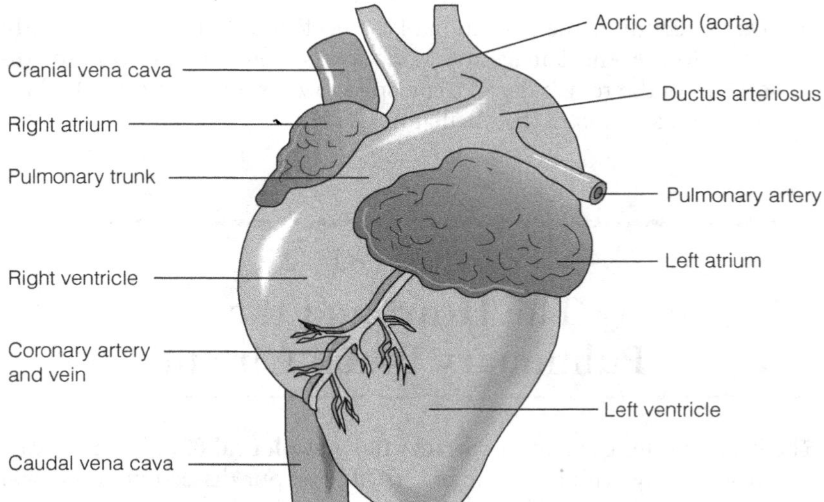

Figure 2.
Enlarged ventral view of a fetal heart, showing the four chambers and the major associated blood vessels. Compare this anatomy with that of an adult heart.

a. The **right atrium** and **left atrium** are small, dark, anteriorly located heart chambers that receive blood from the **venae cavae** and the pulmonary veins, respectively.

b. The **right ventricle** and **left ventricle** are large muscular heart chambers that contract to pump blood. A branch of the **coronary artery** may be seen on the heart surface where the left and right ventricles share a common wall. The coronary artery carries blood to heart tissue.

What is the name of the epithelial lining adhering to the heart surface?

3. Trace the pulmonary circuit. As the heart contracts, blood is forced from the right ventricle into the **pulmonary trunk,** a large vessel lying on the ventral surface of the heart. Another large vessel, the **aorta,** lies just dorsal to the pulmonary trunk.

a. Use forceps to pick away tissue around the pulmonary trunk and trace the pulmonary trunk as it curves cranially, giving off three branches: the right and left **pulmonary arteries** and the **ductus arteriosus.**

b. Identify the ductus arteriosus and the left pulmonary artery (the right pulmonary artery is not readily visible).

The right and left pulmonary arteries are relatively small at this stage of development. They conduct blood to the right and left lungs, respectively. The ductus arteriosus is the short, large-diameter vessel that connects the pulmonary trunk to the aorta. Because the small right and left pulmonary arteries and compact lung tissue present an extremely resistant blood pathway, the greatest volume of blood in the pulmonary trunk will flow through the ductus arteriosus and directly into the aorta and systemic circulation, bypassing the pulmonary arteries and lungs. At the time of the fetus's birth, when air enters the lungs and the tissues expand, blood will more easily flow into the lungs. The ductus arteriosus closes off and eventually becomes a ligament.

4. Observe the isolated adult pig or sheep heart on demonstration and locate the dorsal and ventral surfaces (Figure 2).

a. Identify the **right atrium** with associated **cranial** and **caudal venae cavae** and the **left atrium** with associated **pulmonary veins.**

b. Locate the **right** and **left ventricles** and the **atrioventricular valves** between the atria and the ventricles.

c. Locate the **pulmonary trunk,** which carries blood from the right ventricle, and the **aorta,** carrying blood from the left ventricle. The first two small branches of the aorta are **coronary arteries.** Locate these vessels and the **coronary veins** lying on the surface of the heart between the left and right ventricles. Coronary arteries and veins form a short circuit servicing heart tissues.

Results

Review the heart chambers, blood vessels, and organs in the pathway of the pulmonary circuit in the *adult* heart. To facilitate this review, fill in the blanks in the next paragraph.

Blood entering the heart passes first into the right atrium. From there it flows into the right ventricle. When the heart contracts, this blood is forced out of the ventricle into the _______________ trunk. Branches of this trunk called _____________________ carry blood to the lungs. After birth, the blood will become oxygen-rich in the lungs. Blood from the lungs passes back to the heart through _____________________, thus completing the circuit. It enters the left atrium of the heart.

Discussion

1. Define *artery.* Define *vein.*

2. Why would pulmonary arteries be relatively small at the fetal stage of development?

3. Although a pulmonary circuit exists, the heart in amphibians and most reptiles is made up of only three chambers—two atria and one ventricle. The latter receives blood from both atria. Speculate about possible disadvantages to this circulatory pathway.

EXERCISE 3

The Heart and the Systemic Circuit in the Thorax

Blood returning from the lungs collects in the left atrium and flows into the left ventricle. When the heart contracts, blood is forced out the **aorta,** the origin of which is obscured by the pulmonary trunk. The first branch from the aorta is the small **coronary artery,** previously identified, leading to the heart muscle. The larger volume of blood passes through the aorta to all organs of the body but the lungs. Blood returns to the heart from organs of the body through two large veins, the cranial and caudal venae cavae.

Procedure

1. Identify the venae cavae and their major branches.
   a. Push the heart to the pig's left to see two large veins entering the right atrium; these are the **cranial** and **caudal venae cavae** (Figure 3).

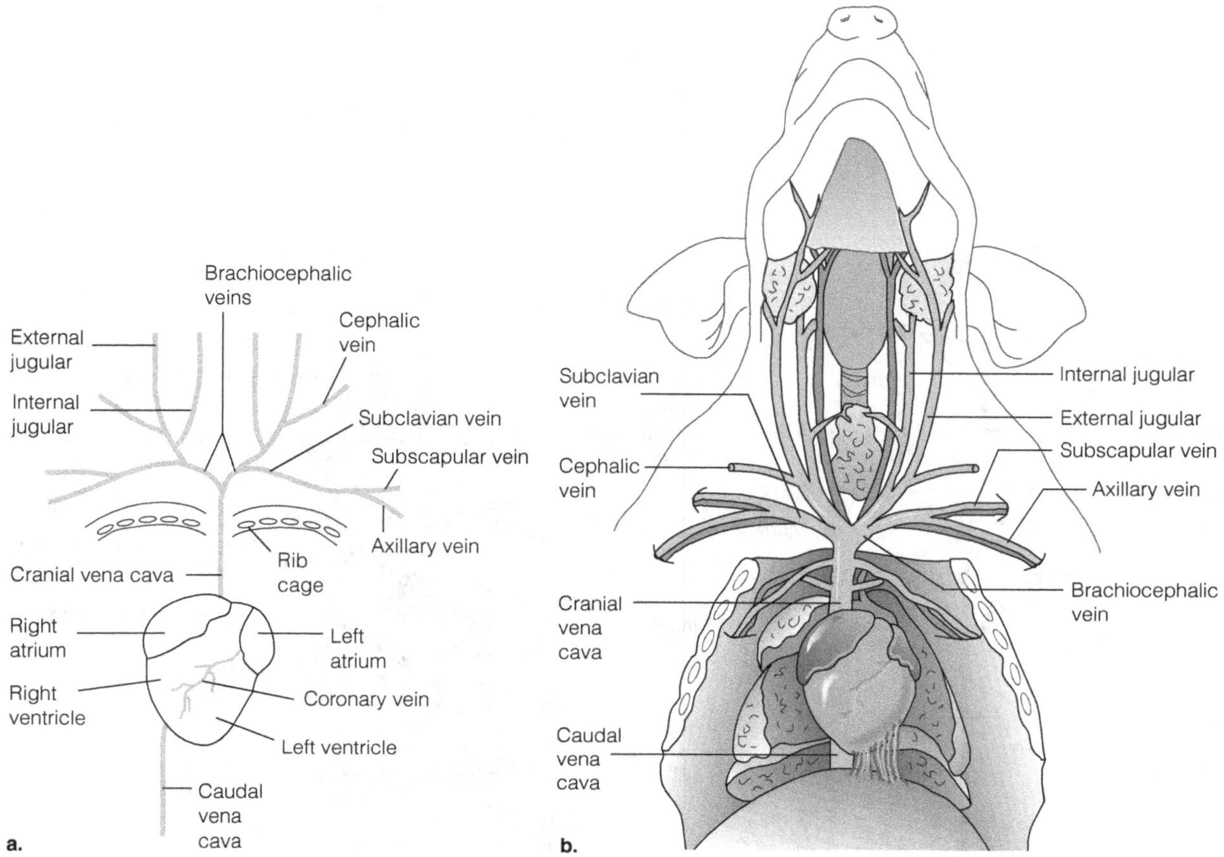

Figure 3.
Veins near the heart. The subclavian vein and the external and internal jugulars carry blood to the brachiocephalic veins, which unite into the cranial vena cava. The caudal vena cava carries blood from the posterior regions of the body.

b. Using the blunt probe to separate the vessels from surrounding tissues, follow the cranial vena cava toward the head and identify the two large **brachiocephalic veins,** which unite in the cranial vena cava.

c. Identify the three major veins that unite to form each brachiocephalic vein: the **external** and **internal jugulars** that carry blood returning from the head, and the **subclavian vein** that drains blood from the front leg and shoulder. Follow the subclavian vein into the front leg. Probe deep into the muscle covering the underside of the scapula (shoulder blade) and you should see the **subscapular vein,** draining blood from the shoulder region. The **axillary vein** carries blood from the front leg, becoming the subclavian vein at the subscapular branch. Occasionally, the subclavian vein is very short, and the subscapular and axillary veins unite close to the brachiocephalic vein. Another vein that is often injected and prominent in the shoulder area is the **cephalic vein.** This vein lies just beneath the skin on the upper front leg. It typically enters the external jugular near its base.

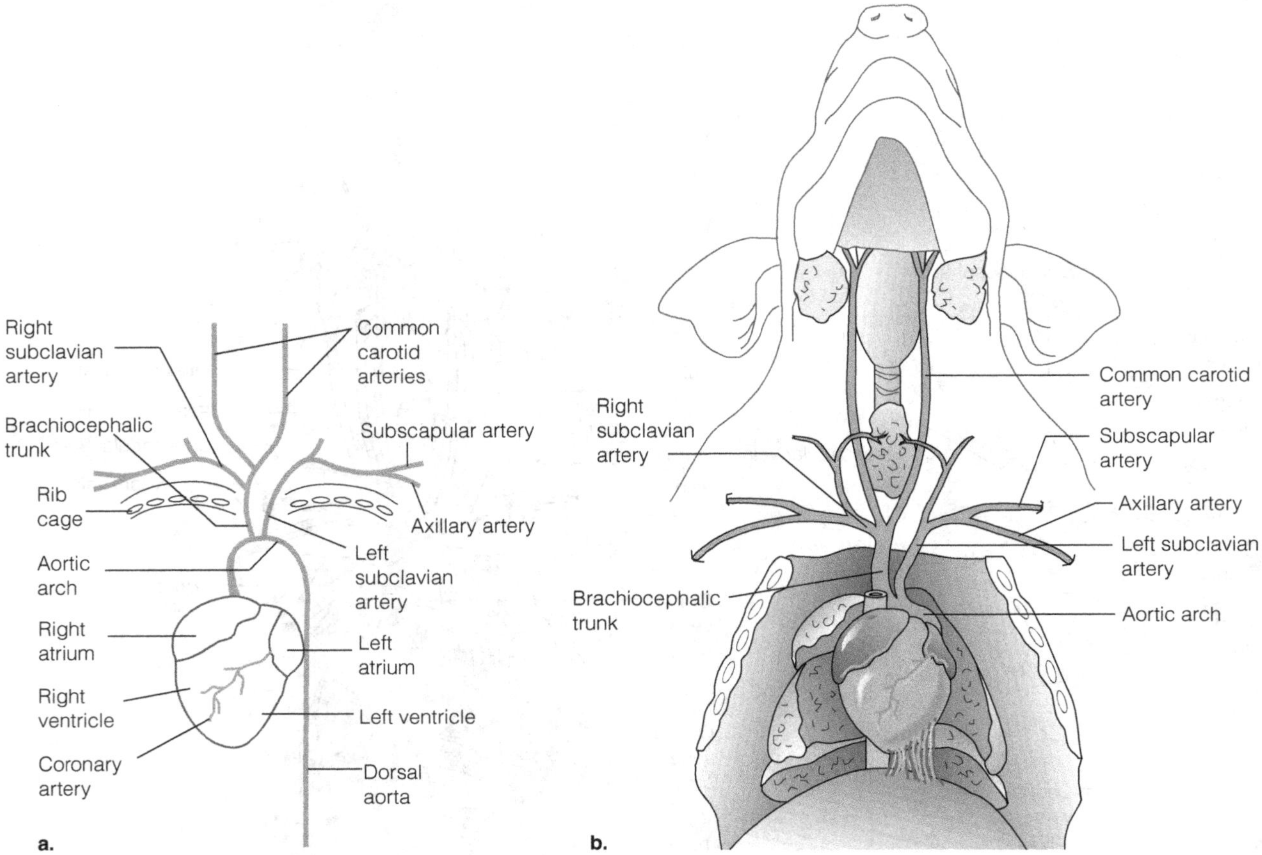

Figure 4.
Branches of the aorta. Branches from the aortic arch carry blood to the head and anterior limbs. The first branch, the brachiocephalic trunk, branches into the right subclavian artery to the right limb and two common carotid arteries to the head. The second branch is the left subclavian to the left limb.

2. Identify branches of the aorta near the heart (Figure 4).
   a. Push the pulmonary trunk ventrally and posteriorly to observe the curve of the aorta, the **aortic arch**, lying behind.
   b. Remove obscuring tissue and expose the first two major branches of the arch, which carry blood anteriorly. It may be necessary to remove the veins to do so. The larger of the branches, the **brachiocephalic trunk,** branches off first. The **left subclavian artery** branches off second.
   c. Identify the three major branches from the brachiocephalic trunk: the **right subclavian artery,** which gives off several branches that serve the right shoulder and limb area, and two **common carotid arteries,** which carry blood to the head. The common carotid arteries lie adjacent to the internal jugular veins.
   d. Trace the branches of the left subclavian artery into the left shoulder and front leg. The branch that passes deep toward the underside of the scapula is the **subscapular artery.** After the subscapular artery branches off, the left subclavian continues into the front leg as the left **axillary artery**. Additional branches of this artery complex may also be visible.

3. Pull the lungs to the pig's right side and trace the dorsal aorta as it extends posteriorly from the aortic arch along the dorsal thoracic wall. Notice again the **ductus arteriosus** connecting from the pulmonary trunk.
4. Note the small branches of the dorsal aorta carrying blood to the ribs. A large conspicuous vein, the **azygos vein,** lies near this region of the aorta. This vein carries blood from the ribs back to the heart.

Results

Modify Figures 3 and 4 or sketch additional details in the margin of your lab manual to indicate particular features of your pig's circulatory system for future reference.

EXERCISE 4

The Systemic Circuit in the Abdominal Cavity

The dorsal aorta passes into the abdominal cavity, where it branches into arteries supplying the abdominal organs, the legs, and the tail. In fetal circulation, it also branches into two large umbilical arteries to the placenta. Blood from the legs, tail, and organs collects in veins that ultimately join the caudal vena cava to return to the heart. Blood draining from organs of the digestive system passes through additional vessels in the hepatic portal system before emptying into the caudal vena cava.

Lab Study A. Major Branches of the Dorsal Aorta and the Caudal Vena Cava

In this lab study, you will identify the major blood vessels branching from the dorsal aorta and those emptying into the caudal vena cava.

Procedure

1. Identify branches of the dorsal aorta (Figures 5 and 7).
   a. The first large branch of the aorta in the abdominal cavity exits the aorta at approximately the level of the diaphragm. Clip the diaphragm where it joins the body wall, pull all the organs (lungs and digestive organs) to the pig's right, and search for the **coeliac artery,** which carries blood to the stomach and the spleen. You may have to pick away pieces of the diaphragm that are attached to the aorta to see this vessel.
   b. Once you have identified the coeliac artery, look for the next branch of the aorta, the **cranial mesenteric artery,** arising slightly caudal to the coeliac artery and carrying blood to the small intestine. The cranial mesenteric artery ultimately branches to the **mesenteric arteries** you observed when you studied the digestive system.
   c. Following the dorsal aorta posteriorly, identify the two **renal arteries** leading to the kidneys.

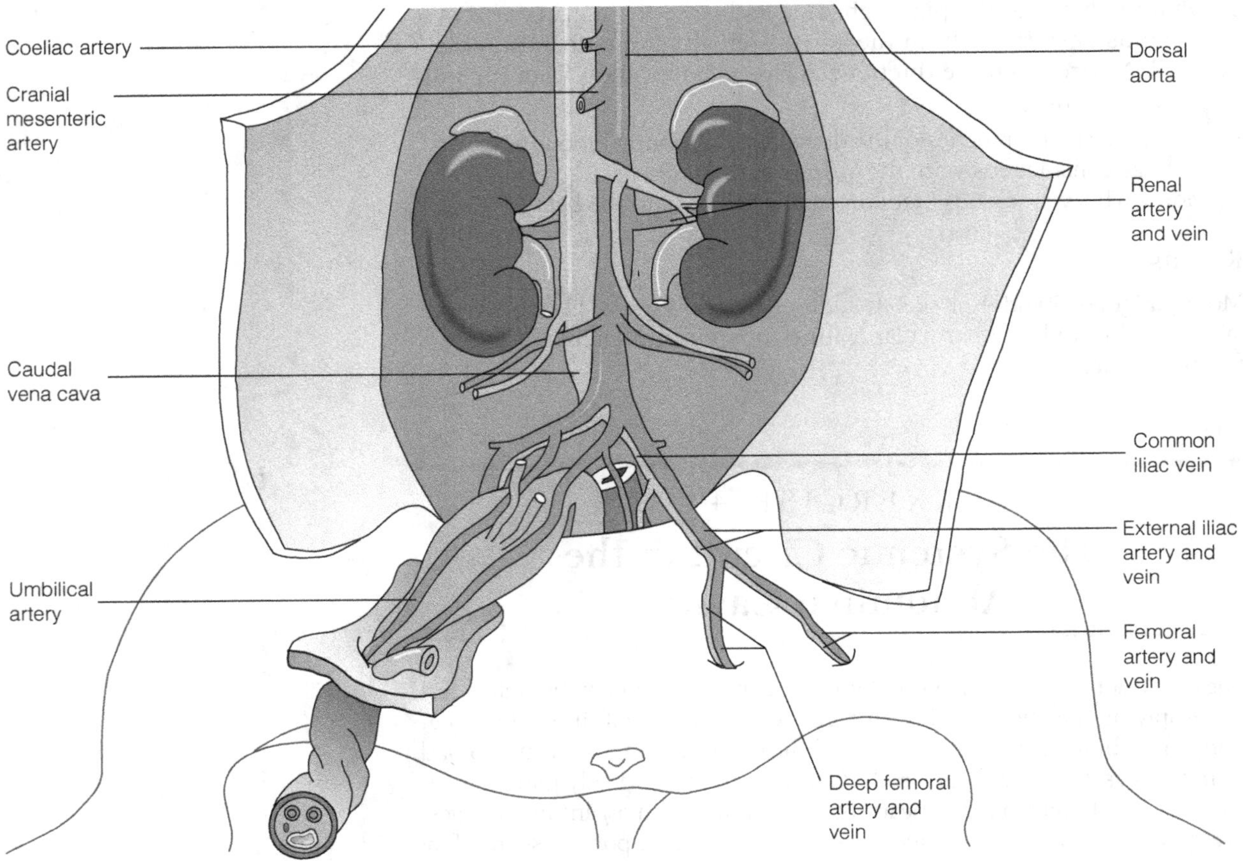

Figure 5.
Branches of the aorta and caudal vena cava in the abdomen. Branches of the aorta supply blood to the stomach (the coeliac artery), the small intestine (the cranial mesenteric artery), the kidney (renal arteries), the hind limbs (iliac arteries), and the placenta (umbilical arteries). Branches of the caudal vena cava drain blood from the kidney (renal veins) and posterior limbs (common iliac veins).

You will observe the posterior branches of the aorta after the dissection of the reproductive system.

d. The dorsal aorta sends branches into the hind legs (the **external iliac arteries**) and to the placenta (the **umbilical arteries**) through the umbilical cord.

e. Separate the muscles of the leg to see that the external iliac artery divides into the **femoral artery** and the **deep femoral artery.** The femoral artery carries blood to the muscles of the lower leg, and the deep femoral artery carries blood to the thigh muscles.

2. Identify branches of the caudal vena cava.
   a. Using Figure 5 as a reference, push the digestive organs to the pig's left and trace the caudal vena cava into the abdominal cavity. It lies deep to the membrane lining the wall of the abdominal cavity, the **parietal peritoneum.** Peel off this membrane to see the vena cava, the dorsal aorta, and the kidneys.
   b. Identify **renal veins** carrying blood from the kidneys. **Common iliac veins** carry blood from the hind legs, and **hepatic veins** carry blood from the liver to the caudal vena cava. Hepatic veins are presented in Lab Study B.

Lab Study B. The Hepatic Portal System

In the usual pathway of circulation, blood passes from the heart to arteries, to capillaries in an organ, and to veins leading from the organ back to the heart (Figure 6a). In a few rare instances, a second capillary bed is inserted in a second organ in the circulation pathway (Figure 6b). When this occurs,

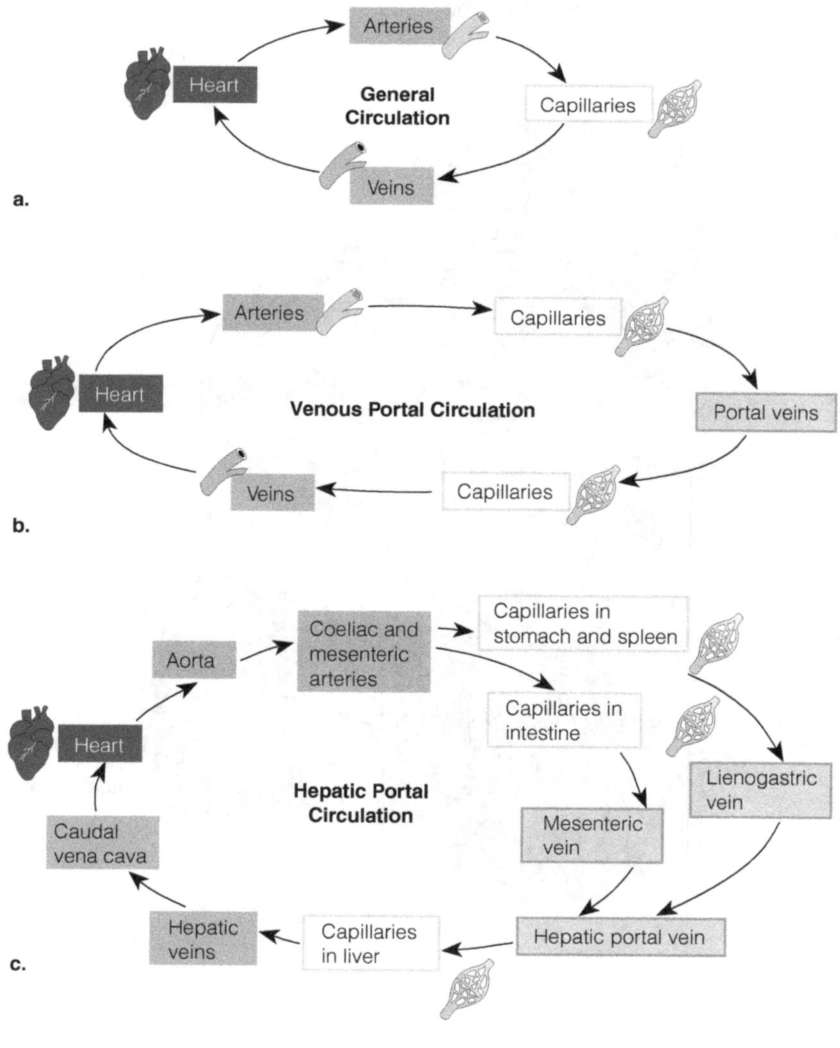

Figure 6.
Circulatory pathways. (a) General circulatory pathway; (b) circulation in a portal system; and (c) circulation in the hepatic portal system. Arteries are depicted in dark blue; veins are gray; portal veins are gray outlined in dark blue.

the circulatory circuit involved is called a **portal system.** Such a system of portal circulation exists in the digestive system (Figure 6c). An understanding of this circulation pathway will increase your understanding of the absorption and processing of nutrients.

You have previously exposed the coeliac and cranial mesenteric arteries, which send branches to the stomach, spleen, and small intestine. These arteries divide into smaller arteries, to arterioles, and, finally, to capillaries, thin-walled vessels that are the site of exchange between blood and the tissues of the organs. Arteries associated with the small intestine are called **mesenteric arteries;** veins leaving the small intestine are called **mesenteric veins,** and they unite to form one large **mesenteric vein.** Veins from the stomach and spleen unite to form the larger **lienogastric vein.** The mesenteric and lienogastric veins unite to form the **hepatic portal vein,** which enters the liver (Figure 7). In the fetal pig, small branches of the **umbilical vein** join the hepatic portal vein as it enters the liver. However, the greatest volume of blood in the umbilical vein passes directly through the liver into the caudal vena cava.

In the liver, the hepatic portal vein branches into a second capillary bed, where exchange takes place between blood and liver tissue. These capillaries reunite into **hepatic veins,** which join the caudal vena cava. To identify these vessels, begin by dissecting the veins.

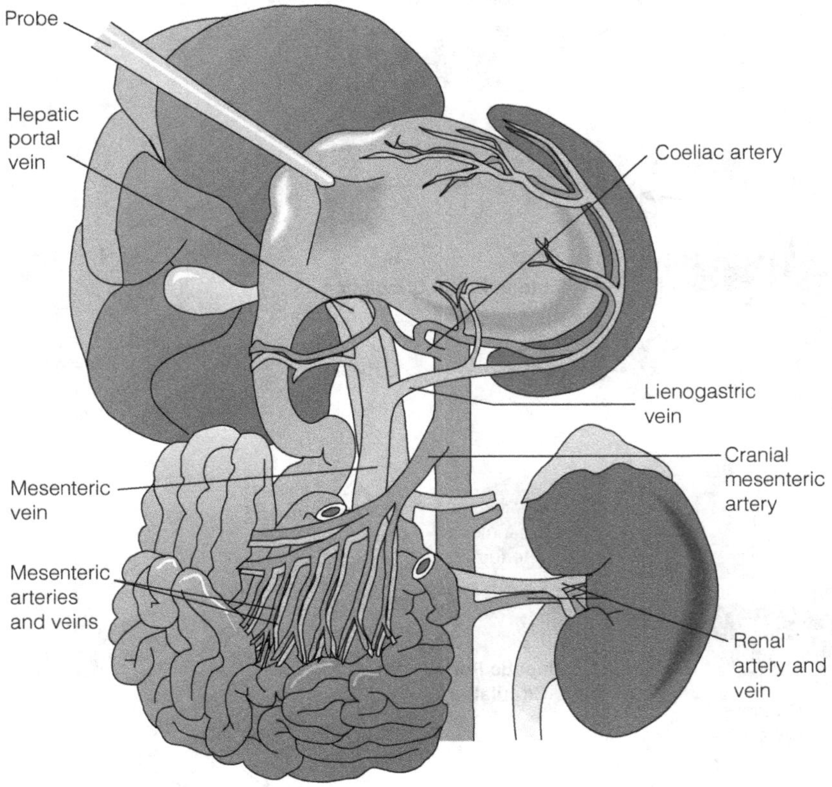

Figure 7.
The hepatic portal system. Blood from the small intestine passes into the mesenteric vein, which unites with the lienogastric vein to form the hepatic portal vein. This vessel leads to the liver, where it breaks into a capillary bed. Blood leaves the liver through the hepatic veins.

Procedure

1. Push the stomach and spleen anteriorly and dissect away the pancreas.
2. Use the blunt probe to expose a vein (it will probably not be injected) leading from the mesenteries of the small intestine. This is the **mesenteric vein.** It is joined by a vein leading from the stomach and spleen, the **lienogastric vein.** The two fuse to form the **hepatic portal vein,** which continues to the liver.
3. Review the flow of blood from the mesenteric arteries to the liver.

Results

Review the blood vessels and organs in the pathway of blood through the hepatic portal system of an adult pig with functioning digestive organs. Fill in the blanks in the next paragraph:

Blood that is poor in nutrients is carried from the aorta to the __________ __________ artery to smaller mesenteric arteries, which divide to a capillary bed in the wall of the __________________, where, in the process of absorption, nutrients enter the blood. This nutrient-rich blood now flows into the __________________ vein, which joins with the ____________ vein from the spleen and stomach and becomes the ______________ vein. This vein now carries blood to the liver, where it breaks into a second capillary bed. Capillaries in the liver converge into the ____________ veins, which empty into the caudal vena cava for transport back to the heart.

Discussion

Referring to your text, review the function of the liver in nutrient metabolism and relate this to the function of the hepatic portal system. Include information on digestive products, drugs, and toxins.

EXERCISE 5

Fetal Pig Circulation

As you dissected the circulatory system in the fetal pig and observed the adult pig heart, you noted differences between the fetal heart and the adult heart, and you identified blood vessels found in the fetus but not in the adult. In this exercise you will review these vessels and structures, tracing blood flow through the fetal pig.

Procedure

1. Return the umbilical cord to the position it occupied before you began your dissection. Locate again the umbilical vein as it passes from the umbilical cord toward the liver. You cut through this vein when you opened the abdominal cavity. The umbilical vein carries blood from the umbilical cord into the liver. In the liver, small branches of this vein join the hepatic portal vein, passing blood into the liver tissue. However, the majority of the blood passes through a channel in the liver called the **ductus venosus** into the caudal vena cava. Would blood be *high* or *low* in oxygen in the caudal vena cava?

2. Review the anatomy of the fetal pig heart, and retrace the flow of blood through the heart into the dorsal aorta by way of the **ductus arteriosus**. This represents one pathway of blood through the fetal heart.
3. A second pathway of blood through the heart is created by a structure in the fetal heart called the **foramen ovale.** To study this pathway, use your scalpel to open the pig heart by cutting it along a frontal plane, dividing it into dorsal and ventral portions. Begin at the caudal end of the heart and carefully slice along the frontal plane, cutting just through the ventricles, keeping the atria intact. Carefully lift the ventricles and look inside the heart for the wall between the two atria. Using your blunt probe, carefully feel along this wall for an opening between the two atria. This hole is the foramen ovale, which makes possible the second pathway of blood through the heart. How would this hole change the flow of blood through the heart?

   In fact, most blood coming into the heart from the caudal vena cava passes from the right atrium through this hole into the left atrium. After leaving the left atrium, where would blood go next?

4. Follow the dorsal aorta into the abdominal cavity to the umbilical artery branches. These branches pass through the umbilical cord to the placenta. Would blood in these branches be *high* or *low* in oxygen?

Results

Trace the pathway of blood from the umbilical vein to the umbilical artery by filling in the blanks in the next paragraph.

Blood from the umbilical vein passes through the liver and into the ________ __________, which carries blood into the heart, specifically into the chamber called the ____________. In one circuit of blood flow, blood goes from this chamber into the right ventricle and out the ______________. A branch from this vessel, the ______________ (present only in fetal circulation), carries most of this blood into the dorsal aorta. The dorsal aorta passes through the body, giving off branches to all organs of the body. Two large branches located near the tail lead into the umbilical cord and are called the ______________.

An alternate route carries blood from the right atrium through a fetal hole called the ______________ into the heart chamber, the ____________. From this chamber, blood next goes into the left ventricle and out the ___________. Branches of this vessel lead to the head.

Discussion

1. What is the advantage of the circuit of fetal blood flow through the ductus arteriosus?

2. What is the advantage of fetal blood flow through the foramen ovale?

EXERCISE 6
Details of the Respiratory System

You have previously located several of the major structures of the respiratory system (Exercise 1). Direct your attention again to the neck region of the pig and complete the study of the respiratory system.

Procedure

1. Identify again the **larynx** and the **trachea** (Figure 8).
2. Follow the trachea caudally to the pleural cavities housing the lungs. The trachea branches into **bronchi** (sing., bronchus), which lead into the

lobes of the **lungs**. It will be necessary to push aside blood vessels to see this. *Take care not to destroy these vessels.*

3. Tease apart lung tissues to observe that the larger bronchi branch into smaller and smaller bronchi. When the tubes are about 1–2 mm in diameter, they are called **bronchioles.** Bronchioles continue to branch and ultimately lead to microscopic **alveoli** (not visible with the unaided eye), thin-walled, blind-ending sacs that are covered with capillaries. It is here that the exchange of oxygen and carbon dioxide takes place between the blood and the atmosphere.
4. Identify the epithelial lining of the pleural cavity. How would this epithelium be named?
5. After you complete this lab topic, return your pig to its plastic bag. Check that your labels are intact and that your name, lab room, and lab day are legible. Add preserving solution and securely close the bag.

Results

List, in order, the structures, tubes, and cellular barriers through which air passes as it travels from outside the body to the circulatory system of a pig, a terrestrial vertebrate.

Discussion

1. In terrestrial vertebrates, what is the advantage of having the surfaces for oxygen and carbon dioxide exchange embedded deep in lung tissue?
2. The capillaries that lie in close contact with alveoli are branches of what blood vessel?
3. The confluence of these capillaries forms what blood vessel?
4. Compare blood composition in adult circulation with reference to oxygen and carbon dioxide between capillaries approaching alveoli and capillaries leaving alveoli.

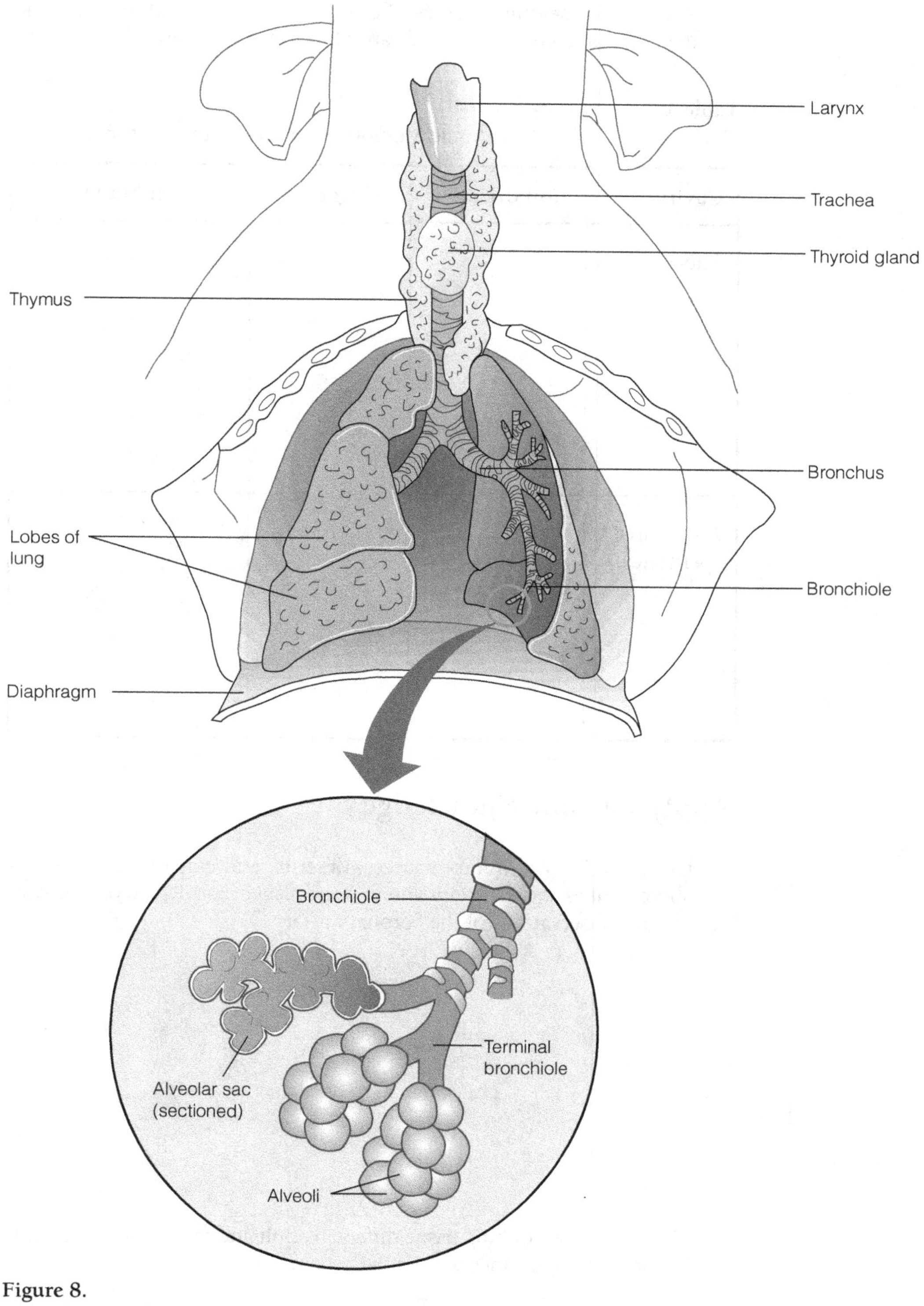

Figure 8.
The respiratory system of the fetal pig. Air passes through a succession of smaller and more numerous tubes: the larynx, trachea, bronchi, bronchioles, and ultimately, microscopic alveoli (see enlarged area).

5. Review the coelomic cavities, the organs contained within them, and the associated coelomic membranes by completing Table 1.

Table 1
Cavities, Organs, and Coelomic Membranes of the Mammalian Body

Cavity	Subdivision	Organ(s)	Membranes
Thoracic			
Abdominal (peritoneal)			

Applying Your Knowledge

1. Using the Web or library sources, describe and compare the medical abnormalities *angina pectoris* and *myocardial infarction*. Relate your answer to your observations of the coronary artery.

2. The appearance of lung tissue differs in adult and fetal pigs. Predict differences in appearance and explain them.

3. Using the Web, materials provided in the lab, your text, or library materials answer the following questions related to the effects of smoking on the structure and function of the human respiratory system.

Disease	Effects and Symptoms
Chronic bronchitis	
Emphysema	
Lung cancer	

a. Describe changes in the cells and tissues of the lungs and describe the concomitant effects on function.

b. Describe the effects and symptoms of each of the following diseases linked to cigarette smoking.

c. What effects does smoking during pregnancy have on the fetus?

4. The trachea is composed of rings of cartilage, while the nearby esophagus is composed of muscle and lacks cartilage. How are these structural differences related to the functions of each?

5. Scientists have concluded that a four-chambered heart is necessary to support the high metabolic rates seen in "warm-blooded" animals (endotherms)—that is, birds and mammals. In 2000 scientists reported that a 66-million-year-old dinosaur found in South Dakota by an amateur fossil hunter in 1993 appeared to contain a fossilized heart with two ventricles, as one would find in a four-chambered heart. What does this discovery suggest about the metabolism of this dinosaur and the position of this species of dinosaur in the evolutionary tree?

References

Burggren, W. "And the Beat Goes On—A Brief Guide to the Hearts of Vertebrates," *Natural History,* 2000, vol. 109, pp. 62–65.

Fisher, P. E., D. A. Russell, M. K. Stoskopf, R. E. Barrick, M. Hammer, and A. A. Kuzmitz. "Cardiovascular Evidence for an Intermediate or Higher Metabolic Rate in an Ornithischian Dinosaur," *Science,* 2000, vol. 288, pp. 503–505.

Marieb, E. N. *Human Anatomy and Physiology,* 6th ed. Menlo Park, CA: Benjamin Cummings, 2004.

"What You Need to Know about Cancer," *Scientific American,* Special Issue, vol. 275, 1996.

Websites

Photographs of fetal pig anatomy:

http://www.biology.ucok.edu/AnimalBiology/pigweb/pig.html

All About Smoking:

http://www.guess-what.com/ske_1.htm

http://whyquit.com/joel/Joel_02_17_smoke_in_lung.html.

Includes photographs of lungs of smokers and nonsmokers and diagrams of microscopic changes in lungs of smokers.

www-med.stanford.edu/medicalreview/smrp14-16.pdf

For information on smoking and pregnancy.

Vertebrate Anatomy III: The Excretory, Reproductive, and Nervous Systems

Laboratory Objectives

After completing this lab topic, you should be able to:

1. Identify and describe the function of all parts of the excretory system of the fetal pig, noting differences between the sexes and noting structures shared with the reproductive system.
2. Identify and describe the function of all parts of the reproductive systems of male and female fetal pigs and trace the pathway of sperm and egg from their origin out of the body.
3. Compare reproductive systems in pigs and humans.
4. Describe the structure of a neuron.
5. Describe the pathway of a simple reflex, relating this to the structure of the spinal cord.
6. Describe the structure of a representative sensory receptor, the eye.
7. Discuss the role played by the nervous and endocrine systems in integrating all vertebrate systems into a functioning whole organism.

Introduction

You have seen that, functionally, the excretory system is closely related to the circulatory and respiratory systems. Developmentally, however, the excretory system shares many embryonic and some adult structures with the reproductive system. In the first two exercises of this lab topic, you will investigate form and functional relationships in the excretory and reproductive systems. In the last exercise of this lab topic, you will study the nervous system, which keeps all organ systems functioning appropriately and in harmony.

The action and interaction of organ systems must be precisely timed to meet specific needs within the animal. Two systems in the body, the nervous system and the endocrine system, coordinate the activities of all organ systems. The nervous system consists of a **sensory component,** made up of **sensory receptors** that detect such stimuli as light, sound, touch, and the concentration

---

of oxygen in the blood, and **sensory nerves,** which carry the data to the **central nervous system.** The central nervous system consists of the brain and spinal cord. It integrates information from all stimuli, external and internal, and, when appropriate, sends signals to the motor system. The **motor system** carries impulses along motor nerves to **effectors** such as glands, muscles, and other organs, bringing about the appropriate response. The nervous system provides rapid, precise, and complex control of body activities.

The endocrine system consists of endocrine glands, which respond to stimuli by secreting hormones into the blood to be transported to target tissues in the body. The target tissues then bring about the response. You have already observed several endocrine glands, including the thymus, thyroid, and pancreas. In this lab topic, you will study additional endocrine glands: ovaries and testes. Control mediated by hormones in the endocrine system is slower and less precise than nervous system control. The interaction of the nervous and endocrine systems brings about the coordination of physiological processes and the maintenance of internal **homeostasis,** the steady state condition in the vertebrate body.

EXERCISE 1
The Excretory System

Materials

preserved fetal pig
dissecting instruments
dissecting pan
disposable gloves

Introduction

Several important functions are performed by the vertebrate excretory system, including **osmoregulation,** the control of tissue water balance, and the elimination of excess salts and urea, a waste product of the metabolism of amino acids. In terrestrial animals, including most mammals, water conservation is an important function of the excretory system. Studying this system in the pig will reveal the organs and structures involved in producing and eliminating metabolic waste with minimal water loss.

Wear disposable gloves when dissecting preserved animals.

Procedure

1. Locate the blood vessels serving the kidneys, exposed in the dissection of the circulatory system. The arteries branch from the dorsal aorta caudal to the cranial mesenteric artery. Blood enters the kidney through the **renal artery** and exits through the **renal vein.** Identify these vessels and the **kidneys** lying deep to the **parietal peritoneum** lining the abdominal cavity.
2. Dissect the left kidney as follows. Leaving the kidney in the body and attached to all blood vessels and tubes, make a frontal section along the

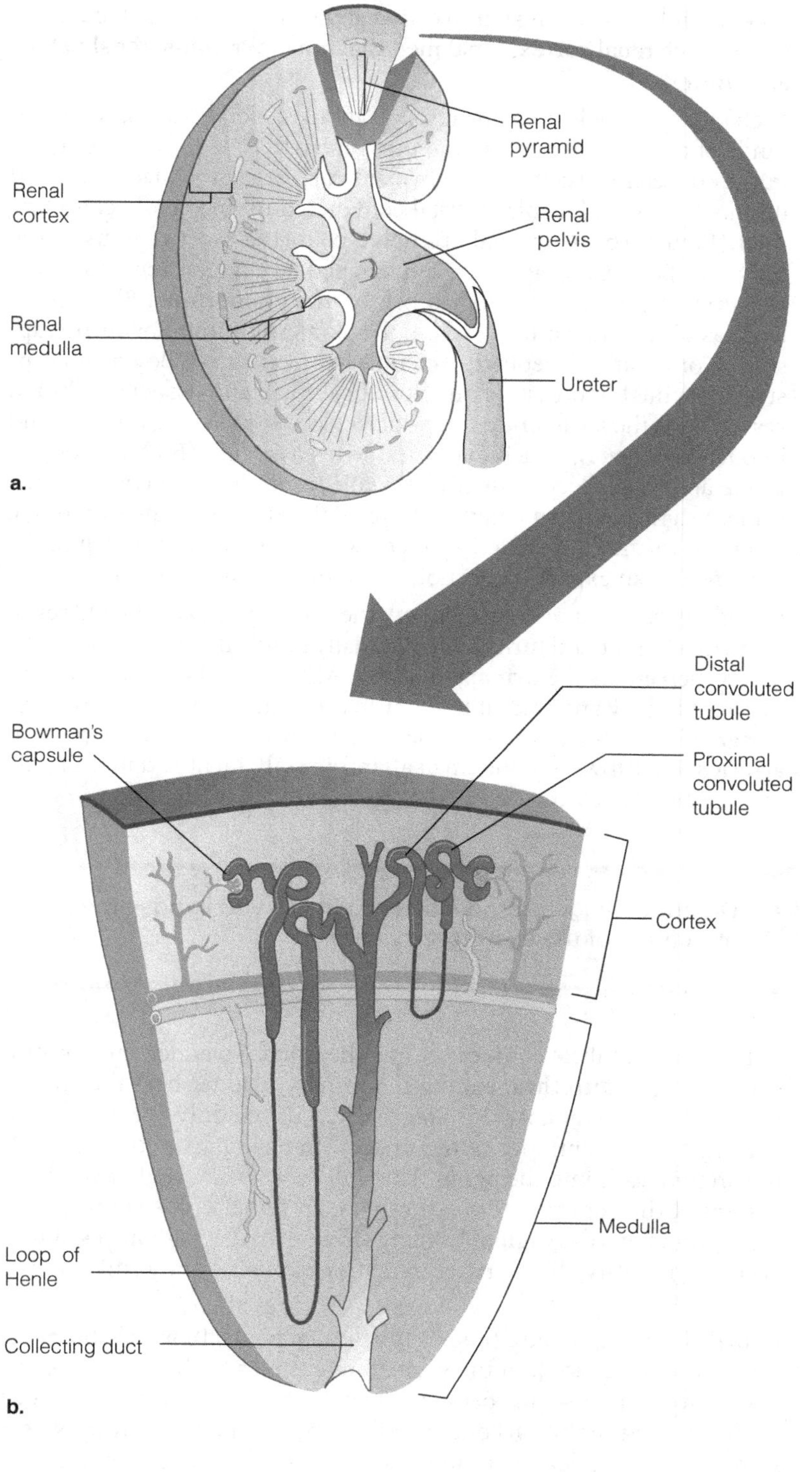

Figure 1.
Structure of the kidney.
(a) The kidney consists of three major regions: the cortex, the medulla, and the pelvis. Renal pyramids make up the medulla, and the pelvis is continuous with the ureter. (b) An enlarged wedge of the kidney, including the cortical region over one pyramid. Nephrons consisting of Bowman's capsule, a proximal convoluted tubule; the loop of Henle, a distal convoluted tubule; and a collecting duct extend over the cortical and medullary regions. Waste carried in the collecting duct ultimately passes into the pelvis and ureter.

outer periphery, dividing it into dorsal and ventral portions (Figure 1a). Observe the **renal cortex, renal medulla, renal pyramids, renal pelvis,** and **ureter.**

Each kidney is made up of microscopic tubules, blood vessels, and thousands of nephrons (over 1 million in humans). A nephron (not visible in your dissections) consists of Bowman's capsule, a proximal convoluted tubule, the loop of Henle, a distal convoluted tubule, and a collecting duct (Figure 1b). Cuboidal epithelial cells line most regions of the nephron. Bowman's capsule, a cup-shaped swelling at the end of the nephron, surrounds a ball of capillaries, the **glomerulus.** Blood is filtered as water and waste pass from the glomerulus into Bowman's capsule. (For details of nephron function, see your text.) Bowman's capsule, proximal and distal convoluted tubules, and associated blood vessels lie in the *renal cortex.* Loops of Henle and collecting ducts extend into *renal pyramids,* which make up the *renal medulla.* Both the loop of Henle and the collecting duct play a role in producing a concentrated urine, a significant adaptation for terrestrial vertebrates. The hypertonic urine passes into the collecting ducts, which ultimately empty into the renal pelvis, an expanded portion of the ureter into the kidney.

3. Using Figure 2 as a reference, follow the ureter as it exits the kidney at its medial border and turns to run caudally beside the dorsal aorta. The ureter then enters the **urinary bladder.** Also locate the ureter draining the right kidney and trace it to the urinary bladder. In the fetal pig, the urinary bladder is an elongate structure lying between the two **umbilical arteries**. It narrows into the small **allantoic stalk** identified in the study of the umbilical cord.

Do not damage reproductive organs as you expose the structures of the excretory system.

---

4. Pull on the umbilical cord, extending the urinary bladder, and locate a single tube, the **urethra,** exiting the urinary bladder near the attachments of the ureters. At this stage, you will see only the end of the urethra near the entrance of the ureters. In male pigs (see Figure 2a), the urethra leads into the **penis.** This will be visible only after you have dissected the reproductive structures. In female pigs (Figure 3a), the urethra joins the **vagina,** forming a chamber, the **vaginal vestibule.** You will identify these structures after exposing the reproductive structures.

   In male humans, the urethra is a tube in the penis. In female humans, the urethra does not join the vagina but empties to the outside of the body through a separate opening. The urethra becomes functional after birth when the umbilical cord and allantois wither and fall away. Waste stored in the bladder passes into the urethra, where it is carried to the outside of the body.

Results

Describe the pathway of metabolic waste from the aorta to the outside of the body in the fetal pig.

Discussion

How does the elimination of metabolic waste in the pig change after birth?

EXERCISE 2
The Reproductive System

Materials

items from Exercise 1

Introduction

Reproduction is perhaps the ultimate adaptive activity of all organisms. It is the means of transmitting genetic information from generation to generation. Less complex animals may reproduce sexually or asexually, but in general, vertebrates reproduce sexually. Sexual reproduction promotes genetic variation, which is important for species to adapt to changing environments. For evolution to occur, heritable variation must exist in populations. Although mutation is the source of variation, sexual reproduction promotes new and diverse combinations of genetic information. Ultimately, all sexual reproduction involves the production of gametes and the bringing together of gametes to enable fertilization to take place.

Lab Study A. Male Reproductive System

The male reproductive system consists of gonads, ducts, and glands. Testes, the male gonads, produce sperm and secrete testosterone and other male sex hormones. Sperm pass from the testes into the epididymis, where they mature and are stored. When ejaculation takes place, sperm pass from the epididymis through the ductus deferens—also called the *vas deferens*—to the urethra. The urethra leads to the penis, which carries the sperm to the outside of the body. As sperm pass through the male tract, secretions from the seminal vesicles, the prostate gland, and the bulbourethral glands are added, producing semen, a fluid containing sperm, fructose, amino acids, mucus, and other substances that produce a favorable environment for sperm survival and motility.

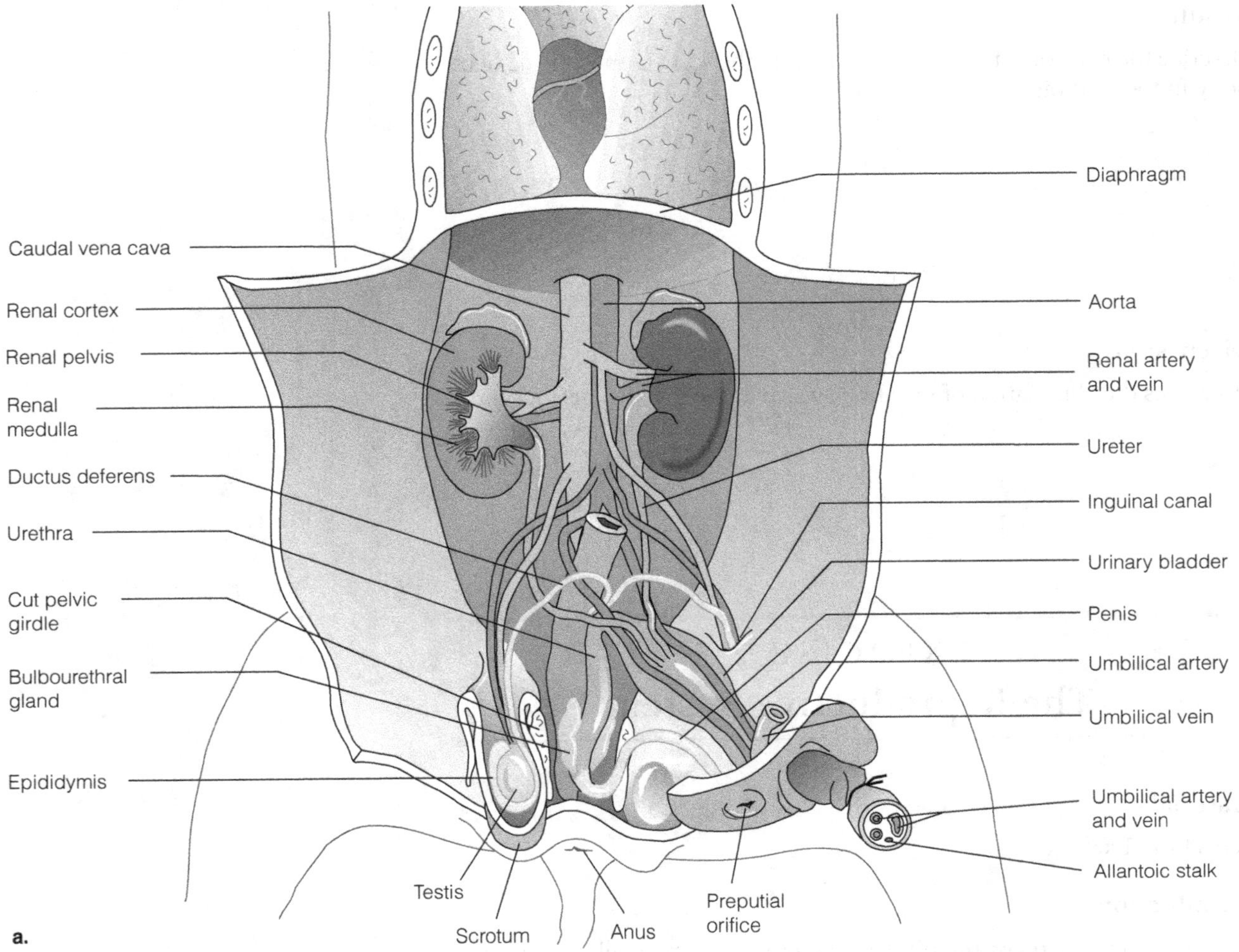

Figure 2a.
Organs of the excretory and reproductive systems in the male fetal pig. The ureters enter the urinary bladder between the umbilical arteries. The urethra exits the urinary bladder and leads to the penis. The penis leads to the preputial orifice. The testes lie in pouches in the scrotum. Sperm are produced in the testes, stored in the epididymis on the testis surface, and pass to the ductus deferens, which leads to the urethra.

Procedure

You will dissect the reproductive system of only one sex. However, you should observe the dissection of a pig of the opposite sex and be able to identify and describe various structures of both sexes.

1. Expose the structures of the male reproductive system (Figure 2a). The penis is located in the flap of ventral body wall caudal to the umbilical cord. To prevent damage to this structure, locate it before you make an

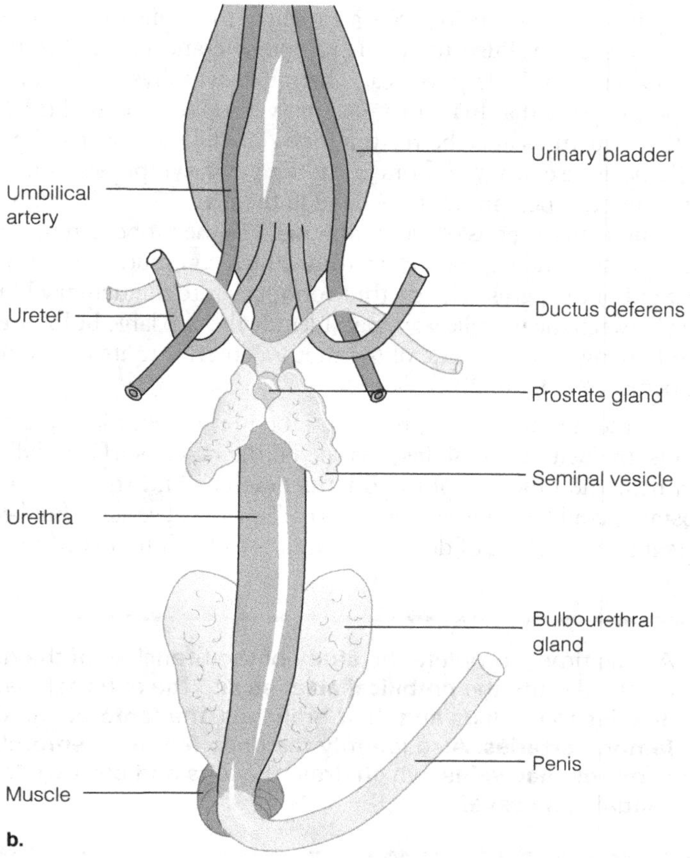

Figure 2b.
Enlarged dorsal view of male excretory and reproductive structures in the fetal pig. Seminal vesicles lie near the junction of the urethra and ductus deferens. Bulbourethral glands lie on either side of the urethra.

incision. Hold the flap between your fingers and feel for the cordlike penis just below the skin. Once you locate the penis, using scissors, begin at the urogenital opening, the **preputial orifice**, and make a longitudinal incision, extending caudally, just through the skin. Push aside the skin and use the probe to locate and expose the long penis from the orifice caudally until it turns dorsally to meet the urethra (see Figure 2b).

2. Next, begin to expose the testis, epididymis, and ductus deferens. To do this, locate the **ureters** (identified in Exercise 1) and observe the right and left **ductus deferentia** (sing., deferens), which loop over the ureters. Follow a ductus deferens outward and caudally to the **inguinal canal** leading into the **scrotum.** Use scissors to cut carefully along the canal to expose the **testis** lying in a membranous sac. Remove this sac and identify the various structures.
   a. Identify the **testis,** a bean-shaped gonad. The testes first develop in the abdominal cavity and descend before birth into the scrotal sacs.
   b. Identify the **epididymis,** a convoluted duct that originates at the cranial end of the testis, extends caudally along one side, then turns and continues cranially as the ductus deferens.
   c. Identify the **ductus deferens,** a duct that leads away from the epididymis back into the abdominal cavity, where it loops over the ureter and enters the urethra. Also locate the ductus deferens from the other testis.

3. Turn your attention again to the area where the penis turns dorsally to meet the urethra. Push the penis to one side and probe through the muscle between the legs to locate the pubic symphysis, the portion of the pelvic girdle that fuses in a position ventral to several of the reproductive structures and the rectum. *Being careful not to go too deep or to cut the penis,* use heavy scissors to cut the pubic symphysis from posterior to anterior beginning at the bend in the penis. Press the hind limbs apart and trim the ends of the symphysis. Use the probe to remove connective tissue, and expose the **urethra,** which continues anteriorly from the bend of the penis. The urethra continues into the **urinary bladder** lying between the umbilical arteries. Identify the two large **bulbourethral glands** lying on either side of the urethra anterior to its junction with the penis (see Figure 2b).
4. Pull on the umbilical cord, reflecting the urethra, and locate a pair of glands, the **seminal vesicles,** that lie on the dorsal surface of the urethra near the junction of the ductus deferens and the urethra. The **prostate gland** lies between the lobes of the seminal vesicles, but because of its immature stage of development, it is difficult to identify.

At this time, complete the study of the branches of the dorsal aorta. Identify the **umbilical arteries** and the **external iliac arteries** to the legs and their branches, the **femoral** and **deep femoral arteries.** Also identify the **deep femoral, femoral,** and **common iliac veins,** which drain the legs and empty into the **caudal vena cava.**

---

5. After you conclude the study of the male pig, find someone with a female pig, and demonstrate the systems to each other.
6. Place your pig in its plastic bag, make sure the labels are legible, add preservative, secure the bag, and store it.

Results

In Table 1, list the organs and ducts through which sperm pass from their origin to the outside of the body. Describe what takes place in each organ or duct, and note glandular secretions when appropriate. Refer to your text if needed.

Discussion

1. Vasectomy is the most common form of human male sterilization used for birth control. Describe this process.

2. What structures identified are common to both reproductive and excretory systems?

Table 1
Pathway of Sperm

Organ/Duct	Activity and Glandular Secretion

3. The testes develop inside the abdominal cavity and descend through the inguinal canal into the scrotum before birth. Explain the significance of the external scrotum and external testes in mammals. Refer to your text if needed.

Lab Study B. Female Reproductive System

The female reproductive system consists of the ovaries (female gonads), short uterine tubes (also called *fallopian tubes,* or *oviducts*), the uterus, the vagina, and the vaginal vestibule. The vaginal vestibule is present in the pig but not in the human. In the pig, the uterus consists of a uterine body and two uterine horns in which embryonic pigs develop. In the human female, the uterus does not have uterine horns but consists of a dome-shaped portion, the fundus, which protrudes above the entrance of the fallopian tubes, and an enlarged main portion, the body of the uterus, where embryos develop.

Procedure

1. To study the female reproductive system (Figure 3a), use scissors and make a median longitudinal incision, cutting through the skin posterior to the umbilical cord. Push aside skin and muscles and probe in the

midline to locate the pubic symphysis, the portion of the pelvic girdle that fuses in a position ventral to many of the female reproductive structures and the rectum. Being careful not to go too deep, use heavy scissors to cut through the muscles and the symphysis. Press apart the hind limbs and trim away the cut ends of the symphysis.

2. Begin observations by locating the **ovaries** in the abdominal cavity just caudal to the kidneys (Figure 3a). They are a pair of small, bean-shaped organs, one caudal to each kidney. (When the testes of the male first develop, they are located in approximately the same position in the abdominal cavity as the ovaries; however, the testes later descend, becoming supported in the scrotal sacs.) A small convoluted tube, the **uterine tube,** can be observed at the border of the ovary.

3. The reproductive structures form a long, continuous tract. Follow a uterine tube from one ovary into the associated **horn of the uterus.** Left and right horns join to form the **body of the uterus.** The body of

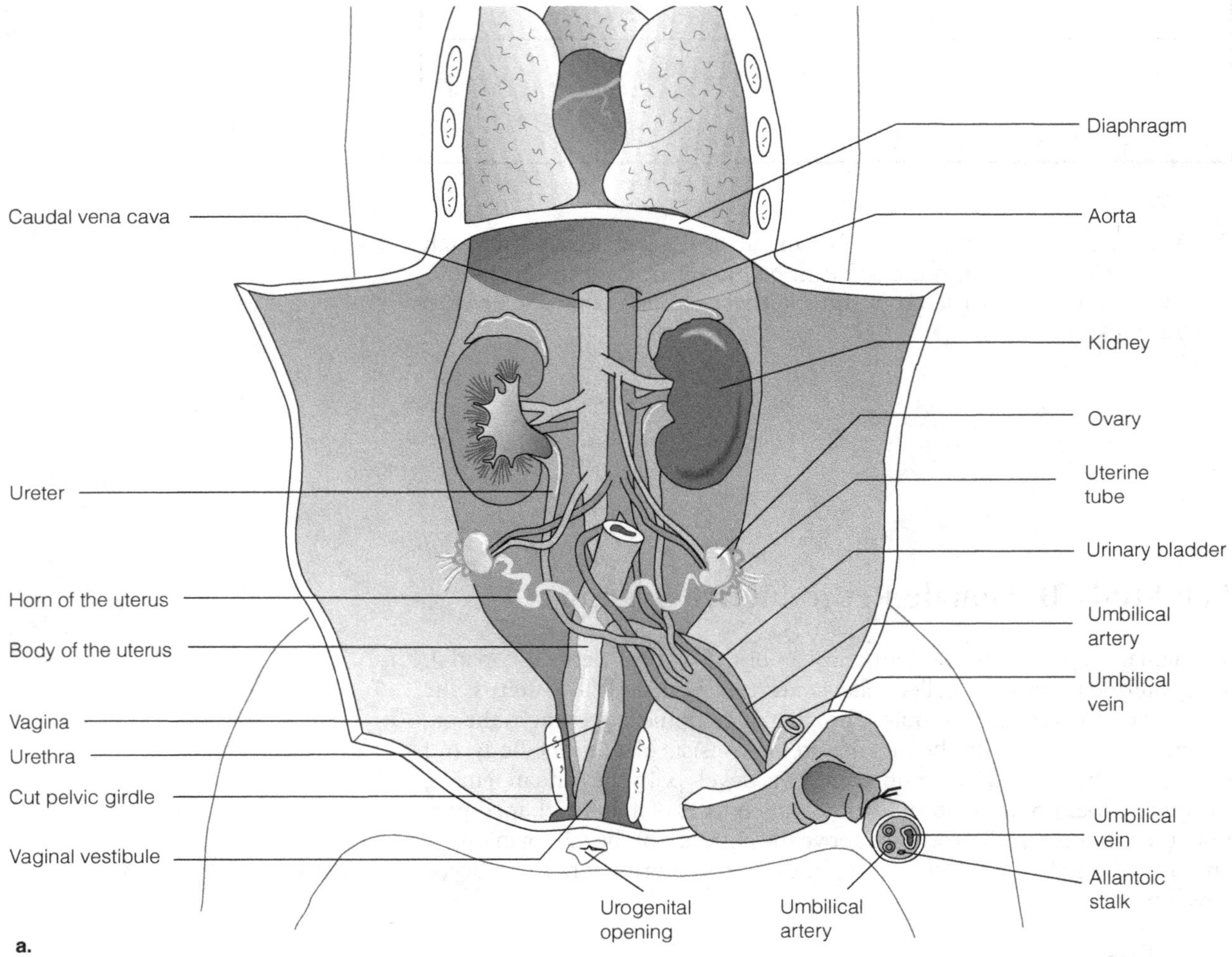

Figure 3a.
Organs of the excretory and reproductive systems in the female fetal pig. The ureters enter the urinary bladder. The urethra exits the urinary bladder and joins the vagina, forming the vaginal vestibule.

the uterus lies dorsal to the urethra. Push the urethra aside and use the probe to separate the urethra from the uterus. Notice that the urethra and the reproductive structures meet.

4. The body of the uterus leads into the **cervix** of the uterus, which leads into the **vagina.** To conclusively identify these regions, you must open the uterus. Without disturbing the junction of the urethra and the reproductive structures, use scissors to make a longitudinal, lateral incision in the reproductive structures and push back the sides, exposing the interior. Your dissection should resemble Figure 3b. Now you should be able to identify all parts of the uterus, the vagina, and the opening of the urethra into the reproductive tract. Identify the cervix, easily identified by the presence of internal ridges. The vagina, which joins the cervix, does not have these ridges. The vagina joins the urethra to form a common chamber, the **vaginal vestibule,** leading to the outside of the body. The outer opening is the **urogenital opening,** ventral to the anus.

At this time, complete the study of the branches of the dorsal aorta. Identify the **umbilical arteries** and the **external iliac arteries** to the legs and their branches, the **femoral** and **deep femoral** arteries. Also identify the **deep femoral, femoral,** and **common iliac veins,** which drain the legs and empty into the **caudal vena cava.**

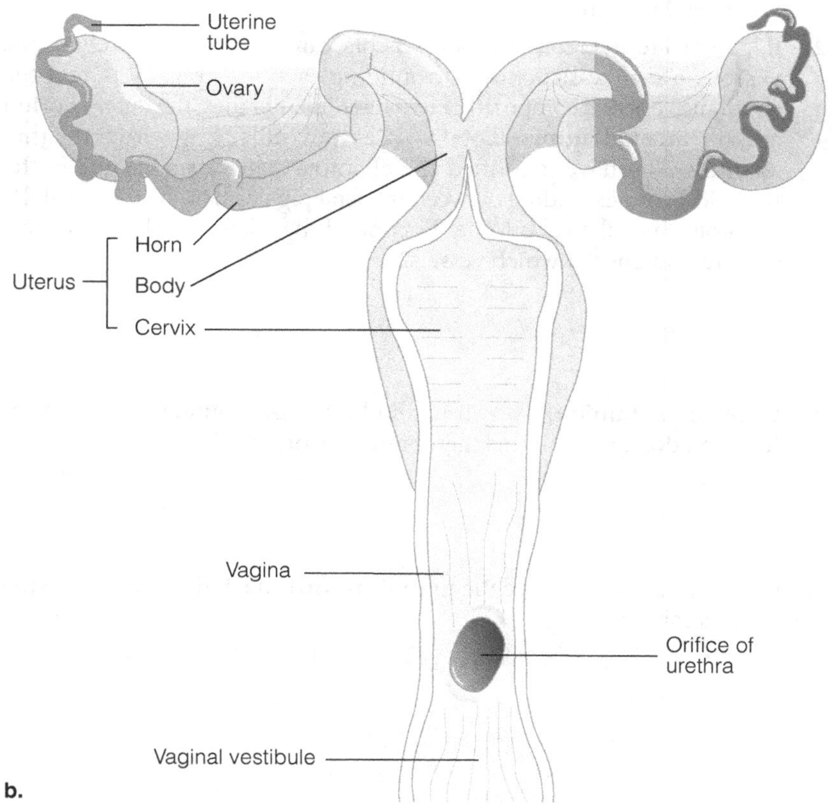

Figure 3b.
Enlarged view of the female reproductive system in a fetal pig. The cervix and vagina have been opened to show the ridges in the cervix, which are absent in the vagina. The vaginal vestibule is the common chamber formed by the confluence of the vagina and the urethra.

5. After you conclude your study of the female pig, find someone with a male pig, and demonstrate the systems to each other.
6. Place your pig in its plastic bag, make sure your labels are legible, add preservative, secure the bag, and store it.

Results

Describe the pathway of an egg from the ovary to the outside of the body in a fetal pig, naming regions of organs when appropriate.

Lab Study C. The Pregnant Pig Uterus

On demonstration is an isolated pregnant pig uterus, which should include uterine horns and the body of the uterus. Ovaries and uterine tubes may be attached. Fetal pigs are located in the uterine horns. Each fetal pig is attached to the mother pig by means of the **placenta,** a structure consisting of tissue from the inner lining of the uterus (maternal tissue) and the **chorionic vesicle** (embryonic tissue). These tissues are convoluted, creating interdigitating folds that increase the surfaces where the exchange of nutrients, oxygen, and wastes takes place between mother and fetus.

Procedure

1. Observe the uterus with one uterine horn partially opened (Figure 4). Some fetal pigs should be visible.
2. If it is not already dissected, using scissors, carefully cut into the **chorionic vesicle,** a saclike structure surrounding each fetal pig. Note that the chorionic vesicle is composed of two fused membranes, the outer **chorion** and the inner **allantois.** Blood vessels are visible lying within the thin allantois. You have identified the allantoic stalk, a small tube in the umbilical cord extending between the fetal pig's urinary bladder and the allantois. Speculate about the function of the allantois. The blood vessels are branches of which vessels?
3. Observe the **amnion,** a very thin, fluid-filled sac around the fetus. What function do you think this membrane performs?
4. Open the amnion and see the **umbilical cord** attaching each fetus to the fetal membranes.

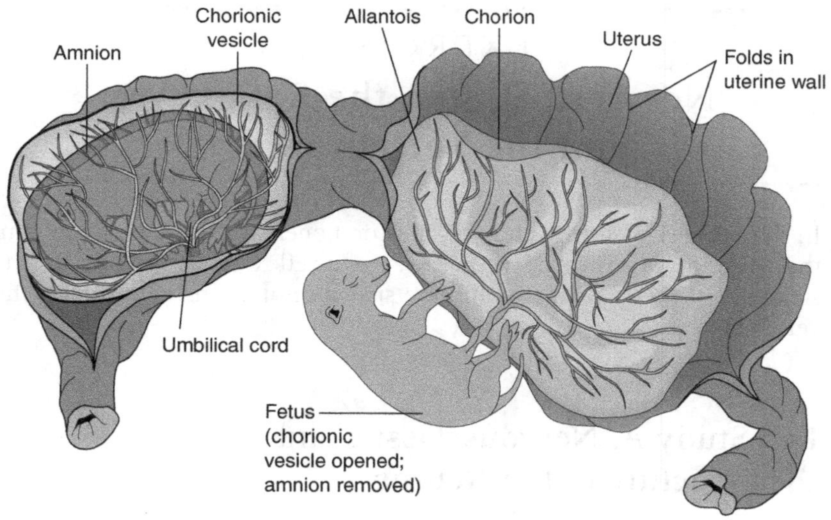

Figure 4.
Section of uterine horn from an adult pig with two fetuses. Two saclike structures, an amnion and a chorionic vesicle, surround the fetus on the left. The chorionic vesicle around the other fetus has been opened and the amnion removed.

Results

Beginning with those membranes closest to the fetal pig, list in order all embryonic and maternal membranes and tissues associated with the fetal pig.

Discussion

1. Using your text if necessary, compare the female reproductive organs in a human and an adult pig with respect to the oviduct and uterus in the human and uterine tube, horns of the uterus, and body of the uterus in the pig. Speculate about the adaptive advantage of the differences.

2. Describe differences in the arrangement of the vagina and urethra in the fetal pig and human.

3. Tubal ligation is a common form of human female sterilization. Describe this process.

EXERCISE 3

Nervous Tissue, the Reflex Arc, and the Vertebrate Eye

In this exercise, you will study several components of the nervous system: the structure of neurons, the pathway of a reflex arc as it relates to the structure of the spinal cord, and the structure of a sensory receptor, the vertebrate eye.

Lab Study A. Nervous Tissue and the Structure of the Neuron

Materials

compound microscope
prepared slide of nervous tissue

Introduction

To understand the function of nervous tissue, review the structure of the **neuron,** the functional cell of nervous tissue. Neuron structure facilitates nervous impulse transmission. Each neuron has three parts: a **cell body,** which contains cytoplasm and the nucleus; **dendrites,** extensions from the cell body that transmit nervous impulses toward the cell body; and an **axon,** an extension that transmits nervous impulses away from the cell body to the next neuron or sometimes to a muscle fiber (Figure 5). Neurons are found in the brain and the spinal cord and in nervous tissue throughout the body. You will study the structure of nervous tissue and neurons in the spinal cord.

Procedure

1. Using the intermediate objective on your compound microscope, scan the prepared slide of nervous tissue provided. This is a smear preparation of tissue taken from the spinal cord. You will see hundreds of small, dark dots, which are the nuclei of **glial cells.** Glial cells are nonconducting cells that support and protect neurons.

Figure 5.
Structure of a neuron. Dendrites and an axon, cytoplasmic processes, extend from the cell body.

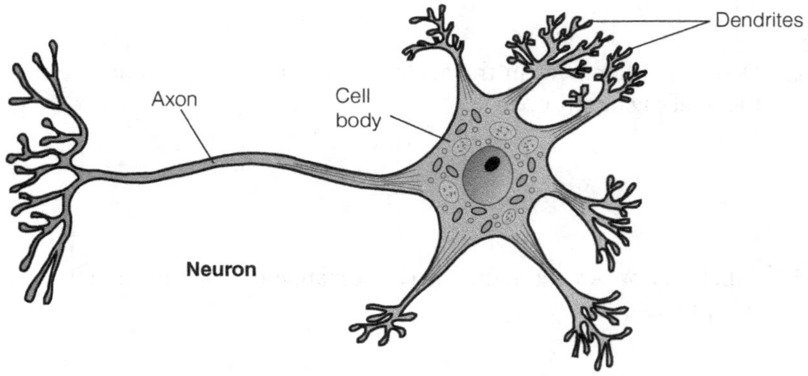

2. Look for large angular **cell bodies** of **motor neurons** scattered among the fibers and glial cells. Study one of these cell bodies on high power and locate the **nucleus,** usually with a prominent **nucleolus.** Try to identify the two types of **processes** extending from the cell body: the **axon** and **dendrites.** Although it is difficult to be certain, you may be able to differentiate between the single, broader axon and one or more slender dendrites extending from the cell body.

Lab Study B. The Reflex Arc and Structure of the Spinal Cord

Materials

stereoscopic microscope
compound microscope
prepared slide of a cross section of spinal cord

Introduction

By studying the anatomy of the spinal cord, you will be able to better envision the interaction of the three components of the nervous system: the sensory component with sensory receptors and sensory nerves; the central nervous system, consisting of the brain and the spinal cord; and the motor system, consisting of motor nerves and effectors. Each of these components plays a role in a simple reflex such as the knee-jerk reflex.

Procedure

1. Using the stereoscopic microscope, examine a prepared slide of a spinal cord cross section taken at a level that shows **dorsal** and **ventral roots.** The roots are collections of processes of neurons in spinal nerves.
2. Identify the dorsal and ventral surfaces of the spinal cord by locating the **ventral fissure** (Figure 6). Recall that vertebrates have a tubular nervous system. Show this by locating the **central canal,** a small channel in the center of the cord.
3. Locate **gray** and **white matter.** In the spinal cord, white matter lies outside the butterfly-shaped gray matter. In sections through the spinal cord at the level where dorsal and ventral roots enter and exit the cord, you will be able to identify the **dorsal root ganglion,** in which cell bodies of sensory neurons lie. Look for the neuronal processes from these cell bodies. These processes continue into the tip of the dorsal "wing" of the gray matter. Sensory neurons receive impulses directly from the environment or from a specific sensory receptor.
4. Locate cell bodies of **motor neurons** in the ventral "wing" of the gray matter. These are best studied using lower powers on the compound microscope. Many of these cell bodies contain conspicuous nuclei and nucleoli. Whereas the simplest reflex involves only one sensory and one motor neuron, most reflexes involve many **interneurons,** lying between sensory and motor neurons. Motor neurons carry impulses to muscles or glands and bring about a **response.**

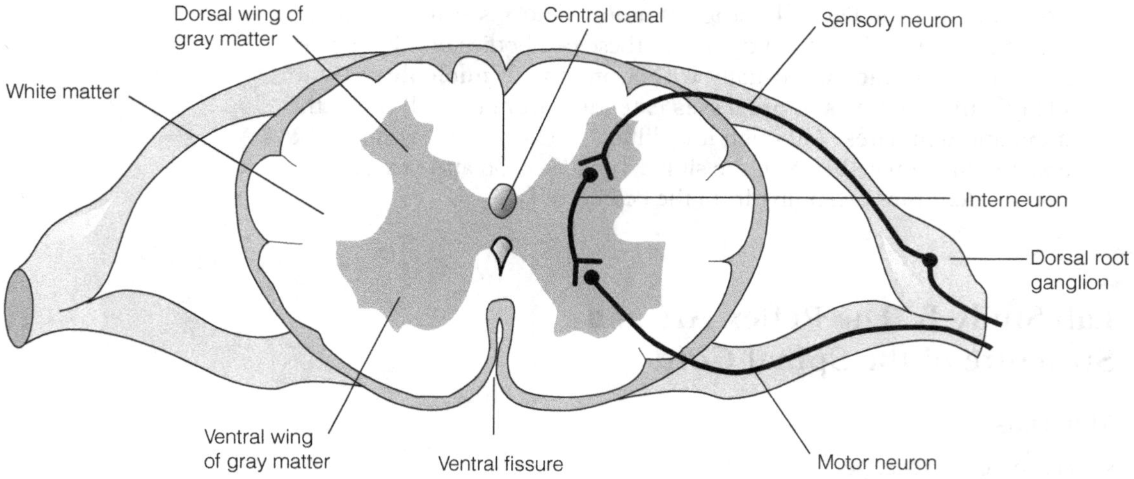

Figure 6.

Cross section of the spinal cord at the level of dorsal and ventral roots. Sensory neurons enter the dorsal wing of the gray matter, and the cell bodies of motor neurons lie in the ventral portion of the gray matter. Interneurons may be present in simple reflex arcs. A simple reflex arc may include two neurons—one motor neuron and one sensory neuron—or three neurons if an interneuron is present.

5. Careful observations may reveal axons from motor neuron cell bodies coursing through the white matter and into the ventral root of the spinal nerve.

Results

Using information from the study of the spinal cord, list in sequence the structures or neurons involved in the simplest reflex.

Discussion

Most reflexes involve a specific sensory receptor (such as the eye, ear, or pain or touch receptors), several sensory neurons, several interneurons, several motor neurons, and effectors (muscles or glands). Propose a reflex arc that would result from your touching a hot plate in the lab.

Lab Study C. Dissection of a Sensory Receptor, the Eye

Materials

preserved cow or sheep eye
dissecting instruments
dissecting pan
disposable gloves

Introduction

The goal of this study is not to perform a comprehensive study of eye structure but rather to identify those structures in the eye that enable it to receive stimuli and transmit the signals in sensory nerves to the central nervous system for processing. After processing, the signals are sent through motor nerves to the effector, bringing about the response.

The vertebrate eye is a complex sensory organ containing nervous tissue capable of being stimulated by light to produce nervous impulses. Sensory neurons carry these impulses to the brain, where they are interpreted, resulting in the perception of sight. The light-sensitive, or photoreceptor, cells in the eye are called *rods* and *cones*. They are the sensory part of a multilayered tissue, the retina. Other structures in the eye protect the retina and regulate the amount and quality of light stimulating the photoreceptor cells.

As you dissect an isolated eyeball from a cow or sheep, determine the contribution of each structure to the production of sight.

Procedure

1. Examine the isolated eye and notice that it is covered with fatty tissue and muscle bands except in the region of the **cornea,** a tough, transparent layer that allows light to enter the eye (Figure 7a).

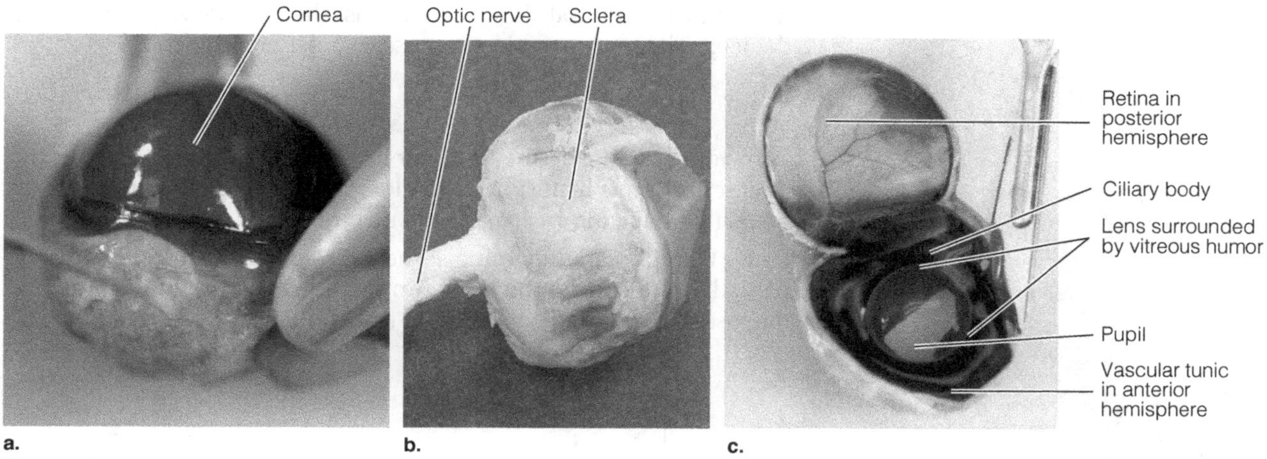

Figure 7.
(a) Isolated cow eye, (b) sheep eye with fatty tissue removed, and (c) cow eye opened to show internal structures.

2. Search through the fatty tissue on the eye sphere approximately opposite the cornea and locate the round stub of the **optic nerve** exiting the eyeball (Figure 7b).
3. Use forceps and scissors to trim away all fat and muscle on the eye surface, taking care to leave the optic nerve undisturbed.
4. Once the fat is removed, you will see that the cornea is the anterior portion of the tough, outer layer of the eyeball, the **fibrous tunic.** The posterior portion of this layer is the white **sclera** (Figure 7b). The fibrous tunic protects the internal eye structures.
5. Use scissors to cut the eye in half, making an equatorial incision and separating the anterior hemisphere (with the cornea) from the posterior hemisphere (bearing the optic nerve). Open the eye by placing it, nerve down, in the dissecting tray and lifting off the front hemisphere. Place this hemisphere in the tray with the cornea down. Your dissection should look like Figure 7c.
6. Identify the various structures in the anterior hemisphere.
   a. Identify the **lens,** a hard, oval-shaped structure that focuses the light on the retina (Figure 7c). In life, this is transparent. Surrounding and attached to the lens may be a jellylike clear substance, the vitreous humor, described in step 8.
   b. Identify the **ciliary body,** a dark, ridged, muscular structure surrounding and attached to the lens by thin ligaments. The ciliary body is a component of the second tunic of the eye, the darkly pigmented **vascular tunic.** Contraction of muscle fibers in the ciliary body changes the shape of the lens. What role does this process play in eye function?

7. Carefully remove the lens (and vitreous humor, if attached) and observe that the ciliary body merges anteriorly into another component of the vascular tunic, the **iris.** The iris surrounds an opening, the **pupil.** In the cow or sheep eye, the pupil is more irregular in shape than in the human eye. The pupil allows light to pass through the vascular tunic to the lens. The iris is a sphincter muscle. What is its function?

8. Turn your attention to the posterior hemisphere of the eye. If dissected as described, this hemisphere should hold the **vitreous humor,** which holds the retina in place and is the major internal support of the eye.
9. Using forceps, carefully remove the vitreous humor and identify the pale, delicate **retina,** the third tunic of the eye. The retina contains microscopic rods and cones. What is the function of the retina?

10. The retina lies on the inside surface of the pigmented **choroid layer,** another component of the vascular tunic. The choroid layer absorbs extraneous light rays passing through the retina. Gently push the retina aside and notice that it appears to be attached to the choroid layer in only one spot. This point of attachment is actually where processes from sensory neurons exit the retina as fibers of the **optic nerve.** You may notice a semicircular area of rainbow-colored tissue in the choroid layer. This is the **tapetum lucidum,** a tissue found in the choroid of some animals (but not humans) that enhances vision in limited light.

Results

Examining your dissected eye, list in sequence all tissues and structures in the eye through which light passes to create an image, beginning outside the eye through to the brain.

Discussion

1. Using your text or library sources, describe each listed functional impairment of the eye.

   myopia (nearsightedness):

   hyperopia (farsightedness):

   astigmatism:

   cataracts:

2. Which of the above impairments is (are) most likely to occur as a result of aging?

Questions for Review

Complete Table 2, naming the three tunics of the eye and their subdivisions, if appropriate. Give the function of each subdivision.

Table 2
Eye Tunics and Their Functions

Tunic	Subdivision	Function

Applying Your Knowledge

1. Normally a fatty encasement surrounds the kidney helping to maintain its normal position in the body. In cases of extreme emaciation in humans—for example, as in anorexia—the kidneys may drop to a lower position. Consider the ducts associated with the kidney and propose one side-effect to the kidney that could result from severe weight loss.

2. Define *homeostasis.* Describe disorders or diseases that may result when homeostasis is disrupted owing to problems in the respiratory, digestive, circulatory, or excretory system.

3. A person who has lost a limb may experience phantom pain, feeling pain in the part of the body that is gone. Suggest an explanation for this phenomenon.

4. Both the eye and a camera focus an image using a lens, but the mechanisms differ. How does the eye lens focus light on the retina? How is this different in a camera?

5. As humans age, the lens loses its elasticity. How would this affect its ability to focus light on the retina?

6. How would hypertrophy (swelling) of the prostate gland (often a symptom of prostate cancer) affect functioning of the excretory system?

References

Fawcett, D. W., and W. Bloom. *A Textbook of Histology*, 11th ed. Philadelphia, PA: Saunders College Publishing, 1986.

Marieb, E. N. *Human Anatomy and Physiology*, 5th ed. Menlo Park, CA: Benjamin Cummings, 2001.

Rust, T. G. *A Guide to Biology Lab.* San Antonio, TX: Southwest Educational Enterprises, 1983.

Websites

Photographs of fetal pig anatomy:

http://www.biology.ucok.edu/AnimalBiology/pigweb/pig.html

Vertebrate eye anatomy:

http://www.stlukeseye.com/anatomy.htm

Vertebrate eye anatomy:

http://www.discoveryfund.org/anatomyoftheeye.html

A Google search for "reflex arc" will yield many informative websites:

http://www.google.com

Animal Behavior

Laboratory Objectives

After completing this lab topic, you should be able to:

1. Define *ethology.*
2. Define and give an example of *taxis, kinesis, agonistic behavior,* and *reproductive behavior.*
3. State the possible adaptive significance of each of these behaviors.
4. Propose hypotheses, make predictions, design experiments to test hypotheses, collect and process data, and discuss results.
5. Present the results of your experiments in a scientific paper.

Introduction

Behavior, broadly defined, is the sum of the responses of an organism to stimuli in its environment. In other words, behavior is what organisms do. **Ethology** is the study of animal behavior in the context of the evolution, ecology, social organization, and sensory abilities of an animal (Gould, 1982). Ethologists concentrate on developing accurate descriptions of animal behavior by carefully observing and experimentally analyzing overt behavior patterns and by studying the physiology of behavior (Barnett, 1981).

Explaining a particular behavior in the broad, multivariable context of evolution or ecology can become a complex undertaking. It is often necessary, therefore, to study behavior in animals that have a limited range of behaviors and for which more is known about their evolution, ecology, and sensory abilities. Understanding simple and isolated behaviors is important in unraveling more complex behaviors.

There are two basic categories of behavior: **learned** and **innate** (inherited) behavior. Experimental evidence suggests that the basis of both lies in the animal's genes. As with all genetically controlled features of an organism, behavior is subject to evolutionary adaptation. As you study animal behavioral activities in this lab topic, think in terms of both **proximate causes,** the immediate physiological events that led to the behavior, and **ultimate causes,** the adaptive value and evolutionary origin of the behavior. To illustrate, a fiddler crab will respond to human intrusion into its feeding area by running into its burrow. The proximate cause of this behavior might be the vibration caused by footsteps stimulating sensory receptors and triggering

---

nervous impulses. The nervous impulses control muscle contractions in the crab's legs. Ultimate causes are the adaptive value of retreating from predators to avoid being eaten.

Note that you will be asking **causal** questions in your investigations. It is inappropriate to ask **anthropomorphic** questions—that is, questions that ascribe human attributes to the animal. Consider, for example, a behavior that places an animal in its best environment. An anthropomorphic explanation for this behavior would be that the animal makes a conscious choice of its environment. There is no way for us to come to this conclusion scientifically. The causal explanation would be that the animal is equipped with a sensory system that responds to environmental stimuli until the favorable environment is reached.

Ethologists have categorized behavioral patterns based on the particular consequence of that behavior for the organism. **Orientation behaviors** place the animal in its most favorable environment. Two categories of orientation behaviors are **taxis** (plural, **taxes**) and **kinesis.** A taxis is movement directly toward or away from a stimulus. When the response is toward a stimulus, it is said to be *positive;* when it is away from the stimulus, it is *negative.* Prefixes such as *photo, chemo,* and *thermo* can be added to the term to describe the nature of the stimulus. For example, an animal that responds to light may demonstrate positive phototaxis and is described as being *positively phototactic.*

A kinesis differs from a taxis in that it is undirected, or random, movement. A stimulus initiates the movement but does not necessarily orient the movement. The intensity of the stimulus determines the rate, or velocity, of movement in response to that stimulus. If a bright light is shined on an animal and the animal responds by moving directly away from it, the behavior is a taxis. But if the bright light initiates random movement or stimulates an increase in the rate of turning with no particular orientation involved, the behavior is a kinesis. The terms *positive* and *negative* and the prefixes mentioned earlier are also appropriately used with *kinesis.* An increase in activity is a positive response; a decrease in activity is a negative response.

Another complex of behaviors observed in some animals is **agonistic behavior.** In this case, the animal is in a conflict situation where there may be a threat or approach, then an attack or withdrawal. Agonistic behaviors in the form of force are called **aggression;** those of retreat or avoidance are called **submission.** Often the agonistic behavior is simply a display that makes the organism look big or threatening. It rarely leads to death and is thought to help maintain territory so that the dominant organism has greater access to resources such as space, food, and mates.

Mating, or **reproductive behavior,** can involve a complex sequence of activities, sometimes spectacular, that facilitate finding, courting, and mating with a member of the same species. It is an adaptive advantage that reproductive behaviors are species-specific. Can you suggest reasons why?

For the first hour of lab, you will perform Experiment A in each of the exercises that follow, briefly investigating the four behaviors just discussed: taxis in brine shrimp, kinesis in pill bugs, agonistic behavior in Siamese fighting fish, and reproductive behavior in fruit flies. After completing every Experiment A, your team will choose one of the systems discussed and perform Experiment B in that exercise. To begin Experiment B, you will propose one or more testable hypotheses and design a simple experiment by which to test your hypotheses. Then you will spend the remainder of the laboratory period carrying out your experiments.

Near the end of the laboratory period, several of you may be asked to present your team's results to the class for discussion. One part of the scientific process involves persuading your colleagues that your experimental design is sound and that your results support your conclusions (either negating or supporting your hypothesis). Be prepared to describe your results in a brief presentation in which you will use your experimental evidence to persuade the other students in your class.

You may be required to submit a laboratory report describing your experiment and results in the format of a scientific paper. You should discuss results and come to conclusions with your team members; however, you must turn in an originally written lab report. Your Materials and Methods section and your tables and figures may be similar, but your Introduction, Results, and Discussion sections must be the product of your own library research and creative thinking.

Remember, first complete Experiment A in each exercise. Then discuss with your research team a possible question for your original experiment, choosing one of the animals investigated in Experiment A as your experimental organism. Be certain you can pose an interesting question from which you can develop a testable hypothesis. Then turn to Experiment B in the exercise for your chosen organism and design and execute an experiment.

EXERCISE 1
Taxis in Brine Shrimp

Brine shrimp (*Artemia salina*) are small crustaceans that live in salt lakes and swim upside down using 11 pairs of appendages. Their sensory structures include two large compound eyes and two pairs of short antennae (Figure 1). They are a favorite fish food and can be purchased in pet stores.

Figure 1.
Brine shrimp (*Artemia salina*) magnified about 20×. A type of fairy shrimp, brine shrimp live in inland salt lakes such as the Great Salt Lake in Utah.

Experiment A. Brine Shrimp Behavior in Environments with Few Stimuli

Materials

brine shrimp
2 large test tubes
black construction paper
1 small finger bowl
salt water
dropper

Introduction

In this experiment, you will place brine shrimp in a test tube of salt water similar to the water of their normal environment. You will not feed them or disturb them in any way. You will observe their behavior in this relatively stimulus-free environment. Notice their positions in the test tube. Are they in groups, or are they solitary? Are they near the top or near the bottom? You should make careful observations of their behavior, asking questions about possible stimuli that might initiate taxes in these animals.

Hypothesis

Hypothesize about the behavior of brine shrimp in an environment with few stimuli.

Prediction

Predict the result of your experiment based on the hypothesis (if/then).

Procedure

1. Place six brine shrimp in a test tube filled two-thirds with salt water. Rest the test tube in the finger bowl in such a way that you can easily see all six shrimp. You may need to use black construction paper as a background.
2. Describe the behavior of the brine shrimp in the Results section; for example, are they randomly distributed throughout the test tube or do they collect in one area?
3. Record your observations in the Results section.

Results

1. By describing the behavior of brine shrimp in an environment with relatively few stimuli, which component of experimental design are you establishing?

2. Describe the behavior of the brine shrimp.

Discussion

On separate paper, list four stimuli that might initiate taxes in brine shrimp and predict the response of the animal to each. What possible adaptive advantage could this behavior provide?

Experiment B. Original Investigation of Brine Shrimp Behavior

Materials

supplies from Experiment A
piece of black cloth
lamp
dropper bottles—solutions of sugar, egg albumin, acid, and base

Introduction

If your team chooses to perform your original experiment investigating taxes in brine shrimp, return to this experiment after you have completed all the introductory investigations (Experiment A of each exercise). Using the materials available and collaborating with other members of your research team, design a simple experiment to investigate taxes in brine shrimp.

Hypothesis

State the hypothesis that you will investigate.

Prediction

Predict the results of your experiment based on your hypothesis (if/then).

Procedure

Allow a conditioning period of several minutes after the shrimp have been disturbed or stimulated. If you add something to the water in one experiment, begin additional experiments with fresh water and shrimp.

1. On separate paper, list in numerical order each step of your procedure. Remember to include the number of repetitions, levels of treatment, the duration of each stimulus, and other time intervals when appropriate.
2. If you have an idea for an experiment that requires materials other than those available, ask your laboratory instructor. If possible, additional supplies will be made available.
3. Quantify your data whenever possible (count, weigh, measure, time).

Results

On separate paper, record your data and describe your results. You should design at least one table and figure.

Discussion

1. Among members of your team, discuss your results in light of your hypothesis. If possible, come to conclusions about the behaviors you have been investigating. Record your conclusions on a separate paper.
2. You may be asked to report the results of your experiments to the class.

EXERCISE 2

Kinesis in Pill Bugs

Kinesis can be studied using a crustacean in the order Isopoda (called *isopods*). These animals are also called *pill bugs, sow bugs,* and *roly-polies* (Figure 2). Although most crustaceans are aquatic, pill bugs are truly terrestrial, and much of their behavior is involved with their need to avoid desiccation. They are easily collected in warm weather under flowerpots, in leaf litter, or in woodpiles. They often respond to mechanical stimuli by rolling up into a ball.

Experiment A. Pill Bug Behavior in Moist and Dry Environments

Materials

pill bugs
2 large petri dishes
filter paper
squirt bottle of water

Figure 2.
Pill bugs magnified about 15×.
These terrestrial isopods are also called *sow bugs* and *roly-polies*.

Introduction

In this experiment, you will investigate pill bug behavior in moist and dry environments by observing the degree of their activity, that is, the number of times they circle and turn. As you observe their behavior, ask questions about possible stimuli that might modify this behavior.

Hypothesis

Hypothesize about the degree of activity of pill bugs in moist and dry environments.

Prediction

Predict the results of the experiment based on your hypothesis (if/then).

Procedure

1. Prepare two large petri dishes, one with wet filter paper, the other with dry filter paper.
2. Place five pill bugs in each dish.
3. Place the dishes in a dark spot, such as a drawer, for 5 minutes.
4. After 5 minutes, carefully observe the pill bugs in the petri dishes. Before you open the drawer or uncover the petri dishes, assign each of the following procedures to a member of your team.
   a. Count the number of pill bugs moving in each dish.
   b. Choose one moving pill bug in each dish and determine the rate of locomotion by counting revolutions per minute (rpm) around the petri dish.

c. Determine the rate of turning by counting turns (reversal of direction) per minute for one pill bug in each dish.

Results

Record your results in Table 1.

Table 1
Kinesis in Pill Bugs: Response to Wet and Dry Environments

Environmental Condition	Number Moving	Rate of Locomotion (rpm)	Rate of Turning (turn/min)
Moist			
Dry			

Discussion

1. Kinetic response to varying moisture in the environment is called *hygrokinesis.* What other environmental factors might influence the behavior of pill bugs?

2. On separate paper, list four factors that might initiate kineses in pill bugs and predict their response to each. What possible adaptive advantage could this behavior provide?

Experiment B. Original Investigation of Pill Bug Behavior

Materials

supplies from Experiment A
white enamel pan
wax pencils
beaker of water
construction paper
manila folder
large pieces of black cloth

Introduction

If your team chooses to perform your original experiment investigating kineses in pill bugs, return to this experiment after you have completed all the introductory investigations (Experiment A of each exercise). Using the materials available and collaborating with other members of your research team, design a simple experiment to investigate kineses in pill bugs.

Hypothesis

State the hypothesis that you will investigate.

Prediction

Predict the results of the experiment based on your hypothesis (if/then).

Procedure

1. On separate paper, list in numerical order each step of your procedure. Remember to include the number of repetitions, the levels of treatment, the duration of stimulus, and other time intervals where appropriate.
2. If you have an idea for an experiment that requires materials other than those available, ask your laboratory instructor. If possible, additional supplies will be made available.
3. Quantify your data whenever possible (count, weigh, measure, time).

Results

On separate paper, record your data and describe your results. You should design at least one table and figure.

Discussion

1. Among members of your team, discuss your results in light of your hypothesis. If possible, come to conclusions about the behaviors you have been investigating. Record your conclusions on a separate paper.
2. You may be asked to report the results of your experiments to the class.

EXERCISE 3

Agonistic Display in Male Siamese Fighting Fish

The innate agonistic behavior of the male Siamese fighting fish *(Betta splendens)* has been widely studied (Simpson, 1968; Thompson, 1969). The sight of another male *Betta* or even its own reflection in a mirror will stimulate a ritualized series of responses toward the intruder. If two fish are placed in the same aquarium, their agonistic behavior usually continues until one fish is defeated or subordinated.

Experiment A. Display Behavior in Male Siamese Fighting Fish

Materials

male Siamese fighting fish in a 1- to 2-L flat-sided fishbowl
mirror

Introduction

The purpose of this experiment is to describe the ritualized agonistic display of a male Siamese fighting fish after being stimulated by its own reflection in a mirror. Before you begin the experiment, become familiar with the fish's anatomy, identifying its dorsal fin, ventral fin, pectoral fin, gill cover, and tail (Figure 3).

When you begin the experiment, you will be looking for several possible responses: frontal approach (facing intruder), broadside display, undulating movements, increased swimming speed, fin elevation (dorsal, ventral, or pectoral), gill cover extension (angle may vary), tail expansion, and enhanced coloration in tail, fin, or body.

Hypothesis

Hypothesize about the response of the fish to its image in the mirror.

Prediction

Predict the result of the experiment based on your hypothesis (if/then).

Figure 3.
Male Siamese fighting fish (*Betta splendens*).

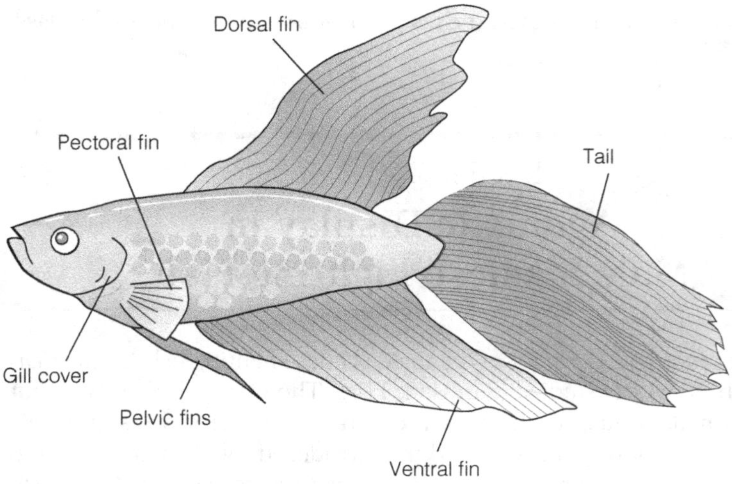

Procedure

1. Plan your strategy.
   a. Be ready with your pencil and paper to record your observations. Behaviors can happen very quickly. Your entire team should observe and record them.
   b. Each team member should be responsible for timing the duration of particular responses (listed in the Introduction). You might also take turns observing different behaviors, alternating from one behavior to another every 30 seconds.
2. Place the mirror against the fishbowl.
3. As the fish reacts to its reflection, list, in order and using the appropriate terminology, the series of responses. Be as quantitative as possible; for example, you might record "gill cover extended 90° for 30 seconds" or "broadside display for 60 seconds."
4. Compare collective results.
5. In the Results section, make a *sequential* list of the recognizable responses involved in the display.
6. Note in the Results section those responses that take place simultaneously.

Results

1. Record your sequential list.

2. Record the responses that take place simultaneously.

Discussion

1. Collaborating with your teammates, write a descriptive paragraph, as quantitative and detailed as possible, describing the agonistic display elicited in the Siamese fighting fish in response to its reflection.

2. What is the obvious adaptive advantage of complex agonistic displays that are not followed by damaging fights? Are there advantages that are not so obvious?

3. Name several other animals that demonstrate a strong display that is seldom followed by a damaging fight.

4. Name several animals that do engage in damaging fights.

Experiment B. Original Investigation of Siamese Fighting Fish Behavior

Materials

supplies from Experiment A
colored pencils
index cards
fish of different species in fishbowls
female Siamese fighting fish

Introduction

If your team chooses to perform your original experiment investigating agonistic behavior in Siamese fighting fish, return to this experiment after you have completed all the introductory investigations (Experiment A of each exercise). Using the materials available and collaborating among your research team, design a simple experiment to investigate this behavior.

Discuss with your team members possible investigations that might be carried out. Several questions follow that might give you ideas.

1. What is the simplest stimulus that will initiate the response? Is color important? Size? Movement?
2. Is the behavior "released" by a specific stimulus or by a complex of all the stimuli?
3. Will another species of fish initiate the response?
4. Will a female *Betta* fish initiate the response, and, if so, how does the response compare with the response to a fish of a different species?
5. Is the response all or none—that is, are there partial displays with different stimuli?
6. Does the fish become "conditioned"—that is, after repeated identical stimuli, does the duration of the display change, or does the display cease?
7. Could chemical stimulation contribute to the response? (Transfer water from one fishbowl to another.)

Hypothesis

After your team has decided on one or more questions to investigate, formulate a testable hypothesis.

Prediction

Predict the results of the experiment based on your hypothesis (if/then).

Procedure

1. On separate paper, list in numerical order each step of your procedure. Remember to include the number of repetitions, the levels of treatment, the duration of a stimulus, and other time intervals where appropriate.
2. If you have an idea for an experiment that requires materials other than those available, ask your laboratory instructor. If possible, additional supplies will be made available.
3. Quantify your data whenever possible (count, weigh, measure, time).

Results

On separate paper, record your data and describe your results. You should design at least one table and figure.

Discussion

1. Among members of your team, discuss your results in light of your hypothesis. If possible, come to conclusions about the behaviors you have been investigating. Record your conclusions on a separate paper.
2. You may be asked to report the results of your experiments to the class.

EXERCISE 4
Reproductive Behavior in Fruit Flies

Spieth (1952, described in Marler, 1968) has classified the mating behavior of the fruit fly *Drosophila melanogaster* as being a complex of at least fourteen behaviors. Described below are ten of the most common and easily recognized of these behaviors. Read the list carefully and become familiar with the behaviors you will be required to recognize. Six of the behaviors are seen in males, four in females. The behavior sequence begins as the male orients his body toward the female (Figure 4a).

Male Behaviors

1. *Tapping.* The forelegs are extended to strike or tap the female (Figure 4b).
2. *Waving.* The wing is extended and held 90° from the body, then relaxed without vibration (Figure 4c).
3. *Wing vibration.* The male extends one or both wings from the resting position and moves them rapidly up and down (Figure 4c).
4. *Licking.* The male licks the female's genitalia (on the rear of her abdomen) (Figure 4d).
5. *Circling.* The male postures and then circles the female, usually when she is nonreceptive.
6. *Stamping.* The male stamps forefeet as in tapping but does not strike the female.

Female Behaviors

1. *Extruding.* A temporary, tubelike structure is extended from the female's genitalia.
2. *Decamping.* A nonreceptive female runs, jumps, or flies away from the courting male.
3. *Depressing.* A nonreceptive female prevents access to her genitalia by depressing her wings and curling the tip of her abdomen down.
4. *Ignoring.* A nonreceptive female ignores the male.

If the behavior display is successful, the flies will copulate (Figure 4e, f).

Figure 4.
Mating behavior in fruit fly, *Drosophila melanogaster*.

Experiment A. Reproductive Behavior in *Drosophila melanogaster*

Materials

stereoscopic microscope
fly vials with 2 or 3 virgin female *D. melanogaster* flies
fly vials with 2 or 3 male *D. melanogaster* flies

Introduction

In this experiment, you will place virgin female *D. melanogaster* flies in the same vial with male flies and observe the behavior of each sex. Working with another student, discuss the behaviors described in the introduction to this exercise and plan the strategy for your experiment. Identify mating behaviors of *D. melanogaster* and record their sequence and duration (when appropriate). As you observe the behavior of the flies, discuss possible original experiments investigating reproductive behavior in flies.

Hypothesis

Hypothesize about the presence of flies of the opposite sex in the same vial.

Prediction

Predict the results of the experiment based on your hypothesis (if/then).

Procedure

1. Set up the stereoscopic microscope.
2. Have paper and pencil ready. The behaviors can happen very rapidly. One person should call out observations while the other person records.
3. Obtain one vial containing virgin females and one vial containing males, and gently tap the male flies into the vial containing females.
4. Observe first with the naked eye. Once flies have encountered each other, use the stereoscopic microscope to make observations.

Results

1. Describe, in sequence, the response of the male to the female and the female to the male. Quantify your observations. To do this, you may consider counting the number of times a behavior takes place and timing the duration of behaviors.

2. Describe rejection if this takes place.

3. In the margin of your lab manual, note any behaviors that can be analyzed quantitatively.

Discussion

Speculate about the adaptive advantage of elaborate courtship behaviors in animals.

Experiment B. Original Investigation of Reproductive Behavior in Fruit Flies

Materials

supplies from Experiment A
fly vials with 2 or 3 virgin females of an alternate fly species (other than *D. melanogaster*)
fly vials with 2 or 3 males of the alternate species

Introduction

If your team chooses to perform your original experiment investigating reproductive behavior in fruit flies, continue with this experiment after you have completed all the introductory investigations (Experiment A of each exercise). Using the materials available and collaborating with your research partner, design a simple experiment to investigate reproductive behavior. Several questions follow that might provide ideas.

1. Will reproductive behavior in another species be identical to that in *D. melanogaster*?
2. Will males placed in the same vial demonstrate courtship behaviors?
3. Will males respond to dead females?
4. What is the response of a male *D. melanogaster* to females of a different species?
5. Do males compete?

Quantify your observations. To do this, you may consider counting the number of times a behavior takes place or timing the duration of behaviors.

Hypothesis

After your team has decided on one or more questions to investigate, formulate a testable hypothesis.

Prediction

Predict the results of your experiment based on your hypothesis (if/then).

Procedure

1. On a separate paper, list in numerical order each step of your procedure. Remember to include the number of repetitions, the levels of treatment, the duration of stimulus, and other time intervals where appropriate.
2. If you have an idea for an experiment that requires materials other than those available, ask your laboratory instructor. If possible, additional supplies will be made available.
3. Quantify your data whenever possible (count, weigh, measure, time).

Results

On a separate paper, record your data and describe your results. You should design at least one table and figure.

Discussion

1. Within your team, discuss your results in light of your hypothesis. If possible, come to conclusions about the behaviors you have been investigating. Record your conclusions on a separate paper.
2. You may be asked to report the results of your experiments to the class.

Questions for Review

Define, compare, and give examples for each item in the following pairs:

1. Learned behavior—innate behavior
2. Proximate cause of behavior—ultimate cause of behavior
3. Causal explanation for a behavior—anthropomorphic explanation for a behavior
4. Taxis—kinesis

Applying Your Knowledge

1. Adult male European robins have red feathers on their breasts. A male robin will display aggressive behavior and attack another male robin that invades his territory during mating season. Immature male robins with all brown feathers do not elicit this behavior in the adult robin. How could you explain this behavior? Design an experiment to test your explanation (hypothesis).

2. In the spring, distinctive and elaborate male cardinal songs may be heard throughout most eastern deciduous forests. You suspect that the function of a bird's song at this time of year has something to do with territorial defense and finding a mate. You also suspect that there must be some environmental trigger that affects the bird's endocrine system leading to the behavior. In lab today, you learned that it is possible to explain behaviors based on anthropomorphic causes but that scientists base explanations on proximate and ultimate causes. In the space below, propose explanations (hypotheses) based on these three perspectives—anthropomorphic, proximate, and ultimate—and then propose a research project for those hypotheses that can be tested scientifically.

a. Anthropomorphic causes:

Possible research project:

b. Proximate causes:

Possible research project:

c. Ultimate causes:

Possible research project:

References

Alcock, J. *Animal Behavior: An Evolutionary Approach,* 7th ed. Sunderland, MA: Sinauer Associates, 2001.

Campbell, N., and J. Reece. *Biology,* 7th ed. Menlo Park, CA: Benjamin Cummings, 2005.

Greenspan, R. J. "Understanding the Genetic Construction of Behavior," *Scientific American,* 1995, vol. 272, no. 4, p. 72.

Johnson, R. N. *Aggression in Man and Animals.* Philadelphia, PA: Saunders College Publishing, 1972.

Marler, P. "Mating Behavior of *Drosophila.*" In *Animal Behavior in Laboratory and Field,* editor A. W. Stokes. San Francisco: Freeman, 1968.

Raham, G. "Pill Bug Biology," *The American Biology Teacher,* 1986, vol. 48, no. 1.

Simpson, M. J. A. "The Threat Display of the Siamese Fighting Fish, *Betta splendens,*" *Animal Behavior Monograph,* 1968, vol. 1, p. 1.

Thompson, T. "Aggressive Behavior of Siamese Fighting Fish," in *Aggressive Behavior,* editors S. Garattini and E. B. Sigg. Proceedings of the International Symposium on the Biology of Aggressive Behavior. New York, NY: Wiley, 1969.

Waterman, M., and E. Stanley. *Biological Inquiry: A Workbook of Investigative Cases.* Menlo Park, CA: Benjamin Cummings, 2005. In this supplement to Campbell and Reece, 7th ed., see "Back to the Bay," a case study applying principles of animal behavior to an environmental problem.

Ecology I: Terrestrial Ecology

Laboratory Objectives

After completing this lab topic, you should be able to:

1. Describe the trophic levels of an ecosystem and provide examples from field experience.
2. Describe the environmental factors that are important components of the ecosystem.
3. Calculate density, frequency, dominance, and species diversity.
4. Describe the relative importance of particular species in the ecosystem as determined by their density, size, or role in the ecosystem.
5. Construct an illustrative model of the ecosystem components.

Introduction

Organisms are influenced by their physical environment and by interactions with other living organisms. The study of the relationships of organisms with their environment (both physical and biological) is called **ecology.** Ecological investigations may address questions at several hierarchical levels: **individuals, populations** (organisms of the same species that share a common gene pool and occur in the same area), **communities** (populations of different species that inhabit the same area), and **ecosystems** (the community of plants and animals plus the physical environment). A physiological ecologist studies the effects of the environment on individual organisms. A population ecologist might be interested in questions about the reproductive biology of a population of endangered plant species. The community ecologist might investigate the sequence of species composition changes in a forest following a disturbance. And the ecosystem ecologist might question how the interactions among members of different trophic levels (feeding levels) are influenced by environmental conditions.

An ecosystem can be divided into **biotic** components (living organisms) and **abiotic** components (physical features). In a forest ecosystem, the abiotic components include the climatic factors, soil type, water availability, and landscape features. The biotic components of the forest include trees, shrubs, wildflowers, squirrels, foxes, caterpillars, eagles, spiders, millipedes, and fungi on the forest floor and in the soil (Figure 1). The biotic components can be further characterized based on **trophic structure,** the ecological role of organisms in the food chain. Plants and some protists are categorized as

---

Figure 1.
Forest ecosystem. A simplified forest system showing trophic (feeding) relationships among primary producers, consumers, detritivores, and decomposers.

primary producers (autotrophic organisms), capable of transforming light energy into chemical energy stored in carbohydrates through the process of photosynthesis. The amount of energy available for all other trophic levels is dependent on the photosynthetic ability of the primary producers. **Consumers** are animals and heterotrophic protists, which literally consume the primary producers or each other or both. They may be divided into **primary consumers (herbivores,** which consume plants) and **secondary** and **tertiary consumers (carnivores,** which eat other consumers). Rarely do ecosystems support additional levels of consumers. In general, only 10–20% of the energy available at one trophic level is transferred to the next trophic level. The number of organisms that can be supported at subsequent higher trophic levels is limited by the available energy. **Detritivores** obtain their nutrients and energy from dead organisms and waste materials, and **decomposers** (fungi and bacteria) absorb nutrients from nonliving organic material.

With the assistance of your lab partner, match each of the following trophic levels with an example of an organism from the forest system just described. Remember that the trophic level reflects who is eating whom.

Primary producers:

Primary consumers:

Secondary consumers:

Tertiary consumers:

Detritivores:

Decomposers:

Note that some organisms fit into more than one trophic level—because, like many humans, some are omnivores, eating whatever is available.

Stating the Problem

In this lab topic, you will investigate the structure and function of a local ecosystem. The exercise is designed for a forest ecosystem but can be adapted easily for use in grasslands or even a weedy urban lot. (An outline for adapting the lab for use in a weedy field is included at the end of the lab topic.) The study site has been selected in advance by your instructor, who may have prepared an introductory description for you.

In the field, spend 5 minutes observing the features of your study site, both biotic and abiotic. Based on your observations and the information provided by your instructor, write in the space below a brief description of the study site, including its physical and biological features.

Study Site

You will work as teams of ecologists to determine the components of the ecosystem. Each team, composed of six to eight students, will sample one plot, thus providing three or four replicate samples, depending on the number

Suggested Organization of Student Teams

Exercise	Sampling	No. of Students
Exercise 1	Biotic Components	
A	Trees	2
B	Shrubs, saplings, and vines	2
C	Seedlings and herbaceous vegetation	2
D	Macroinvertebrates	2
E	Microinvertebrates	2
F	Microorganisms	2*
G	Other forest animals	All
Exercise 2	Abiotic Components	2*

*Two students can complete both Exercise 2 and Field Study F in Exercise 1.

of teams. Within teams, each student will have specific assigned responsibilities, as suggested below and fully described in the following exercises.

Following the field sampling, you will share results with other teams, make calculations, pool and analyze data, and develop a model of the ecosystem. Students should read assignments for all field studies.

EXERCISE 1
Biotic Components

As you begin your observations of the forest, note the vertical layers of the forest from the forest floor up to the tallest and largest trees, which form a canopy. The forest vegetation can be subdivided arbitrarily into categories according to the structural pattern of the forest (Figure 2): forest **trees** (woody plants with a diameter at breast height (DBH) of >10 cm); **shrubs, saplings,** and **vines** (DBH 2.5–10 cm); and **seedlings** and **herbaceous plants** (DBH < 2.5 cm). (Note that DBH is measured at a height of 1.5 m from the base of the tree.) Microorganisms and small animals can be sampled from the forest floor, **litter** (fallen leaves, for example), and soil, with large vertebrates observed directly or indirectly by animal signs (nest sites, feces, tracks).

In your student teams, you will sample part of the study site using circular plots to estimate the abundance of plants and animals in each of the categories described above. The size of the circular plots varies according to the size and abundance of the organisms (Table 1). Thus, trees are sampled using the largest plot, while the herbs of the forest floor are sampled in small plots. Imagine the difficulty of sampling trees in plots of only 1 m^2 or counting all the nonwoody plants in a plot with a diameter of over 10 m!

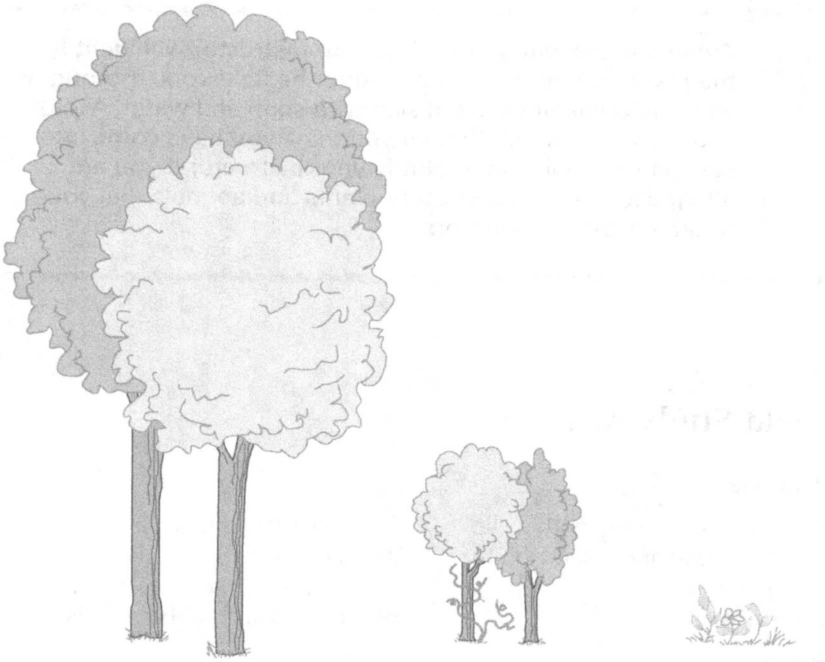

Figure 2.
Vertical stratification of the forest. The forest can be divided into layers: the trees (DBH > 10 cm); shrubs, saplings, and vines (DBH 2.5–10 cm); and seedlings and herbaceous plants (DBH < 2.5 cm).

Table 1
Sampling Design for Determining the Biotic Components of a Forest Ecosystem

Organisms	Plot Size
Trees (DBH > 10 cm)	100 m^2
Shrubs, saplings, and vines (DBH 2.5–10 cm)	50 m^2
Seedlings and herbs (DBH < 2.5 cm)	0.50 m^2
Litter macroinvertebrates	0.50 m^2
Microinvertebrates from litter and soil samples	—
Microorganisms from litter and soil samples	—
Large vertebrates observed by all	—

Avoid contact with poison ivy. Your instructor will identify the plant for you. After completing the fieldwork, thoroughly wash all areas of exposed skin with soap and water. Avoid contact with your clothing if you think you have come into contact with poison ivy. Notify your instructor if you are allergic to bee stings or other plants and animals that you might encounter outdoors.

Field Study A. Trees

Materials

3 lines, 5.64 m long, with a clip on one end and a stake on the other end of each
center post
mallet
DBH measuring tape
index cards
permanent marker
plastic bags and rubber bands

Introduction

Trees form the uppermost layer, or canopy, of the forest. They influence the physical environment, such as the quality and quantity of light reaching all other vegetation, water availability, and temperature. A forest description is usually based on the largest and most abundant species of trees.

Procedure

1. Determine the sample plot location based on recommendations from your instructor.
2. Locate the center of the sample plot and hammer the center post into the ground at that location.
3. Clip one end of a line to the center post. Extend the line, keeping it straight and taut, and hammer the stake into position (Figure 3, line 1).
4. Attach and secure lines 2 and 3 at an angle forming two wedge-shaped sections A and B (see Figure 3). Each wedge should be equal to approximately one-fifth of the plot.
5. Identify and measure DBH (>10 cm) for all trees in sections A and B (see Figure 3). The number of DBH measurements will also provide a record of abundance. If a tree is on the outer perimeter of the plot, it should be counted in the plot if at least 50% of the tree is within the plot.

Diameter at breast height (DBH) is measured 1.5 m above the base of the tree. Measure or estimate this height on your body to ensure that you determine DBH in a consistent fashion. If DBH measuring tapes are not available, measure trees with a circumference of >32 cm.

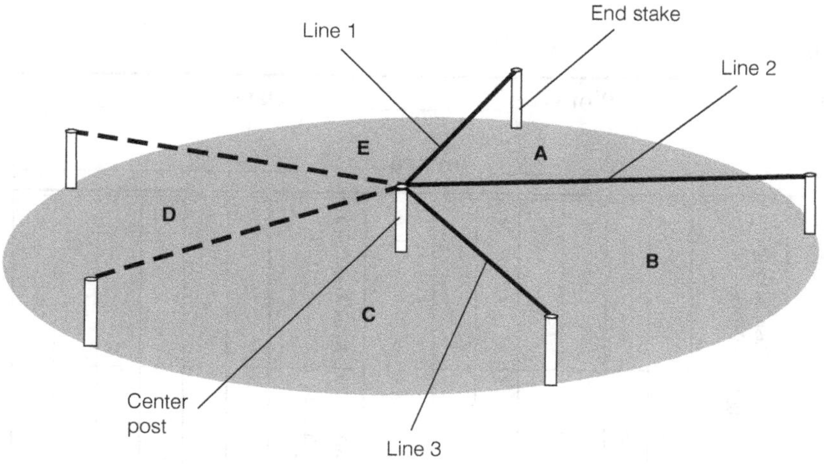

Figure 3.
Establishing and sampling a circular plot. Locate the center post and attach three lines (1, 2, 3) to form two wedge-shaped sections, A and B. After sampling A and B, move line 2 to form section C. After sampling C, move line 3 to form sections D and E.

6. If you cannot identify a tree, assign a number to that type of tree. Collect a leaf sample, if possible, for later identification. Label the sample by attaching a numbered card or by writing the number on the leaf blade. If leaves are not available, write a brief description.
7. Before moving any lines, check with the shrub, sapling, and vine group to be sure they have completed their sampling. Their plot is smaller and lies within the boundary of the tree plot.
8. Do not move line 1. Detach line 2 and move it into position to form the boundary between sections C and D (the first dotted line in Figure 3).
9. Identify and measure DBH for all trees in section C (see Figure 3).
10. Detach line 3 and move it into position to form the boundary between sections D and E (the second dotted line in Figure 3).
11. Identify and measure DBH for all trees in sections D and E (see Figure 3).

Results

1. Record your data in Table 2 on the next page.
2. In Exercise 3, Data Analysis, you will calculate:
   DBH (if measurements were taken of circumference rather than DBH)
   Density and relative density
   Frequency and relative frequency
   Basal area, dominance, and relative dominance
   Importance value

Field Study B. Shrubs, Saplings, and Vines

Materials

circular plot established for trees in Field Study A; the radius lines should be flagged conspicuously at 4 m for the SSV plot
plastic bags and rubber bands
calipers
permanent marker
index cards

Table 2
Sampling Results for **Trees** (DBH > 10 cm)

Locality: ______________ **Plot ID #:** __________ **Plot size:** ______________ **Date:** ______________

Students: ____ **Instructor:** ______________________

Species:

Circumference (cm)	DBH (cm) $= \frac{\text{Circumference}}{\pi}$	Basal Area (cm^2) $= 0.7854\ (\text{DBH})^2$

Species:

Circumference (cm)	DBH (cm) $= \frac{\text{Circumference}}{\pi}$	Basal Area (cm^2) $= 0.7854\ (\text{DBH})^2$

Species:

Circumference (cm)	DBH (cm) $= \frac{\text{Circumference}}{\pi}$	Basal Area (cm^2) $= 0.7854\ (\text{DBH})^2$

Species:

Circumference (cm)	DBH (cm) $= \frac{\text{Circumference}}{\pi}$	Basal Area (cm^2) $= 0.7854\ (\text{DBH})^2$

Species:

Circumference (cm)	DBH (cm) $= \frac{\text{Circumference}}{\pi}$	Basal Area (cm^2) $= 0.7854\ (\text{DBH})^2$

Species:

Circumference (cm)	DBH (cm) $= \frac{\text{Circumference}}{\pi}$	Basal Area (cm^2) $= 0.7854\ (\text{DBH})^2$

Species:

Circumference (cm)	DBH (cm) $= \frac{\text{Circumference}}{\pi}$	Basal Area (cm^2) $= 0.7854\ (\text{DBH})^2$

Species:

Circumference (cm)	DBH (cm) $= \frac{\text{Circumference}}{\pi}$	Basal Area (cm^2) $= 0.7854\ (\text{DBH})^2$

Species:

Circumference (cm)	DBH (cm) $= \frac{\text{Circumference}}{\pi}$	Basal Area (cm^2) $= 0.7854\ (\text{DBH})^2$

Introduction

Lower vertical layers of the forest are inhabited by young trees of the types seen in the upper levels, trees and shrubs unique to this layer, and some vines. The shrub, sapling, and vine (SSV) plot is located within the tree plot (Figure 4). Therefore, each line should be boldly marked to indicate the radius for 50 m^2.

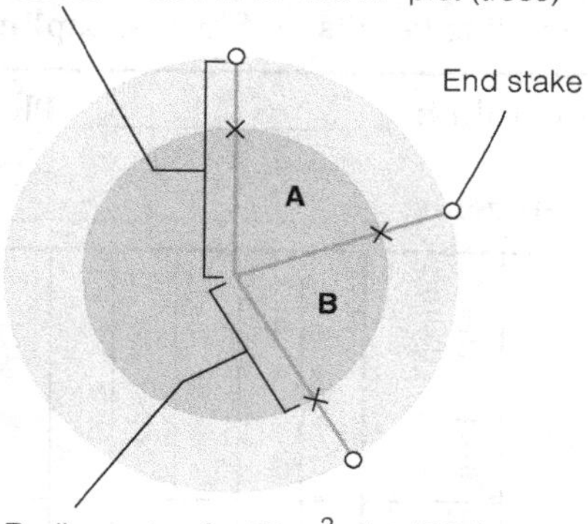

Figure 4.
Placement of circular plot for shrubs, saplings, and vines. A circular plot with a smaller diameter is marked within the boundary of the large tree plot. Radius lines are clearly marked to indicate the outer perimeter for the plot (Xs).

Coordinate your sampling with the tree group, Field Study A.

Procedure

1. Locate the circular plot established by your team members sampling trees. Restrict your sampling to the smaller plot located within the tree plot. The radius of the smaller plot should be marked clearly with flagging or tape along each line. Sample vines and other woody plants with a DBH of 2.5–10 cm within the SSV plot.
2. Begin sampling in section A (see Figure 3). Identify and measure each individual in the SSV category for all sections of the plot. If available, use calipers, rather than a meter tape, to determine DBH.

Diameter at breast height (DBH) is measured 1.5 m above the base of the woody plant. Measure or estimate this height on your body to ensure that you determine DBH in a consistent fashion. If DBH measuring tapes are not available, measure plants with a circumference of 8–32 cm.

3. If you cannot identify a woody plant, assign a number to that type of plant. Collect a leaf sample, if possible, for later identification. Label the sample by attaching a numbered card or writing the number on the leaf blade. If leaves are not available, write a brief description.

Results

1. Record your data in Table 3 on the next page.
2. In Exercise 3, Data Analysis, you will calculate:

   DBH (if measurements were taken of circumference rather than DBH)
   Density and relative density
   Frequency and relative frequency
   Basal area, dominance, and relative dominance
   Importance value

Table 3
Sampling Results for **Shrubs, Saplings,** and **Vines** (DBH 2.5–10 cm)

Locality: ______________ **Plot ID #:** __________ **Plot size:** ______________ **Date:** ______________

Students: ____ **Instructor:** ____________________

Species:

Circumference (cm)	DBH (cm) $= \frac{\text{Circumference}}{\pi}$	Basal Area (cm^2) $= 0.7854\,(\text{DBH})^2$

Species:

Circumference (cm)	DBH (cm) $= \frac{\text{Circumference}}{\pi}$	Basal Area (cm^2) $= 0.7854\,(\text{DBH})^2$

Species:

Circumference (cm)	DBH (cm) $= \frac{\text{Circumference}}{\pi}$	Basal Area (cm^2) $= 0.7854\,(\text{DBH})^2$

Species:

Circumference (cm)	DBH (cm) $= \frac{\text{Circumference}}{\pi}$	Basal Area (cm^2) $= 0.7854\,(\text{DBH})^2$

Species:

Circumference (cm)	DBH (cm) $= \frac{\text{Circumference}}{\pi}$	Basal Area (cm^2) $= 0.7854\,(\text{DBH})^2$

Species:

Circumference (cm)	DBH (cm) $= \frac{\text{Circumference}}{\pi}$	Basal Area (cm^2) $= 0.7854\,(\text{DBH})^2$

Species:

Circumference (cm)	DBH (cm) $= \frac{\text{Circumference}}{\pi}$	Basal Area (cm^2) $= 0.7854\,(\text{DBH})^2$

Species:

Circumference (cm)	DBH (cm) $= \frac{\text{Circumference}}{\pi}$	Basal Area (cm^2) $= 0.7854\,(\text{DBH})^2$

Species:

Circumference (cm)	DBH (cm) $= \frac{\text{Circumference}}{\pi}$	Basal Area (cm^2) $= 0.7854\,(\text{DBH})^2$

Field Study C. Seedlings and Herbaceous Vegetation

Materials

circular 0.50-m^2 plot
compass
index cards
plastic bags and rubber bands
permanent marker

Introduction

Tree seedlings and herbaceous plants appear near the forest floor. These plants may be difficult to count, and, in some cases, it may be almost impossible to determine what is actually one individual. Because of this, the abundance of these plants is estimated based on the percent cover.

The seedling and herb plot is not located within the larger plots but should be placed near the tree plot at a predetermined position.

Procedure

1. Place a 0.50-m^2 plot just outside the tree plot. Determine the exact location for the plot before beginning. For example, it might always be 1 m away from the tree plot at a compass heading of due north.
2. Identify and estimate the abundance of each species by estimating the percent of the plot area covered by the species. Sketching the plot may help determine cover and ensure consistency in your estimates.
3. If you cannot identify a plant, assign a number to that type of plant. Collect a leaf or flower sample if possible for later identification. Label the sample by attaching a numbered card or by writing the number on the leaf blade. If leaves are not available, write a brief description.

Results

1. Record results in Table 4 on the next page.
2. In Exercise 3, Data Analysis, you will calculate average percent cover, frequency, and relative frequency.

Field Study D. Macroinvertebrates

Materials

circular 0.50-m^2 plot
thin plastic sheet
forceps
dissecting probes
vials with 70% alcohol
labeling tape
permanent marker
compass

Introduction

Large invertebrates—for example, grasshoppers, ants, and spiders—can be surveyed by sifting through the dead leaves or litter on the forest floor. These animals may fit into any of the consumer trophic levels. For example, grasshoppers are primary consumers, spiders are secondary consumers, and ants are omnivores.

Table 4
Sampling Results for **Seedlings** and **Herbaceous Vegetation** (DBH < 2.5 cm)

Locality: ________ **Plot ID #:** ________ **Plot size:** ________ **Date:** ________

Students: ________________ **Instructor:** ________

Species	Percent Cover	Species	Percent Cover

Procedure

1. Carefully place a 0.50-m^2 circular plot on the ground in an undisturbed spot outside and near the large vegetation plot. This should be a preselected spot; for example, it might always be 1 m away from the large plot at a compass heading of due south. Avoid disturbing the animals present. Quickly cover the plot with plastic to discourage "escapees."
2. Carefully remove all animals from the vegetation and litter at ground level.
3. Sort animals into similar groups in the field. Place the organisms into vials of 70% alcohol according to their group. If you cannot identify an animal, assign a number to that type of animal. Preserve the animal in alcohol and label the sample using tape and a permanent marker.

Results

1. Record results in Table 5.
2. In Exercise 3, Data Analysis, you will calculate density for the groups.

Table 5
Sampling Results for **Consumers**, **Detritivores**, and **Decomposers**

Locality: ______________________ **Plot ID #:** __________ **Date:** __________

Students: ______________________________ **Instructor:** ______________

Macroinvertebrates		Microinvertebrates
Species/Group	**No. of Individuals**	**Groups Observed**

Microorganisms:

Vertebrates:

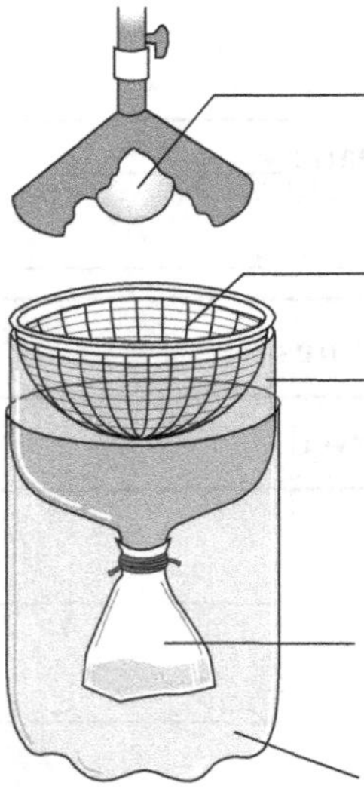

Figure 5.
Berlese-Tullgren funnel used for the extraction of microinvertebrates from litter and soil. The samples are placed on screening beneath a light. The light and heat drive the animals down into the small sampling bag containing preservative.

Field Study E. Microinvertebrates

Materials

circular 0.50-m^2 plot
index cards
self-sealing plastic bags
Berlese-Tullgren funnels
light sources
soil sample collected in Exercise 2, Field Study A

Introduction

A variety of invertebrates, including mites and springtails, inhabit the litter layer and the upper layers of the soil. Many of these animals are not easily seen with the naked eye and would be impossible to collect by inspecting samples. These consumers and detritivores can be sampled by collecting soil and litter and placing these in Berlese-Tullgren funnels (Figure 5). The animals move away from the light and heat source into a small sampling vial. The animals can then be identified in the laboratory using a dissecting microscope. You may be asked to collect samples for extraction later in the lab, or your instructor may have already collected the samples and started the extractions.

Procedure

1. Place the 0.50-m^2 plot in an undisturbed location. Carefully remove half the litter (discard sticks) and place it into the bag provided. Include a card with the plot number in your sample bag. Close the bag securely.
2. Upon return to the lab, extract the microinvertebrates using a Berlese-Tullgren funnel. A soil sample will also be collected by the soil group (see Exercise 2, Field Study A), and microinvertebrates will be extracted using the same procedure.
   a. Place the soil or litter sample on wire mesh in a large funnel under a lightbulb. The soil samples can be wrapped in a layer of cheesecloth to prevent soil particles from sifting into the collection vials.
   b. The light and heat force the animals down the funnel into the collecting vial containing 70% alcohol. (See Figure 5 for extraction funnel setup.)
3. After 24 to 48 hours, the organisms can be sorted and identified using the dissecting scope. Refer to the illustrated key to common microinvertebrates in Figure 6.

Results

1. Record in Table 5 the microinvertebrates present.
2. Sketch the most common organisms in the margin of your lab manual if they are not represented in the illustrated key.

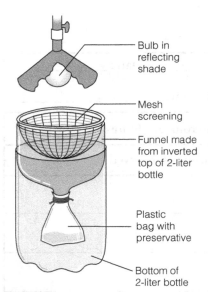

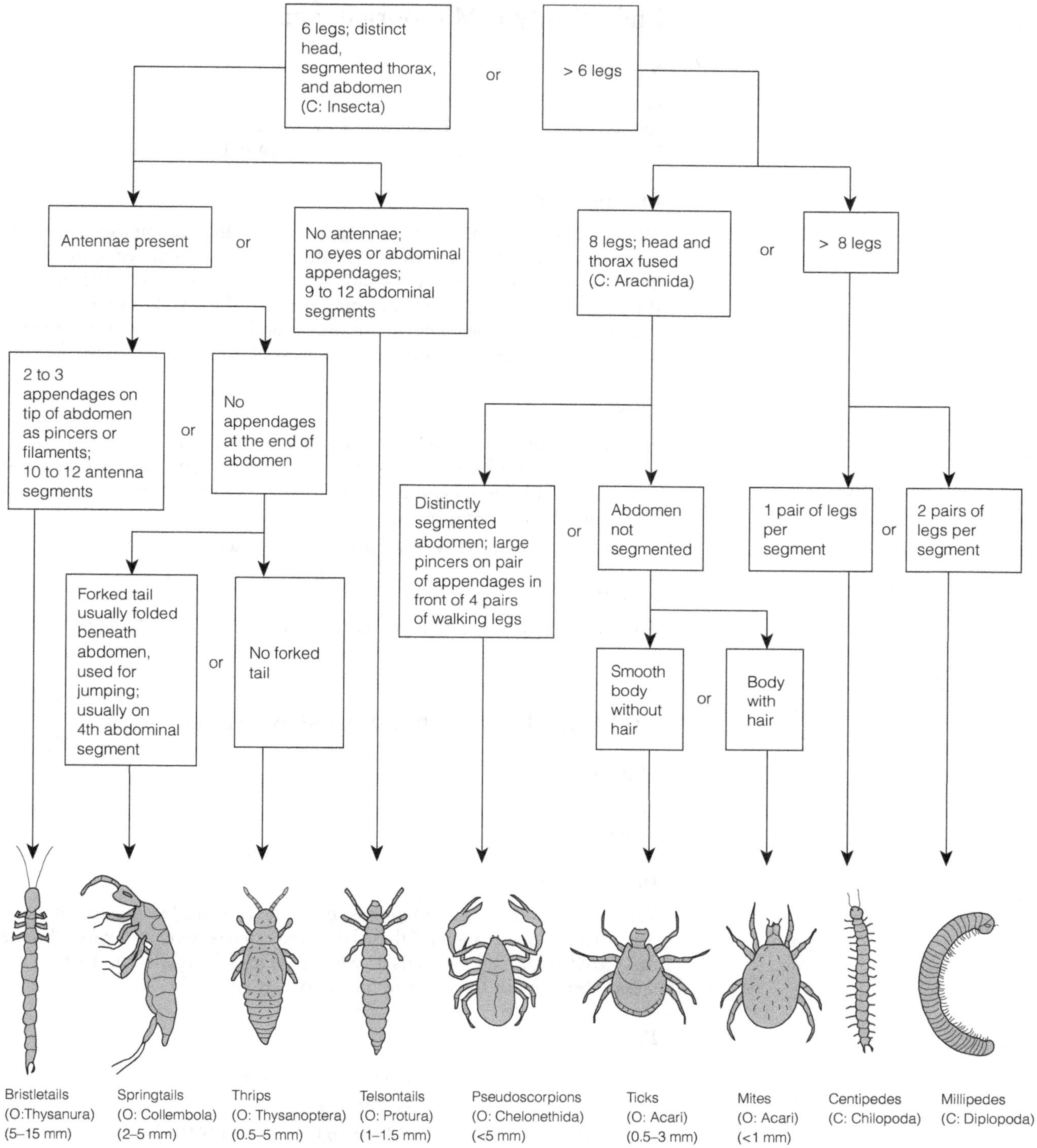

Figure 6.
Picture key to microinvertebrates commonly found in litter and soil samples.
C: class; O: order.

Field Study F. Microorganisms

Materials

petri dishes of nutrient agar
soil sample collected in Exercise 2, Field Study A
litter sample collected in Exercise 1, Field Study E

Introduction

Microorganisms in the litter and soil are important decomposers, the primary functions of which are soil building and nutrient recycling. Your instructor may have collected the samples in advance and begun the cultures. If not, you will need to obtain a small portion of the soil sample from the students sampling the abiotic components and some litter from the microinvertebrate group. You will prepare cultures for later evaluation.

Procedure

1. Upon returning to the lab, place small samples of leaf litter and soil on separate agar plates and incubate them at room temperature for several days until bacterial and fungal growth are abundant. Refrigerate them to prevent further growth.
2. Observe the diversity of colonies present after 2 or 3 days.

Results

Record the presence of different bacterial colony types and fungi in Table 5.

Field Study G. Other Forest Animals

Materials

binoculars
field guides

Introduction

You will not trap forest vertebrates in this field study, but all students will need to make observations of these larger but often secretive animals. Observe the activities of these animals as well as their calls, tracks, nest sites, and feces. Think about their role in the ecosystem.

Procedure

1. After completing your field sampling, survey the surrounding forest for birds, mammals, reptiles, and amphibians.
2. Record observations of animals sighted, plus any tracks, nests, burrows, carcasses, feces, owl pellets, songs, or calls. Field guides are provided to assist with identification.

Results

Record your observations in Table 5.

EXERCISE 2

Abiotic Components

Abiotic components include the physical features of the environment that influence the biotic components and in turn may be influenced by the organisms inhabiting the area. You will record the climatic conditions both for the local environment and for the smaller scale microenvironment within the ecosystem. Two students in each team will measure and record all abiotic features.

Field Study A. Soil

Materials

soil thermometer
soil auger
self-sealing plastic bags
index cards
permanent marker
trowel
diagram of soil profile
soil map of the area
soil test kit

Introduction

The soil contains biotic and abiotic components of the ecosystem. You will determine the soil type and collect samples to be used in extracting microinvertebrates (Exercise 1, Field Study E) and microorganisms (Exercise 1, Field Study F).

Procedure

1. Read about soil temperature (Field Study A) and air temperature (Field Study B); then place thermometers in appropriate locations to equilibrate while you begin your other work.
2. Remove the vegetation from a small undisturbed area near the tree plot. Place the soil thermometer in the soil and allow it to equilibrate for 10 to 15 minutes before recording the temperature.
3. Carefully remove the leaf litter. Using the soil auger, remove two soil cores approximately 30–45 cm long.
4. Sketch the profile of the soil layers in the margin of your lab manual. (See an example of a soil profile in your materials.) Note changes in color and texture. How much sand or clay or dark organic matter appears to be present?
5. Place each soil sample in a separate plastic (self-sealing) bag. Follow the directions provided with the soil test kit. Determine the soil pH and any other characteristics suggested by your instructor for one sample. Instructions are included with the soil test kit. Save the other sample to share with your team.
6. Remove a third sample of soil to be used for determining the presence and types of microinvertebrates and microorganisms. Collect this sample by using a trowel to dig some of the upper loose dirt. Seal this sample in a third plastic bag. Label it "organisms" with the plot number. The organisms will be extracted as described in Exercise 1, Field Studies E and F.

7. Study the soil association map of this general area and determine the type of soil typical of this region.

Results

1. Record the soil temperature and pH in Table 6.
2. Sketch the soil profile in the margin of your lab manual.
3. Record in Table 6 the soil type and other pertinent information from soil maps.

Field Study B. Climatology

Materials

NOAA climatological data sheets	light meter
sling psychrometer (with directions)	thermometers
min/max thermometer (with directions)	wind anemometer (with directions)

Introduction

The climatic conditions of the environment can be viewed on the local level or on a smaller scale (microclimate) within the forest ecosystem. Not only does the microclimate affect the organisms that are present, but the process is mutual: Organisms will influence the microclimatic conditions as well. For example, the air temperature above bare ground and open grassland may differ significantly owing to differences in water loss and the shading effect of the vegetation.

Procedure

1. *Local climate.* For general climate patterns in your area, consult the local climatological data sheets provided. You should record in Table 6 the average annual rainfall for this month, temperature averages, and the relative humidity at 1300 hours (1 P.M.).
2. *Microclimate.* Variation in microclimate due to such factors as elevation, slope, and shade can result in temperatures, humidities, and light intensities quite different from those of surrounding areas only a few meters away. For example, the microclimate conditions near ground level will be different from those a few meters above the surface. Measure the following microclimate conditions and record your results in Table 6.
   a. *Air temperature.* Record the temperature at the soil surface and 2 m or so above the ground for a sunny spot and a shady spot. Allow 5 to 10 minutes for the thermometer to equilibrate at each position. Record the minimum and maximum temperature for the previous 24 hours if a min/max thermometer was left in the forest overnight.
   b. *Light.* Using a light meter, measure the light intensity in the forest and in full sunlight. Calculate the percentage of full sun that reaches the forest floor.
   c. *Humidity.* Humidity refers to the amount of water vapor in the air. It has important biological effects on respiration, transpiration, and evaporation. **Relative humidity** (the most common measurement)

Table 6
Characteristics of the Physical Environment

Locality: ____________ **Plot ID #:** __________ **Date:** _________
Students: ______________________ **Instructor:** _____________
Soil
Temperature (°C): pH: Other: Description:
Local Climate
Annual rainfall: Annual average temperature: Relative humidity:
Microclimate
Temperature Soil surface: sun: ______ shade: ______ 2 m above surface: sun: ______ shade: ______ Min ____________ Max ____________ Light Forest __________ Full sun __________ % full sun __________ Relative humidity __________ Wind speed __________
Topography **Disturbance** **Comments**

is the actual amount of water vapor in the air divided by the total possible water vapor (or saturation vapor) in the air at its temperature. Refer to the directions provided and measure relative humidity with a **sling psychrometer.** Do not hit anyone with the psychrometer!

d. *Wind.* Using the **wind anemometer,** measure the wind speed in the sampling area. What factors can you suggest that affect wind speed?

Results

Record in Table 6 the results of your measurements for air temperature, light, humidity, and wind.

Field Study C. Topographic Features

Materials

field notebook
pencil

Introduction

Before completing your study of the abiotic components, you should stand back and observe the general features of the landscape that are difficult to measure but that may influence other physical factors and the organisms as well.

Procedure

Observe the topography of the sampling site. Is the area sloping, eroded, on a hillside, or cut by a stream or ditch? Record in Table 6 indications of past or present disturbance—for example, scarring from past fires, cut stumps, old fences, or terracing.

Results

1. Record the results of your observations in Table 6.
2. In the margin of your lab manual, sketch the topographic features that appear to influence your sample site.

EXERCISE 3
Data Analysis

Materials

summary of all student data
calculator

Introduction

Students will need to pool data with team members and other teams. You may determine the abundance (density or cover), distribution (frequency), overall size (dominance), and importance (the sum of relative density, frequency, and dominance) for each species in the sampling categories (trees, SSV, and so on).

Density, the number of individuals per unit area, provides a summary of abundance by species. **(Percent cover** is the measure of abundance used for seedlings and herbaceous plants.) However, the density of a species does not necessarily reflect the distribution of the species on the landscape. **Frequency** provides information on the distribution of a species and is calculated as the percent of plots sampled that have at least one individual of the species present. **Dominance** is a measure of the influence of a species based on the size of individuals. (Dominance is determined from the area, called basal area, calculated from DBH measurements.) Adding the relative values for each of these measures provides an estimate of overall **importance,** which includes abundance, distribution, and size. The equations for calculating these parameters are provided in Table 7 on the next page.

Procedure

Trees, Shrubs, Saplings, and Vines

1. If circumference was measured for trees and shrubs, saplings, and vines, then calculate DBH for individuals in each sample plot and record the results in Tables 2 and 3, respectively.
2. Calculate basal area for each tree and shrub, sapling, and vine. Record your results in Tables 2 and 3, respectively.
3. Pool the data for all sample plots and record for each species the total number of individuals, number of plots in which a species was present, and total basal area. Summarize tree data in Table 8, SSV data in Table 9.
4. Calculate density. Total the densities for all species and calculate the relative density of each species.
5. Calculate frequency. Total the frequencies for all species and calculate the relative frequency of each species.
6. Calculate dominance. Total the dominance for all species and calculate the relative dominance of each species.
7. Calculate importance value by totaling the relative density, relative frequency, and relative dominance for each species.

Table 7
Calculating Density, Frequency, Dominance, and Importance Values for the Biotic Components of the Ecosystem

DBH $= \frac{\text{circumference}}{\pi}$	**Basal area** $= 0.7854\ (\text{DBH})^2$
Dominance $= \frac{\text{total basal area}}{\text{total area sampled}}$	
Relative dominance $= \frac{\text{dominance for a species}}{\text{total dominance for all species}} \times 100$	
Density $= \frac{\text{no. of individuals}}{\text{total area sampled}}$	
Relative density $= \frac{\text{density for a species}}{\text{total density for all species}} \times 100$	
Frequency $= \frac{\text{number of plots in which species recorded}}{\text{total number of plots sampled}}$	
Relative frequency $= \frac{\text{frequency for a species}}{\text{total frequency for all species}} \times 100$	
Average percent cover $= \frac{\text{total percent cover}}{\text{total number of plots sampled}}$	
Importance value = relative density + relative dominance + relative frequency	

Seedlings and Herbs

1. Pool the data for all sample plots and record in Table 10 the percent cover for each species and the number of plots in which a species was present.
2. Calculate average percent cover.
3. Calculate frequency. Sum the frequencies for all species and calculate the relative frequency of each species.

Macroinvertebrates

1. Pool the data for all sample plots and record in Table 11 the total number of individuals for each species and the number of plots in which a species was present.
2. Calculate density. Sum the densities for all species and calculate the relative density of each species.
3. Calculate frequency. Sum the frequencies for all species and calculate the relative frequency of each species.

Abiotic Components

Pool the data for all sample plots and record it in Table 12.

Results

1. Record all summary results for *trees* in Table 8 and those for *shrubs, saplings,* and *vines* in Table 9.
2. List in the spaces provided the three most important tree species and the three most important shrub, sapling, and vine species.

   Trees:

   Shrubs, saplings, and *vines:*

3. Record the summary results of *seedlings* and *herbs* in Table 10.
4. List in the space provided the three most common species based on their abundance.

   Seedlings and *herbs:*

5. Record summary results for *macroinvertebrates* in Table 11.
6. List in the space provided the three most common macroinvertebrate species based on abundance. Indicate, if possible, the appropriate trophic level: *primary* (1°) or *secondary* (2°) *consumers,* or *detritivores* (D) by placing the appropriate letter or number by each. To make these determinations, observe mouthparts or other body structures. Consult reference books or handouts provided in the laboratory or from the library. See "Who Eats What" (Hogan, 1994).

   Macroinvertebrates:

Table 8
Summary of Results for **Trees**

Locality: ______________________ **Size class:** Trees **Date:** ______________

No. of plots sampled: ______________________ **Total area sampled:** ______________

Species	Total No. of Individuals	Density	Relative Density	No. of Plots Present	Frequency	Relative Frequency	Total Basal Area	Dominance	Relative Dominance	Importance Value
Totals			100			100			100	

Table 9
Summary of Results for **Shrubs**, **Saplings**, and **Vines**

Locality: ______________________ **Size class:** SSV **Date:** ______________

No. of plots sampled: ______________________ **Total area sampled:** ______________

Species	Total No. of Individuals	Density	Relative Density	No. of Plots Present	Frequency	Relative Frequency	Total Basal Area	Dominance	Relative Dominance	Importance Value
Totals			100			100			100	

Table 10
Summary of Results for **Seedlings** and **Herbaceous Vegetation**

Locality: ______________________ **Size class:** S/Herb **Date:** ________

No. of plots sampled: ______________ **Total area sampled:** ____________

Species	Average Percent Cover	No. of Plots Present	Frequency	Relative Frequency
Totals				100

Table 11
Summary of Results for **Macroinvertebrates**

Locality: ______________________ **Size class:** Macroinvert. **Date:** ________

No. of plots sampled: __________________ **Total area sampled:** ____________

Species	Total No. of Individuals	Density	Relative Density	No. of Plots Present	Frequency	Relative Frequency
Totals			100			100

7. List in the space below the five most common *microinvertebrates* observed in all plots. Indicate, if possible, the appropriate trophic level: *primary* (1°), *secondary* (2°), or *tertiary* (3°) *consumers*, or *detritivores* (D) by placing the appropriate letter or number by each. To determine trophic level, observe mouthparts and other body structures. Consult reference books or handouts provided in the laboratory or from the library. See "Who Eats What" (Hogan, 1994).

   Microinvertebrates:

8. What types of microorganisms grew in your agar plates? Did you observe fungal hyphae (filaments)? Did you observe bacterial colonies? Describe them briefly.

9. Record the summary results for all *abiotic* components in Table 12.

10. List the abiotic features that appear to be important influences in the ecosystem.

11. Describe any summary information not included in the tables.

Table 12
Summary of Results for **Physical Environment**

	Plot				
	1	2	3	4	5
Soil					
Description					
pH					
Temperature					
Climate					
Annual rainfall					
Annual avg. temp.					
Microclimate					
Temperature					
°C soil surface					
°C 2 m above					
°C min					
°C max					
Light intensity					
Forest					
Full sun					
% full sun					
Relative humidity					
Wind speed					
Topography					
Comments					

Figure 7.
Profile diagram of a typical forest system. Using your results, label the important species in each of the vertical layers of the forest, from trees to herbs on the forest floor.

Discussion

1. Prepare ecosystem profiles. Using the results from your study of the forest, label the profile diagram provided in Figure 7. Label the trees, shrubs, saplings, vines, and herbs to illustrate the species composition of each vertical layer of the forest ecosystem. If you are not investigating a forest system, construct a profile diagram that will illustrate the specific composition and patterns of your study site. Refer to Figure 7.
2. Incorporating all components of the ecosystem, complete the model of the ecosystem in Figure 8, indicating the trophic levels and interactions observed in the forest. Provide examples for each trophic level, from producers to top carnivores to decomposers.
3. Write a one-page discussion of your results. Characterize the forest by vegetation type. Describe trophic levels and provide examples, using your model as an illustration. Propose features of the physical environment that appear to influence or be influenced by the biotic community.

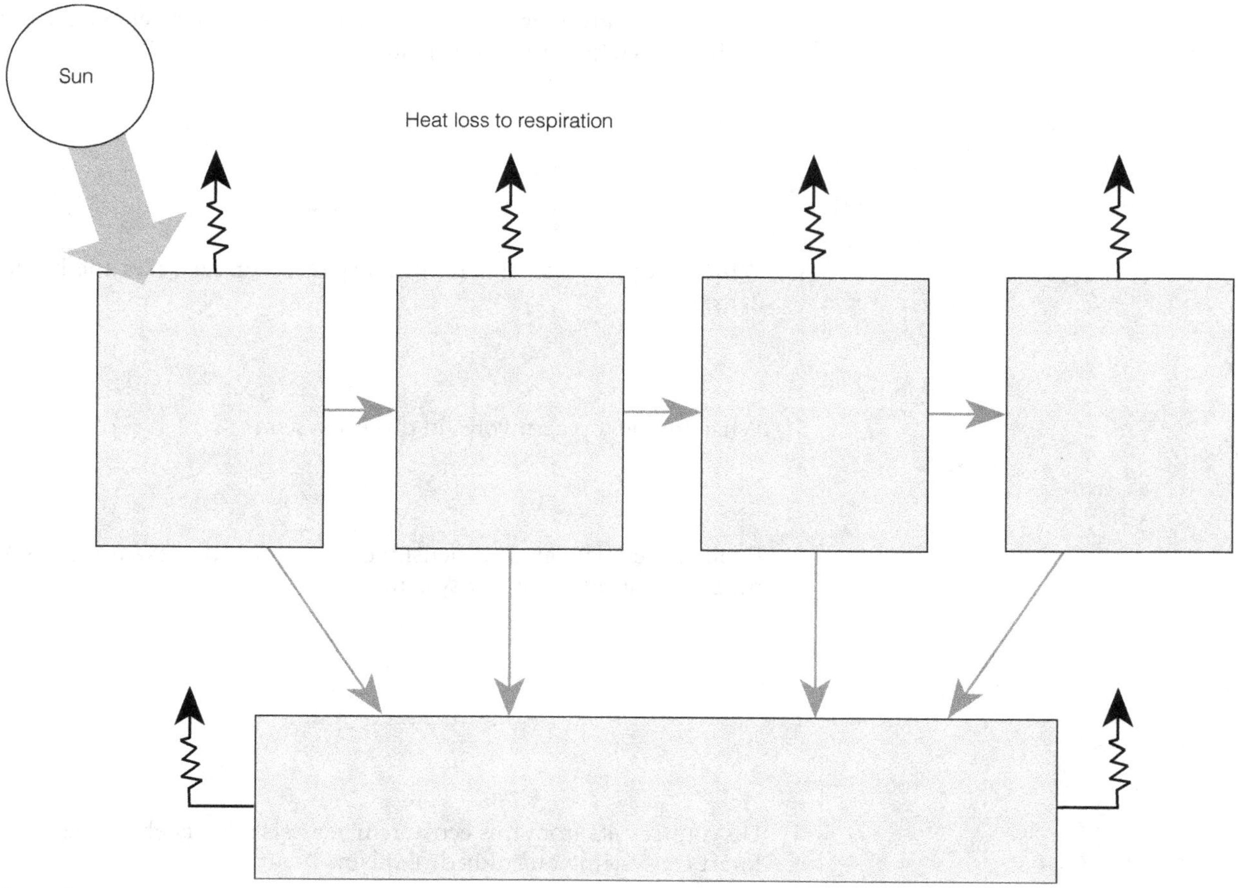

Figure 8.
Compartmental model for trophic relationships in an ecosystem. Heat losses to respiration are represented by zigzag arrows. Label the trophic levels and add arrows to represent energy flow from trophic level to trophic level. For each trophic level, list examples from organisms observed in this laboratory.

Questions for Review

1. What are the factors that determine the importance of species in the tree category?

2. Are the same species important in the tree and SSV categories?

3. What are the advantages and disadvantages of using cover as a measure of abundance for herbaceous plants?

4. Which group of consumers, primary or secondary, had the highest density?

5. What are the top carnivores in this ecosystem?

   Explain the relatively low density of carnivores (for example, hawks, owls, or snakes) in this ecosystem.

6. Do your results from this ecosystem analysis adequately represent the forest ecosystem you studied? Explain.

Applying Your Knowledge

1. To investigate the structure and function of ecosystems, ecologists may construct a microcosm using organisms and materials from the ecosystem. Properly constructed, these model systems should be self-sustaining. If you remove the primary producers from the microcosm, would you predict that your model would continue to be self-sustaining? Explain.

   If you remove the decomposers and detritivores, would the microcosm be self-sustaining? Explain.

2. Using your knowledge of ecosystem structure and function, compare the trophic structure of a desert to that of a temperate hardwood forest. Include the relative number of organisms and energy availability for the different trophic levels.

3. Sudden oak death, the rapid decline of red oaks and tanoaks, was first described for central California forests in 1994. The disease is caused by the pathogen *Phytopthora ramorum,* which infects and kills tanoak seedlings and trees. However, mature red oaks are more susceptible, developing large lesions on their stem, with clusters of trees rapidly dying. The death of saplings could have very different effects on the forest community compared with the death of mature trees. How might forest structure and regeneration be affected by the loss of mature oaks that dominate the canopy? How might the forest be affected by the loss of young saplings?

4. Wolves did not inhabit Yellowstone National Park from the 1930s until 1995, when 14 gray wolves were introduced by the National Park Service and U.S. Fish and Wildlife Service. In 2004, there were 16 packs with about 10 wolves per pack. Some of the changes in the ecosystem were expected, for example the decline of elk, a major food source for the wolves. However changes in other animals and vegetation over 10 years provide a study of trophic structure and ecological connections. Between 1930 and 1990, there was no growth of young aspen, cottonwood, and willows along creeks, but now young saplings are thriving. No beavers were seen in these areas, but they have now returned. Draw a simple model of interactions among these components in the Yellowstone ecosystem, including wolves, elk, aspen, and beavers.

Explain how the introduction of a top carnivore could affect vegetation in an ecosystem.

5. Design a sampling regimen to answer the following question: Are there differences in the abundance and species composition of microinvertebrates found in the tree litter from forests of different ages? Include the types of plots, organisms, and physical features to be measured and the selection of sample sites.

OPTIONAL EXERCISE 1
Biotic Components: Weedy Lots or Fields

If a forest system is not accessible for study, small and more numerous plots can be used to study weedy fields, which are ubiquitous in both urban and rural environments. The scale for environmental factors can also be reduced and will require sampling at intervals that correspond to the smaller plot sizes. If the weedy field has woody vegetation, then refer to the plot sizes recommended earlier for the forest ecosystem. If only a few woody plants are present, consider recording the presence of these in the general description of the study site, but do not sample them. If the field has only seedlings or nonwoody (herbaceous) vegetation (or both), then use 0.50-m^2 plots to sample the vegetation and invertebrates.

It may be necessary to modify your field studies to correspond to the ecosystem being studied.

Students should work in teams of four: two for seedlings, herbaceous plants, and macroinvertebrates, and two for microinvertebrates and abiotic factors. A class of 24 could sample 6 to 12 plots.

Suggested Outline for Weedy Fields

Exercise 1, Biotic Components
  Field Study C. Seedlings and Herbaceous Plants
  D. Macroinvertebrates
  E. Microinvertebrates
  F. Microorganisms
  G. Other Forest Animals

Exercise 2, Abiotic Components
  Field Study A. Soil
  B. Climatology

Exercise 3, Data Analysis

Complete sections that are appropriate to the biotic components sampled.

References

Barbour, M., J. H. Burk, and W. D. Pitts. *Terrestrial Plant Ecology,* 3rd ed. Menlo Park, CA: Benjamin Cummings, 1999.

Brower, J. E., and J. H. Zar. *Field and Laboratory Methods for General Ecology.* Dubuque, IA: William C. Brown, 1972. This edition is more comprehensive than later editions.

Cox, G. W. *Laboratory Manual of General Ecology,* 8th ed. Columbus, OH: McGraw Hill, 2001.

Hogan, K. "Who Eats What," *Eco-Inquiry,* Appendix A. Dubuque, IA: Kendall-Hall Publishing, 1994, pp. 355–382.

Meuller-Dombois, D., and H. Ellenberg. *Aims and Methods of Vegetation Ecology.* New York: Wiley, 1974.

Rizzo, D. M. and M. Garbelotto. "Sudden Oak Death: Endangering California and Oregon Forest Ecosystems," *Frontiers in Ecology and the Environment* 1(5):197–204, 2003.

Robbins, J. "Lessons from the Wolf," *Scientific American.* 290(6):76–81.

Waterman, M. and E. Stanley. *Biological Inquiry: A Workbook of Investigative Cases.* Menlo Park, CA: Benjamin Cummings, 2005.

Ecology II: Computer Simulations of a Pond Ecosystem

Laboratory Objectives

After completing this lab topic, you should be able to:

1. Develop a computer model to investigate a pond ecosystem.
2. Calibrate the model using information from field investigations.
3. Determine the steady-state values for the model ecosystem.
4. Answer questions and test hypotheses using a computer model.
5. Evaluate the effects of disturbance on the model ecosystem.
6. Apply the results of computer simulations to predict the results in real ecosystems.

Introduction

Ecosystems are difficult to investigate using the experimental method because they are so large and complex. Scientists are nevertheless studying ecosystem structure and function in a selected number of systems across the United States as part of the Long Term Ecological Research Program, effectively implementing experiments at the landscape level in places such as the Okefenokee Swamp in Georgia, Konza Prairie in Kansas, the hardwood forest of Coweeta Hydrological Station in North Carolina, and the urban ecosystem of Baltimore, Maryland. However, to understand these complex systems and to make predictions concerning their responses to disturbance (both natural and human), ecologists often depend on computer models that correspond to the ecosystem of interest. Information obtained in field investigations is used to determine the structure of the model, the appropriate interactions among components, and the actual values used in the model.

You have already worked with models in other laboratory topics, including the bead models of cellular reproduction and population genetics and the diagrammatic models in terrestrial ecology. Models generally provide a simplified and amplified (or reduced) view of the phenomenon of interest. In this lab topic, you will actually construct a computer model of a simple ecosystem, the pond. As you develop your model, you can simulate a variety of conditions, including the effects of disturbance.

Table 1
Definitions of Ecological Terms

Primary producer:
Consumer:
Trophic level:
Ecosystem:
Biotic component:
Abiotic component:
Food chain:

You should be able to construct a compartmental model of a forest ecosystem and develop a general model based on the trophic levels present in ecosystems. Before continuing this lab, complete Table 1, providing definitions and examples.

The Pond Ecosystem

The primary producers in a pond are generally the algae floating in the surface layers and some plants growing at the pond edge, or margin. These autotrophic organisms convert the energy of sunlight into chemical energy stored in organic compounds. The producers, in turn, are consumed by primary consumers (herbivores such as aquatic invertebrates), which are ingested by secondary consumers (carnivores such as sunfish) and even tertiary consumers (carnivores such as bass) (Figure 1). The movement of energy through these systems is called **energy flow** (energy does not cycle), and at each trophic level, the amount of available energy is reduced. All organisms expend some energy in the activities of life, and this energy is dissipated as heat. The efficiency of transfer from one level to another is only about 10%.

The rate at which light energy is converted to chemical energy is called **primary productivity.** Productivity is measured as the amount of **biomass,** or organic matter, added to the system per unit area per unit time (for example, $kg/m^2/yr$). In tropical rain forests, for example, the primary productivity is 2.2 $kg/m^2/yr$; in temperate grassland, 0.6 $kg/m^2/yr$; and in lakes and streams, 0.25 $kg/m^2/yr$ (Campbell and Reece, 2005). **Secondary productivity** is the rate at which consumers and detritivores accumulate new biomass from organic matter that was consumed. In the computer model of the pond, the changes in each trophic level will be measured as biomass.

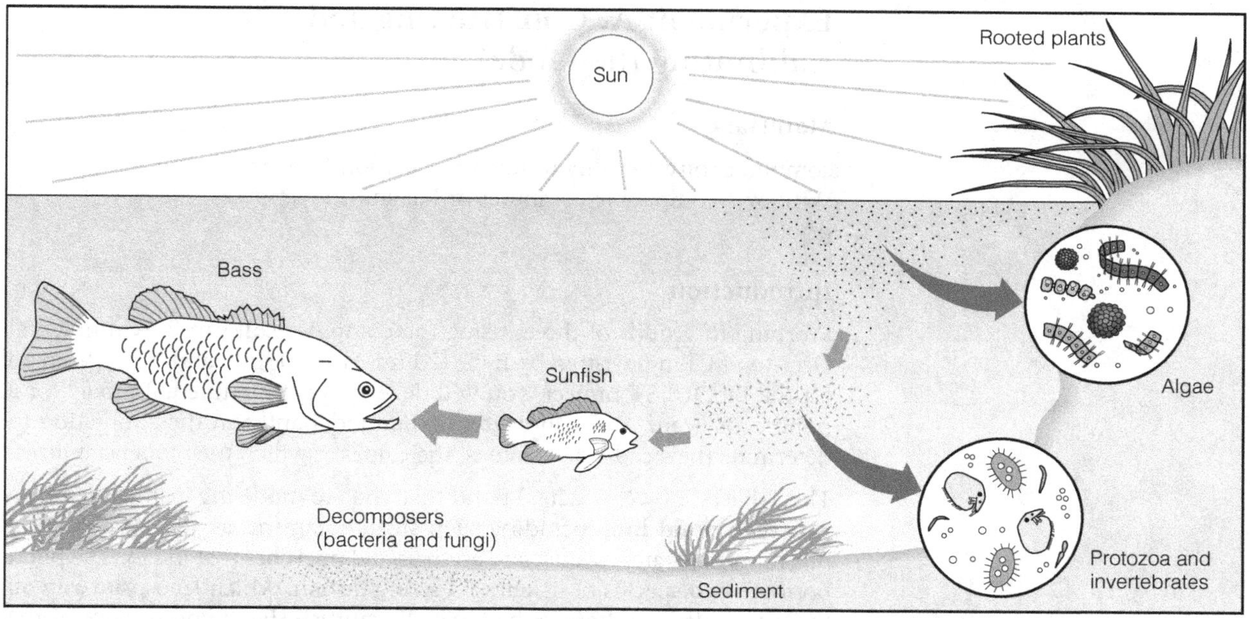

Figure 1.
The food web of a pond ecosystem. The primary producers (algae) are consumed by primary consumers (protozoa and invertebrates), which in turn are consumed by secondary consumers (sunfish and bass). In this pond, bass also may be tertiary consumers.

Refer to the food web in Figure 1, and in the margin of your lab manual, sketch a compartmental model of a pond ecosystem. Indicate connections between compartments (inputs and outputs).

EXERCISE 1

Computer Model of the Pond Ecosystem

The computer model of an ecosystem must be based on observations of the natural ecosystem in the field. Your compartmental model, which includes biotic components and interactions, represents the first step in constructing a model. You must also determine the biomass associated with each compartment based on data collected from field investigations. These data are used to **calibrate** the model—that is, to set the starting values for each component.

In this exercise, you will construct and calibrate a computer model for a pond ecosystem. You will run an initial simulation to determine the **steady-state,** or stable, values for your pond, then compare your results with those expected from a field study. In the process, you will practice changing components of the model, graphing, and printing your results. Once you have determined that your model adequately represents a natural ecosystem, you can begin to ask questions, formulate hypotheses and predictions, and test these using the model ecosystem. This process will continue as you adjust the model, analyze your results, and simulate conditions.

Experiment A. Constructing and Calibrating the Model

Materials

computer software (Environmental Decision Making)
Windows-compatible computer or Macintosh computer
printer

Introduction

Working in groups of three, using the computer software Environmental Decision Making, written by E. C. Odum, H. T. Odum, and N. S. Peterson for the BioQUEST project, you will develop a compartmental model for a pond ecosystem. You will calibrate the model and run the simulation to determine the steady-state values, the values at which the model stabilizes.

The 1-hectare (= 2.47 acres) pond that you are modeling is inhabited by a variety of **pond life,** including such small organisms as algae, micro- and macroinvertebrates, plants, and animals and microbes that inhabit the pond bottom. Two species of fish are present: **sunfish,** which feed primarily off the pond life, and **bass,** which eat the sunfish. Each component of the ecosystem is represented by an icon (Figure 2).

Procedure

Your instructor will review how to use the computer, including use of the mouse, and guidelines for use of the computer facilities. Environmental Decision Making is now available in both Mac and Windows™ versions. Depending on the version you are using, the screens may be slightly different.

1. Open the program by double-clicking on the icon Environmental Decision Making (EDM), then double-click on *Pond Worksheet.* (Double-click on *Pondwork* in the Windows version.) Click on the *Extend* screen. You should see an empty window with the plotter icon in the corner with the label "Quantity."
2. Construct the model to incorporate pond life, sunfish, and bass.
   a. Choose BioQUEST Library from the Library menu, and then choose BIOQULIB.LIX from the Library menu. Select Sunlight from the submenu.
   b. When you select an icon and hold down the mouse button, the pointer changes to a hand that allows you to move the icon. Move the sunlight icon to the left of the window.
   c. Choose Pond Life from the BioQUEST Library submenu and position it to the right of the sunlight icon.

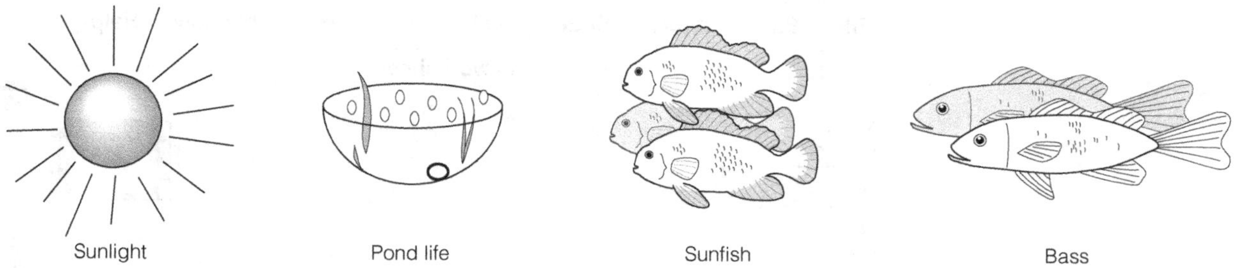

Figure 2.
Icons for the components of the model ecosystem.

d. To connect the sunlight and pond life components, draw a line from one icon to another, connecting the small boxes on each icon. To do this, move the pointer over the small dark box by the sunlight icon. The pointer changes to a pen. Drag the pen from the dark box of the sunlight icon to the open box of pond life (Figure 3). Release the button. The solid line should connect the dark box of the sunlight icon (indicating flows out of this component) with the open box of the pond life icon (indicating flows into the second component). For example, sunlight provides the energy input to the ecosystem through pond life. Therefore, the dark box of sunlight is connected to the open box of pond life.

e. Connect the pond life to the plotter (Figure 4) by drawing a line connecting the upper dark box of the pond life icon to the first open box on the plotter. The plotter can connect up to four components.

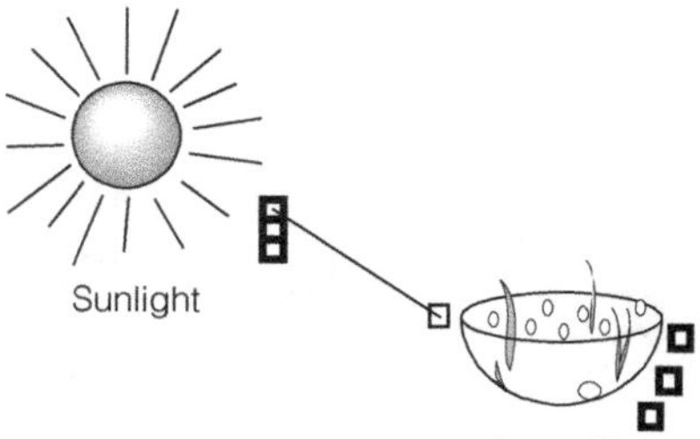

Figure 3.
Drawing lines with the mouse to connect icons. Position the mouse over the dark box, click the mouse, and hold. A pen will appear, and you can draw a connecting line.

To erase an icon, move the pointer to the icon, and a hand should appear. Select the icon and press *Delete.*

To erase a line, move the pointer to the line and click it to select it. Press *Delete.*

---

f. Choose Sunfish from the BioQUEST Library and position it to the right of the pond life icon. Connect the open box of the sunfish icon to a dark box of the pond life icon. Connect the upper dark box of the sunfish to the second box of the plotter.

g. Choose Bass from the BioQUEST Library and position the icon to the right of the sunfish icon. Connect one of the open boxes of the bass icon to one of the dark boxes of the sunfish icon. Connect the

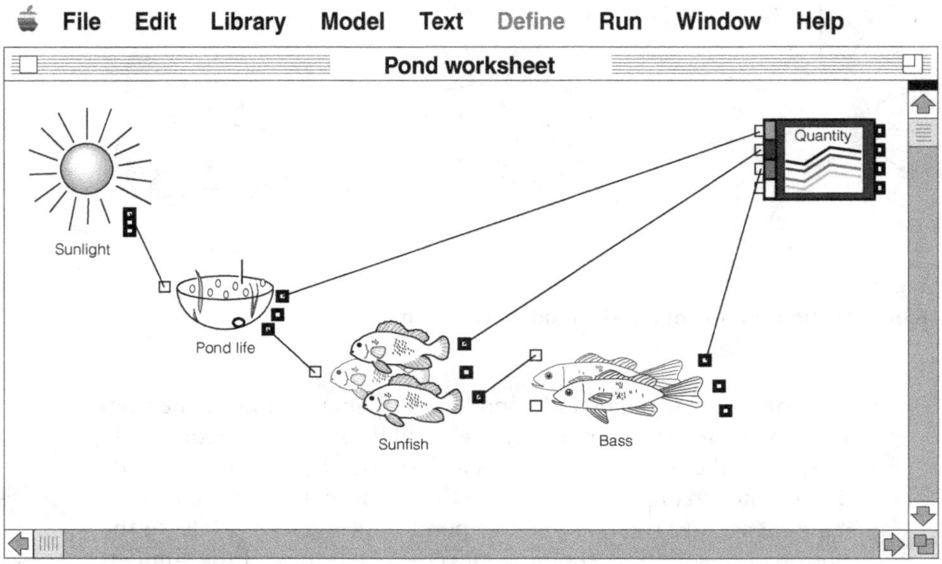

Figure 4.
An example of the model ecosystem.

upper dark box of the bass icon to the third box of the plotter. Beginning on the left side of the screen, you should have sunlight connected to pond life; pond life should in turn be connected to sunfish, which consume the pond life. Finally, the bass should be connected to the sunfish. All the organisms should be connected to the plotter (Figure 4). What trophic level is represented by the bass?

3. Calibrate the model by determining the starting values for the components of the ecosystem: sunlight, pond life, sunfish, and bass.
   a. Refer to the map of solar radiation for the United States (Figure 5). Determine the solar energy for your location in kilocalories per meter squared. If your location is not included on the map, ask your instructor for appropriate values to use.
   b. Double-click on the sunlight icon. A box, called a *dialog box,* should appear on the screen. Calibrate the model by entering the appropriate energy values in the box and click on OK.
   c. Double-click on the pond life icon. Enter *1,000 kg/ha (kilograms per hectare) for your starting value.* Click on OK.
   d. Double-click on the sunfish icon and enter the total biomass of sunfish in kilograms in the dialog box. An appropriate starting value for sunfish might be 500 sunfish for a 1-ha pond. (*Assume 10 sunfish per kilogram, or 50 kg/ha.*) Click on OK.
   e. Double-click on the bass icon and enter the total biomass of bass in kilograms in the dialog box. *The starting value for bass might be 10 large bass, 1 kg each, or 10 kg/ha.* Click on OK.
   f. Record the starting values for all components in Table 2.

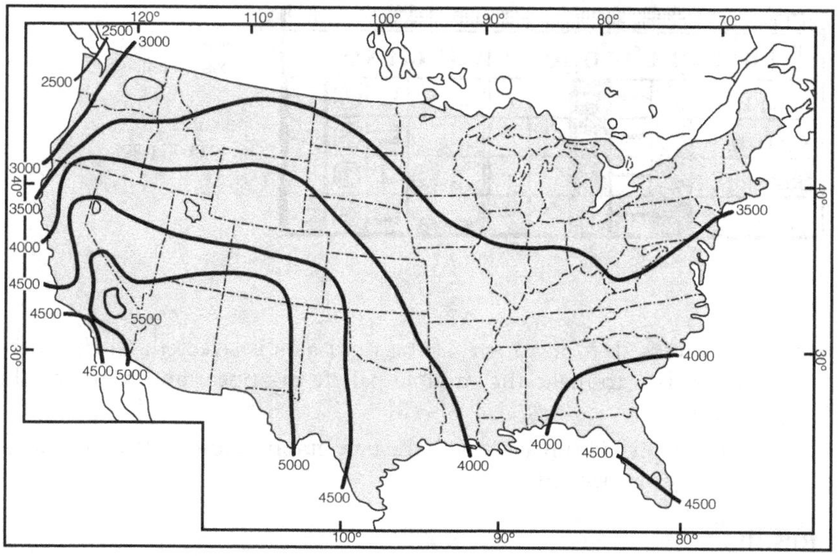

Figure 5.
Solar radiation for regions of the United States. Select the kilocalories of solar radiation for your location.

4. To calibrate the plotter, choose Simulation Setup from the Run menu. In the time dialog box that appears, change the time to end the simulation to 2 years (730 days). Enter *730* in the first box and click on OK.
5. Run the simulation: Choose Run Simulation from the Run menu.The simulation should run and the simulation graph, similar to the screen shown in Figure 8, should be plotted.
   a. Check the lines on the graph. There should be three, representing pond life, sunfish, and bass. If not, the icons on the model are not correctly attached to the plotter or each other. Return to the model by closing the Pond System window. Correct the model and run the simulation again.
   b. Check the axes of the graph. You can modify the graph and table, if needed, to accommodate all the components of the ecosystem and to scale axes appropriately. To change the values on the axes, click on the lower or upper value for the axis. Type in the new number and press *Enter.* To modify the labels, click in the space above the axis and type in the appropriate label. Press *Enter.*
   c. Label the axes for your graph. The controls for changing the features of the graph appear in a bar at the top of the screen. You may want to experiment with these in a later simulation. (Refer to Figure 6.) Click on the icon in the first box of the display bar. A palette showing the variables in the graph will appear. *Pond life* should appear in the first box, *Sunfish kg/ha* in the second, and *Bass kg/ha* in the third (Figure 7). Click and type in the box to change the variables. To read the small values for the bass, you will use a different scale on the right axis (Y2). If the right axis is not selected, click on the graph icon (eighth column) on the same row for Bass. The graph icon should now

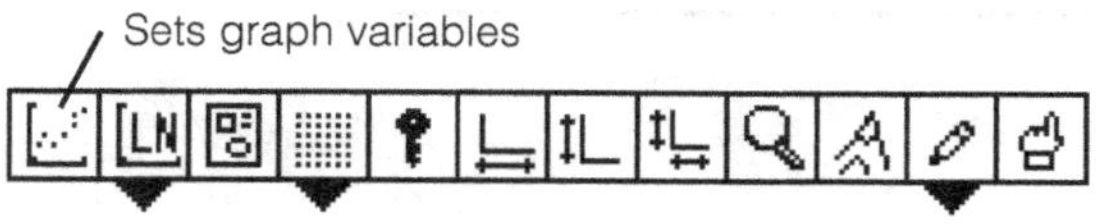

Figure 6.
Display bar for graph. Select the graph icon to adjust the axes and labels for the simulation graph.

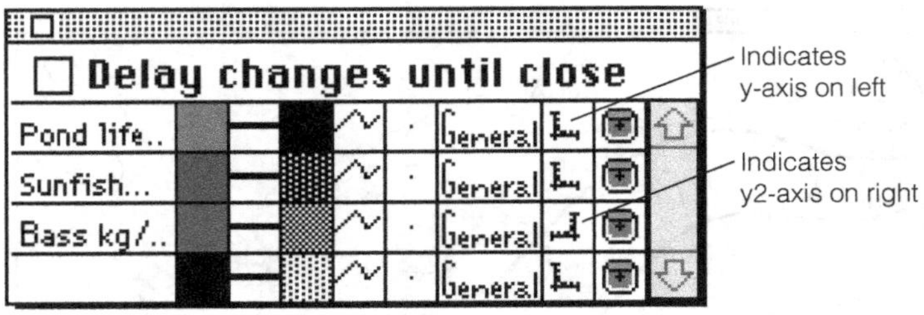

Figure 7.
Example of palette for modifying graph variables. Modify the axes and labels by entering information in this palette.

be reversed, indicating that the right axis is selected. Click on the Close box to make the variable palette disappear and return to the graph.

d. The graph will run again with the new graph features. Make additional changes as needed.

Results

1. On the simulation graph, note the point at which biomass levels off for the ecosystem components. These various points indicate the steady state values for the energy levels used in your model, showing that the system has stabilized. *To read values from the graph, move the cursor to the point of interest (for example, the steady-state point) and read the corresponding biomass in the table at the bottom of the graph (Figure 8).* The top row of the table should show the time and biomass at the position on the graph indicated by the cursor line. By moving along the graph, you can follow the values on the top row, indicating increases, decreases, and relative stability. Other values and times are listed in the table.
2. Record the steady-state values and the time it took to reach steady state in Table 2.

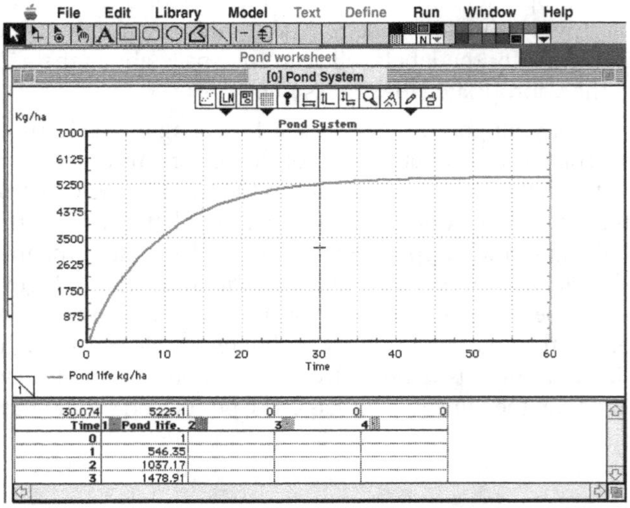

Figure 8.
Example of reading values from a simulation graph. To determine the values at any point on the graph, move the cursor to the position. Read the values on the top row of the table below the graph. The cursor line is at 5,225 kg/ha of pond life on day 30.

Table 2
Starting and Steady-State Values for Computer Simulation, Experiment A

Component	Starting Value	Steady-State Value
Sunlight		
Pond life		
Sunfish		
Bass		
Time to steady state:		

3. Choose *Print Plotter* from the File menu. If you want to print only the graph, then click on the *Top Plot Only* button. If *Plot Data Tables* is selected (a ✓ appears in the box), then click on this box to remove the table option. Click on *Print.*
4. Close the simulation graph window.

Discussion

1. Describe the changes in the biomass of each component of the ecosystem over time.

   Pond life:

Sunfish:

Bass:

2. Did the highest and lowest values for the three components occur at the same time? Explain why or why not.

3. What do you predict would happen to the steady-state values if you increased or decreased the amount of sunlight available?

Experiment B. Steady-State Model

Materials

computer software (Environmental Decision Making)
Windows-compatible computer or Macintosh computer
printer

Introduction

Your initial calibration was based on data from field observations and investigations. Having run the model, you should have estimates for the steady-state values. In this simulation, you will calibrate and run the model using the steady-state values from Experiment A.

Hypothesis

State a hypothesis for changes in the components of the ecosystem at steady state.

Predictions

Based on your hypothesis, predict the appearance of the simulation.

Procedure

1. Calibrate the model. (Refer to Experiment A, Procedure step 3.) Double-click on each of the icons and set the starting value for each component at the steady-state value based on results in Table 2.
2. Record the new starting values in Table 3.
3. Run the simulation.

Table 3
Starting and Steady-State Values for Computer Simulation, Experiment B

Component	Starting Value	New Steady-State Value
Sunlight		
Pond life		
Sunfish		
Bass		
Time to steady state:		

Results

1. Compare the graph of this simulation with the results from the first simulation (Experiment A). If the starting values for this experiment are not similar to the ending steady-state values from the first simulation, check the starting value for each component. Rerun the simulation if necessary.

2. Record your results in Table 3.
3. Print the graph. Choose *Print* from the File menu.
4. Label each line on your graph.

Discussion

1. Did your results match your predictions? If not, explain.

2. Were the values you set for this simulation actually at steady state? If not, consider using new steady-state values from this simulation and repeat the simulation.
3. The steady-state value for each component represents the biomass that can be sustained by this ecosystem. This is referred to as the **carrying capacity** for each component of the ecosystem. At carrying capacity, how many bass can be sustained by this pond system? (*Hint:* Refer to Experiment A; The values used in the model are biomass.)

4. Does the biomass increase or decrease as you move from producers to the secondary and tertiary consumers? Would you ever expect the pond biomass to be the same in all the components? Explain.

EXERCISE 2

Effects of Disturbance on the Pond Ecosystem

Materials

computer software (Environmental Decision Making)
Macintosh computer with mouse
printer
computer disk, CD, or USB flash drive

Introduction

In this exercise, you will discuss questions that interest your group and design experiments to determine the effects of disturbance on the components of the pond ecosystem. You will run a series of three or more simulations.

In groups of three, discuss with your teammates possible options for *simulating disturbance of the pond ecosystem.* Using Environmental Decision Making, you can change a number of factors. Consider the following options as you discuss your ideas:

1. What happens to biomass and steady-state values for a pond receiving more or less sunlight (see Figure 5)?
2. What would happen to each trophic level if more (or fewer) sunfish (or bass) inhabited the pond?
3. What changes would occur to the biomass of the sunfish and bass if another fish (e.g., gar) were added to the pond? (Gar eat sunfish, but not bass.)
4. What changes would you expect in each trophic level if sunfish (or bass) were eliminated due to a massive fish kill?

The questions you pose should have a biological basis; that is, they should be meaningful questions based on your understanding of ecosystems, particularly pond ecosystems. Just because you can change the model does not mean the question is appropriate. If necessary, consult your textbook or additional readings supplied by your instructor.

List the questions of interest to your group.

Questions

You will run three computer simulations of your own design. You may choose to pursue one or more questions, depending on your results. With a computer model, you can make any number of changes easily, but, depending on what you do, you may have difficulty in stating predictions and interpreting your results. *It is best to begin with one change at a time, increasing the level of complexity in subsequent simulations.*

In the third simulation (Experiment C), you will investigate the effects of fishing on the components of the pond ecosystem. You may choose to add fishing to one of your previous models or design an entirely new simulation model.

Be prepared to describe one of your questions, explain the model, and present your results at the end of the lab period.

Experiment A. Computer Simulation 1

Choose one question that you want to pursue. Formulate a hypothesis and make a prediction for your computer simulation.

Question

Hypothesis

Formulate a hypothesis about the effects of disturbance on the pond ecosystem.

Prediction

State a prediction based on your hypothesis. (This is an if/then statement that predicts the results of changes in the steady-state model in Exercise 1.)

Test your prediction using the computer simulation model.

Procedure

1. In Table 4 on the next page, describe the disturbance problem you have chosen to simulate. Record the selected starting values for your model and indicate, by circling, the values that differ from the steady-state model.
2. Note any other changes in the model—for example, changes in interactions, solar radiation, or addition or removal of components.
3. Calibrate the model based on your changes. Modify the model according to your problem. You should be able to make changes in the model based on your experience in Exercise 1, Experiment A, Procedure step 2. For additional help, refer to the EDM manual provided with the software.
4. Run the simulation until steady-state values are reached. At steady state, the biomass for each component should change only slightly or not at all.
5. Modify the graph features if necessary.

Results

1. Record the new steady-state values and the time to steady state in Table 4.
2. Print the simulation graph.

Table 4
Starting and Steady-State Values for Exercise 2, Experiment A

Problem:		
Component	**Starting Value**	**Steady-State Value**
Sunlight		
Pond life		
Sunfish		
Bass		
Time to steady state:		

3. If instructed to do so, save your model on a disk. Refer to the following instructions for assistance.

To Save a Model

a. Insert your new formatted disk into the disk drive. (Ask your instructor for assistance if your disk is not formatted.)

b. Click on *File* and pull down to *Save Model As.* Enter the name of the file, which might be, for example, your name and the experiment number (Stef1.A). Select the formatted disk. (Ask for assistance if the disk does not appear on the screen.) Click on *Save.* The file is saved on your disk.

c. If the file has been saved previously, click on *File* and *Save.* The current version of the file will be saved with the existing name. Save your files to a disk for future use. You may choose to save each model for Experiments A to D with a different name. Ask your instructor.

Discussion

1. Describe the interactions among the trophic levels in the pond ecosystem.

2. Do your results match your predictions? Discuss any differences between results and predictions.

3. How did the disturbance simulated in this experiment affect the pond ecosystem? How might these results be applied to a natural ecosystem?

Experiment B. Computer Simulation 2

Your research group should evaluate the questions you listed earlier in light of the results from your first computer simulation. Select a related question or pose new or modified questions that you want to pursue in this simulation. An appropriate choice might be to increase the disturbance factor or to add another level of complexity to the first simulation. State the question of interest below.

Question

Hypothesis

Formulate a hypothesis about the effects of disturbance on the pond ecosystem.

Prediction

State a prediction based on your hypothesis. (This is an if/then statement that predicts the results of changes in the steady-state model in Exercise 1.)

Test your prediction using the computer simulation model.

Procedure

1. In Table 5, describe the disturbance problem you have chosen to simulate. Record the selected starting values for your model and indicate, by circling, the values that differ from the steady-state model.
2. Note any other changes in the model, such as changes in interactions, solar radiation, or addition or removal of components.

3. Calibrate the model based on your changes. Modify the model according to your problem.
4. Run the simulation until steady-state values are reached. At steady state, the biomass for each component should change only slightly or not at all.
5. Modify the graph features if necessary.

Results

1. Record the new steady-state values and the time to steady state in Table 5.
2. Print the simulation graph.

Table 5
Starting and Steady-State Values for Exercise 2, Experiment B

Problem:		
Component	**Starting Value**	**Steady-State Value**
Sunlight		
Pond life		
Sunfish		
Bass		
Time to steady state:		

3. If instructed to do so, save your model on a disk. Refer to the instructions in Experiment A for assistance.

Discussion

1. Describe the interactions among the trophic levels in the pond ecosystem.

2. Do your results match your predictions? Discuss any differences between results and predictions.

3. How did the disturbance simulated in this experiment affect the pond ecosystem? How might these results be applied to a natural ecosystem?

Experiment C. Simulation of Fishing Activities

Although we often think of our human activities as being separate from natural ecosystems, we can have a dramatic effect on these systems. Ponds support not only carnivores such as bass, but also humans, who fish selectively. In this simulation, you will add fishing as a component to the model. Your objective might be to allow fishing at levels that will maintain a stable pond ecosystem. You might choose to challenge the system by increasing fishing on one or more species. You do not have to begin with the original steady-state model but can choose to add fishing to one of your previous models. Consider what type of fish will be caught—sunfish, bass, or gar. Is it possible to catch more than one type of fish? Does fishing compound disturbance factors that you may have introduced in previous simulations? State the question of interest below.

Question

Hypothesis

State a hypothesis about the effect of fishing on the pond ecosystem.

Prediction

State a prediction based on your hypothesis.

Test your prediction using the computer simulation model.

Procedure

1. In Table 6, describe the problem you have chosen to simulate. Record the selected starting values for your model.
2. Record in the space provided the proposed changes to the model. What fish will be caught? Are any other interactions being changed?

3. Modify the model. Select Fishing from the Library. Connect the open box for fishing to the dark box for the fish of choice. Connect the dark box for catch to the fourth plotter line.
4. Calibrate the model based on your changes. The level for fishing is set at 1 hour of fishing per day. Begin with this level. You may adjust the model according to your hypothesis.
5. Run the simulation until steady-state values are reached. At steady state, the biomass for each component should change only slightly or not at all.
6. You will need to modify the graph features. Fishing should now be displayed on the right (Y2) axis. Select the first box on the display bar over the graph. In the fourth row, type in *Fishing kg/ha/d* and select the right axis by clicking in the eighth column. Return to the graph and adjust the right axis values as needed.The right axis label is now *Catch/day* (for fishing) and *kg/ha* (for fish). Refer to the Procedure section for the first simulation for additional assistance. (See also Figures 7 and 8.)

Results

1. Record the new steady-state values and the time to steady state in Table 6.
2. Print the simulation graph.
3. If instructed to do so, save your model on a disk. Refer to the instructions in Experiment A for assistance.

Discussion

1. Describe the interactions among the trophic levels in the pond ecosystem.

Table 6
Starting and Steady-State Values for Exercise 2, Experiment C (Fishing)

Problem:		
Component	**Starting Value**	**Steady-State Value**
Sunlight		
Pond life		
Sunfish		
Bass		
Fishing		
Time to steady state:		

2. Do your results match your predictions? Discuss any differences between results and predictions.

3. Discuss the effects of fishing on the pond ecosystem. How might these results be applied to a natural ecosystem?

Experiment D. Computer Simulation of an Invasive Species

Problem

Jake, a fish farmer, counted the number of dead striped bass in his net. Twenty more today! He skillfully cut one open, exposing intestines and the mottled mass of muscles riddled with worms. "I'm not sure I can even harvest enough stripers to cover my expenses, much less make a profit. At this rate, it looks like the worm has turned. They're eatin' my fish instead of the other way 'round." Bud, the fishery's technician, suggested, "Can't you just kill those worms? You know, worm the fish." Jake countered, "I can't kill the worms because they reproduce in the snails. I can't kill the snails, because every chemical I could use would also kill the fish and contaminate my fish farm." "How about a biological control, like we use grass carp to keep the plants down in the pond?" suggested Bud. Jake thought about this idea. He knew that black carp would eat the snails. No snails, no worms. But he remembered that black carp is considered an invasive species, when it escapes from ponds into streams and lakes. Maybe he should find out more before investing in snail-crunching black carp.

News Focus from *Science:*

"Will Black Carp Be the Next Zebra Mussel?" by Dan Ferber, vol. 292. pp. 203–204, April 13, 2001.

> *There's good reason to worry about black carp, says ichthyologist Jim Williams of the U.S. Geological Survey (USGS) Caribean Research Center in Gainesville, Florida. In a detailed 1996 risk assessment of the fish, Williams and USGS colleague Leo Nico concluded that black carp would survive and reproduce in U.S. rivers, consuming native mollusks and competing with native mollusk-eating fish such as redear sunfish and freshwater drum.*

Additional Information

If Jake adds black carp to his pond and they escape to a natural pond, there could be problems. The structure and function of the pond ecosystem would change. Black carp will eat the snails (part of the pond life in the computer model). The bass prefer to eat the sunfish, because carp are too bony. Therefore, black carp would be competing with the sunfish for food, but with little or no predation by bass. (Assume no bass predation.)

Questions

What might be the consequences if black carp were to escape to a nearby natural pond? What do you think would happen to the pond life, sunfish, and bass in a natural pond?

Hypothesis

Formulate a hypothesis about the effects of introducing black carp to the pond ecosystem.

Test your hypothesis using the computer simulation model.

Prediction

State a prediction based on your hypothesis. (This is an if/then statement that predicts the results of changes in the model.)

Test your prediction using the computer simulation model.

Procedure

1. In Table 7, describe the components of the model you will simulate. Record the selected starting values for your model. The starting value for black carp should be small relative to sunfish. For example, if sunfish is 30 kg/ha, then black carp might be 10 kg/ha.
2. Note below any other changes to the model, such as changes in interactions or additions or removal of components.

3. Calibrate the model based on your changes. Modify the model according to your problem. Select a new fish icon from the Library menu to represent the black carp. (Black carp does not appear as an icon, so you should select the gar icon or add another sunfish icon.) Connect the dark box of pond life to the open box of the new fish icon. Connect the new icon to the plotter. Double-click on the new icon to set the starting value for black carp (Table 7). Remember, the starting value for carp should be less than for sunfish. (You may want to check the starting values for all components at this time.) The carp should not be connected to bass.
4. Run the simulation until steady-state values are reached.
5. You will need to modify the graph features. Select the first box on the display bar over the graph. In the fourth row, type in *Black carp kg/ha* and select the right axis by clicking in the eighth column. Return to the graph and adjust the right axis as needed. Refer to the Procedure section of the first simulation for additional assistance. (See also Figures 7 and 8.)

Results

1. Record the new steady-state values and the time to steady state in Table 7.
2. Print the simulation graph.

Table 7
Starting and Steady-State Values for Exercise 2, Experiment D

Problem:		
Component	**Starting Value**	**Steady-State Value**
Sunlight		
Pond life		
Sunfish		
Bass		
Black carp		
Time to steady state:		

3. If instructed to do so, save your model on a disk. Refer to the instructions in Experiment A for assistance.

Discussion

1. Describe the interactions among the trophic levels in the pond ecosystem.

2. Do your results match your predictions? Discuss any differences between results and predictions.

3. Do you think that Jake should add black carp to his pond? Why or why not? Remember that Jake wants to increase his yield of striped bass (after all, he is a fish farmer). Should the federal government ban the sale of black carp, given your prediction of what will happen if black carp invade natural aquatic ecosystems?

Questions for Review

1. Define *model* and provide examples from several areas in biology. Consider areas of biology other than those studied in the laboratory.

2. Critique the computer model used in this lab topic. In what ways is it an appropriate model of the pond ecosystem? In what ways does it fail to model the pond adequately?

3. Even when you adjust the starting values for components in the model, the steady-state values remain the same. However, if you change the energy from the sun, new steady-state values will emerge. Explain.

4. Which disturbance factors had the greatest effect on the pond ecosystem? How are you measuring the effect?

Applying Your Knowledge

1. Where would you expect more primary productivity in a pond, in Georgia or in Michigan? Why? What factors would be limiting in these two environments?

2. In 1997, nonnative and invasive Asian swamp eels were collected in Florida for the first time at two sites near Tampa and Miami. These fish are extremely adaptable to a wide range of freshwater habitats, from wetlands to streams and ponds. They are predators that feed on worms, insects, crayfish, frogs, and other fishes, including bluegill and bass. Swamp eels have the ability to gulp air, which allows them to survive in only a few inches of water and to move over land to a nearby body of water. Scientists are tracking their movements and increasing numbers in the Southeast. In one pond, several species of fish have been completely eliminated.

   Based on your understanding of the pond ecosystem, predict the effect of introducing swamp eels on the following components of the pond.

   Bluegill:

   Bass:

   Pond life:

3. Using your knowledge of ecosystem structure and function, propose a plan of action for eliminating the swamp eels (described in question 2 above) from the pond before they eliminate the other organisms. You cannot use toxins, since the local anglers fish in this pond.

4. A local television news bulletin urges you not to eat fish caught in nearby Lake Ketchum because water levels of the pollutant PCB have reached 0.0001 part per million (ppm). With such a small reading, why should you be concerned?

Investigative Extension

Environmental Decision Making has two other ecosystem models, Grasslands and Forestry and Logging, as well as an option for creating your own model using general symbols. These programs can be used to pursue additional topics, including ecosystem dynamics and management.

References

Campbell, N., and J. Reece. *Biology,* 7th ed. Menlo Park, CA: Benjamin Cummings, 2005.

Cox, G. W. *Alien Species in North America and Hawaii.* Washington, DC: Island Press, 1999.

Mack, R. N., D. Simberloff, W. M. Lonsdale, H. Evans, M. Clout, and F. Bazzaz. "Biotic Invasions: Causes, Epidemiology, Global Consequences and Control," *Issues in Ecology,* 2000, No. 5, Spring.

Odum, E. C., H. T. Odum, and N. S. Peterson. *Environmental Decision Making, The BioQUEST Library Volume V.* San Diego, CA: Academic Press, 2002. Lab written to correspond to software by permission of publisher.

Odum, H. T., and E. C. Odum. *Computer Minimodels and Simulation Exercises,* Gainesville, FL: Center for Wetlands, Phelps Laboratory, University of Florida, 1989. Examples using BASIC with program listings for Apple II, PC, and Macintosh.

SOS for America's Streams (video). Gaithersburg, MD: Izaak Walton League of America, 1990. See the Preparation Guide for ordering information.

Waterman, M. and E. Stanley. *Biological Inquiry: A Workbook of Investigative Cases.* Menlo Park, CA: Benjamin Cummings, 2005.

Website

The BioQUEST Curriculum Consortium:
http://bioquest.org

Appendix: Chi-Square Test

Chi-square is a statistical test commonly used to compare observed data with data we would expect to obtain according to a specific scientific hypothesis. For example, if according to Mendel's laws, you expect 10 of 20 offspring from a cross to be male and the actual observed number is 8 males out of 20 offspring, then you might want to know about the "goodness of fit" between the observed and the expected. Were the deviations (differences between observed and expected) the result of chance, or were they due to other factors? How much deviation can occur before the investigator must conclude that something other than chance is at work, causing the observed to differ from the expected? The chi-square test can help in making that decision. The chi-square test is always testing what scientists call the **null hypothesis,** which states that there is no significant difference between the expected and the observed result.

The formula for calculating chi-square (χ^2) is:

$$\chi^2 = \Sigma(o - e)^2 / e$$

That is, chi-square is the sum of the squared difference between observed (o) and expected (e) data (or the deviation, d), divided by the expected data in all possible categories.

For example, suppose that a cross between two pea plants yields a population of 880 plants, 639 with green seeds and 241 with yellow seeds. You are asked to propose the genotypes of the parents. Your scientific hypothesis is that the allele for green is dominant to the allele for yellow and that the parent plants were both heterozygous for this trait. If your scientific hypothesis is true, then the predicted ratio of offspring from this cross would be 3 : 1 (based on Mendel's laws), as predicted from the results of the Punnett square (Figure 1). The related null hypothesis is that there is no significant difference between your observed pea offspring and offspring produced according to Mendel's laws. To determine if this null hypothesis is rejected or not rejected, a χ^2 value is computed.

To calculate χ^2, first determine the number expected in each category. If the ratio is 3 : 1 and the total number of observed individuals is 880, then the expected numerical values should be 660 green and 220 yellow ($\frac{3}{4} \times 880 = 660$; $\frac{1}{4} \times 880 = 220$).

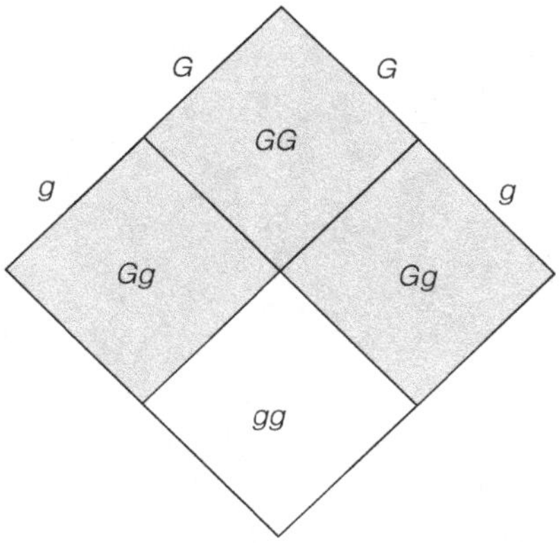

Figure 1.
Punnett square. Predicted offspring from cross between green- and yellow-seeded plants. Green (*G*) is dominant (3/4 green; 1/4 yellow).

From *Investigating Biology Laboratory Manual*, Fifth Edition, Judith G. Morgan and M. Eloise Brown Carter.

Chi-square analysis requires that you use numerical values, not percentages or ratios.

Then calculate χ^2 using the formula, as shown in Table 1. Note that we get a value of 2.673 for χ^2. But what does this number mean? Here's how to interpret the χ^2 value:

1. Determine **degrees of freedom** (df). Degrees of freedom can be calculated as the number of categories in the problem minus 1. For example, if we had four categories, then the degrees of freedom would be 3. In our example, there are two categories (green and yellow); therefore, there is 1 degree of freedom.
2. Determine a relative standard to serve as the basis for rejecting the hypothesis. Scientists allow some level of error in their decision making for testing their hypotheses. The relative standard commonly used in biological research is $p < 0.05$. The ***p* value** is the *probability* of rejecting the null hypothesis (that there is no difference between observed and expected), when the null hypothesis is true. In other words, the p value gives an approximate value for the error of falsely stating that there is a significant difference between your observed numbers and the expected numbers, when there is *not* a significant difference. *When we pick* $p < 0.05$*, we state that there is less than a 5% chance of error of stating that there is a difference when, in fact, there is no significant difference.* Although scientists and statisticians sometimes select a lower significance value, in this manual we will assume a value of 0.05.
3. Refer to a chi-square distribution table (Table 2). Using the appropriate degrees of freedom, locate the value corresponding to the p value of 0.05, the error probability that you selected. If your χ^2 value is *greater* than the value corresponding to the p value of 0.05, then you reject the null hypothesis. You conclude that the observed numbers are significantly different from the expected. In this example your calculated value, $\chi^2 = 2.673$, is not larger than the table χ^2 value of 3.84 (df = 1, $p = 0.05$). *Therefore, your observed distribution of plants with green and yellow seeds is not significantly different from the distribution that would be expected under Mendel's laws. Any minor differences between your offspring distribution and the expected Mendelian distribution can be attributed to chance or sampling error.*

Step-by-Step Procedure for Testing Your Hypothesis and Calculating Chi-Square

1. State the hypothesis being tested and the predicted results.
2. Gather the data by conducting the relevant experiment (or, if working genetics problems, use the data provided in the problem).
3. Determine the expected numbers for each observational class. Remember to use numbers, not percentages.

Chi-square should *not* be calculated if the expected value in any category is less than 5.

Table 1
Calculating Chi-Square

	Green	Yellow
Observed (o)	639	241
Expected (e)	660	220
Deviation ($o - e$)	–21	21
Deviation^2 (d^2)	441	441
d^2/e	0.668	2.005
$\chi^2 = \Sigma d^2/e = 2.673$		

Table 2
Chi-Square Distribution

Degrees of Freedom (df)	Probability (p)										
	0.95	**0.90**	**0.80**	**0.70**	**0.50**	**0.30**	**0.20**	**0.10**	**0.05**	**0.01**	**0.001**
1	0.004	0.02	0.06	0.15	0.46	1.07	1.64	2.71	3.84	6.64	10.83
2	0.10	0.21	0.45	0.71	1.39	2.41	3.22	4.60	5.99	9.21	13.82
3	0.35	0.58	1.01	1.42	2.37	3.66	4.64	6.25	7.82	11.34	16.27
4	0.71	1.06	1.65	2.20	3.36	4.88	5.99	7.78	9.49	13.28	18.47
5	1.14	1.61	2.34	3.00	4.35	6.06	7.29	9.24	11.07	15.09	20.52
6	1.63	2.20	3.07	3.83	5.35	7.23	8.56	10.64	12.59	16.81	22.46
7	2.17	2.83	3.82	4.67	6.35	8.38	9.80	12.02	14.07	18.48	24.32
8	2.73	3.49	4.59	5.53	7.34	9.52	11.03	13.36	15.51	20.09	26.12
9	3.32	4.17	5.38	6.39	8.34	10.66	12.24	14.68	16.92	21.67	27.88
10	3.94	4.86	6.18	7.27	9.34	11.78	13.44	15.99	18.31	23.21	29.59
	Nonsignificant								Significant		

Source: R. A. Fisher and F. Yates, *Statistical Tables for Biological, Agricultural, and Medical Research*, 6th ed., Table IV, Longman Group UK Ltd., 1974.

4. Calculate χ^2 using the formula. Complete all calculations to three significant digits.
5. Use the chi-square distribution table to determine the significance of the value.
   a. Determine the degrees of freedom, one less than the number of categories. Locate that value in the appropriate column.
   b. Locate the χ^2 value for your significance level ($p = 0.05$ or less).
   c. Compare this χ^2 value (from the table) with your calculated χ^2.
6. State your conclusion in terms of your hypothesis.
   a. If your calculated χ^2 value is greater than the χ^2 value for your particular degrees of freedom and *p* value (0.05), then *reject the null hypothesis* of no difference between expected and observed results. *You can conclude that there is a significant difference between your observed distribution and the theoretical expected distribution* (for example, under Mendel's laws).
   b. If your calculated χ^2 value is less than the χ^2 value for your particular degrees of freedom and *p* value (0.05), then *fail to reject the null hypothesis* of no difference between observed and expected results. *You can conclude that there does not seem to be a significant difference between your observed distribution and the theoretical expected distribution* (for example, under Mendel's laws). *You can conclude that any differences between your observed results and the expected results can be attributed to chance or sampling error.* (Note: It is incorrect to say that you "accept" the null hypothesis. Statisticians either "reject" or "fail to reject" the null hypothesis.)

The chi-square test will be used to test for the goodness of fit between observed and expected data from several laboratory investigations in this lab manual.

References

Motulsky, M. *Intuitive Biostatistics.* New York: Oxford University Press, 1995.

Triola, M. *Elementary Statistics Update,* 9th ed. San Francisco: Addison-Wesley, 2005.

Appendix: Scientific Writing

For the scientific enterprise to be successful, scientists must clearly communicate their work. Scientific findings are never kept secret. Instead, scientists share their ideas and results with other scientists, encouraging critical review and alternative interpretations from colleagues and the entire scientific community. Communication, both verbal and written, occurs at every step along the research path. While working on projects, scientists present their preliminary results for comments from their coworkers at laboratory group meetings and in written research reports. At a later stage, scientists report the results of their research activities as a poster or oral presentation at a scientific meeting. Then the final report is prepared in a rather standard scientific paper format and submitted for publication in an appropriate scientific journal. At each stage in this process, scientists encourage and require critical review of their work and ideas by their peers. The final publication in a peer-reviewed journal generally promotes additional research and establishes this contribution to current knowledge.

One of the objectives of every lab topic in this manual is to develop your writing skills. You will generate and write hypotheses, observations, answers to questions, and more, as one way of learning biology. Also, you will practice writing in a scientific paper format and style to communicate the results of your investigations. The scientific process is reflected in the design of a scientific paper and the format you will use for your laboratory papers.

A scientific paper usually includes the following parts: a **Title** (statement of the question or problem), an **Abstract** (short summary of the paper), an **Introduction** (background and significance of the problem), a **Materials and Methods** section (report of exactly what you did), a **Results** section (presentation of data), a **Discussion** section (interpretation and discussion of results), and **References Cited** (books and periodicals used). A **Conclusion** (concise restatement of conclusions) and **Acknowledgments** (recognition of assistance) may also be included.

We propose that you practice writing throughout the biology laboratory program by submitting individual sections of a scientific paper. Your instructor will determine which sections you will write for a given lab topic and will evaluate each of these sections, pointing out areas of weakness and suggesting improvements. By the time you have completed these assignments, you will have submitted the equivalent of one scientific paper. Having practiced writing each section of a scientific paper in the first half of the laboratory program, you will then write one or two complete laboratory papers

---

in scientific paper format during the second half of the laboratory program, reporting the results of experiments, preferably those that you and your research team have designed and performed.

Successful Scientific Writing

The following notes for success apply to writing throughout all sections of a scientific paper.

- Your writing should be clear and concise. Delete unnecessary words—for example, adjectives and adverbs have limited use in describing your work. Write clearly in short and logical, but not choppy sentences. Avoid run-on sentences and use grammatically correct English. Avoid long introductions. (See Appendix 4, "Sentences Requiring Revision," in Knisely [2002] for basic rules of writing and practice in editing for common errors.)
- Your audience is your peers, other student-scientists. Write as though they are scientists: professional and knowledgeable.
- Use the past tense in the Abstract, Materials and Methods, and Results sections. Also use the past tense in the Introduction and Discussion sections when referring to *your* work. Use the present tense when relating the background information as you refer to other investigator's published work. Previously published research is considered established in the present body of knowledge.
- Use the active voice whenever possible. Doing so makes the paper easier to read and more understandable. However, in the Materials and Methods section you may use the passive voice so that the focus of your writing is the methodology, rather than the investigator.
- When referring to the scientific name of an organism, the genus and species should be in italics or underlined. The first letter of the genus is capitalized, but the species is written in lowercase letters, for example, *Drosophila melanogaster.*
- Use metric units for all measurements. Use numerals when reporting measurements, percentages, decimals, and magnifications. When beginning a sentence, write the number as a word. Numbers of ten or less that are not measurements are written out. Numbers greater than ten are given as numerals. Decimal numbers less than one should have a zero in the one position (e.g., 0.153; not .153).
- Clearly label each section (except the title page), placing the title of the section against the left margin on a separate line. Each section does not begin a new page but continues in order.
- Begin writing early to allow time for researching your topic, analyzing your results, and revising your writing. Revise, revise, and then revise! For suggestions and examples of how to revise your work, see Chapter 5, "Revision," in Knisely (2002) and Chapter 5, "Revising," in Pechenik (2001).
- Note the word "data" is plural.
- Remember the results cannot "prove" the hypothesis, but rather they may "support" or "falsify" the hypothesis.
- Carefully proofread your work even if your word processor has checked for grammatical and spelling errors. These programs cannot distinguish between "your" and "you're," for example.

- Save a copy of your work on a disk or USB flash drive, and print a copy of your paper before turning in the original.

Plagiarism

Students will write their papers independently. Because performing the experiment will be a collaborative effort, you and your teammates will share the results of your investigation. The Introduction, Discussion, and References Cited (or References) sections must be the product of your own personal library research and creative thinking. If you are not certain about the level of independence and what constitutes plagiarism in this laboratory program, ask your instructor to clarify the class policy. *In the most extreme case of plagiarism, a student presents another student's report as his or her own. However, representing another person's ideas as your own without giving that person credit is also plagiarism and is a serious offense.*

Plan for Writing a Scientific Paper

The sections of a scientific paper and particular material to be covered in each section are described in this appendix in order of appearance in the paper. However, most scientists do not follow that sequence in the actual writing of the paper, but rather begin with the methodology. A typical plan for writing a scientific paper follows.

- Begin writing the Materials and Methods section. The first draft of this section can be written before all the results are completed. Remember to review and carefully edit after completing all work. (See Materials and Methods).
- Construct the tables and figures. Compose the text for the Results section based on the tables and figures.
- Consult references for background information and interpretation of results. Locate and review primary and secondary references for use in the Discussion and Introduction sections. (See References Cited)
- Develop the Introduction section and begin the References Cited section. (See Introduction and References Cited) Most scientists prefer to write the Introduction before the Discussion. Both sections require background information and a clear understanding of the results of the work. Remember to carefully check and revise your Introduction if you write it first.
- Write the Discussion section and complete the References Cited section. (See Discussion)
- Write the Title and Abstract.
- Review checklist, if available, before preparing final version of the paper.

Title Page and Title

The title page is the first page of the paper and includes the title of the paper, your name, the course title, your lab time or section, your instructor's name, and the due date for the paper. *The title should be as short as possible and as long as necessary to communicate to the reader the question being answered in the paper.* For example, if you are asking a question about the inheritance patterns of the gene for aldehyde oxidase production in *Drosophila melanogaster,* a possible title might be "Inheritance of the Gene for Aldehyde Oxidase in *Drosophila melanogaster.*" Something like "Inheritance in Fruit Flies" is too general, and "A Study of the Inheritance of the Enzyme Aldehyde Oxidase in the Fruit Fly *Drosophila melanogaster*" is too wordy. The words "A Study of the" are superfluous, and "Enzyme" and "Fruit Fly" are redundant. The suffix *-ase* indicates that aldehyde oxidase is an enzyme, and most scientists know that *Drosophila melanogaster* is the scientific name of a common fruit fly species. However, it is appropriate to include in the title both common and scientific names of lesser known species.

Place the title about 7 cm from the top of the title page. Place "by" and your name in the center of the page, and place the course name, lab section, instructor's name, and due date, each on a separate centered line, at the bottom of the page. Leave about 5 cm below this information.

Abstract

The abstract, if one is requested by the instructor, is placed at the beginning of the second page of the paper, after the title page. *The abstract concisely summarizes the question being investigated in the paper, the methods used in the experiment, the results, and the conclusions drawn.* The reader should be able to determine the major topics in the paper without reading the entire paper. The abstract should be no more than 250 words, and fewer if possible. Compose the abstract after the paper is completed.

Introduction

The introduction has two functions: (1) to provide the context for your investigation and (2) to state the question asked and the hypothesis tested in the study. Begin the introduction by reviewing background information that will enable the reader to understand the objective of the study and the significance of the problem, relating the problem to the larger issues in the field. Include only information that directly prepares the reader to understand the question investigated. Most ideas in the introduction will come from outside sources, such as scientific journals or books dealing with the topic you are investigating. All sources of information must be referenced and included in the References Cited (or References) section of the paper, but the introduction must be in your own words. Refer to the references when appropriate. Unless otherwise instructed, place the author of the reference cited and the year of publication in parentheses at the end of the sentence or paragraph relating the idea; for example, "(Finnerty, 1992)." Additional information on citing references is provided in References Cited. Do not use citation forms utilized in other disciplines. Do not use footnotes and avoid the use of direct quotes.

As you describe your investigation, include only the question and hypothesis that you finally investigated. Briefly describe the experiment performed and the outcome predicted for the experiment. Although these items are usually presented after the background information near the end of the introduction, you should have each clearly in mind before you begin writing the introduction. It is a good idea to write down each item (question, hypothesis, prediction) before you begin to write your introduction.

Materials and Methods

The Materials and Methods section describes your experiment in such a way that it can be repeated. This section should be a narrative description that integrates the materials with the procedures used in the investigation. Do not list the materials and do not list the steps of the procedure. Rather, write the Materials and Methods section concisely in paragraph form in the past tense. Be sure to include levels of treatment, numbers of replications, and controls. If you are working with living organisms, include the scientific name and the sex of the organism if that information is relevant to the experiment. If you used computer software or any statistical analyses, include these in the Materials and Methods section.

The difficulty in writing this section comes as you decide the level of detail to include in your paragraphs. You must determine which details are essential for another investigator to repeat the experiment. For example, if in your experiment you incubated potato pieces in different concentrations of sucrose solution, it would not be necessary to explain that the pieces were incubated in plastic cups labeled with a wax marking pencil or to provide the numbers of the cups. In this case, the molarity of the sucrose solutions, the size of the potato pieces and how they were obtained, and the amount of incubation solution are the important items to include. Do not include failed attempts unless the technique used may be tried by other investigators. Do not try to justify your procedures in this section.

The Materials and Methods section is often the best place to begin writing your paper. The writing is straightforward and concise, and you will be reminded of the details of the work.

Results

The Results section consists of at least four components: (1) one or two sentences reminding the reader about the nature of the research, (2) one or more paragraphs that describe the results, (3) figures (graphs, diagrams, pictures), and (4) tables. *The Results is the central section of a scientific paper.* Therefore, you should think carefully about the best way to present your results to the reader. The data included in tables and graphs should be summarized and emphasized in the narrative paragraph. Draw the reader's attention to the results that are important. Describe trends in your data and provide evidence to support your claims. This section also is written in the past tense.

Before writing the Results section, prepare the tables and figures. Remember to number figures and tables consecutively throughout the paper (*see Lab Topic 1, Scientific Investigation, for instructions on creating figures and tables and their presentation*). Refer to figures and tables within the paragraph as you describe your results, using the word Figure or Table, followed by its number; for example, "(Figure 1)." If possible, place each figure or table at the end of the paragraph in which it is cited.

If you have performed a statistical analysis of your data, such as chi-square, include the results in this section.

Report your data as accurately as possible. Do not report what you expected to happen in the experiment nor whether your data supported your hypothesis. Do not discuss the meaning of your results in this section. Do not critique the results. Any data you plan to include in the Discussion section must be presented in the Results. Conversely, do not include data in the Results that you do not mention in the Discussion.

Write the Results section before attempting the Discussion section. This will ensure that the results of your investigation are clearly organized, logically presented, and thoroughly understood before they are discussed. For this reason, some scientists begin with the Results section when writing a paper.

Discussion

In the Discussion section, you will analyze and interpret the results of *your experiment.* Simply restating the results is not interpretation. The Discussion must provide a context for understanding the significance of the results. Explain why you observed these results and how these results contribute to our knowledge. Your results either will support or confirm your hypothesis or will negate, refute, or contradict your hypothesis; but the word *prove is* not appropriate in scientific writing. If your results do not support your hypothesis, you must still state why you think this occurred. Support your ideas from other work (books, lectures or outside reading of scientific literature). State your conclusions in this section.

Complete your Introduction and Results sections before you begin writing the Discussion. The figures and tables in the Results section will be particularly important as you begin to think about your discussion. The tables allow you to present your results clearly to the reader, and graphs allow you to visualize the effects that the independent variable has had on the dependent variables in your experiment. Studying these data will be one of the first steps in interpreting your results. As you study the information in the Introduction section and your data in the Results section, write down relationships and integrate these relationships into a rough draft of your discussion.

The following steps may be helpful as you begin to outline your discussion and before you write the narrative:

- Restate your question, hypothesis, and prediction.
- Write down the specific data, including results of statistical tests.
- State whether your results did or did not confirm your prediction and support or negate your hypothesis.
- Write down what you know about the biology involved in your experiment. How do your results fit in with what you know? What is the significance of your results?
- How do your results support or conflict with previous work? Include references to this work.
- Clearly state your conclusions.

- List weaknesses you have identified in your experimental design that affected your results. List any problems that arose during the experiment itself that affected your results. The weaknesses of the experiment should not dominate the Discussion. *Include one or two sentences only if these problems affected the results.* Remember the focus of the Discussion is to convey the significance of the results.
- You are now ready to write the narrative for the Discussion. Integrate all of the above information into several simple, clear, concise paragraphs. Discuss the results; do not simply restate the data. Refer to other work to support your ideas.

References Cited (or References)

A References Cited section lists only those references cited in the paper. A References section (bibliography), on the other hand, is a more inclusive list of all references used in producing the paper, including books and papers used to obtain background knowledge that may not be cited in the paper. Most references will be cited in the Introduction and Discussion sections of your paper. For your paper you should have a References Cited section that includes only those references cited in the paper.

Locating Appropriate References

Textbooks and review articles are an excellent starting place for developing background information for your independent investigations. Consult texts and books that are more specific than your general biology textbook. For example, if your project is on plant hormones, you might consult a plant physiology textbook to provide foundational information. Books will often have lists of articles and other references that may be helpful. (Also see the References section for each Lab Topic in this manual.) Textbooks, review articles, and articles from popular science magazines are **secondary references,** which generally provide a summary and interpretation of research (for example, *Annual Review of Genetics, Science News* and *Scientific American*).

Scientific papers in general rely on **primary references,** reports of original research that present the work of scientists in such a way that it can be repeated. Primary references are journal articles that have been reviewed by other scientists and the journal editor. In addition to articles in journals (e.g., *American Journal of Botany, Cell, Ecology,* and *Science*), primary references include conference papers, dissertations, and technical reports. Many scientific journals are available in a full-text version online; these are still primary references. However, websites are not primary references, because they are not required to participate in the peer review process. Your instructor will indicate the number of primary references required for your paper. Knisely (2002) and Pechenik (2001) provide useful suggestions for how to read scientific papers. Also Knisely (2002) has a helpful guide to searching for references using three computer databases: *Science Citation Index, Basic BIOSIS,* and *Article Finder.*

Record the citation information for any references, including online sources, at the time you read the information. Refer to the citation format to record the complete citation.

Examples of Reference Citations

The format for the References Cited section differs slightly from one scientific journal to the next. How does an author know which format to use? Every scientific journal provides "Instructions to Authors" that describe specific requirements for this important section and all other aspects of the paper. You may use the format used in this lab manual and provided in the examples below, select the format in a scientific journal provided by your instructor, or use another accepted format for listing your references. Your instructor may provide additional instructions. Be sure to read the references that you cite in your paper.

Journal article, one author:

Whittaker, R. H. "New Concepts of Kingdoms of Organisms." *Science,* 1969, vol. 163, pp. 150–160.

Journal article, two or more authors:

Watson, J. D., and F. H. Crick. "Molecular Structure of Nucleic Acids: A Structure for Deoxyribose Nucleic Acid." *Nature,* 1953, vol. 171, pp. 737–738.

Book:

Darwin, C. R. *On the Origin of Species.* London: John Murray, 1859.

Chapter or article in an edited book:

Baker, H. G. "Characteristics and Modes of Origin of Weeds" in *Genetics and Colonizing Species,* eds. H. G. Baker and G. L. Stebbins. New York: Academic Press, 1965, pp. 147–152.

Government publication:

Office of Technology Assessment. *Harmful Non-indigenous Species in the United States.* Publication no. OTA-F-565. Washington, D.C.: U.S. Government Printing Office, 1993.

Citing References in Text

In the text of the paper, cite the references using the author's name and the year. For example: "The innate agonistic behavior of the male Siamese fighting fish has been widely studied (Simpson, 1968)." "Simpson (1968) has described the agonistic behavior of the male Siamese fighting fish." If there are more than two authors, use the first author's name followed by *et al.* (and others). For example: (Simpson *et al.,* 1968).

Using Information Sources from the Internet

The Internet can provide access to online reference resources and databases including *Biological Abstracts, Current Contents, Medline,* and *Annual Reviews* among many others. These search tools provide access to a wide range of published papers, some of which may be available online as full text journals. For suggestions and examples of how to locate sources using the Internet, see Harnack and Kleppinger (2001) and Knisely (2002). Scientific papers published in professional journals have gone through an extensive review process by other scientists in the same field. Most scientific articles have been revised based on comments by the reviewers and the editors. Sources of information that lack this critical review process do not have the same validity and authority.

The Internet is an exciting, immediate, and easily accessible source of information. However, unlike traditional bibliographic resources in the sciences, the Internet includes websites with material that has not been critically reviewed. Your instructor may prefer that you use the Internet only for locating peer-reviewed primary references or as a starting point to promote your interest and ideas. You may not be allowed to use Internet sources at all. Consult your instructor concerning use of Internet information.

If you do use the Internet to locate information, you should be prepared to evaluate these sites critically. Remember always to record the online address for any site you use as a reference. Tate and Alexander (1996) suggest the following five criteria for evaluating Internet sources:

1. **Authority.** Determine the author and sponsor for the Internet site. What is the professional affiliation of the author? Are phone numbers and addresses included? Is there a link to the sponsor's home page? Does the author list his or her qualifications? If the material is copyrighted, who owns the copyright?
2. **Accuracy.** Look for indications of professional standards for writing, citations, figures, and tables. Are there typographical, spelling, and grammatical errors? Are sources of information cited? Are the data presented or simply summarized?
3. **Objectivity.** Is the site provided as a public service, free of advertising? If advertising is present, is it clearly separate from the information? Does the site present only the view of the sponsor or advertiser?
4. **Currency.** Determine the date of the site and whether it is regularly revised. How long has the site existed? When was it last updated? Are figures and tables dated? Some Internet sites disappear overnight. Always record the date that you visited the site and retrieved information.
5. **Coverage.** Is the information offered in a complete form or as an abstract or summary of information published elsewhere? Is the site under construction? When was the site last revised?

Below find a model format and examples for citing Internet sources in the References Cited section of your paper. Other formats may be suggested by your instructor or librarian.

Model:

Author's last name and initials. Date of Internet publication. Document title. <URL> or other retrieval information. Date of access.

Examples:

(Professional site)

[CBE] Council of Biology Editors. 1999, Oct. 5. CBE home page. <http://www.councilscienceeditors.org>. Accessed Oct. 7, 1999.

(e-journal)

Browning T. 1997. Embedded visuals: student design in Web spaces. *Kairos: A Journal for Teachers of Writing in Webbed Environments* 3(1). <http://english.ttu.edu/kairos/2.1/features/browning/bridge.html>. Accessed Oct. 4, 1999.

(Government publication)

Food and Drug Administration, 1996, Sep. "Outsmarting Poison Ivy and Its Cousins." *FDA Consumer Magazine.* <http://www.fda.gov/fdac/features/796_ivy.html>. Accessed Aug. 9, 2004.

References

The following sources are recommended to give additional help and examples in scientific writing:

Harnack, A. and E. Kleppinger. *Online! A Reference Guide to Using Internet Sources.* Boston: St. Martins, 2001.

Knisely, K. *A Student Handbook for Writing in Biology.* Sunderland, MA: Sinauer Associates, 2002.

McMillan, V. E. *Writing Papers in the Biological Sciences.* New York, NY: St. Martin's Press, 1997.

Pechenik, J. A. *A Short Guide to Writing about Biology,* 4th ed., New York, NY: Addison Wesley, 2001.

Style Manual Committee, Council of Biology Editors. *Scientific Style and Format: The CBE Manual for Authors, Editors and Publishers.* 6th ed. Cambridge, MA: Cambridge Univ. Press, 1994.

Tate, M., and J. Alexander. "Teaching Critical Evaluation Skills for World Wide Web Resources." *Computers in Libraries,* Nov/Dec 1996, pp. 49–55.

Websites

How to cite Internet sources:
http://www.bedfordstmartins.com/online/cite8.html

Appendix: Terminology and Techniques for Dissection

Orientation Terminology

Orientation terminology used with quadrupeds (four-legged animals such as the fetal pig) differs from terminology used with bipeds (such as humans). Become familiar with the following terms, which refer to quadrupeds (Figure 1).

Right/left: always refer to the animal's right or left, not yours.

Anterior, cranial: toward the head.

Posterior, caudal: toward the tail.

Dorsal: backside; from the Latin *dorsum,* meaning "back."

Ventral: bellyside; from the Latin *venter,* meaning "belly."

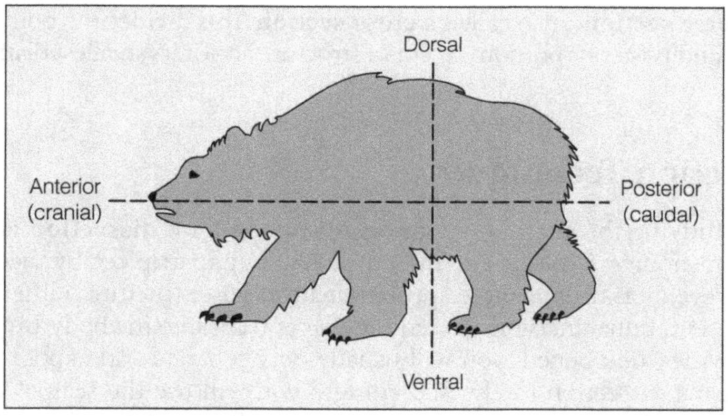

Figure 1.
Orientation terminology for quadrupeds.

Terms Relating to Position in the Body

Proximal: near the trunk, attached portion, or point of reference, for example: "The pig's elbow is *proximal* to its wrist."

Distal: farther from the trunk, attached portion, or point of reference, for example: "The toes are *distal* to the ankle."

Superficial: lying on top or near the body surface.

Deep: lying under or below.

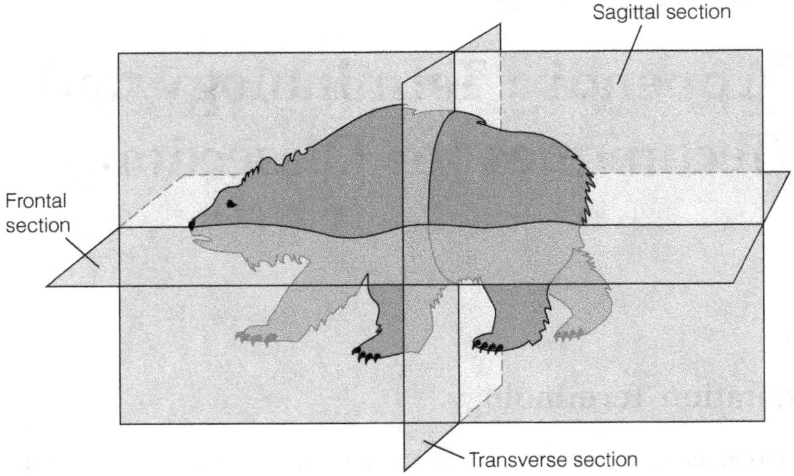

Figure 2.
Sections of an organism.

Planes and Sections

A **section** is a cut through a structure. A **plane** is an imaginary line through which a section can be cut. Anatomists generally refer to three planes or sections (Figure 2).

Sagittal section: divides the body into left and right portions or halves. This is a longitudinal or lengthwise section from anterior to posterior.

Frontal section: A longitudinal or lengthwise section from anterior to posterior, this divides the body into dorsal and ventral portions or halves.

Transverse section: Also called a **cross section,** this divides the body into anterior and posterior portions or cuts a structure across its smallest diameter.

Dissection Techniques

When studying the anatomy of an organism, the term **dissection** is perhaps a misnomer. *Dissection* literally means to cut apart piece by piece. In lab, however, it is usually more appropriate to expose structures rather than dissect them. Initial incisions do require that you cut into the body, but after body cavities are opened, you will usually only separate and expose body parts, using dissection rarely. Accordingly, you will use the scalpel when you make initial incisions into the body wall of large animals, but seldom when studying small animals or organs of large animals.

Scissors are used to deepen initial cuts made by the scalpel in large animals and to cut into the bodies of smaller animals. When using scissors, direct the tips upward to prevent gouging deeper organs. Once the animal's body is open, use forceps and the blunt probe to carefully separate organs and to pick away connective tissue obstructing and binding organs and ducts. Needle probes are only minimally useful. Never cut away an organ or cut through a blood vessel, nerve, or duct unless given specific instructions to do so.

Producing a good dissection takes time and cannot be rushed. As you study the anatomy of animals, your goal should be to expose all parts so that they can be easily studied and demonstrated to your lab partner or instructor.